Maria Lewis is an author, screenwriter and film curator based in Australia. Getting her start as a police reporter, her writing on pop culture has appeared in publications such as the *New York Post*, *Guardian*, *Penthouse*, *The Daily Mail*, *Empire Magazine*, *Gizmodo*, *Huffington Post*, *The Daily* and *Sunday Telegraph*, *i09*, *Jun*__ and many more. A journalist for over 16 years, she tran___ed into working in television as a segment producer, ___ and guest presenter on live nightly news program *The* ___ n SBS. She has worked as a screenwriter on docume___ n and scripted television projects.

Her best-selling ___ vel *Who's Afraid?* was published in 2016, followed ___ quel *Who's Afraid Too?* in 2017, which was nominat___ 3est Horror Novel at the Aurealis Awards. *Who's Afra___ urrently being developed for television. Her Young Ad___ but, *It Came From The Deep*, was released globally in 2___, followed by her fourth book, *The Witch Who Courted ___ h*, which won Best Fantasy Novel at the Aurealis Awards ___)19.

Her fifth novel set ___ in the shared supernatural universe – *The Wailing Wom___* – was nominated for Best Fantasy Novel at the Aurealis ___wards in 2020, followed by the publication of her sixth novel, *Who's Still Afraid?*, and book seven *The Rose Daughter*. The host, writer and producer of the limited podcast series *Josie & The Podcats* about the 2001 cult film, she's a film curator at Australia's national museum of screen culture.

Visit Maria Lewis online:

Twitter: @moviemazz
Instagram: @maria___lewis
www.marialewis.com.au

Dennis DeNitto and Daniel J. Leary

CONTRASTS
CONTRASTS
CONTRASTS
CONTRASTS

Essays, Short Stories, and Poems

CONTRASTS:

ESSAYS,
SHORT STORIES,
AND
POEMS

CONTRASTS:

ESSAYS,
SHORT STORIES,
AND POEMS

Dennis DeNitto
Daniel J. Leary

The Macmillan Company

ACKNOWLEDGMENTS

Copyrighted works, listed in the order of appearance, are reprinted in the United States, its possessions and dependencies, and The Philippines, by permission of the following.

"Fashions in Love." From COLLECTED ESSAYS by Aldous Huxley; renewed 1957 by Aldous Huxley. Reprinted by permission of Harper & Row, Publishers, Inc.

"Love or the Life and Death of a Value" by Joseph Wood Krutch. From THE MODERN TEMPER by Joseph Wood Krutch, copyright 1929 by Harcourt, Brace & World, Inc.; renewed, 1957, by Joseph Wood Krutch. Reprinted by permission of the publishers.

"Love or Marriage" by Ernest van den Haag. Copyright © 1962 by Harper's Magazine, Inc. Reprinted from the May 1962 issue by permission of the author.

"Sex" by Edmund Wilson. From A PIECE OF MY MIND, Farrar, Straus & Giroux, Inc., 1956. Reprinted by permission of the author.

"William and Mary" by Max Beerbohm. From AND EVEN NOW by Max Beerbohm. Copyright 1921 by E. P. Dutton & Co., Inc. Renewal 1949, by Max Beerbohm. Reprinted by permission of the publishers.

"The She-Wolf" by Giovanni Verga. From THE SHE-WOLF AND OTHER STORIES by Giovanni Verga, translated by Giovanni Cecchetti. Reprinted by permission of University of California Press.

"Suicides" by Cesare Pavese. From STORIES OF MODERN ITALY edited by Ben Johnson. © Copyright 1960 by Random House, Inc. Reprinted by permission of the publisher.

"Francesca" by Ezra Pound. From PERSONAE by Ezra Pound. Copyright 1926, 1954 by Ezra Pound. Reprinted by permission of New Directions Publishing Corporation.

"somewhere i have never travelled, gladly beyond" by E. E. Cummings. Copyright 1931, 1959, by E. E. Cummings. Reprinted from his volume, POEMS 1923–1954 by permission of Harcourt, Brace & World, Inc.

"The Farmer's Bride" by Charlotte Mew. From COLLECTED POEMS by Charlotte Mew. Reprinted by permission of Gerald Duckworth & Co. Ltd.

"Not Marble Nor the Gilded Monuments" by Archibald MacLeish. From COLLECTED POEMS OF ARCHIBALD MACLEISH 1917–1952. Copyright, 1952, by Archibald MacLeish. Reprinted by permission of the publisher, Houghton Mifflin Company.

PREFACE

This anthology is intended primarily as a reader for introductory college English courses. The twenty-seven essays, twenty-one short stories, and one hundred poems, though selected on the basis of individual merit, are divided into seven sections, arranged to serve both as a basis for student compositions and as an introduction to prose and poetry. *Contrasts,* as the name suggests, is an anthology of juxtapositions. By offering a wide spectrum of contrasting approaches and attitudes in an equally wide range of categories, such as love, violence, death, and religion, this anthology is designed to encourage students to explore ideas and emotions.

Each of the seven main divisions opens with a group of essays that provide several different views of the central subject. These are followed by three short stories and a varying number of poems that cast the light of creative imagination upon the subject. The foreword to each section indicates the contrasts to be found there. Finally, of course, it is the material itself that establishes the basic contrasts, and these contrasts are as complex and diverse as the selections themselves.

Since each section provides examples of essayists, poets, and short story writers dealing, each in his own way, with the same subject, the student can become aware of some of the differing imaginative perspectives and artistic techniques possible within the various genres. Moreover, since the sections are arranged according to subject rather than period, a teacher can demonstrate how a topic

of perennial interest is modified by individual talent and changing times. For example, an affirmative love poem by Andrew Marvell can be more fully understood as its form and content are compared to and contrasted with those of a poem on the same complex theme by E. E. Cummings.

We have considered the question of stylistic attitudes so important that we have devoted the last section to it. Although "Perspectives of Style and Structure" focuses upon the twentieth century, it is possible to contrast the works in this section with selections in the anthology from earlier periods. With the essays, we chose to include not only standard expository works, but also examples of essays that are descriptive, such as George Orwell's "Hanging"; familiar, such as E. B. White's "Death of a Pig"; and journalistic, such as Norman MacKenzie's "Dreams and Dreaming."

The nine poems by William Butler Yeats constitute another feature of the anthology. We have concluded each section with at least one of his poems—three of them in Part VI—thus providing a consistent referent, a transitional device, and a small but representative selection from one major poet.

We have excluded drama because we were dissatisfied with the inevitable limitations in the number and range of plays that could be included in a one-volume collection. We believe that when drama is a part of the course, a separate, inexpensive anthology of perhaps a dozen plays would be more useful and practical than the four or five plays we might have chosen.

Apparatus in this anthology has been kept to a minimum. The teacher thus has freedom to choose the means by which his students may be led to their own intellectual and emotional insights. A teacher's manual, however, is available; it contains suggestions on analyzing the selections, topics for discussion, and subjects for compositions.

We are grateful to a number of people for their help in the preparing of this anthology. To Mr. J. G. Case, our editor at The Macmillan Company, we owe a special debt of gratitude, which is not lessened by this public statement. Others also have given generously of helpful criticism and encouragement. In particular we would thank Professors Leo Hamalian, Edmond Volpe, Theodore Gross, and Arthur Zeiger, of the City College of the City University of New York. Of a more personal nature is our indebtedness to Elisabeth DeNitto and Judith Jobin.

D. D. N.
D. J. L.

CONTENTS

I

LOVE

THE FACES
OF VIOLENCE

DEATH

IV

SOME VARIETIES
OF
RELIGIOUS
BELIEF

xvi

V

DREAMS AND THE UNCONSCIOUS

VI

THE INDIVIDUAL AND SOCIETY

I

LOVE

FOREWORD

The works in this section on love are limited to the complex emotional and physical relations between a man and a woman. Each essayist's approach to heterosexual love may be characterized by his predominant perspective: Aldous Huxley, social; Joseph Wood Krutch, moral; Ernest van den Haag, cultural; Edmund Wilson, physiological.

Once again, in the short stories and poems, contrasts are evident. Max Beerbohm presents a social, idealistic, perhaps sentimental picture of a married couple. In the relationship depicted by Giovanni Verga, the heroine abandons all social restraints in her primitivistic, all-consuming passion. Cesare Pavese, on the other hand, describes the feelings of a man who is isolated and unable to commit himself more than tentatively to a woman.

The poems in this section have been grouped on the basis of whether the poet's primary attitude toward love is affirmative or negative. The poets in the first group emphasize the attractions of love. Less sanguine are the poets in the second group; they view this subject with colder eyes. The Yeats poem is ambiguous, balanced between the misery and the delight of love.

ESSAYS

FASHIONS IN LOVE

Aldous Huxley
(1894–1963)

Human nature does not change, or, at any rate, history is too short for any changes to be perceptible. The earliest known specimens of art and literature are still comprehensible. The fact that we can understand them all and can recognize in some of them an unsurpassed artistic excellence is proof enough that not only men's feelings and instincts, but also their intellectual and imaginative powers, were in the remotest times precisely what they are now. In the fine arts it is only the convention, the form, the incidentals that change: the fundamentals of passion, of intellect and imagination remain unaltered.

It is the same with the arts of life as with the fine arts. Conventions and traditions, prejudices and ideals and religious beliefs, moral systems and codes of good manners, varying according to the geographical and historical circumstances, mold into different forms the unchanging material of human instinct, passion, and desire. It is a stiff, intractable material—Egyptian granite, rather than Hindu bronze. The artists who carved the colossal statues of Rameses II may have wished to represent the Pharaoh standing on one leg and waving two or three pairs of arms over his head, as the Indians still represent the dancing Krishna. But with the best will in the world they could not have imposed such a form upon the granite. Similarly, those artists in social life whom we call statesmen, moralists, founders of religions, have often wished to mold human nature into forms of superhuman elegance; but the material has proved too stubborn for them, and they have had to be content with only a relatively small alteration in the form which their predecessors had given it. At any given historical moment human behavior is a compromise (enforced from without by law and custom, from within by belief in religious or philosophical myths) between the raw instinct on the one hand and the unattainable ideal on the other—a compromise, in our sculptural metaphor, between the unshaped block of stone and the many-armed dancing Krishna.

Like all the other great human activities, love is the product of unchanging passions, instincts, and desires (unchanging, that is to say, in the mass of humanity; for, of course, they vary greatly in quantity and quality from individual to individual), and of laws and conventions, beliefs and ideals, which the circumstances of time and place, or the arbitrary fiats of great personalities, have imposed on a more or less willing society. The history of love, if it were ever written (and doubtless some learned German, unread, alas, by me, *has* written it, and in several volumes), would be like the current histories of art—a record of succeeding "styles" and "schools," of "influences," "revolutions," "technical discoveries." Love's psychological and physiological material remains the same; but every epoch treats it in a different manner, just as every epoch cuts its unvarying cloth and silk and linen into garments of the most diverse fashion. By way of illustration, I may mention that vogue of homosexuality which seems, from all accounts, to have been universal in the Hellenic world. Plutarch attributes the inception of this mode to the custom (novel in the fifth century, according to Thucydides) of exercising naked in the Palestra.[1] But whatever may have been its origin, there can be no doubt that this particular fashion in love spread widely among people who were not in the least congenitally disposed to homosexuality. Convention and public opinion molded the material of love into forms which a later age has chosen to call "unnatural." A recrudescence of this amorous mode was very noticeable in Europe during the years immediately following the War. Among the determining causes of this recrudescence a future Plutarch will undoubtedly number the writings of Proust and André Gide.

The present fashions in love are not so definite and universal as those in clothes. It is as though our age were dubiously hesitating between crinolines and hobble skirts, trunk hose and Oxford trousers. Two distinct and hostile conceptions of love coexist in the minds of men and women, two sets of ideals, of conventions,

---

[1] Plutarch, who wrote some five hundred years after the event, is by no means an unquestionable authority. The habit of which he and Thucydides speak may have facilitated the spread of the homosexual fashion. But that the fashion existed before the fifth century is made sufficiently clear by Homer, not to mention Sappho. Like many modern oriental peoples, the ancient Greeks were evidently, in Sir Richard Burton's expressive phrase, "omnifutuent."

of public opinions, struggle for the right to mold the psychological and physiological material of love. One is the conception evolved by the nineteenth century out of the ideals of Christianity on the one hand and romanticism on the other. The other is that still rather inchoate and negative conception which contemporary youth is in process of forming out of the materials provided by modern psychology. The public opinion, the conventions, ideals, and prejudices which gave active force to the first convention and enabled it, to some extent at least, to modify the actual practice of love, had already lost much of their strength when they were rudely shattered, at any rate in the minds of the young, by the shock of the War. As usually happens, practice preceded theory, and the new conception of love was called in to justify existing post-War manners. Having gained a footing, the new conception is now a cause of new behavior among the youngest adolescent generation, instead of being, as it was for the generation of the War, an explanation of war-time behavior made after the fact.

Let us try to analyze these two coexisting and conflicting conceptions of love. The older conception was, as I have said, the product of Christianity and romanticism—a curious mixture of contradictions, of the ascetic dread of passion and the romantic worship of passion. Its ideal was a strict monogamy, such as St. Paul grudgingly conceded to amorous humanity, sanctified and made eternal by one of those terrific exclusive passions which are the favorite theme of poetry and drama. It is an ideal which finds its most characteristic expression in the poetry of that infinitely respectable rebel, that profoundly anglican worshiper of passion, Robert Browning. It was Rousseau who first started the cult of passion for passion's sake. Before his time the great passions, such as that of Paris for Helen, of Dido for Æneas, of Paolo and Francesca for one another, had been regarded rather as disastrous maladies than as enviable states of soul. Rousseau, followed by all the romantic poets of France and England, transformed the grand passion from what it had been in the Middle Ages —a demoniac possession—into a divine ecstasy, and promoted it from the rank of a disease to that of the only true and natural form of love. The nineteenth-century conception of love was thus doubly mystical, with the mysticism of Christian asceticism and sacramentalism, and with the romantic mysticism of nature. It claimed an absolute rightness on the grounds of its divinity and of its naturalness.

Now, if there is one thing that the study of history and psychology makes abundantly clear, it is that there are no such things as either "divine" or "natural" forms of love. Innumerable gods have sanctioned and forbidden innumerable kinds of sexual behavior, and innumerable philosophers and poets have advocated the return to the most diverse kinds of "nature." Every form of amorous behavior, from chastity and monogamy to promiscuity and the most fantastic "perversions," is found both among animals and men. In any given human society, at any given moment, love, as we have seen, is the result of the interaction of the unchanging instinctive and physiological material of sex with the local conventions of morality and religion, the local laws, prejudices, and ideals. The degree of permanence of these conventions, religious myths, and ideals is proportional to their social utility in the given circumstances of time and place.

The new twentieth-century conception of love is realistic. It recognizes the diversity of love, not merely in the social mass from age to age, but from individual to contemporary individual, according to the dosage of the different instincts with which each is born, and the upbringing he has received. The new generation knows that there is no such thing as Love with a large L, and that what the Christian romantics of the last century regarded as the uniquely natural form of love is, in fact, only one of the indefinite number of possible amorous fashions, produced by specific circumstances at that particular time. Psychoanalysis has taught it that all the forms of sexual behavior previously regarded as wicked, perverse, unnatural, are statistically normal (and normality is solely a question of statistics), and that what is commonly called amorous normality is far from being a spontaneous, instinctive form of behavior, but must be acquired by a process of education. Having contracted the habit of talking freely and more or less scientifically about sexual matters, the young no longer regard love with that feeling of rather guilty excitement and thrilling shame which was for an earlier generation the normal reaction to the subject. Moreover, the practice of birth-control has robbed amorous indulgence of most of the sinfulness traditionally supposed to be inherent in it by robbing it of its socially disastrous effects. The tree shall be known by its fruits: where there are no fruits, there is obviously no tree. Love has ceased to be the rather fearful, mysterious thing it was, and become a perfectly normal, almost commonplace, activity—an activity, for many young people, especially in America, of the same nature as dancing or tennis, a sport, a recreation, a pastime. For those who hold this conception of love, liberty and toleration are prime necessities. A strenuous offensive against the old taboos and repressions is everywhere in progress.

Such, then, are the two conceptions of love which oppose one another today. Which is the better? Without presuming to pass judgment, I will content myself with pointing out the defects of each. The older conception was bad, in so far as it inflicted unnecessary and undeserved sufferings on the many human beings whose congenital and acquired modes of love-making did not conform to the fashionable Christian-romantic pattern which was regarded as being uniquely entitled to call itself Love. The new conception is bad, it seems to me, in so far as it takes love too easily and lightly. On love regarded as an amusement the last word is surely this of Robert Burns:

> I waive the quantum of the sin,
> The hazard of concealing;
> But oh! it hardens all within
> And petrifies the feeling.

Nothing is more dreadful than a cold, unimpassioned indulgence. And love infallibly becomes cold and unimpassioned when it is too lightly made. It is not good, as Pascal remarked, to have too much liberty. Love is the product of two opposed forces—of an instinctive impulse and a social resistance acting on the individual by means of ethical imperatives justified by philosophical or religious myths. When, with the destruction of the myths, resistance is removed, the impulse wastes itself on emptiness; and love, which is only the product of conflicting forces, is not born. The twentieth century is reproducing in a new form the error of the early nineteenth-century romantics. Following Rousseau, the romantics imagined that exclusive passion was the "natural" mode of love, just as virtue and reasonableness were the "natural" forms of men's social behavior: Get rid of priests and kings, and men will be for ever good and happy; poor Shelley's faith in this palpable nonsense remained unshaken to the end. He believed also in the complementary paralogism that you had only to get rid of social restraints and erroneous mythology to make the Grand Passion universally chronic. Like the Mussets and Sands, he failed to see that the Grand Passion was produced by the restraints that opposed themselves to the sexual impulse, just as the deep lake is produced by the dam that bars the passage of the stream, and the flight of the aeroplane by the air which resists the impulsion given to it by the motor. There would be no air-resistance in a vacuum; but precisely for that reason the machine would not leave the ground, or even move at all. Where there are no psychological or external restrains, the Grand Passion does not come into existence and must be artificially cultivated, as George Sands and Musset cultivated it—with what painful and grotesque results the episode of Venice made only too ludicrously manifest.

"J'aime et je veux pâlir; j'aime et je veux souffrir," says Musset, with his usual hysterically masochistic emphasis. Our young contemporaries do not wish to suffer or grow pale; on the contrary, they have a most determined desire to grow pink and enjoy themselves. But too much enjoyment "blunts the fine point of seldom pleasure." Unrestrained indulgence kills not merely passion, but, in the end, even amusement. Too much liberty is as life-destroying as too much restraint. The present fashion in love-making is likely to be short, because love that is psychologically too easy is not interesting. Such, at any rate, was evidently the opinion of the French, who, bored by the sexual license produced by the Napoleonic upheavals, reverted (so far, at any rate, as the upper and middle classes were concerned) to an almost anglican strictness under Louis-Philippe. We may anticipate an analogous reaction in the not distant future. What new or what revived mythology will serve to create those internal restraints without which sexual impulse cannot be transformed into love? Christian morality and ascetic ideals will doubtless continue to play their part, but there will no less certainly be other moralities and ideals. For example, Mr. D.

H. Lawrence's new mythology of nature (new in its expression, but reassuringly old in substance) is a doctrine that seems to me fruitful in possibilities. The "natural love" which he sets up as a norm is a passion less self-conscious and high-falutin, less obviously and precariously artificial, than that "natural love" of the romantics, in which Platonic and Christian notions were essential ingredients. The restraints which Mr. Lawrence would impose on sexual impulse, so as to transform it into love, are not the restraints of religious spirituality. They are restraints of a more fundamental, less artificial nature—emotional, not intellectual. The impulse is to be restrained from promiscuous manifestations because, if it were not, promiscuity would "harden all within and petrify the feeling." The restraint is of the same personal nature as the impulse. The conflict is between a part of the personality and the personality as an organized whole. It does not pretend, as the romantic and Christian conflict pretends, to be a battle between a diabolical Lower Self and certain transcendental Absolutes, of which the only thing that philosophy can tell us is that they are absolutely unknowable, and therefore, for our purposes, nonexistent. It only claims to be, what in fact it is, a psychological conflict taking place in the more or less known and finite world of human interests. This doctrine has several great advantages over previous systems of inward restraint. It does not postulate the existence of any transcendental, non-human entity. This is a merit which will be increasingly appreciated as the significance of Kant's and Nietzsche's destructive criticism is more widely realized. People will cease to be interested in unknowable absolutes; but they will never lose interest in their own personalities. True, that "personality as a whole," in whose interests the sexual impulse is to be restrained and turned into love, is, strictly

speaking, a mythological figure. Consisting, as we do, of a vast colony of souls—souls of individual cells, of organs, of groups of organs, hunger-souls, sex-souls, power-souls, herd-souls, of whose multifarious activities our consciousness (the Soul with a large S) is only very imperfectly and indirectly aware—we are not in a position to know the real nature of our personality as a whole. The only thing we can do is to hazard a hypothesis, to create a mythological figure, call it Human Personality, and hope that circumstances will not, by destroying us, prove our imaginative guesswork too hopelessly wrong. But myth for myth, Human Personality is preferable to God. We do at least know something of Human Personality, whereas of God we know nothing and, knowing nothing, are at liberty to invent as freely as we like. If men had always tried to deal with the problem of love in terms of known human rather than of grotesquely imagined divine interests, there would have been less "making of eunuchs for the kingdom of heaven's sake," less persecution of "sinners," less burning and imprisoning of the heretics of "unnatural" love, less Grundyism, less Comstockery, and, at the same time, less dirty Don Juanism, less of that curiously malignant and vengeful love-making so characteristic of the debauchee under a Christian dispensation. Reacting against the absurdities of the old mythology, the young have run into absurdities no less inordinate at the other end of the scale. A sordid and ignoble realism offers no resistance to the sexual impulse, which now spends itself purposelessly, without producing love, or even, in the long-run, amusement, without enhancing vitality or quickening and deepening the rhythm of living. Only a new mythology of nature, such as, in modern times, Blake, Robert Burns, and Lawrence have defined it, an untranscendental and (relatively speaking) realistic mythology of Energy, Life, and Human Personality, will provide, it seems to me, the inward resistances necessary to turn sexual impulse into love, and provide them in a form which the critical intelligence of Post-Nietzschean youth can respect. By means of such a conception a new fashion in love may be created, a mode more beautiful and convenient, more healthful and elegant, than any seen among men since the days of remote and pagan antiquity.

LOVE—OR THE LIFE AND DEATH OF A VALUE

Joseph Wood Krutch
(1893–   )

I

In one of these popular phrases too generally current to be attributed to any particular person, and hence seeming to have been uttered by a whole and united folk, our Victorian ancestors were accustomed to say that "love is best." Perhaps no other cultural group had ever set itself more resolutely to discipline this most unruly of passions by laying down the conditions under which one might permissibly indulge in it, and perhaps no other had expressed a more inflexible disapproval of any violation of the taboos with which it was surrounded; but, for all the strictness of its definition, it gave to "virtuous love" the highest place in its hierarchy of values.

The age was, though we sometimes forget the fact, an age of many skepticisms, during which many things were called in question, but it never doubted the worth of that which we are accustomed to call, in a phrase whose downrightness would have shocked it profoundly, "sublimated sex." It looked with loathing and fear at any of the cruder manifestations of the sexual instincts, but when those instincts had been adorned with poetry, and submitted to the discipline of society, it regarded them as the source not only of the most admirable virtues, but of the most intrinsically valuable of human experiences as well. In theory, at least, a successful love crowned all other successes and obliterated all other failures. It made all men equal because all men were capable of it, and it stood between man and any ultimate pessimism because, so long as love was possible, life could not be either meaningless or not worth the living. Nor was this evaluation questioned by the leaders in any school of thought, for upon this point even Gladstone and Huxley would have agreed. Whether man were son of God or great-grandson of the ape, it was in love that he fulfilled himself. If he were the former, then love brought him nearer than anything else to the divine state from which he had fallen; if he were the latter, then at least love carried him to the highest level of which he was capable.

Now faiths such as this lie deeper than religious or political creeds. The Christian knows that he is a Christian and that other people are not; the Democrat is aware of theories of government other than his; but such tacit evaluations as that set upon love are accepted as matters of fact almost as something established by the scheme of nature. These Victorians knew that they were, in the literal sense of the word, puritans here as elsewhere. They knew, that is to say, that they had insisted upon a soberness in love as well as in religion, and that they looked upon the antisocial tendencies of extravagant passion in the same way that they looked upon the antisocial tendencies of extravagant religion; but that it was in love that the meaning of life must inevitably be sought they never stopped to doubt. They did not much consider the fact that the ability to live for love in any form was a relatively recent accomplishment on the part of the human race; that the tacit assumption which lay behind all their literature and all their thinking was not, after all, part of the unchangeable nature of man, but merely an assumption, seemingly inevitable because it had been handed on and accepted by one generation after another, which had changed the rules of the game, but never doubted that it was worth the playing. And it was in part because love seemed to them so inevitably valuable that they were able to hold so firmly to their belief in its supreme importance.

We, however, have specialized in origins, and it requires no more than a glance at the past to show that the high values set upon love are not inevitable. Certainly the savage—the American Indian, for example—knows little of what we call romance. When he sings his songs or addresses his gods, when, that is to say, his consciousness reaches the intensest level of which he is capable, it is upon thoughts of agriculture and of war that he dwells. These are the activities which seem to him to be most worthy to be realized or adorned in contemplation, because they are the ones which seem to bring him closest to the meaning of life; and when he thinks of wooing he does so chiefly not because he regards love as the most significant of human emotions, but because his wife will bear him sons to help guide the destiny of the tribe or to slay its enemies. Like all human beings, the savage considers certain experiences as ends in themselves, but he still regards the act of sexual union as a relatively simple process, important chiefly because of its biological function; it is only somewhere between savagery and civilization that love is born.

At first it holds, no doubt, a relatively low place in the hierarchy of values. The stories which deal with it are at first fewer than those which deal with the struggle against the elements and warfare with neighboring tribes; the lover is still far less than the warrior the type of the hero; and soft emotions are still a matter for surprise, almost for shame. But, once these emotions have been accepted into song and story, they reveal an amazing capacity to elaborate and complicate themselves. They come to be regarded with respect and awe; a mythology quite as elaborate as that concerning the combats of warriors grows up around them; and tacitly it is assumed that a great love is a subject hardly less worthy, hardly less near the divine, than a great heroism.

Perhaps the sterner members of the society set themselves up against it and shake their heads when amorous songs or poems win more applause than warlike ones, but at least the romantic view of life has come to set itself against what, for want of a better name, we must call the heroic one, and a value is born.

Love is, then, not a fact in nature of which we become aware, but rather a creation of the human imagination; and this is true not only when we think of the word as implying some complicated system of attitudes like that of the Victorians, but even when we think of it as referring to no more than a mere physical act to which considerable importance is attached. The very singling out of this particular desire as one more significant than others must precede any attribution of transcendental values to it, and even this singling out took place recently enough for us to be aware of it. If mere lust cannot play any very large part in human life until the imagination has created it, how much more conspicuously is it true that we must regard as purely a creation of the human mind so complex a system of emotional attitudes—interwoven with all sorts of aesthetic, sociological and mystical conceptions—as that which was implied by the Victorian in the word

quite as complete as that of any Victorian novel; and if one reads the six volumes of Havelock Ellis's *Studies in the Psychology of Sex*—which will stand perhaps as the completest and most characteristic of those works which made a rationalist attitude toward sex an important feature of the spirit of the age—one will see that to Ellis, too, love has its element of transcendental value. Neither the scientist nor the romancer dreamed of questioning the fact that love was the most significant of human experiences and that in it men might find the ultimate justification of life. If both were frequently concerned with an attack upon what were beginning to be called, even in popular language, the "taboos" which surround the theory and the practice of love, both were so concerned because they thought of love as too obviously the supreme privilege of man to be burdened with irrational proscriptions; and their ultimate purpose was, in a word, not to cheapen or tarnish, but merely to free it.

The Victorians, for all their romantic system of values, had accepted the frustrations and the sacrifices entailed by their social code with a complacency which seemed to the new generation hardly less than heartless. They had seemed to take even a sort of perverse satisfaction in contemplating the bowed head with which people were supposed to acknowledge the inviolability of the rules and which Matthew Arnold had celebrated in two of his most characteristic stanzas:

Each in his own strict line we move,
And some find death ere they find love;
So far apart their lives are thrown
From the twin soul that halves their own.

And sometimes, by still harder fate,
The lovers meet, but meet too late.
—Thy heart is mine; *True, true. Ah, true,*
—Then, love, thy hand; *Ah, no! Adieu!*

They had, moreover, visited their punishments mercilessly, and they had even —witness George Eliot in *Adam Bede*— persuaded themselves that the punishment visited by society upon those who violated its taboos were the result of a law of nature, and the new generation was merely anxious to avoid the commoner tragedies of love which it regarded as avoidable. It looked forward to an individual who, free from a corroding sense of sin, should live in a society which placed no unnecessary restrictions upon emotional fulfillment, and, far from anticipating any cynical devaluation of love itself, it hoped only for an age in which men should love more feely, more fully, and more perfectly.

Yet it requires no more than a casual acquaintance with either contemporary life or its reflec in contemporary literature to enabl to perceive that this life hardly cor nds to the anticipation.

Freedom has come, but with it a certain lessened sense of the importance of the passions that are thus freely indulged; and, if love has come to be less often a sin, it has come also to be less often a supreme privilege. If one turns to the smarter of those novelists who describe the doings of the more advanced set of those who are experimenting with life— to, for example, Mr. Aldous Huxley or Mr. Ernest Hemingway—one will discover in their tragic farces the picture of a society which is at bottom in despair because, though it is more completely absorbed in the pursuit of love than in anything else, it has lost the sense of any ultimate importance inherent in the experience which preoccupies it; and if one turns to the graver of the intellectual writers—to, for example, Mr. D. H. Lawrence, Mr. T. S. Eliot, or Mr. James Joyce —one will find both explicitly and implicitly a similar sense that the transcendental value of love has become somehow attenuated, and that, to take a perfectly concrete example, a conclusion which does no more than bring a man and woman into complete possession of one another is a mere bathos which does nothing except legitimately provoke the comment, "Well, what of it?" One can hardly imagine them concerned with what used to be called, in a phrase which they have helped to make faintly ridiculous, "the right to love." Individual freedom they have inherited and assumed as a right, but they are concerned with something which their more restricted forefathers assumed—with, that is to say, the value of love itself. No inhibitions either within or without restrain them, but they are asking themselves, "What is it worth?" and they are certainly no longer feeling that it is obviously and of itself something which makes life worth the living.

To Huxley and Hemingway—I take them as the most conspicuous exemplars of a whole school—love is at times only a sort of obscene joke. The former in particular has delighted to mock sentiment with physiology, to place the emotions of the lover in comic juxtaposition with quaint biological lore, and to picture a romantic pair "quietly sweating palm to palm." But the joke is one which turns quickly bitter upon the tongue, for a great and gratifying illusion has passed away, leaving the need for it still there. His characters still feel the physiological urge, and, since they have no sense of sin in connection with it, they yield easily and continually to that urge; but they have also the human need to respect their chief preoccupation, and it is the capacity to do this that they have lost. Absorbed in the pursuit of sexual satisfaction, they never find love and they are scarcely aware that they are seeking it, but they are far from content with themselves. In a generally devaluated world they are eagerly endeavoring to get what they can in the pursuit of satisfactions which are sufficiently in-

stinctive to retain inevitably a modicum of animal pleasure, but they cannot transmute that simple animal pleasure into anything else. They themselves not infrequently share the contempt with which their creator regards them, and nothing could be less seductive, because nothing could be less glamorous, than the description of the debaucheries born of nothing except a sense of the emptiness of life.

Now it is gratifyingly appropriate that this Huxley should be the grandson of the great Victorian exponent of life rationally conducted in the light of natural knowledge, since the predicament which he recognizes is a direct result of the application of the principles advocated by the grandfather. It is true, of course, that Thomas Henry Huxley felt too strongly the influence of Victorian taboos ever to indulge in any extended naturalistic consideration of the problems of sex, but the Ellises and the Wellses, whom we have taken as the type of those who have concerned themselves with such an effort, did little more than apply the principles which he laid down. They used analysis in an effort to clarify an illusion, and the result, which now seems as though it might have been foretold, was to destroy that illusion.

They were, to be sure, successful in the immediate objects which they proposed to themselves; they did, that is to say, succeed in freeing love, both by relaxing somewhat the ferocity with which society had punished conduct which deviated from even the mere letter of its code and by lifting from mankind the burden of that sense of guilt which had oppressed so many and not infrequently poisoned what would have been otherwise a mighty and perfect experience. But when the consequences of love were made less momentous, then love itself became less momentous too, and we have discovered that the now-lifted veil of mystery was that which made it potentially important as well as potentially terrible. Sex, we learned, was not so awesome as once we had thought; God does not care so much about it as we had formerly been led to suppose; but neither, as a result, do we. Love is becoming gradually so accessible, so unmysterious, and so free that its value is trivial.

That which the Victorians regarded as possessed of a supreme and mystical value was, as we have already pointed out, a group of related ideas and emotional aptitudes whose elements had, during a long period of time, been associated by means of connections not always logical. Analysis can dissociate them and has indeed done so, but in so doing it destroys the importance which only as a group they possessed. We know that the social consequences which once followed a surrender to love need no longer do so, and hence the nexus between the sexual act and those elements of the love complex which are predominantly social has disappeared. More important yet, we know, or rather we feel, that this act is a simple biological one which sends no reverberations through a spiritual universe, and so it no longer has any transcendental implications. With vertiginous rapidity it is being reduced to that which it was in savage or prehuman society, and threatens to become again no more than a simple physiological act with no more than a simple physiological act's importance or value.

For many generations the adolescence of the individual has repeated the miracle achieved in the first place by the human race as a whole; it has, that is to say, associated the new impulses suddenly discovered in itself with various duties to society and with all the other aspirations of which it is capable; but this miracle is one which is becoming constantly more difficult of performance. Certain individuals have always and for different reasons failed to achieve it, and they have been compelled in consequence to lead jangled lives; but more and more people find themselves victims of a disharmony which results from the fact that they cannot escape a continual preoccupation with a passion which seems to their intellect trivial, and it would not be wholly fanciful to say that this sense of disharmony, of the unworthiness of their aims, is the modern equivalent of the conviction of sin.

It is not to be supposed, I take it, that any mood so disrupted as this is destined to endure. It represents an unstable equilibrium of forces in which one or the other is bound sooner or later to yield; for if the passion of love is to be devaluated, then it must be made to play in human life a part as small as our slight estimate of its importance makes appropriate. Such was the position to which the early Church Fathers attempted to reduce it, and they were unsuccessful because the conflict which they felt between their instincts and their intellectual convictions was resolved in the religion of love; but the modern consciousness is surely destined either to evolve some equally mighty fiction or, while surrendering the erotic instinct as a source of important values, to dispose of it in some fashion involving a minimum of inconvenience and distraction. Nor is the fact that the ferocious and deliberate nastiness of some current writers suggests that of the Fathers, that, for example, Huxley has even in the midst of one of his novels quoted in the Latin from which he hardly dared translate it one of the most brutally scornful of their comments upon the flesh, merely an accident, since there is a certain similarity between the early saint and the contemporary sophisticate which is due to the fact that, however different their experiences may be, each rejects love for the same reason —each, that is to say, has refused to surround it with mystical implications, and each, looking at it as a mere biological fact, has found it ridiculous and disgusting. Certainly the nastiness of, let us say, James Joyce's *Ulysses* is the nastiness of an ascetic reviling the flesh in order that he may be free of it.

Now, if we set aside the ascetic ideal which in the past, at least, has generally proved itself radically impracticable, and if we set aside also the romantic ideal which the rationalizing tendencies of the human mind seem certain to destroy, there is only one way in which the artist —by which term is here meant whoever is distinctly human enough to have a plan for his life which he sets up in opposition to the simple plan of nature—may deal with sex, and that way is the one in which it is accepted as something ineluctable, perhaps, but nevertheless uncomplex and trivial. The man who follows it may feel no need to battle against the flesh; he may have no desire to waste his energies in a futile struggle against the inclinations of the natural man, and he may preach no stern denials; but he makes of love a game, a joke, a ribaldry even, in order that, since it no longer seems really significant, it may be reduced to a mere incident.

And if, leaving the Huxleys and the Hemingways, who are concerned with characters still in the midst of confusion, we turn to certain other novelists, poets, and critics, we shall find them at least adumbrating such a solution, as may be illustrated by the words put into the mouth of a by no means ascetic painter in one of the most powerful of contemporary novels. "The tendency of my work," he remarks, "is, as you may have noticed, that of an invariable severity. Apart from its being good or bad, its character is ascetic rather than sensuous, and divorced from immediate life. There is no slop of sex in *that*."

Such a character is merely the novelist's projection of a type which logically results from the effort to think one's way through the confusions just outlined. This painter —Tarr is his name—represents the direction in which we are moving, and he ex-

plains the growing popularity of abstract design in the plastic arts and of pure intellectualism in literature, since both represent a reaction from that diffusion of sublimated sex through all the arts which is one of the chief characteristics of romanticism. But however logical and inevitable such a tendency may be, and however preferable it is to an absorption in things which can no longer be respected, it must be remembered that it is, nevertheless, based upon a complete surrender of something which we have been accustomed to regard as one of the chief values in human life, and that it leaves a mighty blank in existence.

Whatever else love may still be—game, puerility, or wry joke played by the senses and the imagination upon the intellect—it no longer is the ultimate self-justifying value which once it was. We may still on occasion surrender to it, but surrender is no longer a paradoxical victory and the world is no longer well lost for love. Many other things we have come to doubt —patriotism, self-sacrifice, respectability, honor—but in the general wreck the wreck of love is conspicuous and typical. Rationalism having destroyed the taboos which surrounded it, and physiology having rudely investigated its phenomena upon the same level as other biological processes, it has been stripped of the mystical penumbra in whose shadow its transcendental value seemed real, though hid; and somehow, in the course of the very process of winning the right to love, love itself has been deprived of its value.

Such, in outline, is the process by which is accomplished what has here been called the death of a value. Many of us, not yet old, were born at a time when the religion of love was all but unquestioned, when it seemed to stand more firmly than even the religion of the Church, whose foundations science was already known to have slowly undermined. But if we have followed the course of modern thought we have seen it rapidly disintegrate. We have seen how works, of which Havelock Ellis's *magnum opus* is a type, claimed love as a legitimate subject for rationalistic consideration, and how, though Ellis himself believed that the superstructure of poetry would remain after its foundations had been subject to rational examination, just as Thomas Huxley believed that the superstructure of Christian morality would stand after the supernatural props had been removed from under it, the mystical values lingered as ghosts for only one generation after rationalism had attacked the mythology upon which they rested.

We have seen the rise of an atheism quite as significant in the history of the human soul as that which has regard to religion in the more conventional sense, and one whose result may be summed up by a consideration of the fact that, though the phrase "love is best" meant to our grandfathers more things than a volume could describe, it is to us so completely denuded that we can only repeat it as we repeat one of those formulæ of theology which, though once rich with meaning, are to us only words, words, words.

III

Others who have described, though perhaps in somewhat different terms, the disintegration of the love complex have been concerned chiefly with its effect upon human society. They have stressed their fear that, for example, the progressive tendency to dissociate love from family life would involve the most thoroughgoing reconstruction of our social organization, even if it did not destroy the possibility of any stable society, and in general they have thought of modified sexual customs in terms of their effect upon the race. We, however, are here concerned with the individual and with the consequences which the process we have been describing may have for the intimate emotional life of the separate soul—with, in a word, the changes involved by the death of love in the character of what we may call the experience of living.

We will, if we must, give up the illusion of love. The time may come when it will mean to us even less than it now means to the philosophical Chinese and no more than it did to the savage; when, to state the case somewhat differently, romance will be, either as a motive in art or an aim in living, as fundamentally incomprehensible to us as it is to the American Indian, and when it will be so, not because we have not yet developed the complex system of associations upon which it depends, but because the analytical tendencies of our intelligence forbid our imagination to create the values once deemed so precious.

We may realize now that the effort to develop the possibilities of love as an adornment of life by understanding it more completely wrecks itself upon the fact that to understand any of the illusions upon which the values of life depend inevitably destroys them; but we realize that fact too late, and even if we should convince ourselves that we have paid too high a price for our rationality, that we should willingly reassume all the taboos of the Victorian if we could feel again his buoyant sense that the meaning of life had been revealed to him through love, we could no more recapture his illusions by means of an intellectual conviction than we could return to the passionate faith of the Middle Ages merely because, having read Ruskin, we should like to build a cathedral.

Nor is human life so rich in values as to justify us in surrendering any one of them complacently. At bottom, life is worth living only because certain of our conscious activities allowed themselves to be regarded as though they were possessed of some importance or significance in themselves, and even the number of such conscious activities is too strictly limited to permit us to accept without foreboding the reduction of so important a one as that of sexual union to the status of a mere triviality. Many of the life processes—and by no means the least important—are carried on without the accompaniment of any awareness whatsoever. The beating of the heart and the slow churning of the stomach, to say nothing of the infinitely complicated activities with which the glands are busy, are as little a part of that consciousness which we know of as ourselves as is the shifting of the earth upon its axis or the explosive disintegration of an atom of radium. In one sense man cannot either "know himself" or "live completely," for the simple reason that only a fragment of his total organism is connected with that part of the brain wherein resides all that he is accustomed to call his ego or self. The body keeps itself alive by processes which we neither will nor recognize, and death may be preparing itself for months before a warning finally bursts its way into that relatively small mass of cells to which our awareness and hence our emotions confine themselves. When the life of any individual rises above the dim level of the mere toiler whose existence is scarcely more than a round of duties, and reaches that distinctly human level upon which contemplation in some form or other furnishes the motive for living, it does so because he has attributed a meaningfulness to some aspect of consciousness, but the possibilities for such attribution are limited.

Eating, because it is a conscious and not an unconscious process, because the taste buds of the tongue happen to be connected by nerves with the cerebrum and not the cerebellum, can be made into one of the ceremonies by which life is elaborated and can pass as a symbol into poetry and philosophy. So, for the same reason, can the act of sexual union; but both digestion and gestation, because they are controlled without the intervention of consciousness, are destined to remain merely unadorned processes of nature. Man has wanted to live in order to love or even in order to eat, but hardly in order either to gestate or to digest. Yet it is merely an accident of our nervous organization that this is so.

Thus it is that of the infinitely complicated processes of life, in the biological sense, only a few are subject to that elaboration and poetization which make them even potentially a part of significant human experience. Just as the ears can hear only a certain limited class of the innumerable kinds of waves which roll incessantly through the air, and the eyes can see only a certain few of those vibrations in the ether which, after ranging from red to violet, pass on into invisibility, so, too, only a few of the processes of life furnish materials available to the mind. From a limited number of colors we must paint our pictures, from a limited number of sounds compose our symphonies, and from a limited number of conscious processes construct our "good life." But we are no more aware through our minds of the totality of what living involves than we are through our sense of the entire natural world. To ultraviolet light we are as blind as a man without eyes, and, similarly, most of our biological existence is as meaningless to us as the life of an insect is to it. Whatever does not happen within a few square inches upon the surface of our forebrain does not, so far as we are concerned, happen at all. It cannot be made the source of any human value, because it is a part of us which lives as the plant lives, without any knowledge of itself.

Nature, then, has imposed a certain rigid selection upon us. Grudgingly, perhaps, she has permitted us to be aware of certain of her activities, and has bid us do what we may by way of contemplating or elaborating them until they seem to become not, as to her all things are, merely the means by which life is kept going, but ends to be enjoyed or valued in themselves. Within the limits which she has set we have, moreover, made certain choices of our own. Certain of the available conscious processes have seemed to us more suitable than others for this contemplation or elaboration, and we have devoted ourselves to them, leaving the others merely upon the fringe of awareness. Thus we made mere animal combativeness into chivalry, surrounded lair-making with all the association which belongs to the idea of home, and created a sense of the presence of God out of the fears for our security; but the greatest and most elaborate of our creations was love, and the process by which it is stripped of its meaning is a process by which man is dehumanized and life is made to sink back to a level nearer that of the animal, for whom life is a phenomenon in which there is no meaning except the biological urge.

At the very least it means that a color has faded from our palette, a whole range of effects dropped out of our symphony. Intellectually we may find romantic people and romantic literature only ridiculous, intellectually we may convince ourselves that we regret the passing of love no more than the passing of the spring festival or even the disappearance of those passionate convictions which made civil war seem to the Middle Ages intrinsically worth while; but we cannot deny that life is made paler and that we are carried one step nearer to that state in which existence is seen as a vast emptiness which the imagination can no longer people with fascinating illusions.

For the more skeptical of the Victorians, love performed some of the functions of the God whom they had lost. Faced with it, many of even the most hard-headed turned, for the moment, mystical. They found themselves in the presence of something which awoke in them that sense of reverence which nothing else claimed, and something to which they felt, even in the very depths of their being, that an unquestioning loyalty was due. For them love, like God, demanded all sacrifices; but like Him, also, it rewarded the believer by investing all the phenomena of life with a meaning not yet analyzed away. We have grown used —more than they—to a Godless universe, but we are not yet accustomed to one which is loveless as well, and only when we have so become shall we realize what atheism really means.

LOVE OR MARRIAGE?

Ernest van den Haag
(1914–   )

If someone asks, "Why do people marry?" he meets indignation or astonishment. The question seems absurd if not immoral: the desirability of marriage is regarded as unquestionable. Divorce, on the other hand, strikes us as a problem worthy of serious and therapeutic attention. Yet marriage precedes divorce as a rule, and frequently causes it.

What explains marriage? People divorce often but they marry still more often. Lately they also marry—and divorce, of course—younger than they used to, particularly in the middle classes (most statistics understate the change by averaging all classes). And the young have a disproportionate share of divorces. However, their hasty exertions to get out of wedlock puzzle me less than their eagerness to rush into it in the first place.

A hundred years ago there was every reason to marry young—though middle-class people seldom did. The unmarried state had heavy disadvantages for both sexes. Custom did not permit girls to be educated, to work, or to have social, let alone sexual, freedom. Men were free but since women were not, they had only prostitutes for partners. (When enforced, the double standard is certainly self-defeating.) And, though less restricted than girls shackled to their families, single men often led a grim and uncomfortable life. A wife was nearly indispensable, if only to darn socks, sew, cook, clean, take care of her man. Altogether, both sexes needed marriage far more than now—no TV, cars, dates, drip-dry shirts, cleaners, canned foods—and not much hospital care, insurance, or social security. The family was all-important.

Marriage is no longer quite so indispensable a convenience; yet we find people marrying more than ever, and earlier. To be sure, prosperity makes marriage more possible. But why are the young exploiting the possibility so sedulously? Has the yearning for love become more urgent and widespread?

What has happened is that the physical conveniences which reduced the material usefulness of marriage have also loosened the bonds of family life. Many other bonds that sustained us psychologically were weakened as they were extended: beliefs became vague; associations impersonal, discontinuous, and casual. Our contacts are many, our relationships few: our lives, externally overcrowded, often are internally isolated; we remain but tenuously linked to each other and our ties come easily undone. One feels lonely surrounded by crowds and machines in an unbounded, abstract world that has become morally unintelligible; and we have so much time now to feel lonely. Thus one longs, perhaps more acutely than in the past, for somebody to be tangibly, individually, and definitely one's own, body and soul.

This is the promise of marriage. Movies,

songs, TV, romance magazines, all intensify the belief that love alone makes life worthwhile, is perpetual, conquers the world's evils, and is fulfilled and certified by marriage. "Science" hastens to confirm as much. Doesn't popular psychology, brandishing the banner of Freud with more enthusiasm than knowledge, tell us, in effect, that any male who stays single is selfish or homosexual or mother-dominated and generally neurotic? and any unmarried female frustrated (or worse, not frustrated) and neurotic? A "normal" person, we are told, must love and thereupon marry. Thus love and marriage are identified with each other and with normality, 3000 years of experience notwithstanding. The yearning for love, attended by anxiety to prove oneself well-adjusted and normal, turns into eagerness to get married.

The young may justly say that they merely practice what their parents preached. For, indeed, the idea that "love and marriage go together like a horse and carriage" has been drummed into their heads so much that it finally has come to seem entirely natural. Yet, nothing could be less so. Love has long delighted and distressed mankind, and marriage has comforted us steadily and well. Both, however, are denatured—paradoxically enough, by their stanchest supporters— when they are expected to "go together." For love is a very unruly horse, far more apt to run away and overturn the carriage than to draw it. That is why, in the past, people seldom thought of harnessing marriage to love. They felt that each has its own motive power: one primed for a life-long journey; the other for an ardent improvisation, a voyage of discovery.

Though by no means weaker, the marital bond is quite different from the bond of love. If you like, it is a different bond of love—less taut, perhaps, and more durable. By confusing these two related but in many ways dissimilar bonds, we stand to lose the virtues and gain the vices of both: the spontaneous passion of love and the deliberate permanence of marriage are equally endangered as we try to live up to an ideal which bogs down one and unhinges the other.

Marriage is an immemorial institution which, in some form, exists everywhere. Its main purpose always was to unite and to continue the families of bride and groom and to further their economic and social position. The families, therefore, were the main interested parties. Often marriages were arranged (and sometimes they took place) before the future husbands or wives were old enough to talk. Even when they were grown up, they felt, as did their parents, that the major purpose of marriage was to continue the family and produce children. Certainly women hoped for kind and vigorous providers and men for faithful mothers and good housekeepers; both undoubtedly hoped for affection, too; but love did not strike either as indispensable and certainly not as sufficient for marriage.

Unlike marriage, love has only recently come to be generally accepted as something more than a frenzied state of pleasure and pain. It was a welcome innovation —but easily ruined by marriage; which in turn has a hard time surviving confusion with love. Marriage counselors usually recognize this last point; but people in love seldom consult them. Perhaps their limited clientele colors the views of too many marriage counselors: instead of acknowledging that love and marriage are different but equally genuine relationships, they depict love as a kind of dependable wheel horse that can be harnessed to the carriage of married life. For them, any other kind of love must be an "immature" or "neurotic" fantasy, something to be condemned as Hollywood-inspired, "unrealistic" romanticism. It is as though a man opposed to horse racing— for good reasons perhaps—were to argue that race horses are not real, that all real horses are draft horses. Thus marriage counselors often insist that the only "real" and "true" love is "mature"—it is the comfortable workaday relation Mommy and Daddy have. The children find it hard to believe that there is nothing more to it.

In a sense, they are right. And they have on their side the great literature of the world, and philosophers from Plato to Santayana. What is wrong with Hollywood romance surely is not that it is romantic, but that its romances are shoddy cliches. And since Hollywood shuns the true dimensions of conflict, love in the movies is usually confirmed by marriage and marriage by love, in accordance with wishful fantasy, though not with truth.

Was the love Tristan bore Isolde "mature" or "neurotic"? They loved each other before and after Isolde was married —to King Mark. It never occurred to them to marry each other; they even cut short an extramarital idyll together in the forest. (And Tristan too, while protesting love for Isolde, got married to some other girl.) Dante saw, but never actually met Beatrice, until he reached the nether world, which is the place for permanent romance. Of course, he was a married man.

It is foolish to pretend that the passionate romantic longing doesn't exist or is "neurotic"—just as it is foolish to pretend that romantic love can be made part of a cozy domesticity. The truth is simple enough, though it can make life awfully complicated: There are two things, love and affection (or marital love), not one; they do not usually pull together as a team; they tend to draw us in different directions, if they are present at the same time. God nowhere promised to make this a simple world.

In the West, love came to be socially approved around the twelfth century. It became a fashionable subject of discussion then and even of disputation in formal "courts of love" convoked to argue its merits and to elaborate its true characteristics. Poets and singers created the models and images of love. They still do—though mass production has perhaps affected the quality; what else makes the teen-age crooners idols to their followers and what else do they croon about? In medieval times, as now, manuals were written codifying the behavior recommended to lovers. With a difference, though. Today's manuals are produced not by men of letters, but by doctors and psychologists, as though love, sex, and marriage were diseases or therapeutic problems—which they promptly become if one reads too many of these guidebooks (and one is one too many). Today's manuals bear titles like "Married Love" (unmarried lovers must manage without help, I guess); but regardless of title, they concentrate on sex. In handbooks on dating they tell how to avoid it; in handbooks on marriage, how to enjoy it. The authors are sure that happiness depends on the sexual mechanics they blueprint. Yet, one doesn't make love better by reading a book any more than one learns to dance or ride a bicycle by reading about it.

The sexual engineering (or cook-book) approach is profitable only for the writer: in an enduring relationship, physical gratification is an effect and not a cause. If a person does not acquire sexual skill from experience, he is not ready to do so. Whenever such inhibitions exist, no book can remove them. Where they do not, no book is necessary. I have seen many an unhappy relationship in my psychoanalytic practice, but none ever in which sexual technique or the lack of it was more than a symptom and an effect. The mechanical approach never helps.

The troubadours usually took sex and marriage for granted and dealt with love —the newest and still the most surprising and fascinating of all relationships. And also the most unstable. They conceived love as a longing, a tension between desire and fulfillment. This feeling, of course, had been known before they celebrated it. Plato described love as a desire for something one does not have, implying that it is a longing, not fulfillment. But in ancient Greece, love was regarded diffidently as rather undesirable, an intoxication, a bewitchment, a divine punishment —usually for neglecting sex. The troubadours thought differently, although, unlike many moderns, they did not deny that love is a passion, something one suffers.[1] But they thought it a sweet suffering to be cultivated, and they cele'rated it in song and story.

The troubadours clearly distinguished love from sex. Love was to them a yearning for a psychic gratification which the lover feels only the beloved can give; sex, an impersonal desire anybody possessing certain fairly common characteristics can gratify by physical actions. Unlike love, sex can flourish without an intense personal relationship and may erode if it exists. Indeed, the Romans sometimes wondered if love would not blunt and tame their sexual pleasures, whereas the troubadours fretted lest sex abate the fervor of love's longing. They never fully resolved the contest between love and sex, nor has anyone else. (To define it away is, of course, not to solve it.)

We try to cope with this contest by fusing love and sex. (Even high-school students have no doubt the two go together.) This, as Freud pointed out, does not always succeed and may moderate both, but, as he also implied, it is the best we can hope for. In the words of William

---

[1] . . . *I am in love*
And that is my shame.
What hurts the soul
My soul adores,
No better than a beast
Upon all fours.
So says W. B. Yeats. Seven hundred years earlier, Chrestien de Troyes expressed the same sentiment.

Butler Yeats, "Desire dies because every touch consumes the myth and yet, a myth that cannot be consumed becomes a specter. . . ."

Romantics, who want love's desiring to be conclusive, though endless, often linked it to death: if nothing further can happen and rival its significance, if one dies before it does, love indeed is the end. But this is ending the game as much as winning it—certainly an ambiguous move. The religious too perpetuate longing by placing the beloved altogether out of physical reach. The "bride of Christ" who retires to a convent longs for her Redeemer—and she will continue to yearn, as long as she lives, for union with a God at once human and divine, incarnating life and love everlasting. In its highest sense, love is a reaching for divine perfection, an act of creation. And always, it is a longing.

Since love is longing, experts in the Middle Ages held that one could not love someone who could not be longed for—for instance, one's wife. Hence, the Comtesse de Champagne told her court in 1174: "Love cannot extend its rights over two married persons." If one were to marry one's love, one would exchange the sweet torment of desire, the yearning, for that which fulfills it. Thus the tension of hope would be replaced by the comfort of certainty. He who longs to long, who wants the tension of desire surely should not marry. In former times, of course, he married—the better to love someone else's wife.

When sexual objects are easily and guiltlessly accessible, in a society that does not object to promiscuity, romantic love seldom prospers. For example, in imperial Rome it was rare and in Tahiti unknown. And love is unlikely to arouse the heart of someone brought up in a harem, where the idea of uniqueness has a hard time. Love flowers best in a monogamous environment morally opposed to unrestrained sex, and interested in cultivating individual experience. In such an environment, longing may be valued for itself. Thus, love as we know it is a Christian legacy, though Christianity in the main repudiates romantic love where the love object is human, and accepts passion only when transcendent God is the object—or when muted into affection: marital love.

Let me hazard a Freudian guess about the genesis of the longing we call love. It continues and reproduces the child's first feeling for his parent—the original source of unconditioned and unconditional love. But what is recreated is the child's image, the idealized mother or father, young and uniquely beautiful, and not the empirical parent others see. The unconsummated love for this ideal parent (and it could be someone else important in the child's experience) remains an intense longing. Yet any fulfillment now must also become a disappointment—a substitute, cheating the longing that wants to long. Most of us, however, marry and replace the ideal with an imperfect reality; we repudiate our longing or we keep it but shift its object. If we don't, we may resent our partners for helping us "consume the myth," and leaving us shorn of longing—which is what Don Giovanni found so intolerable, and what saddens many a faithful husband.

Sexual gratification, of course, diminishes sexual desire for the time being. But it does more. It changes love. The longing may become gratitude; the desire tenderness; love may become affectionate companionship—"After such knowledge, what forgiveness?" Depending on character and circumstance, love may also be replaced by indifference or hostility.

One thing is certain though: if the relationship is stabilized, love is replaced by other emotions. (Marriage thus has often been recommended as the cure for love. But it does not always work.) The only way to keep love is to try to keep up—or re-establish—the distance between lovers that was inevitably shortened by intimacy and possession, and thus, possibly, regain desire and longing. Lovers sometimes do so by quarreling. And some personalities are remote enough, or inexhaustible enough, to be longed for even when possessed. But this has disadvantages as well. And the deliberate and artificial devices counseled by romance magazines and marriage manuals ("surprise your husband . . .") are unlikely to yield more than the pretense of love—even when they do not originate with love of pretense.

The sexual act itself may serve as a vehicle for numberless feelings: lust, vanity, and self-assertion, doubt, and curiosity, possessiveness, anxiety, hostility, anger, or indifferent release from boredom. Yet, though seldom the only motive, and often absent altogether, love nowadays is given as the one natural and moral reason which authorizes and even ordains sexual relations. What we have done is draw a moral conclusion from a "rule" of popular psychology: that "it is gratifying, and therefore healthy and natural, to make love when you love, and frustrating, and therefore unhealthy and unnatural, not to; we must follow nature; but sex without love is unnatural and therefore immoral."

Now, as a psychological rule, this is surely wrong; it can be as healthy to frustrate as it is to gratify one's desires. Sometimes gratification is very unhealthy; sometimes frustration is. Nor can psychological health be accepted as morally decisive. Sanity, sanitation, and morality are all desirable—but they are not identical, and simply to want all of them is to pose a problem, not to solve it. It may be quite "healthy" to run away with your neighbor's wife, but not, therefore, right. And there is nothing unhealthy about wishing to kill someone who has injured you—but this does not morally justify doing so. Finally, to say "we must follow nature" is always specious: we follow nature in whatever we do—we can't ever do what nature does not let us do. Why then identify nature only with the non-intellectual, the sensual, or the emotional possibilities? In this view, it would be unnatural to read: literacy is a gift of nature only if we include the intellect and training in nature's realm. If we do, it makes no sense to call a rule unnatural merely because it restrains an urge: the urge is no more natural than the restraint.

The combination of love and sex is no more "natural" than the separation. Thus, what one decides about restraining or indulging an emotion, or a sexual urge, rests on religious, social, or personal values, none of which can claim to be more natural than any other.

Not that some indulgences and some inhibitions may not be healthier than others. But one cannot flatly say which are good and bad for every man. This depends on their origins and effects in the personalities involved. Without knowing these, more cannot be said—except, perhaps, that we should try not to use others, or even ourselves, merely as a means—at least not habitually and in personal relations. Sex, unalloyed, sometimes leads to this original sin which our moral tradition condemns. Psychologically, too, the continued use of persons merely as instruments ultimately frustrates both the user and the used. This caution, though it justifies no positive action, may help perceive problems; it does not solve them; no general rule can.

What about marriage? In our society, couples usually invite the families to their weddings, although the decision to marry is made exclusively by bride and groom. However, a license must be obtained and the marriage registered; and it can be dissolved only by a court of law. Religious ceremonies state the meaning of marriage clearly. The couple are asked to promise "forsaking all others, [to] keep thee only unto her [him], so long as ye both shall live." The vow does not say, "as long as we both shall want to," because marriage is a promise to continue even when one no longer wishes to. If marriage were to end when love does, it would be redundant: why solemnly ask two people to promise to be with each other for as long as they want to be with each other?

Marriage was to cement the family by tying people together "till death do us part" in the face of fickleness of their emotions. The authority of state and church was to see to it that they kept a promise voluntarily made, but binding, and that could not be unmade. Whether it sprang from love did not matter. Marriage differed from a love affair inasmuch as it continued regardless of love. Cupid shoots his arrows without rhyme or reason. But marriage is a deliberate rational act, a public institution making the family independent of Cupid's whims. Once enlisted, the volunteers couldn't quit, even when they didn't like it any longer. That was the point.

The idea that marriage must be coextensive with love or even affection nullifies it altogether. (That affection should coincide with marriage is, of course, desirable, though it does not always happen.) We would have to reword the marriage vow. Instead of saying, "till death do us part," we might say, "till we get bored with each other"; and, instead of "forsaking all others," "till someone better comes along." Clearly, if the couple intend to stay "married" only as long as they want to, they only pretend to be married: they are having an affair with legal trimmings. To marry is to vow fidelity regardless of any future feeling, to vow the most earnest attempt to avoid contrary feelings altogether, but, at any rate, not to give in to them.

Perhaps this sounds grim. But it needn't be if one marries for affection more than for love. For affection, marital love may grow with knowledge and intimacy and shared experience. Thus marriage itself, when accepted as something other than a love affair, may foster affection. Affection differs from love as fulfillment differs from desire. Further love longs for what desire and imagination make uniquely and perfectly lovable. Possession erodes it. Affection, however—which is love of a different, of a perhaps more moral and less aesthetic kind—cares deeply also for what is unlovable without transforming it into beauty. It cares for the unvarnished person, not the splendid image. Time can strengthen it. But the husband who wants to remain a splendid image must provide a swan to draw him away, or find a wife who can restrain her curiosity about his real person—something that Lohengrin did not succeed in doing. Whereas love stresses the unique form perfection takes in the lover's mind, affection stresses the uniqueness of the actual person.

One may grow from the other. But not when this other is expected to remain unchanged. And affection probably grows more easily if not preceded by enchantment. For the disenchantment which often follows may turn husband and wife against each other, and send them looking elsewhere for re-enchantment—which distance lends so easily.

SEX

Edmund Wilson
(1895–   )

The purpose of sexual intercourse, and hence of what we call love, is to secure the survival of the human race and, if possible, to improve its breed.

This would seem to be obvious enough, yet I have found, on several occasions, when I have emphasized this truism in conversation, that I have provoked the most vehement protests, and have had a suspicion confirmed that for educated people at the present time this objective has been so far lost sight of that it is hard for them to see "love" in terms of it. The sentimentalities, romanticisms ideal isms that make up so much of modern literature have concealed from such people the pattern and the purpose of the mating of human beings, which is basically identical with those of the mating of the other animals. The male makes a play for the female, competing with other males and attempting to impress the female not only by fighting off these competitors, but also by strutting before her, displaying his accomplishments, his prowess, his charms. The Australian lyre-bird has a whole repertoire of devices for dazzling and amusing the female. He dances, he parades the magnificent tail which he specially grows for this season, he gives brilliant imitations of other birds. Not only does he woo her by these means: he keeps her entertained through her period of setting—lyre-birds, as a rule, lay only one egg, and its hatching seems rather precarious. When he is done with this, he loses his tail and retires into the forest, where he works at learning new numbers for his repertoire. It is possible that, as some believe, an element of what we call the aesthetic is involved in such non-human phenomena as the lyre-bird's virtuosity. His range is remarkable: he can even reproduce such mechanical sounds as the scratch of a saw. He acquires new imitations as a singer acquires new songs. Nor is his mate his only audience. In the off-season, he practices his act on the other deplumaged males. Now, a man in his mating time behaves very much like the lyre-bird, and he does so to

achieve the same end: to produce baby human beings, as the lyre-bird to produce little lyre-birds. When the female has been won and impregnated, when the offspring have been hatched or born, the attitude of the father changes. He may apply himself more or less effectually to feeding and protecting his family, but he no longer need strain to please. The biological cycle is now complete, the intensity of passion relieved. It may never recur for the man in connection with that particular woman, or he may like her so much that he woos her again and makes her produce more offspring.

One difference, however, between human life and the life of the lyre-bird is to be found in the much greater frequency with which, in the case of humanity, this cycle becomes frustrated or complicated. It would seem that, in the lyre-bird world, there are actually unhappy males who form in the forest a group by themselves and—as seems to be implied in a report on this bird—engage in homosexual practices. One wonders whether the performance of the lyre-bird male may not sometimes prove so unsatisfactory that it fails to hold the hen to her nest. Yet, relatively effete though the lyre-bird is, he manages, in propagating his species, more easily than the human animal. Even a tomcat who cannot get the tabby he wants will prowl around her prison for days, and it is plain that he actually suffers from unappeased desire; but eventually he may slake this desire with another female cat. Compare the mating behavior of any of these non-human creatures with those of the creatures we read about in contemporary imaginative literature. Our novels, our plays and our poetry are concerned to what may seem an appalling degree— may seem so, that is, to persons who have known the completed cycle—with people who are shown as feeling in relation to one another a definite biological attraction yet are prevented from experiencing, or are incapable of experiencing, the full cycle of courtship, fruition, relief. Modern literature has become so addicted to presenting situations of this kind that one cannot always be sure whether its writers are fully aware that the anguish of their lovers arises not merely from estrangements, from not being able to enjoy or to renew the ecstasy of love-making, from being deprived by some obstacle of one another's congenial company, but from the basic biological bafflement of the failure to produce children. And of course there is the complication that one does not want just any children. There is the principle of sexual selection. One wants children by a mate one admires. One wants to produce better children. A conflict between the attractions of different possible mates, a falling-back on a *pis-aller* where something much better was aimed at, may provide a situation that interests. Yet in all this it is rather surprising how frequently the prime motivation—the impulse to propagate—is lost sight of in modern life. The various substitutes for the child-getting cycle to which people are often driven by the codes and neuroses of modern life have come so to preoccupy us that we lose sight of the original process. We have had in modern literature, at various epochs, the doomed guilty passion of the British Victorians and the accepted adultery of the French, the long and uncertain engagements and the rejections of irregular relationships of the James and Howells period in the United States, the glorification of intercourse for its own sake as you get it in D. H. Lawrence, the feminine promiscuity of Edna Millay, the homosexuality of Proust that is really a stunted and embittered form of an intense admiration for women, the adolescent sexuality of Gide that does not much transcend masturbation, the homosexual narcissism of Nor-man Douglas and the dynamic narcissism of Bernard Shaw, who tries to make his women approximate men and who never went to bed with his wife.

The literature of sexual sterility is, however, as old as Plato, and it is curious to contrast these modern works with the point of view of Saadia Ben Joseph, the tenth-century Jewish teacher, who lived in a part of the world where—among the Greeks and the Arabs—homosexual love was accepted. Saadia was quite puritanical even in relation to women and believed that it was "proper for men to satisfy this appetite only in order to produce offspring." The difficulties, the agonies and the scandals of the current Platonic love therefore seem to him quite fantastic. He might be dealing with the world of Proust when he deplores the loss of appetite and the failure of "all other functions basic to his well being," "the inflammation and the fainting and the heart throbs and the worry and the excitement and the agitation" experienced by the unlucky lover: "The slavish submission to the object of one's passion and to his retinue, and the sitting at the gates and waiting upon him everywhere"; and what about the vigils at night and the rising at dawn and the secrecy practised so as not to be surprised in the act, and the deaths one dies whenever one is discovered in one's shame? . . . and what about the murder of the lover or the beloved or of one of their retinue or of both them and those attached to them and of a great many human beings together with them that often results from being madly in love, as Scripture says: *Because they are adulteresses, and blood is on their hands?* (Ezekiel 23:45) . . . This emotional state . . . has its appropriate place only in the relationship between husband and wife. They should be affectionate to one another for the sake of the maintenance of the world, as Scripture says: *A lovely hind and a graceful doe, let her breasts satisfy thee at all times; with her love be thou ravished always* (Proverbs 5:19)." I find it admirable of this stout rabbi to insist upon the straight path of procreation while surrounded by Platonic lovers tying themselves into knots. (The romantic adoration of *women* —which in our own day has resulted in similar antics—was not even imagined in Saadia's world.) The Jews have owed much of their strength to their steady concentration on the family line, their loyalty to the family unit. The only great modern writer who has occupied himself seriously with this unit—James Joyce in *Ulysses* and *Finnegans Wake*—has, it seems to me, on that account, been fashionable rather for the brilliance of his technical innovations than for the family situations that always make the core of his work. A short story by Dorothy Parker—a girl who is hanging in anguish on the ring of the telephone—is, from this point of view, not so far from Proust as either of them is from Joyce, with his middle-aged married people, more or less comfortably mated and bound to one another by their children. This is the reason why critics of *Ulysses* can grasp Molly Bloom's promiscuity but not her underlying fidelity to Bloom that makes of her a true Penelope, and why students of *Finnegans Wake* are likely to be preoccupied exclusively with the verbal tricks and facets of reference at the expense of the commonplace household whose relationships are being explored.

This is not, of course, to say that the biologically sterile relationships with which modern literature deals are devoid of importance or interest, or that sexual desires ungratified, or which, gratified, produce no children, may not set off consuming passions or stimulate noble virtues. It is true that there is nothing in the world that can become more completely demoralizing, more wasteful of emotional energy, than a prolonged affair with a married woman; that nothing can be more depressing than the situation of unmarried lovers who are not in a position to marry; that homosexuality is, in every sense, a cul-de-sac. Yet in the world in which we are living the problems of neurotic incapacitation, the shakiness of economic security, the difficulties in a mixed society of living up to principles of sexual selection which must always be to some extent inherited—all these obstacles to procreation must drive many to *pis-allers* which themselves become tests of character and pressures toward "sublimation." Nor should I advocate as a general policy—as Theodore Roosevelt did—that everyone should get married young and beget as many children as possible. These sterile arrangements should be recognized as the modi vivendi they are: they ought not to be glorified. The renunciations of Henry James, the hysterical orgasms of Lawrence, the impotent and obsessive suspicions of Proust are all equally sexual monstrosities, dislocations of the reproductive instinct. Yet, for all we know, such states of mind may mark—as extreme symptoms—a period of difficult transition from our previous habits of reproduction to the mastery of new methods, a period in the course of which a continual process of dislocation will give rise to confusion and anguish. I mean that humanity may be reaching a phase in which the improvement of the human breed will no longer be entrusted entirely to our present hit-or-miss practice, to the pairing-off of individuals who at the moment happen to look good on one another.

To the young, such a prospect as this is likely to appear forbidding; but to one who has passed sixty, the exercise of the sexual functions can hardly be made a cult or the longing for it give rise to extravagant idealization. The attainment of this satisfaction can no longer present itself as a supremely desired end, as it sometimes does in youth—when, however, we may not be aware that what we are aiming at is offspring more viable than we are. We have not yet arrived, at sixty, at the state of the aged Sophocles, who is made to say, in Plato's *Republic,* that he is glad to have escaped at last from a mad and cruel master. We still may desire, touch rapture, we still may be left as if drunken with the aftermath of love. We may even feel occasional symptoms of falling in love again, as we do those of some old ailment—gout or a sneezing from roses—to which we have become accustomed and which by this time we know how to cure. Yet sex has come to seem more irrelevant to the other things that occupy our minds, and we may sometimes push it away with impatience when we are busy with something else. We do not now want any more children. It is as much as we can do to give adequate attention to those we already have. And at this time of life, in this state of mind, we can just begin to catch a glimpse of a world in which what we call love would be demoted to a place less important than it has occupied for our part of the world in the past. It has never been so important among certain other peoples —with the Japanese, for example—as it is supposed to be in the West. In every country, as a matter of fact, the word *love* means something different. Our American ideal of love has come to us by way of romanticist Europe from the code of the age of chivalry. We depend on it for sexual selection, for the betterment of the human stock. We demand that prospective parents shall be what we call "in love." But that is not the only principle that has been applied to get this result. The predominant practice in Europe was to build up a social group which would aim to breed for certain qualities. Hence

the various aristocracies, and the custom —so solidly established in France—of assigning one's daughter to a good *parti,* no matter how little he might thrill her, who would be certain to carry on the manners and the virtues one prized. There was no question of sexual passion: for that, both the mates could take lovers, who, according to the rules of the game, would try to avoid illegitimate children. Romanticism ran counter to this system, for it championed the exception, the rebel—the rights of sexual passion. But with us in the United States, where the social groups were so much less solid—where the money so often changed hands and the classes were less clearly defined—the ideal of romantic love became the dominating convention. It has always disguised a good deal that is mercenary, prosaic or sordid; and I doubt whether it will last indefinitely. The situations I have mentioned above—in James and Lawrence and Proust—are reductions to absurdity of it; and they may be at the same time, I suggest, the symptoms of an obsolescence, eventually a scrapping, of this ideal. We can no longer depend for breeding on the maintenance of certain families accustomed to certain conditions and marrying only among themselves. That has always been difficult in the United States, and it is becoming equally difficult in Europe, where the levellings and upheavals of war and the impoverishment of the landowning classes have been making it more and more impossible to preserve these groups intact. In Russia, it has quite gone by the board. The old upper classes were exiled, and even under the Soviet regime, the dictator—jealous of power— kept changing, by dismissal or murder, the personnel of the upper ranks, in order to avert the danger of a powerful governing group who might dig themselves in and displace him. It is said that since Stalin's demise there is a tendency for such a group to coagulate and leave to its children its resources as well as its traditions. Such tendencies are bound to appear. They exist in every American town that more or less respects its "first families"; in every African tribe that cultivates a princely caste. But how much scope will they have in the future? How much will they be encouraged?

What I am getting at is that some new technique of breeding will very soon have to be found. The pretensions of the aristocracies, though never entirely justified, were never perhaps completely false; but that road seems forever closed. A possible new method has already appeared in artificial insemination. I find at the county fairs of the dairy country of upstate New York that the semen of prize bulls is now advertised and sold like any other agricultural commodity. Nobody worries about the cows, who, in addition to losing their calves, are deprived of the pleasure of begetting them. And, as I learn from the English press, the same kind of thing is sometimes done, in Britain, for human beings. This is a method which, I do not doubt, will come to be practised more widely, but always, I should imagine, exceptionally—in the case of a husband's sterility or a woman's non-marriageability. It is more probable that the breeding of the future will be managed through the systematic practice of what used to be called eugenics. That remarkable prophet John Humphrey Noyes (1811–1886) founded the Oneida Community in Oneida County, New York, with the object of producing a better stock by the supervised interbreeding—"planned parenthood"— of a carefully selected group. I have heard that the Oneida people were not always satisfied with the partners with whom they had been put to bed, and that the couples officially paired would sometimes, by mutual consent, escape to other rooms through the transoms and themselves

plan a different parenthood. Yet I do not find it hard to imagine a movement of this kind in the future, either promoted in some way by the State or carried out by a private group. Such a movement might well begin with a bureau which should ask for volunteers for the breeding of a new élite and which should make a selection among them based on both intellectual and physical equipment. I do not believe that such unions would necessarily be entered into as coldbloodedly as might be supposed. The very ideal of a new élite would act as a stimulus to enthusiasm—I assume that, among these recruits and the children produced by their breeding, there would be time for acquaintanceship and freedom of choice. We have already seen something of the kind in the German Youth Movement of Hitler and the Russian Komsomols. You may well think the Germans absurd, with their pretensions to Aryan purity, and the Komsomols naïve and priggish. But unless some such new principle is introduced, I do not know how we are going to be saved from the dominance of mediocrity and from a letting-down of all standards with the exception of the mechanical and technical ones which are necessary for our engineering and in which a kind of mass training seems possible. The republican and socialist centuries have insisted on equality of opportunity; but, assuming a civilization where everyone does enjoy equal right— to employment, to education, to justice before the law, to do what he can with his life—this would certainly not be enough. Equality is not enough, and is, besides, only possible in the limited sense of the kind of rights mentioned above. There is always the drive to excel. Work, literacy, food and shelter, hygienic conditions of living are minimum requirements of civilization, but they will not appease this ambition.

It seems to me, therefore, inevitable

that the future will see a great movement for the betterment of the race by breeding. Think what we have done with dogs. Think what we have done with horses. Think what, since Neanderthal man or beginning whenever you like—by methods of deliberate discipline and selection that has been half-unconscious—we have already done with the human race. Do not say that you turn in distaste from a selection so calculated and conscious, which does not depend on "the heart." In how many marriages and liaisons in the society we actually inhabit does not calculation enter or the heart play a cardinal role?

SHORT STORIES

WILLIAM AND MARY

Max Beerbohm
(1872–1956)

Memories, like olives, are an acquired taste. William and Mary (I give them the Christian names that were indeed theirs —the joint title by which their friends always referred to them) were for some years an interest in my life, and had a hold on my affection. But a time came when, though I had known and liked them too well ever to forget them, I gave them but a few thoughts now and then. How being dead, could they keep their place in the mind of a young man surrounded with large and constantly renewed consignments of the living? As one grows older, the charm of novelty wears off. One finds that there is no such thing as novelty—or, at any rate, that one has lost the faculty for perceiving it. One sees every newcomer not as something strange and special, but as a ticketed specimen of this or that very familiar genus. The world has ceased to be remarkable; and one tends to think more and more often of the days when it was so very remarkable indeed.

I suppose that had I been thirty years older when first I knew him, William would have seemed to me little worthier of attention than a twopenny postage-stamp seems to-day. Yet, no: William

really had some oddities that would have caught even an oldster's eye. In himself he was commonplace enough (as I, coæval though I was with him, soon saw). But in details of surface he was unusual. In them he happened to be rather ahead of his time. He was a socialist, for example. In 1890 there was only one other socialist in Oxford, and he not at all an undergraduate, but a retired chimney-sweep, named Hines, who made speeches, to which nobody, except perhaps William, listened, near the Martyrs' Memorial. And William wore a flannel shirt, and rode a bicycle—very strange habits in those days, and very horrible. He was said to be (though he was short-sighted and wore glasses) a first-rate "back" at football; but, as football was a thing frowned on by the rowing men, and coldly ignored by the bloods, his talent for it did not help him: he was one of the principal pariahs of our College; and it was rather in a spirit of bravado, and to show how sure of myself I was, that I began, in my second year, to cultivate his acquaintance.

We had little in common. I could not think Political Economy "the most exciting thing in the world," as he used to call it. Nor could I without yawning listen to more than a few lines of Mr. William Morris' interminable smooth Icelandic Sagas, which my friend, pious young socialist that he was, thought "glorious."

He had begun to write an Icelandic Saga himself, and had already achieved some hundreds of verses. None of these pleased him, though to me they seemed very like his master's. I can see him now, standing on his hearth-rug, holding his MS. close to his short-sighted eyes, declaiming the verses and trying, with many angular gestures of his left hand, to animate them—a tall, broad, raw-boned fellow, with long brown hair flung back from his forehead, and a very shabby suit of clothes. Because of his clothes and his socialism, and his habit of offering beer to a guest, I had at first supposed him quite poor; and I was surprised when he told me that he had from his guardian (his parents being dead) an allowance of £350, and that when he came of age he would have an income of £400. "All out of dividends," he would groan. I would hint that Mr. Hines and similar zealots might disembarrass him of this load, if he asked them nicely. "No," he would say quite seriously, "I can't do that," and would read out passages from *Fabian Essays* to show that in the present anarchical conditions only mischief could result from sporadic dispersal of rent. "Then, twelve years hence—" he would muse more hopefully. "But by that time," I would say, "you'll probably be married, and your wife mightn't quite—," whereat he would hotly repeat what he had said many times: that he would never marry. Marriage was an anti-social anachronism. I think its survival was in some part due to the machinations of Capital. Anyway, it was doomed. Temporary civil contracts between men and women would be the rule "ten, twelve years hence"; pending which time the lot of any man who had civic sense must be celibacy, tempered perhaps with free love.

Long before that time was up, nevertheless, William married. One afternoon in the spring of '95 I happened to meet him at a corner of Cockspur Street. I wondered at the immense cordiality of his greeting; for our friendship, such as it was, had waned in our two final years at Oxford. "You look very flourishing, and," I said, "you're wearing a new suit!" "I'm married," he replied, obviously without a twinge of conscience. He told me he had been married just a month. He declared that to be married was the most splendid thing in all the world; but he weakened the force of this generalisation by adding that there never was any one like his wife. "You must see her," he said; and his impatience to show her proudly off to some one was so evident, and so touching, that I could not but accept his invitation to go and stay with them for two or three days—"why not next week?" They had taken and furnished "a sort of cottage" in ——shire, and this was their home. He had "run up for the day, on business—journalism" and was now on his way to Charing Cross. "I know you'll like my wife," he said at parting. "She's—well, she's glorious."

As this was the epithet he had erst applied to "Beowulf" and to "Sigurd the Volsung" it raised no high hopes. And indeed, as I was soon to find, he had again misused it. There was nothing glorious about his bride. Some people might even have not thought her pretty. I myself did not, in the flash of first sight. Neat, insignificant, pleasing, was what she appeared to me, rather than pretty, and fair rather than glorious. In an age of fringes, her brow was severely bare. She looked "practical." But an instant later, when she smiled, I saw that she was pretty, too. And presently I thought her delightful. William had met me in a "governess cart," and we went to see him unharness the pony. He did this in a fumbling, experimental way, confusing the reins with the traces, and profiting so little by his wife's directions that she began to laugh. And her laugh was a lovely thing; quite a small sound, but exquisitely clear and gay, coming in a sequence of notes that neither rose nor fell, that were quite even; a trill of notes, and then another, and another, as though she were pulling repeatedly a little silver bell . . . As I describe it, perhaps the sound may be imagined irritating. I can only say it was enchanting.

I wished she would go on laughing; but she ceased, she darted forward and (William standing obediently aside, and I helping unhelpfully) unharnessed the pony herself, and led it into its small stable. Decidedly, she was "practical," but—I was prepared now to be lenient to any quality she might have.

Had she been feckless, no doubt I should have forgiven her that, too; but I might have enjoyed my visit less than I did, and might have been less pleased to go often again. I had expected to "rough it" under William's roof. But everything thereunder, within the limits of a strict Arcadian simplicity, was well-ordered. I was touched, when I went to my bedroom, by the precision with which the very small maid had unpacked and disposed my things. And I wondered where my hostess had got the lore she had so evidently imparted. Certainly not from William. Perhaps (it only now strikes me) from a handbook. For Mary was great at handbooks. She had handbooks about gardening, and others about poultry, and one about "the stable," and others on cognate themes. From these she had filled up the gaps left in her education by her father, who was a widower and either a doctor or a solicitor—I forget which—in one of the smallest towns of an adjoining county. And I daresay she may have had, somewhere hidden away, a manual for young hostesses. If so, it must have been a good one. But to say this is to belittle Mary's powers of intuition. It was they, sharpened by her adoration

of William, and by her intensity for everything around him, that made her so efficient a housewife.

If she possessed a manual for young house-hunters, it was assuredly not by the light of this that she had chosen the home they were installed in. The "sort of cottage" had been vacant for many years —an unpromising and ineligible object, a mile away from a village, and three miles away from a railway station. The main part of it was an actual cottage, of seventeenth-century workmanship; but a little stuccoed wing had been added to each side of it, in 1850 or thereabouts, by an eccentric old gentleman who at that time chose to make it his home. He had added also the small stable, a dairy, and other appanages. For these, and for garden, there was plenty of room, as he had purchased and enclosed half an acre of the surrounding land. Those two stuccoed, very Victorian wings of his, each with a sash-window above and a French window below, consorted queerly with the old red brick and the latticed panes. And the long wooden veranda that he had invoked did not unify the trinity. But one didn't want it to. The wrongness had a character all its own. The wrongness was right—at any rate after Mary had hit on it for William. As a spinster, she would, I think, have been happiest in a trim modern villa. But it was a belief of hers that she had married a man of strange genius. She had married him for himself, not for his genius; but this added grace in him was a thing to be reckoned with, ever so much; a thing she must coddle to the utmost in a proper setting. She was a year older than he (though, being so small and slight, she looked several years younger), and in her devotion the maternal instinct played a great part. William, as I have already conveyed to you, was not greatly gifted. Mary's instinct, in this one matter, was at fault. But endearingly, rightly at fault. And, as William *was* outwardly odd, wasn't it well that his home should be so, too? On the inside, comfort was what Mary always aimed at for him, and achieved.

The ground floor had all been made one room, into which you stepped straight from the open air. Quite a long big room (or so it seemed, from the lowness of the ceiling), and well-freshened in its antiquity, with rushmats here and there on the irregular red tiles, and very white whitewash on the plaster between the rafters. This was the dining-room, drawing-room, and general focus throughout the day, and was called simply the Room. William had a "den" on the ground floor of the left wing; and there, in the mornings, he used to write a great deal. Mary had no special place of her own: her place was wherever her duties needed her. William wrote reviews of books for the *Daily——*. He did also creative work. The vein of poetry in him had worked itself out—or rather, it expressed itself for him in Mary. For technical purposes, the influence of Ibsen had superseded that of Morris. At the time of my first visit, he was writing an extraordinarily gloomy play about an extraordinarily unhappy marriage. In subsequent seasons (Ibsen's disc having been somehow eclipsed for him by George Gissing's) he was usually writing novels in which everyone—or do I exaggerate?—had made a disastrous match. I think Mary's belief in his genius had made him less diffident than he was at Oxford. He was always emerging from his den, with fresh pages of MS., into the Room. "You don't mind?" he would say, waving his pages, and then would shout "Mary!" She was always promptly forthcoming—sometimes from the direction of the kitchen, in a white apron, sometimes from the garden, in a blue one. She never looked at him while he read. To do so would have been

lacking in respect for his work. It was on this that she must concentrate her whole mind, privileged auditor that she was. She sat looking straight before her, with her lips slightly compressed, and her hands folded on her lap. I used to wonder that there had been that first moment when I did not think her pretty. Her eyes were of a very light hazel, seeming all the lighter because her hair was of so dark a brown; and they were beautifully set in a face of that "pinched oval" kind which is rather rare in England. Mary as listener would have atoned to me for any defects there may have been in dear old William's work. Nevertheless, I sometimes wished this work had some comic relief in it. Publishers, I believe, shared this wish; hence the eternal absence of William's name from among their announcements. For Mary's sake, and his, I should have liked him to be "successful." But at any rate he didn't need money. He didn't need, in addition to what he had, what he made by his journalism. And as for success—well, didn't Mary think him a genius? And wasn't he Mary's husband? The main reason why I wished for light passages in what he read to us was that they would have been cues for Mary's laugh. This was a thing always new to me. I never tired of that little bell-like euphony; those funny little lucid and level trills.

There was no stint of that charm when William was not reading to us. Mary was in no awe of him, apart from his work, and in no awe at all of me: she used to laugh at us both, for one thing and another—just the same laugh as I had first heard when William tried to unharness the pony. I cultivated in myself whatever amused her in me; I drew out whatever amused her in William; I never let slip any of the things that amused her in herself. "Chaff" is a great bond; and I should have enjoyed our bouts of it even without Mary's own special *obbligato.* She used to call me (for I was very urban in those days) the Gentleman from London. I used to call her the Brave Little Woman. Whatever either of us said or did could be twisted easily into relation to those two titles; and our bouts, to which William listened with a puzzled, benevolent smile, used to cease only because Mary regarded me as a possible purveyor of what William, she was sure, wanted and needed down there in the country, alone with her: intellectual conversation, after his work. She often, I think, invented duties in garden or kitchen so that he should have this stimulus, or luxury, without hindrance. But when William was alone with me it was about her that he liked to talk, and that I myself liked to talk too. He was very sound on the subject of Mary; and so was I. And if, when I was alone with Mary, I seemed to be sounder than I was on the subject of William's wonderfulness, who shall blame me?

Had Mary been a mother, William's wonderfulness would have been less greatly important. But he was her child as well as her lover. And I think, though I do not know, she believed herself content that this should always be, if so it were destined. It was not destined so. On the first night of a visit I paid them in April, 1899, William, when we were alone, told me news. I had been vaguely conscious, throughout the evening, of some change; conscious that Mary had grown gayer, and less gay—somehow different, somehow remote. William said that her child would be born in September, if all went well. "She's immensely happy," he told me. I realised that she was indeed happier than ever. . . . "And of course it would be a wonderful thing, for both of us," he said presently, "to have a son—or a daughter." I asked him which he would rather it were, a son

or a daughter. "Oh, either," he answered wearily. It was evident that he had misgivings and fears. I tried to reason him out of them. He did not, I am thankful to say, ever let Mary suspect them. *She* had no misgivings. But it was destined that her child should live only for an hour, and that she should die in bearing it.

I had stayed again at the cottage in July, for some days. At the end of that month I had gone to France, as was my custom, and a week later had written to Mary. It was William that answered this letter, telling me of Mary's death and burial. I returned to England next day. William and I wrote to each other several times. He had not left his home. He stayed there, "trying," as he said in a grotesque and heart-rending phrase, "to finish a novel." I saw him in the following January. He wrote to me from the Charing Cross Hotel, asking me to lunch with him there. After our first greetings, there was a silence. He wanted to talk of— what he could not talk of. We stared helplessly at each other, and then, in the English way, talked of things at large. England was engaged in the Boer War. William was the sort of man whom one would have expected to be violently Pro-Boer. I was surprised at his fervour for the stronger side. He told me he had tried to enlist, but had been rejected on account of his eyesight. But there was, he said, a good chance of his being sent out, almost immediately, as one of the *Daily* ——'s special correspondents. "And then," he exclaimed, "I shall see something of it." I had a presentiment that he would not return, and a belief that he he did not want to return. He did not return. Special correspondents were not so carefully shepherded in that war as they have since been. They were more at liberty to take risks, on behalf of the journals to which they were accredited.

William was killed a few weeks after he had landed at Cape Town.

And there came, as I have said, a time when I did not think of William and Mary often; and then a time when I did more often think of them. And especially much did my mind hark back to them in the late autumn of last year; for on the way to the place I was staying at I had passed the little railway station whose name had always linked itself for me with the names of those two friends. There were but four intervening stations. It was not a difficult pilgrimage that I made some days later—back towards the past, for that past's sake and honour. I had thought I should not remember the way, the three miles of way, from the station to the cottage; but I found myself remembering it perfectly, without a glance at the finger-posts. Rain had been falling heavily, driving the late leaves off the trees; and everything looked rather sodden and misty, though the sun was now shining. I had known this landscape only in spring, summer, early autumn. Mary had held to a theory that at other seasons I could not be acclimatised. But there were groups of trees that I knew, even without their leaves; and farm-houses and small stone bridges that had not at all changed. Only what mattered was changed. Only what mattered was gone. Would what I had come to see be there still? In comparison with what it had held, it was not much. But I wished to see it, melancholy spectacle though it must be for me if it were extant, and worse than melancholy if it held something new. I began to be sure it had been demolished, built over. At the corner of the lane that had led to it, I was almost minded to explore no further, to turn back. But I went on, and suddenly I was at the four-barred iron gate, that I remembered, between the laurels. It was rusty, and was fastened with a rusty padlock, and beyond it there was grass where a

winding "drive" had been. From the lane the cottage never had been visible, even when these laurels were lower and sparser than they were now. Was the cottage still standing? Presently, I climbed over the gate, and walked through the long grass, and—yes, there was Mary's cottage; still there; William's and Mary's cottage. Trite enough, I have no doubt were the thoughts that possessed me as I stood gazing. There is nothing new to be thought about the evanescence of human things; but there is always much to be felt about it by one who encounters in his maturity some such intimate instance and reminder as confronted me, in that cold sunshine, across that small wilderness of long rank wet grass and weeds.

Incredibly woebegone and lonesome the house would have looked even to one for whom it contained no memories; all the more because in its utter dereliction it looked so durable. Some of the stucco had fallen off the walls of the two wings; thick flakes of it lay on the discoloured roof of the veranda, and thick flakes of it could be seen lying in the grass below. Otherwise, there were few signs of actual decay. The sash-window and the French window of each wing were shuttered, and, from where I was standing, the cream-coloured paint of those shutters behind the glass looked almost fresh. The latticed windows between had all been boarded up from within. The house was not to be let perish soon.

I did not want to go nearer to it; yet I did go nearer, step by step, across the wilderness, right up to the edge of the veranda itself, and within a yard of the front door.

I stood looking at that front door. I had never noticed it in the old days, for then it had always stood open. But it asserted itself now, master of the threshold.

It was a narrow door—narrow even for its height, which did not exceed mine by more than two inches or so; a door that even when it was freshly painted must have looked mean. How much meaner now, with its paint all faded and mottled, cracked and blistered! It had no knocker, not even a slit for letters. All that it had was a large-ish key-hole. On this my eyes rested; and presently I moved to it, stooped down to it, peered through it. I had a glimpse of—darkness impenetrable.

Strange it seemed to me, as I stood back, that there the Room was, the remembered Room itself, separated from me by nothing but this unremembered door . . . and a quarter of a century, yes. I saw it all, in my mind's eye, just as it had been: the way the sunlight came into it through this same doorway and through the lattices of these same four windows; the way the little bit of a staircase came down into it, so crookedly yet so confidently; and how uneven the tiled floor was, and how low the rafters were, and how littered the whole place was with books brought in from his den by William, and how bright with flowers brought in by Mary from her garden. The rafters, the stairs, the tiles, were still existing, changeless in despite of cobwebs and dust and darkness, all quite changeless on the other side of the door, so near to me. I wondered how I should feel if by some enchantment the door slowly turned on its hinges, letting in light. I should not enter, I felt, not even look, so much must I hate to see those inner things lasting when all that had given to them a meaning was gone from them, taken away from them, finally. And yet, why blame them for their survival? And how know that *nothing* of the past ever came to them, revisiting, hovering? Something—sometimes—perhaps? One knew so little. How not be tender to what, as it seemed to me, perhaps the dead loved?

So strong in me now was the wish to see again all those things, to touch them

and, as it were, commune with them, and so queerly may the mind be wrought upon in a solitude among memories, that there were moments when I almost expected that the door would obey my will. I was recalled to a clearer sense of reality by something which I had not before noticed. In the door-post to the right was a small knob of rusty iron—mocking reminder that to gain admission to a house one does not "will" the door: one rings the bell—unless it is rusty and has quite obviously no one to answer it; in which case one goes away. Yet I did not go away. The movement that I made, in despite of myself, was towards the knob itself. But, I hesitated, suppose I did what I half meant to do, and there were no sound. That would be ghastly. And surely there *would* be no sound. And if sound there were, wouldn't that be worse still? My hand drew back, wavered, suddenly closed on the knob. I heard the scrape of the wire—and then, from somewhere within the heart of the shut house, a tinkle.

It had been the weakest, the puniest of noises. It had been no more than is a fledgling's first attempt at a twitter. But I was not judging it by its volume. Deafening peals from steeples had meant less to me than that one single note breaking the silence—in there. In there, in the dark, the bell that had answered me was still quivering, I supposed, on its wire. But there was no one to answer *it*, no footstep to come hither from those recesses, making prints in the dust. Well, *I* could answer it; and again my hand closed on the knob, unhesitatingly this time, pulling further. That was my answer; and the rejoinder to it was more than I had thought to hear—a whole quick sequence of notes, faint but clear, playful, yet poignantly sad, like a trill of laughter echoing out of the past, or even merely out of this neighbouring darkness. It was so like something I had known, so recognisable and, oh, recognising, that I was lost in wonder. And long must I have remained standing at that door, for I heard the sound often, often. I must have rung again and again, tenaciously, vehemently, in my folly.

THE SHE-WOLF

Giovanni Verga
(1840–1922)

She was tall, thin; she had the firm and vigorous breasts of the olive-skinned— and yet she was no longer young; she was pale, as if always plagued by malaria, and in that pallor, two enormous eyes, and fresh red lips which devoured you.

In the village they called her the She-wolf, because she never had enough—of anything. The women made the sign of the cross when they saw her pass, alone as a wild bitch, prowling about suspiciously like a famished wolf; with her red lips she sucked the blood of their sons and husbands in a flash, and pulled them behind her skirt with a single glance of those devilish eyes, even if they were before the altar of Saint Agrippina. Fortunately, the She-wolf never went to church, not at Easter, not at Christmas, not to hear Mass, not for confession.— Father Angiolino of Saint Mary of Jesus, a true servant of God, had lost his soul on account of her.

Maricchia, a good girl, poor thing, cried in secret because she was the She-wolf's daughter, and no one would marry her, though, like every other girl in the village, she had her fine linen in a chest and her good land under the sun.

One day the She-wolf fell in love with a handsome young man who had just returned from the service and was mowing hay with her in the fields of the notary; and she fell in love in the strongest sense of the word, feeling the flesh afire beneath her clothes; and staring him in the eyes, she suffered the thirst one has in the hot hours of June, deep in the plain. But he went on mowing undisturbed, his nose bent over the swaths.

"What's wrong, Pina?" he would ask.

In the immense fields, where you heard only the crackling flight of the grasshoppers, as the sun hammered down overhead, the She-wolf gathered bundle after bundle, and sheaf after sheaf, never tiring, never straightening up for an instant, never raising the flask to her lips, just to remain at the heels of Nanni, who mowed and mowed and asked from time to time:

"What is it you want, Pina?"

One evening she told him, while the men were dozing on the threshing floor, tired after the long day, and the dogs were howling in the vast, dark countryside.

"It's you I want. You who're beautiful as the sun and sweet as honey. I want you!"

"And I want your daughter, instead, who's a maid," answered Nanni laughing.

The She-wolf thrust her hands into her hair, scratching her temples, without saying a word, and walked away. And she did not appear at the threshing floor any more. But she saw Nanni again in October, when they were making olive oil, for he was working near her house, and the creaking of the press kept her awake all night.

"Get the sack of olives," she said to her daughter, "and come with me."

Nanni was pushing olives under the millstone with a shovel, shouting "Ohee" to the mule, to keep it from stopping.

"You want my daughter Maricchia?" Pina asked him.

"What'll you give your daughter Maricchia?" answered Nanni.

"She has all her father's things, and I'll give her my house too; as for me, all I need is a little corner in the kitchen, enough for a straw mattress."

"If that's the way it is, we can talk about it at Christmas," said Nanni.

Nanni was all greasy and filthy, spattered with oil and fermented olives, and Maricchia didn't want him at any price. But her mother grabbed her by the hair before the fireplace, muttering between her teeth:

"If you don't take him, I'll kill you!"

The She-wolf was almost sick, and the people were saying that when the devil gets old he becomes a hermit. She no longer roamed here and there, no longer lingered at the doorway, with those bewitched eyes. Whenever she fixed them on his face, those eyes of hers, her son-in-law began to laugh and pulled out the scapular of the Virgin to cross himself. Maricchia stayed at home nursing the babies, and her mother went into the fields to work with the men, and just like a man too, weeding, hoeing, feeding the animals, pruning the vines, despite the northeast and levantine winds of January or the August sirocco, when the mules' heads drooped and the men slept face down along the wall, on the north side. "In those hours between nones and vespers when no good woman goes roving around," [1] Pina was the only living soul to be seen wandering in the countryside, over the burning stones of the paths, through the scorched stubble of the immense fields that became lost in the suffocating heat, far, far away toward the foggy Etna, where the sky was heavy on the horizon.

"Wake up!" said the She-wolf to Nanni,

who was sleeping in the ditch, along the dusty hedge, his head on his arms. "Wake up. I've brought you some wine to cool your throat."

Nanni opened his drowsy eyes wide, still half asleep, and finding her standing before him, pale, with her arrogant breasts and her coal-black eyes, he stretched out his hands gropingly.

"No! no good woman goes roving around in the hours between nones and vespers!" sobbed Nanni, throwing his head back into the dry grass of the ditch, deep, deep, his nails in his scalp. "Go away! go away! don't come to the threshing floor again!"

The She-wolf was going away, in fact, retying her superb tresses, her gaze bent fixedly before her as she moved through the hot stubble, her eyes as black as coal.

But she came to the threshing floor again, and more than once, and Nanni did not complain. On the contrary, when she was late, in the hours between nones and vespers, he would go and wait for her at the top of the white, deserted path, with his forehead bathed in sweat; and he would thrust his hands into his hair, and repeat every time:

"Go away! go away! don't come to the threshing floor again!"

Maricchia cried night and day, and glared at her mother, her eyes burning with tears and jealousy, like a young she-wolf herself, every time she saw her come, mute and pale, from the fields.

"Vile, vile mother!" she said to her. "Vile mother!"

"Shut up!"

"Thief! Thief!"

"Shut up!"

"I'll go to the Sergeant, I will!"

"Go ahead!"

And she really did go, with her babies in her arms, fearing nothing, and without shedding a tear, like a madwoman, because now she too loved that husband

[1] An old Sicilian proverb, which refers to the hours of the early afternoon, when the Sicilian countryside lies motionless under a scorching sun and no person would dare walk on the roads. Those hours are traditionally believed to be under the spell of malignant spirits. [Translator's note.]

who had been forced on her, greasy and filthy, spattered with oil and fermented olives.

The Sergeant sent for Nanni; he threatened him even with jail and the gallows. Nanni began to sob and tear his hair; he didn't deny anything, he didn't try to clear himself.

"It's the temptation!" he said. "It's the temptation of hell!"

He threw himself at the Sergeant's feet begging to be sent to jail.

"For God's sake, Sergeant, take me out of this hell! Have me killed, put me in jail; don't let me see her again, never! never!"

"No!" answered the She-wolf instead, to the Sergeant. "I kept a little corner in the kitchen to sleep in, when I gave him my house as dowry. It's my house. I don't intend to leave it."

Shortly afterward, Nanni was kicked in the chest by a mule and was at the point of death, but the priest refused to bring him the Sacrament if the She-wolf did not go out of the house. The She-wolf left, and then her son-in-law could also prepare to leave like a good Christian; he confessed and received communion with such signs of repentance and contrition that all the neighbors and the curious wept before the dying man's bed.—And it would have been better for him to die that day, before the devil came back to tempt him again and creep into his body and soul, when he got well.

"Leave me alone!" he told the She-wolf. "For God's sake, leave me in peace! I've seen death with my own eyes! Poor Maricchia is desperate. Now the whole town knows about it! If I don't see you it's better for both of us . . ."

And he would have liked to gouge his eyes out not to see those of the She-wolf, for whenever they peered into his, they made him lose his body and soul. He did not know what to do to free himself from the spell. He paid for Masses for the souls in purgatory and asked the priest and the Sergeant for help. At Easter he went to confession, and in penance he publicly licked more than four feet of pavement, crawling on the pebbles in front of the church—and then, as the She-wolf came to tempt him again:

"Listen!" he said to her. "Don't come to the threshing floor again; if you do, I swear to God, I'll kill you!"

"Kill me," answered the She-wolf, "I don't care; I can't stand it without you."

As he saw her from the distance, in the green wheat fields, Nanni stopped hoeing the vineyard, and went to pull the ax from the elm. The She-wolf saw him come, pale and wild-eyed, with the ax glistening in the sun, but she did not fall back a single step, did not lower her eyes; she continued toward him, her hands laden with red poppies, her black eyes devouring him.

"Ah! damn your soul!" stammered Nanni.

Translated by *Giovanni Cecchetti.*

SUICIDES

Cesare Pavese
(1908–1950)

There are days when everything in the city I live in—the people in the streets, the traffic, trees—awakens in the morning with a strange aspect, the same as always yet unrecognizable, like the times when you look into the mirror and ask: "Who's that?" These for me are the loveliest days of the year.

On such mornings, whenever I can, I leave the office a little earlier and go into the streets, mingling with the crowd, and I don't mind staring at all who pass in

the very way, I suspect, that some of them look at me, for in truth at these moments I have a feeling of assurance that makes me another man.

I am convinced that I shall obtain from life nothing more precious perhaps than the revelation of how I may stimulate these moments at will. One way of making them longer which I have sometimes found successful is to sit in a new cafe, glassed-in and bright, and absorb the noise of all the hurry-scurry and the street, the flare of colors and of voices, and the peaceful interior moderating all the tumult.

In only a few years I have suffered keen stabs of disappointment and regret; still, I may say that my most heartfelt prayer is for this peace, this tranquility alone. I am not cut out for storms and struggle: even though there are mornings when I go forth to walk the streets vibrant with life and my stride may be taken for a challenge, I repeat, I ask of life no more than that she let herself be observed.

And yet even this modest pleasure sometimes leaves me with a bitterness which is precisely that of a vice. It wasn't only yesterday that I realized that in order to live one had to exercise cunning with oneself, and only then with others. I envy the people—they are women mostly— who are able to commit a misdeed or an injustice, or merely to indulge a whim, having contrived beforehand a chain of circumstances so as to give their conduct. in their own eyes, the appearance of being altogether proper. I do not have serious vices—provided this withdrawal from the struggle from lack of confidence, in search of lonely serenity, is not the most serious vice of all—but I do not even know how to handle myself wisely and to hold myself in check when enjoying the little that comes my way.

It sometimes happens, in fact, that I stop in my tracks, glancing about, and ask myself whether I have any right to enjoy my assurance. This occurs especially when my moments out have been rather frequent. Not that I take time off from my work: I provide decently for myself, and support in boarding school an orphaned niece whom the old lady who calls herself my mother doesn't want around the house. But the thing I ask myself is whether—on these ecstatic strolls of mine—I am not ludicrous, ludicrous and disgusting; for I think sometimes that I am not really due my ecstasy.

Or else, as happened the other morning, I need only to assist offhand at some singular scene in a cafe, which intrigues me from the outset by the normalness of its participants, in order to fall a prey to a guilt-ridden sense of loneliness and to so many bleak memories that the farther they recede the more they reveal to me, in their immutable natures, twisted and terrible meanings.

It was five minutes of play between the young cashier and a customer in a light-colored topcoat, accompanied by a friend. The young man was shouting that the cashier owed him change from a hundred-lira note and was slamming his fist on the desk top as he pretended to check through her handbag and pockets.

"Young lady, that's certainly no way to treat customers," he said, winking at his friend, who stood by looking ill at ease. The cashier laughed. The young man then concocted some story about a ride they would take in the elevator of a public bath. Between controlled bursts of laughter they finally decided that they would deposit the money in a bank—once they had it.

"Good-by, young lady," he shouted back as he left at last. "Think of me tonight."

The cashier, exhilarated and laughing, turned to the waiter: "What a character!"

I had noticed her on other mornings,

and sometimes smiled without looking at her, in moments of abstraction. But my peace is too flimsy, a tissue of nothing. The usual stab of remorse returns.

"We are all sordid, but there's a good-natured sordidness, with a smile, that provokes a smile from others, and there's another sordidness that is lonely and holds people off. The sillier, after all, is not the former."

It is on such mornings that I am surprised, each time anew, by the thought that what is truly sinful in my life is only silliness. Others may achieve out-and-out evil by design, sure of themselves, taking an interest in their victims and in the sport—and I suspect that a life so spent may afford many satisfactions—but as for myself, I have never done anything but suffer from great bumbling uncertainty, and writhe, when brought into contact with others, in my own stupid cruelty. Because—and there's no solution—it's enough that I give in to that remorse of my loneliness for an instant or so and I think again of Carlotta.

She has been dead for more than a year, and now I know all the routes that my memory of her may take to surprise me. I can, so wishing, even recognize the initial state of mind that announces her appearance, abruptly diverting my thoughts. But I do not always wish it; and even now my remorse provides me with dark corners, new points, that I study with the trepidation of a year ago. I was so tortuously true with her that each of those far-off days stands in my memory not as a fixed thing, but as an elusive face possessing for me the same reality of today.

Not that Carlotta was a mystery. She was, rather, one of those transparently simple souls—pitiful women—who become irritating if they cease for only an instant being themselves and attempt subterfuge or flirtation. But so long as they are simple no one notices them. I have never understood how she could bear to earn her living as a cashier. She had the makings of an ideal sister.

What I have not fathomed, even yet, are feelings and my behavior then. What, for instance, should I say of the evening in Carlotta's two-room lodgings when she had put on a velvet dress—an old dress—to receive me, and I told her that I should have preferred her in a bathing suit? It was one of my first visits and I had not even kissed her.

Well, making a shy grimace, Carlotta withdrew into the anteroom and—of all things—actually reappeared in a bathing suit! That evening I took her into my arms and forced her down onto the davenport; but then—the moment it was over—I told her I liked being alone and left, and I did not return for three days; and when I did I addressed her formally.

Thereupon another ridiculous courtship began, consisting of timid confidences on her part and few words on my own. Suddenly I addressed her familiarly, but she resisted. Then I asked her if she had reconciled with her husband. Carlotta began to whimper. "He never treated me the way you do," she said.

It was easy to press her head to my chest and caress her and to tell her I loved her; after all, being so alone, couldn't I love a grass widow? And Carlotta let herself go; softly, she confessed that she had loved me from the very beginning, that I struck her as being an extraordinary man, but already, in the short time we had known each other, I had caused her to suffer miserably, and she—she didn't know why—all men treated her the same.

"Blowing hot and cold," I smiled into her hair: "that's how you keep love alive."

Carlotta was sallow, with enormous eyes a little worn with fatigue, and her body was pale too. In the shadows of her bedroom that night, I asked myself if it was because I didn't like her body that I had hurried off the time before.

But even this time I didn't have pity on her: in the middle of the night I dressed and, making no excuses, announced that I had to be going, and went. Carlotta wanted to come along.

"No, I like being alone."

And, giving her a kiss, I left.

When I met Carlotta I was just emerging from a tempest that had nearly cost me my life; and now, returning to the empty streets, retreating from a woman who loved me, I was possessed by a wry mirth. For quite some time I had had to spend days and nights browbeaten and in a fury on account of a woman's whims.

I am convinced now that no passion is so strong as to alter the nature of one who endures it. One may die of it, but that doesn't change a thing. When the frenzy has passed, one returns to being the decent man or the rogue, the family man or the boy, whatever one was, and proceeds with one's life. Or more precisely: from the ordeal our true nature comes out, and it horrifies us; normality disgusts us; and we would wish even to be dead, the insult is so unspeakable, but we have no one to blame but ourselves. I owe it to that woman if I am reduced to this singular life I lead, from day to day, aimlessly, incapable of securing ties with the world, estranged from my fellows—estranged even from my mother whom I only just tolerate, and from my niece whom I don't love—I owe it all to her; but might I not have fared better in the end with another woman? With a woman, I mean, capable of humbling me as my nature required?

Nonetheless, at the time, the thought that I had been wronged, that my mistress could be called treacherous, did afford me a measure of comfort. There is a point in suffering when it is inevitable—it is a natural anesthetic—that one should believe oneself to be suffering unjustly: this brings into force again, according to our most coveted desires, fascination for life; it restores a sense of our worth in the face of things; it is flattering. I had found, and I should have liked, injustice, ingratitude, to be even more unspeakable. I recall—during those interminable days and those evenings of anguish—being aware of a pervasive and secret feeling, like an atmosphere or an irradiance: wonderment that it all happened—that the woman was indeed the woman, that the periods of delirium and stabbing pains were quite what they were, that the sighs, the words, the deeds, that I myself—that it all happeend just as it did.

And now here I was, having suffered injustice, repaying, as inevitably happens, not the guilty one, but another.

I would leave Carlotta's little apartment at night satisfied and absent of mind, delighted to be walking alone, retreating from all solicitude, freely enjoying the long avenue, in vague pursuit of the sensations and thoughts of early youth. The simplicity of the night—darkness and street lamps—has always welcomed me with tenderness, and made for the wildest and most precious fantasies, heightening them with its contrasts and magnifying them. There, even the blind rancor I showed toward Carlotta for her eager humility had full rein, freed of a kind of awkwardness which pitying her made me feel when we were together.

But I was not young any longer. And the better to disengage myself from Carlotta, I reconsidered and anatomized her body and her caresses. Crudely, I considered that separated from her husband as she was, still young and without children, she was simply jumping at the chance for whatever outlet she could find in me. But—poor Carlotta—she was too simple a mistress, and it may have been precisely for this that her husband betrayed her.

I remember returning arm in arm with her from the cinema one evening, wandering through the semilit streets, when she said to me: "I'm happy. It's nice going to the movies with you."

"Did you ever go with your husband?"

Carlotta smiled at me. "Are you jealous?"

I shrugged. "In any case, it doesn't change anything."

"I'm tired," Carlotta would say, pressing against my arm; "this good-for-nothing chain that holds us is ruining both his his life and mine, and making me respect a name that has brought me nothing but suffering. Divorce ought to be possible, at least when there aren't children."

I was lulled that evening by my long, warm contact with her, and by desire. "You have scruples, in other words?"

"Oh, darling," Carlotta said, "why aren't you good all the time, like you are this evening? Think, if only I could have a divorce."

I didn't say anything. Once before when she had mentioned divorce I had burst out: "Now just look here, can anyone be better off than you? You do whatever you please—and I'll wager he still slips you a little, if it's true it was he who betrayed you."

"I have never accepted a thing," Carlotta had replied. "I've worked from that day on"—and she had looked at me. "Now that I have you I'd feel as if I were betraying you."

The evening we went to the movies I shut her up with a kiss. Then I took her to the station cafe where I bought her a couple of glasses of liquor.

We sat like a pair of lovers in the steamy light of the glass panes. I downed quite a few jiggers myself. Presently, in a loud voice, I said to her: "Carlotta, shall we make a baby tonight?"

Some of the people looked at us because Carlotta, radiant and flushed, closed my mouth with her hand.

I talked and talked. Carlotta talked about the film, making silly remarks—passionately—finding comparisons between us and the characters in it. And I—aware that only by drinking could I love her—I drank.

Outside, the cold was invigorating and we hurried home. I spent the night with her, and waking in the morning I felt her by my side, disheveled and full of sleep, fumbling to hug me. I did not repulse her; but when I got up my head was aching and Carlotta's repressed joy as she got my coffee, humming to herself, grated on my nerves. Then we had to leave together, but remembering the concierge, Carlotta sent me out first, not without a wifely hug and a kiss behind the door.

My keenest memory of waking that morning is of the boughs of the trees bordering the walk, stark and dripping in the fog, visible through the curtains in the room. The warmth and solicitude inside, and the raw morning air awaiting me, charged my blood; however, I should have liked to be alone, thinking and smoking by myself, imagining an altogether different waking and another mate.

The tenderness that Carlotta extracted from me at such moments was something I reproached myself for the instant I was alone. I underwent moments of fury, scouring my soul to be rid of the slightest memory of her; I made up my mind to be hard and then was even too hard. It must have been apparent that we loved each other out of indolence, out of some vice—for all the reasons except the very one she sought to delude herself about. The memory of her grave, blissful look after the embrace irritated me, noticing it on her face angered me; whereas the only woman on whom I had wanted to see it had never given me that satisfaction.

"If you accept me as I am, fine," I told her once; "but get it out of your head that you can ever mean anything to me."

"Don't you love me?" Carlotta stammered.

"The little bit of love I was capable of I burned out in my youth."

But there were also times when I lost my temper, having admitted, out of shame or desire, that I did love her a little.

Carlotta would force a smile. "We're good friends at least, aren't we?"

"Listen," I told her seriously, "all this nonsense repels me; we're a man and a woman who are bored; we get on in bed—"

"Oh, yes, that we do!" she said; she clutched my arm, hiding her face. "I like you, I do like you—"

"—period."

It was enough to have just one of these exchanges, in which I struck myself as spineless, for me to avoid her for weeks on end; and if she rang me up at the office from her cafe I told her I was busy. The first time Carlotta tried being angry, I let her spend the evening in torment, while I sat frigid on the davenport—the lampshade cast a white light on her knees—and in the half-light I could sense the contained spasms of her glances. It was I, in the unbearable tension, who finally said: "Thank me, Signora: you're likely to remember this session more than many others."

Carlotta didn't stir.

"Why don't you kill me, Signora? If you think you can play the woman with me, you're wasting your time. The flighty one I'll play myself."

She was breathing heavily.

"Not even your bathing suit," I said to her, "will help you this evening. . . ."

Suddenly Carlotta bounded at me. I saw her blackhaired head go through the white light like some hurled object. I thrust out my hands. But Carlotta collapsed at my knees in tears. I laid a hand on her head two or three times. Then I rose.

"I ought to be crying too, Carlotta. But I know that tears are no use. All this you're going through I've been through myself. I've been on the point of killing myself, and then my nerve failed me. This is the rub: a person so weak as to think of suicide is also too weak to commit it. . . . Come now, Carlotta, be good."

"Don't treat me like that . . ." she stammered.

"I'm not treating you like anything. But you know I like being alone. If you let me be alone, I'll come back; if not, we'll never see each other again. Look, would you like me to love you?"

Beneath my hand, Carlotta looked up with her swollen face.

"Well, then, you must stop loving me. There's no other way. The hare's the hunter."

Scenes of this sort shook Carlotta too deeply for her to consider giving me up. But didn't they also denote a fundamental similarity in temperament? At bottom, Carlotta was a simple soul—too simple— and incapable of clearly recognizing it; but certainly she sensed it. She tried— poor creature—to hold me by being lighthearted, and would sometimes say things like "Such is life!" and "Poor little me!"

I believe that if at that time she had firmly repulsed me I should have suffered a little. But it wasn't in her power. If I remained away for two evenings running, I found her with sunken eyes. And whenever, on occasion, I took pity on her or was kind, and stopped by her cafe and asked her to come out with me, she got up flushed and flustered, even more beautiful.

My rancor was not directed at her; rather, at all the restrictions and the enslavement our liaison seemed likely to produce. Since I didn't love her, her smallest claim on me struck me as an outrage. There were days when addressing her in the *tu*-form disgusted and degraded me Who was this woman clamped onto my arm?

In return, I seemed to experience a rebirth, certain half days, certain hours when, after hurrying through my work, I was able to go out into the cool sun and walk the sunlit streets, unencumbered by her, by anything, feeling satisfied of body, my old sorrow soothed: eager to see, to smell, to feel as I had when I was young. That Carlotta might suffer on my account alleviated my past griefs and made them paltry, and estranged them from me a little, as from a laughable world; and far removed from her, I found myself whole again, more adept. She was the sponge I used to cleanse myself. I thought this often of her.

Some evenings when I talked and talked, engrossed in the game, I was a youngster again and I put my rancor behind me.

"Carlotta," I would say, "what is it like to be a lover? It's so long since I was one. All told, it must be a fine thing, I imagine. When all goes well, you enjoy it; when it doesn't, you hope. You live from day to day, they say. What is it like, Carlotta?"

Carlotta would shake her head, smiling.

"Another thing, you have so many wonderful thoughts, Carlotta. Whoever takes love lightly will never be happy like the lover. Unless," I smiled, "'he sleeps with another woman and then makes game of the lover."

Carlotta knitted her brows.

"Love is a fine thing," I concluded. "And no one escapes it."

Carlotta served as my public. I was talking to myself, those evenings. It's the pleasantest of talks.

"There is love and there is betrayal. In order really to enjoy love there's also got to be betrayal. This is the thing young boys don't realize. You women learn it earlier. Did you betray your husband?"

Carlotta essayed a cunning smile, going red.

"We boys were stupider. Scrupulously, we fell in love with an actress or schoolmate and offered her our finest thoughts. Except that we never got around to telling them. To my knowledge there wasn't a girl our age who didn't realize that love is a matter of craft. It doesn't seem possible, but boys go to brothels and conclude that the women outside are different. What were you up to at sixteen, Carlotta?"

But Carlotta's thoughts were elsewhere. With her eyes, before answering, she told me that I was hers, and I hated the hardness of the solicitude her glance gave off.

"What were you doing at sixteen?" I asked her again, staring down at the floor.

"Nothing," she replied gravely. I knew what she was thinking.

Then she asked me to forgive her—she was acting the poor forlorn creature and she knew she hadn't the right—but her glance was enough. "Do you know you're stupid? For all I care, your husband could take you back!" And off I went with a feeling of relief.

Next day in the office I received a timid telephone call, to which I replied dryly. That evening I saw her again.

Carlotta was amused whenever I talked about my niece who was away at boarding school, and she shook her head with disbelief when I told her that I would rather have shut my mother up in school and lived with the child. She pictured us as two quite different beings, playing at being uncle and niece, but actually having a whole world of secrets and petty grievances to delight and occupy us. She asked me, put out, if the girl were not my daughter.

"Of course. Born when I was sixteen. She decided to be blond just to spite me. How can one be born blond? Blonds for me are creatures like monkeys or lions. It must be like always being in the sun, I should imagine."

Carlotta said: "I was blond when I was little."

"I was bald myself."

My interest in Carlotta's past, during that final period, was a bored curiosity which from time to time allowed me to forget all she had previously told me. I scanned her as one scans the page of local news in the paper. I delighted in puzzling her with whimsical sallies, I put cruel questions to her and then supplied the answers. I was actually listening to no one but myself.

But Carlotta had seen through me. "Tell me about yourself," she would say some evenings, pressing my arm. She knew that only by getting me to talk about myself could she make a friend of me.

"Carlotta, did I ever tell you that a man once killed himself because of me?" I asked her one evening.

She looked at me radiant and half amazed.

"It's nothing to laugh at," I went on. "We killed ourselves together—but he actually died. Youthful shenanigans." Wasn't it curious, I thought suddenly, I had never told a soul, and of all people Carlotta would be the first. "He was a friend of mine, a fine-looking blond boy. And he really did look a lion. You girls, you don't make friendships like that. At that age you're already too jealous. We were schoolmates, but we always met afterward, in the evening. We talked in the dirty ways boys will, but we were in love with a woman. She must still be living. She was our first love, Carlotta. We

spent our evenings talking about love and death. No one in love has ever been more certain of being understood by his best friend than we were of each other. Jean —his name was Jean—had a bold sadness that used to put me to shame. All by himself he created the melancholy of those evenings we spent walking together through the fog. We didn't believe one could suffer so much—"

"You were in love, too?"

"I suffered for being less melancholy than Jean. Finally I discovered that we might kill ourselves, and I told him. Jean took to the idea slowly, he who was normally so imaginative. We had a revolver between us. We went out to the hills to test it, in case it should explode. It was Jean who fired. He had always been foolhardy, and I think that if he had stopped loving the woman I should have stopped too. After the test—we were on a barren footpath, halfway up; it was winter—I was still thinking about the force of the shot when Jean put the barrel into his mouth and said: 'Some guys do it this way . . .' And the gun went off and killed him."

Carlotta stared at me horrified.

"I didn't know what to do and ran away."

Later that evening Carlotta said to me: "And you really loved that woman?"

"What woman? I loved Jean; I told you."

"And did you want to kill yourself too?"

"Naturally. It would have been foolish, though. But not doing it was rank cowardice. I'm sorry I didn't."

Carlotta often returned to the story, and spoke to me of Jean as though she had known him. She had me describe him and asked me what I myself was like then. She wanted to know if I had kept the revolver.

"Don't go killing yourself now. Have

you never thought of killing yourself?" So saying, she rested her eyes on me.

"Every time you fall in love you think of it."

Carlotta didn't even smile. "Do you think of it still?"

"I think of Jean sometimes."

At noon, the thought of Carlotta distressed me terribly when, after I had left the office, I passed her cafe window, hurrying by so as not to have to look in and kid with her a little. I did not go home at noon. I especially liked seating myself alone in an eating house and whiling away that part of an hour I had, with my eyes barely open, smoking. Carlotta, in her chair, would be ringing up change automatically, tilting and nodding her head, smiling and frowning, at times with a customer joking with her.

She was there, in her blue dress, from seven in the morning till four in the afternoon. They paid her four hundred and eighty lire a month. Carlotta liked rushing through the day in a single sitting, and would take lunch, with a big cup of milk, without rising from her place. It would have been an easy job, she told me, except for the way the door banged with all the coming and going. There were times when she felt it like punches on the raw surface of her brain.

Ever since, on entering cafes, I have closed the doors carefully. With me, Carlotta tried to describe the little scenes with the customers, but she could never bring off my way of talking, just as she was never able to get a rise out of me with her sly allusions to the proposals some old goat was making to her.

"Go right ahead," I told her; "just don't let me see him. Receive him on odd days. And take care you don't pick up any diseases."

Carlotta made a wry mouth.

For some days a thought had been gnawing at her. "Are we in love again, Carlotta?" I said to her one evening.

Carlotta looked at me like a whipped dog. And I lost patience with her again. Those shining glances of hers, that evening, in the half-light of the little room, her squeezing my hand—it all infuriated me. With Carlotta I was forever afraid of being tied down. I hated the very thought of it.

I grew sullen again; surly. But Carlotta had stopped taking my outbursts with her former injured paroxysms. She simply looked at me, without moving, and sometimes when, to comfort her, I reached out to caress her, she would draw back in an affectionate motion.

Which was something I liked even less. Being compelled to court her in order to have her was repugnant to me. But it would not begin without a prelude. Carlotta would start: "I have a headache . . . oh, that door! Let's be good this evening. Talk to me."

The moment I realized she was really serious, regarding herself as a poor unfortunate, dredging up regrets, my outbursts would end: I simply betrayed her. I relived one of those colorless evenings of the past when, returning from a brothel, I had sat in any wretched, cheap cafe to rest, neither happy nor sad, muzzy. It seemed only just: one either accepted love with all its hazards or nothing remained but prostitution.

I believed Carlotta's jealousy to be an act, and it amused me. She suffered. But she was too simple a soul to turn it to her gain. Rather, as happens to those who really suffer, it made her ugly. I was sorry, but I would have to have done with her, I felt.

Carlotta saw the blow coming. One evening when we were in bed together, while I was instinctively avoiding conversation, she suddenly thrust me away and curled up toward the wall.

"What's eating you?" I demanded, annoyed.

"If I were to disappear tomorrow," she said, suddenly turning back, "would it make any difference to you?"

"I don't know," I stammered.

"And if I betrayed you?"

"Life itself is a betrayal."

"And if I returned to my husband?"

She was serious. I shrugged.

"I'm only a poor woman," Carlotta continued. "And I'm not able to betray you . . . I've seen my husband."

"What?"

"He came to the cafe."

"But didn't he go to America?"

"I don't know," Carlotta said. "I saw him at the cafe."

She may not have meant to tell me, but it came out that her husband had also come with a woman in a fur coat.

"In that case, you weren't able to talk?"

Carlotta hesitated. "He came back the next day. He talked to me then, and afterward saw me home."

I must confess that I felt uncomfortable. I said softly: "Here?"

Carlotta clung to me with all her body. "But I love you," she whispered. "You mustn't think—"

"Here?"

"It was nothing, darling. He simply talked about his business. Only, seeing him again I realized how much I love you. He can beg and I won't go back to him."

"Then he begged you?"

"No. He just said that if he were to marry again he would still marry me."

"Have you seen him since?"

"He came to the cafe again, with that woman . . ."

That was the last time I spent the night with Carlotta. Without taking leave of her body, without regrets, I stopped ringing her up and stopped visiting her at her flat. I let her telephone me and then wait to meet me in cafes—nor was it every evening: only now and then. Carlotta would come each time and devour me with her eyes, and when we were about to leave her voice would quaver.

"I haven't seen him again," she whispered one evening.

"You're making a mistake," I answered; "you ought to try to get him back."

It annoyed me that Carlotta missed her husband—as she unquestionably did—and that with such talk she hoped to entice me. That unconsummated love of hers was worth neither her regrets nor my own risks.

One evening I told her over the telephone that I'd call on her. She let me in with a look of disbelief and anxiety. I glanced around the entry hall, a little apprehensive. Carlotta was wearing velvet. And I recall that she had a cold and kept squeezing her hankerchief and pressing it to her red nose.

At once, I saw that she understood. She was quiet and meek, and she answered me with pitiful looks. She let me do all the talking, while she cast furtive glances over the top of her handkerchief. Then she rose and came to me, leaning her body against my face, and I had to place an arm around her.

Softly, in the same tone, she said: "Won't you come to bed?"

We went to bed, and through all of it I disliked her damp face, inflamed by her cold. At midnight I jumped out of bed and began dressing. Carlotta turned on the light, looking at me for an instant. Then she turned it off and said: "Yes, go if you wish." Embarrassed, I stumbled out.

In the days that followed I feared a telephone call, but nothing disturbed me, and I was able to work in peace for weeks on end. And then, one evening, desire for Carlotta took hold of me again, but shame helped me to overcome it. Even so, I knew that if I had rung at that door I would have brought happiness. This certainty I have always had.

I didn't yield; but, the day after, I went by her cafe. There was a blond at the cash register. They must have changed hours. But she wasn't there in the evening, either. I thought that perhaps she was ill or that her husband had taken her back. This was not an appealing idea.

But my legs shook when the concierge, with extreme ill grace, fixing me with a hard beady gaze, told me that they had found her in bed a month before, dead, with the gas jets on.

Translated by *Ben Johnson*.

POEMS

NOT MARBLE, NOR THE GILDED MONUMENTS
(Sonnet LV)

William Shakespeare
(1564–1616)

Not marble, nor the gilded monuments
Of princes, shall outlive this powerful
    rime;
But you shall shine more bright in these
    contents
Than unswept stone, besmeared with slut-
    tish time.
When wasteful war shall statues over-
    turn,   5
And broils root out the work of masonry,
Nor Mars his sword nor war's quick fire
    shall burn
The living record of your memory.
'Gainst death and all-oblivious enmity
Shall you pace forth; your praise shall
    still find room   10
Even in the eyes of all posterity
That wear this world out to the ending
    doom.
    So, till the judgment that yourself arise,
You live in this, and dwell in lovers'
    eyes.

4. *stone:* tomb or effigy.
6. *broils:* conflicts or battles.
12. *ending doom:* Judgment Day.
13. *that:* when.

TO HIS COY MISTRESS

Andrew Marvell
(1621–1678)

Had we but world enough, and time,
This coyness, lady, were no crime.
We would sit down, and think which way
To walk, and pass our long love's day.
Thou by the Indian Ganges' side   5
Shouldst rubies find: I by the tide
Of Humber would complain. I would
Love you ten years before the flood,
And you should, if you please, refuse
Till the conversion of the Jews;   10
My vegetable love should grow
Vaster than empires and more slow;
An hundred years should go to praise
Thine eyes, and on thy forehead gaze;
Two hundred to adore each breast,   15
But thirty thousand to the rest;
An age at least to every part,
And the last age should show your heart.
For, lady, you deserve this state;
Nor would I love at lower rate.   20

But at my back I always hear

7. *Humber:* a river in Yorkshire where Marvell lived.

Time's wingéd chariot hurrying near;
And yonder all before us lie
Deserts of vast eternity.
Thy beauty shall no more be found,   25
Nor in thy marble vault shall sound
My echoing song; then worms shall try
That long preserved virginity;
And your quaint honor turn to dust,
And into ashes all my lust: 30
The grave's a fine and private place,
But none, I think, do there embrace.

Now therefore, while the youthful hue
Sits on thy skin like morning dew,
And while thy willing soul transpires   35
At every pore with instant fires,
Now let us sport us while we may,
And now, like amorous birds of prey,
Rather at once our time devour
Than languish in his slow-chapped
   power,   40
Let us roll all our strength and all
Our sweetness up into one ball,
And tear our pleasures with rough strife
Thorough the iron gates of life:
Thus, though we cannot make our sun   45
Stand still, yet we will make him run.

29. *quaint:* proud.
40. *slow-chapped:* having slow-moving jaws.

TO ———

Percy Bysshe Shelley
(1792–1822)

Music, when soft voices die,
Vibrates in the memory—
Odors, when sweet violets sicken,
Live within the sense they quicken.

Rose leaves, when the rose is dead,   5
Are heaped for the belovéd's bed;
And so thy thoughts, when thou art gone,
Love itself shall slumber on.

THE EVE OF ST. AGNES *

John Keats
(1795–1821)

St. Agnes' Eve—Ah, bitter chill it was!
The owl, for all his feathers, was a-cold;
The hare limped trembling through the
   frozen grass,
And silent was the flock in woolly fold:
Numb were the Beadsman's fingers, while
   he told   5
His rosary, and while his frosted breath,
Like pious incense from a censer old,
Seemed taking flight for heaven, without
   a death,
Past the sweet Virgin's picture, while his
   prayer he saith.

His prayer, he saith, this patient, holy
   man;   10
Then takes his lamp, and riseth from his
   knees,
And back returneth, meager, barefoot,
   wan,
Along the chapel aisle by slow degrees:
The sculptured dead, on each side, seem
   to freeze,
Emprisoned in black, purgatorial rails: 15
Knights, ladies, praying in dumb orat'ries,
He passeth by; and his weak spirit fails
To think how they may ache in icy hoods
   and mails.

Northward he turneth through a little
   door,
And scarce three steps, ere Music's golden
   tongue   20
Flattered to tears this aged man and poor;
But no—already had his death-bell rung:
The joys of all his life were said and sung:
His was harsh penance on St. Agnes' Eve:

* The night of January 20, at which time,
according to legend, a maiden who performed
the proper ritual would dream of the man she
was destined to marry.
5. *Beadsman:* a poor man paid to pray for his
benefactor.
16. *orat'ries:* chapels.

Another way he went, and soon among 25
Rough ashes sat he for his soul's reprieve,
And all night kept awake, for sinners'
　　sake to grieve.

That ancient Beadsman heard the prelude
　　soft;
And so it chanced, for many a door was
　　wide,
From hurry to and fro. Soon, up aloft, 30
The silver, snarling trumpets 'gan to
　　chide:
The level chambers, ready with their
　　pride,
Were glowing to receive a thousand
　　guests:
The carvéd angels, ever eager-eyed,
Stared, where upon their heads the cor-
　　nice rests,　　　　　　　　　　35
With hair blown back, and wings put
　　crosswise on their breasts.

At length burst in the argent revelry,
With plume, tiara, and all rich array,
Numerous as shadows haunting faerily
The brain, new-stuffed, in youth, with tri-
　　umphs gay　　　　　　　　　40
Of old romance. These let us wish away,
And turn, sole-thoughted, to one Lady
　　there,
Whose heart had brooded, all that wintry
　　day,
On love, and winged St. Agnes' saintly
　　care,
As she had heard old dames full many
　　times declare.　　　　　　　45

They told her how, upon St. Agnes' Eve,
Young virgins might have visions of de-
　　light,
And soft adorings from their loves receive
Upon the honeyed middle of the night,
If ceremonies due they did aright;　　50
As, supperless to bed they must retire,
And couch supine their beauties, lily
　　white;

37. *argent revelry:* revelers clad in silver.

Nor look behind, nor sideways, but re-
　　quire
Of Heaven with upward eyes for all that
　　they desire.

Full of this whim was thoughtful Made-
　　line:　　　　　　　　　　55
The music, yearning like a god in pain,
She scarcely heard: her maiden eyes
　　divine,
Fixed on the floor, saw many a sweeping
　　train
Pass by—she heeded not at all: in vain
Came many a tiptoe, amorous cavalier, 60
And back retired; not cooled by high dis-
　　dain,
But she saw not: her heart was other-
　　where;
She sighed for Agnes' dreams, the sweet-
　　est of the year.

She danced along with vague, regardless
　　eyes,
Anxious her lips, her breathing quick and
　　short:　　　　　　　　　　65
The hallowed hour was near at hand: she
　　sighs
Amid the timbrels, and the thronged re-
　　sort
Of whisperers in anger, or in sport;
'Mid looks of love, defiance, hate, and
　　scorn,
Hoodwinked with faery fancy; all
　　amort,　　　　　　　　　　70
Save to St. Agnes and her lambs unshorn,
And all the bliss to be before tomorrow
　　morn.

So, purposing each moment to retire,
She lingered still. Meantime, across the
　　moors,
Had come young Porphyro, with heart on
　　fire　　　　　　　　　　75
For Madeline. Beside the portal doors,

70. *amort:* dead
71. *St. Agnes . . . unshorn:* On St. Agnes'
Day lambs were blessed and their wool shorn to
be woven into cloth by nuns.

Buttressed from moonlight, stands he,
and implores
All saints to give him sight of Madeline,
But for one moment in the tedious hours,
That he might gaze and worship all un-
seen;   80
Perchance speak, kneel, touch, kiss—in
sooth such things have been.

He ventures in: let no buzzed whisper tell:
All eyes be muffled, or a hundred swords
Will storm his heart, Love's fev'rous cita-
del:
For him, those chambers held barbarian
hordes,   85
Hyena foemen, and hot-blooded lords,
Whose very dogs would execrations howl
Against his lineage: not one breast affords
Him any mercy, in that mansion foul,
Save one old beldame, weak in body and
in soul.   90

Ah, happy chance! the aged creature
came,
Shuffling along with ivory-headed wand,
To where he stood, hid from the torch's
flame,
Behind a broad hall-pillar, far beyond
The sound of merriment and chorus
bland: 95
He startled her; but soon she knew his
face,
And grasped his fingers in her palsied
hand,
Saying, "Mercy, Porphyro! hie thee from
this place;
They are all here tonight, the whole blood-
thirsty race!

"Get hence! get hence! there's dwarfish
Hildebrand;   100
He had a fever late, and in the fit
He cursèd thee and thine, both house and
land:
Then there's that old Lord Maurice, not a
whit
More tame for his gray hairs—Alas me!
flit!

Flit like a ghost away."—"Ah, Gossip
dear,   105
We're safe enough; here in this armchair
sit,
And tell me how"—"Good Saints! not
here, not here;
Follow me, child, or else these stones will
be thy bier."

He followed through a lowly archéd way,
Brushing the cobwebs with his lofty
plume;   110
And as she muttered, "Well-a—well-a-
day!"
He found him in a little moonlight room,
Pale, latticed, chill, and silent as a tomb.
"Now tell me where is Madeline," said he,
"O tell me, Angela, by the holy loom 115
Which none but secret sisterhood may see,
When they St. Agnes' wool are weaving,
piously."

"St. Agnes! Ah! it is St. Agnes' Eve—
Yet men will murder upon holy days:
Thou must hold water in a witch's
sieve,   120
And be liege-lord of all the Elves and
Fays,
To venture so: it fills me with amaze
To see thee, Porphyro!—St. Agnes' Eve!
God's help! my lady fair the conjuror
plays
This very night: good angels her de-
ceive!   125
But let me laugh awhile, I've mickle time
to grieve."

Feebly she laugheth in the languid moon;
While Porphyro upon her face doth look,
Like puzzled urchin on an aged crone
Who keepeth closed a wond'rous riddle-
book,   130
As spectacled she sits in chimney nook.

105. *Gossip:* an appellation for god-mother or
old woman.
120. *witch's sieve:* a sieve made by supernatural powers to hold water.
126. *mickle:* much.

But soon his eyes grew brilliant, when she
    told
His lady's purpose; and he scarce could
    brook
Tears, at the thought of those enchant-
    ments cold,
And Madeline asleep in lap of legends
    old.   135

Sudden a thought came like a full-blown
    rose,
Flushing his brow, and in his painéd
    heart
Made purple riot: then doth he propose
A stratagem, that makes the beldame
    start:
"A cruel man and impious thou art: 140
Sweet lady, let her pray, and sleep, and
    dream
Alone with her good angels, far apart
From wicked men like thee. Go, go! I
    deem
Thou canst not surely be the same that
    thou didst seem."

"I will not harm her, by all saints I
    swear,"   145
Quoth Porphyro: "O may I ne'er find
    grace
When my weak voice shall whisper its last
    prayer,
If one of her soft ringlets I displace,
Or look with ruffian passion in her face:
Good Angela, believe me by these
    tears;   150
Or I will, even in a moment's space,
Awake, with horrid shout, my foemen's
    ears,
And beard them, though they be more
    fanged than wolves and bears."

"Ah! why wilt thou affright a feeble soul?
A poor, weak, palsy-stricken, churchyard
    thing,   155
Whose passing-bell may ere the midnight
    toll;

Whose prayers for thee, each morn and
    evening,
Were never missed." Thus plaining, doth
    she bring
A gentler speech from burning Porphyro;
So woeful, and of such deep sorrow-
    ing,   160
That Angela gives promise she will do
Whatever he shall wish, betide her weal or
    woe.

Which was, to lead him, in close secrecy,
Even to Madeline's chamber, and there
    hide
Him in a closet, of such privacy   165
That he might see her beauty unespied,
And win perhaps that night a peerless
    bride,
While legioned faeries paced the coverlet,
And pale enchantment held her sleepy-
    eyed.
Never on such a night have lovers met, 170
Since Merlin paid his Demon all the mon-
    strous debt.

"It shall be as thou wishest," said the
    Dame:
"All cates and dainties shall be storéd
    there
Quickly on this feast-night: by the tam-
    bour frame
Her own lute thou wilt see: no time to
    spare,   175
For I am slow and feeble, and scarce dare
On such a catering trust my dizzy head.
Wait here, my child, with patience; kneel
    in prayer
The while: Ah! thou must needs the lady
    wed,
Or may I never leave my grave among the
    dead."   180

So saying, she hobbled off with busy fear.

171. *Merlin . . . debt:* There is a legend that
Merlin, the magician of Arthur's court, revealed
a secret spell to the enchantress Vivian, who
used it against him.
173. *cates:* delicacies.
174. *tambour frame:* embroidery frame in the
shape of a drum.

133. *brook:* endure; Keats apparently meant
"restrain."
156. *passing-bell:* bell that announces death.

The lover's endless minutes slowly passed;
The Dame returned, and whispered in his
    ear
To follow her—with agéd eyes aghast
From fright of dim espial. Safe at last, 185
Through many a dusky gallery, they gain
The maiden's chamber, silken, hushed,
    and chaste;
Where Porphyro took covert, pleased
    amain.
His poor guide hurried back with agues in
    her brain.

Her faltering hand upon the balus-
    trade,   190
Old Angela was feeling for the stair,
When Madeline, St. Agnes' charméd
    maid,
Rose, like a missioned spirit, unaware:
With silver taper's light, and pious care,
She turned, and down the aged gossip
    led   195
To a safe level matting. Now prepare,
Young Porphyro, for gazing on that bed;
She comes, she comes again, like ring-
    dove frayed and fled.

Out went the taper as she hurried in;
Its little smoke, in pallid moonshine,
    died: 200
She closed the door, she panted, all akin
To spirits of the air, and visions wide:
No uttered syllable, or, woe betide!
But to her heart, her heart was voluble,
Paining with eloquence her balmy side; 205
As though a tongueless nightingale should
    swell
Her throat in vain, and die, heart-stifled
    in her dell.

A casement high and triple-arched there
    was,
All garlanded with carven imag'ries
Of fruits, and flowers, and bunches of
    knot-grass,   210

And diamonded with panes of quaint de-
    vice,
Innumerable of stains and splendid dyes,
As are the tiger-moth's deep-damasked
    wings;
And in the midst, 'mong thousand herald-
    ries,
And twilight saints, and dim emblazon-
    ings,   215
A shielded scutcheon blushed with blood
    of queens and kings.

Full on this casement shone the wintry
    moon,
And threw warm gules on Madeline's fair
    breast,
As down she knelt for heaven's grace and
    boon;
Rose-bloom fell on her hands, together
    pressed,   220
And on her silver cross soft amethyst,
And on her hair a glory, like a saint:
She seemed a splendid angel, newly
    dressed,
Save wings, for heaven—Porphyro grew
    faint:
She knelt, so pure a thing, so free from
    mortal taint.   225

Anon his heart revives: her vespers done,
Of all its wreathéd pearls her hair she
    frees;
Unclasps her warméd jewels one by one;
Loosens her fragrant bodice; by degrees
Her rich attire creeps rustling to her
    knees: 230
Half-hidden, like a mermaid in sea-weed,
Pensive awhile she dreams awake, and
    sees,
In fancy, fair St. Agnes in her bed,
But dares not look behind, or all the charm
    is fled.

Soon, trembling, in her soft and chilly
    nest,   235
In sort of wakeful swoon, perplexed she
    lay,

188. *amain:* greatly.
198. *frayed:* frightened.

218. *gules:* red, as used in heraldry.

Until the poppied warmth of sleep op-
    pressed
Her soothéd limbs, and soul fatigued
    away;
Flown, like a thought, until the morrow-
    day;
Blissfully havened both from joy and
    pain;   240
Clasped like a missal where swart Pay-
    nims pray;
Blinded alike from sunshine and from
    rain,
As though a rose should shut, and be a
    bud again.

Stol'n to this paradise, and so entranced,
Porphyro gazed upon her empty dress, 245
And listened to her breathing, if it
    chanced
To wake into a slumberous tenderness;
Which when he heard, that minute did he
    bless,
And breathed himself: then from the
    closet crept,
Noiseless as fear in a wide wilderness, 250
And over the hushed carpet, silent,
    stepped,
And 'tween the curtains peeped, where,
    lo!—how fast she slept.

Then by the bedside, where the faded
    moon
Made a dim, silver twilight, soft he set
A table, and, half anguished, threw
    thereon   255
A cloth of woven crimson, gold, and jet—
O for some drowsy Morphean amulet!
The boisterous, midnight, festive clarion,
The kettle-drum, and far-heard clarionet,
Affray his ears, though but in dying
    tone—   260
The hall door shuts again, and all the
    noise is gone.
And still she slept an azure-lidded sleep,

In blanchéd linen, smooth, and laven-
    dered,
While he from forth the closet brought a
    heap
Of candied apple, quince, and plum, and
    gourd;   265
With jellies soother than the creamy curd,
And lucent syrups, tinct with cinnamon;
Manna and dates, in argosy transferred
From Fez; and spicéd dainties, every one,
From silken Samarcand to cedared Leb-
    anon.   270

These delicates he heaped with glowing
    hand
On golden dishes and in baskets bright
Of wreathéd silver: sumptuous they stand
In the retiréd quiet of the night,
Filling the chilly room with perfume
    light.—   275
"And now, my love, my seraph fair,
    awake!
Thou art my heaven, and I thine eremite:
Open thine eyes, for meek St. Agnes' sake,
Or I shall drowse beside thee, so my soul
    doth ache."

Thus whispering, his warm, unnervéd
    arm   280
Sank in her pillow. Shaded was her dream
By the dusk curtains—'twas a midnight
    charm
Impossible to melt as icéd stream:
The lustrous salvers in the moonlight
    gleam;
Broad golden fringe upon the carpet
    lies: 285
It seemed he never, never could redeem
From such a steadfast spell his lady's eyes;
So mused awhile, entoiled in wooféd
    phantasies.

Awakening up, he took her hollow lute

---

241. *Clasped . . . pray:* held tightly or cherished as a prayer book would be in a land of
pagans.
   257. *Morphean amulet:* sleep-inducing charm.

269. *Fez:* a Moroccan trading city.
270. *Samarcand:* a city in Russia.
     Lebanon: a mountain range in Spain.
277. *eremite:* hermit.

Tumultuous—and, in chords that tender-
    est be,   290
He played an ancient ditty, long since
    mute,
In Provence called "La belle dame sans
    merci";
Close to her ear touching the melody;—
Wherewith disturbed, she uttered a soft
    moan:
He ceased—she panted quick—and sud-
    denly   295
Her blue affrayéd eyes wide open shone:
Upon his knees he sank, pale as smooth-
    sculptured stone.

Her eyes were open, but she still beheld,
Now wide awake, the vision of her sleep:
There was a painful change, that nigh
    expelled   300
The blisses of her dream so pure and deep
At which fair Madeline began to weep,
And moan forth witless words with many
    a sigh;
While still her gaze on Porphyro would
    keep;
Who knelt, with joinéd hands and piteous
    eye,   305
Fearing to move or speak, she looked so
    dreamingly.

"Ah, Porphyro!" said she, "but even now
Thy voice was at sweet tremble in mine
    ear,
Made tuneable with every sweetest vow;
And those sad eyes were spiritual and
    clear: 310
How changed thou art! how pallid, chill,
    and drear!
Give me that voice again, my Porphyro,
Those looks immortal, those complainings
    dear!
Oh, leave me not in this eternal woe,
For if thou diest, my Love, I know not
    where to go."   315

Beyond a mortal man impassioned far

At these voluptuous accents, he arose,
Ethereal, flushed, and like a throbbing star
Seen mid the sapphire heaven's deep re-
    pose;
Into her dream he melted, as the rose 320
Blendeth its odor with the violet—
Solution sweet; meantime the frost-wind
    blows
Like Love's alarum pattering the sharp
    sleet
Against the window-panes; St. Agnes'
    moon hath set.

'Tis dark; quick pattereth the flaw-blown
    sleet;   325
"This is no dream, my bride, my Made-
    line!"
'Tis dark; the icéd gusts still rave and beat;
"No dream, alas! alas! and woe is mine!
Porphyro will leave me here to fade and
    pine.—
Cruel! what traitor could thee hither
    bring?   330
I curse not, for my heart is lost in thine
Though thou forsakest a deceivéd thing;—
A dove forlorn and lost with sick un-
    prunéd wing."

"My Madeline! sweet dreamer! lovely
    bride!
Say, may I be for aye thy vassal blest? 335
Thy beauty's shield, heart-shaped and
    vermeil-dyed?
Ah, silver shrine, here will I take my rest
After so many hours of toil and quest,
A famished pilgrim—saved by miracle.
Though I have found, I will not rob thy
    nest   340
Saving of thy sweet self; if thou think'st
    well
To trust, fair Madeline, to no rude infidel.

"Hark! 'tis an elfin storm from faery land,
Of haggard seeming, but a boon indeed:
Arise—arise! the morning is at hand— 345
The bloated wassailers will never heed—

---

292. *"La . . . merci":* "the beautiful lady
without mercy."

325. *flaw-blown:* blown by a wind.
336. *vermeil:* crimson.

Let us away, my love, with happy speed;
There are no ears to hear, or eyes to see—
Drowned all in Rhenish and the sleepy
   mead;
Awake! arise! my love, and fearless be,   350
For o'er the southern moors I have a home
   for thee."

She hurried at his words, beset with fears,
For there were sleeping dragons all
   around,
At glaring watch, perhaps, with ready
   spears—
Down the wide stairs a darkling way they
   found.—   355
In all the house was heard no human
   sound.
A chain-drooped lamp was flickering by
   each door;
The arras, rich with horseman, hawk, and
   hound,
Fluttered in the besieging wind's uproar;
And the long carpets rose along the gusty
   floor.   360

They glide, like phantoms, into the wide
   hall;
Like phantoms to the iron porch they
   glide,
Where lay the Porter, in uneasy sprawl,
With a huge empty flagon by his side;
The wakeful bloodhound rose, and shook
   his hide,   365
But his sagacious eye an inmate owns:
By one, and one, the bolts full easy slide—
The chains lie silent on the footworn
   stones;—
The key turns, and the door upon its
   hinges groans.

And they are gone: aye, ages long ago   370
These lovers fled away into the storm.
That night the Baron dreamt of many a
   woe,
And all his warrior-guests, with shade and
   form

358. *arras:* tapestry.

Of witch, and demon, and large coffin-
   worm,
Were long be-nightmared. Angela the old
Died palsy-twitched, with meager face
   deform;   376
The Beadsman, after thousand aves told,
For aye unsought-for slept among his
   ashes cold.

FRANCESCA

Ezra Pound
(1884–   )

You came in out of the night
And there were flowers in your hands,
Now you will come out of a confusion of
   people,
Out of a turmoil of speech about you.

I who have seen you amid the primal
   things   5
Was angry when they spoke your name
In ordinary places.
I would that the cool waves might flow
   over my mind,
And that the world should dry as a dead
   leaf,
Or as a dandelion seed-pod and be swept
   away,   10
So that I might find you again,
Alone.

SOMEWHERE I HAVE NEVER TRAVELLED, GLADLY BEYOND

E. E. Cummings
(1894–1962)

Somewhere i have never travelled,gladly
   beyond

any experience,your eyes have their
    silence:
in your most frail gesture are things
    which enclose me,
or which i cannot touch because they are
    too near

your slightest look easily will unclose
    me   5
though i have closed myself as fingers,
you open always petal by petal myself as
    Spring opens
(touching skilfully,mysteriously)her first
    rose

or if your wish be to close me,i and
my life will shut very beautifully,sud-
    denly,   10
as when the heart of this flower imagines
the snow carefully everywhere descend-
    ing;

nothing which we are to perceive in this
    world equals
the power of your intense fragility:whose
    texture
compels me with the colour of its coun-
    tries,   15
rendering death and forever with each
    breathing

(i do not know what it is about you that
    closes
and opens;only something in me under-
    stands
the voice of your eyes is deeper than all
    roses)
nobody,not even the rain, has such small
    hands   20

▣   ▣   ▣

MY MISTRESS' EYES ARE
NOTHING LIKE THE SUN
(Sonnet CXXX)

William Shakespeare
(1564–1616)

My mistress' eyes are nothing like the sun;
Coral is far more red than her lips' red;
If snow be white, why then her breasts
    are dun;
If hairs be wires, black wires grow on her
    head.
I have seen roses damask'd, red and
    white,   5
But no such roses see I in her cheeks;
And in some perfumes is there more de-
    light
Than in the breath that from my mistress
    reeks.
I love to hear her speak; yet well I know
That music hath a far more pleasing
    sound.   10
I grant I never saw a goddess go:
My mistress, when she walks, treads on
    the ground.
    And yet, by heaven, I think my love as
        rare
    As any she belied with false compare.

5. *damask'd:* patterned.

SINCE THERE'S NO HELP,
COME LET US KISS AND PART

Michael Drayton
(1563–1631)

Since there's no help, come let us kiss and
    part;
Nay I have done, you get no more of me;
And I am glad, yea, glad with all my
    heart,
That thus so cleanly I myself can free;

Shake hands for ever, cancel all our
    vows,   5
And when we meet at any time again,
Be it not seen in either of our brows
That we one jot of former love retain.
Now at the last gasp of love's latest breath,
When his pulse failing, passion speechless
    lies,   10
When faith is kneeling by his bed of death,
And innocence is closing up his eyes,
Now if thou would'st, when all have given
    him over,
From death to life thou might'st him yet
    recover.

THE SICK ROSE

William Blake
(1757–1827)

    O Rose, thou art sick!
    The invisible worm
    That flies in the night,
    In the howling storm,

    Has found out thy bed   5
    Of crimson joy;
    And his dark secret love
    Does thy life destroy.

THE FARMER'S BRIDE

Charlotte Mew
(1869–1928)

Three Summers since I chose a maid,
Too young maybe—but more's to do
At harvest-time than bide and woo.
    When us was wed she turned afraid
Of love and me and all things human;   5
Like the shut of a winter's day.
Her smile went out, and 'twasn't a
    woman—

More like a little frightened fay.
    One night, in the Fall, she runned
    away.

"Out 'mong the sheep, her be," they
    said,   10
'Should properly have been abed;
But sure enough she wasn't there
Lying awake with her wide brown stare.
So over seven-acre field and up-along
    across the down
We chased her, flying like a hare   15
Before our lanterns. To Church-Town
    All in a shiver and a scare
We caught her, fetched her home at last
    And turned the key upon her, fast.

She does the work about the house   20
As well as most, but like a mouse:
    Happy enough to chat and play
    With birds and rabbits and such as they,
    So long as men-folk keep away.
"Not near, not near!" her eyes beseech 25
When one of us comes within reach.
    The women say that beasts in stall
    Look round like children at her call.
    I've hardly heard her speak at all.

Shy as a leveret, swift as he,   30
Straight and slight as a young larch tree,
Sweet as the first wild violets, she
To her wild self. But what to me?

The short days shorten and the oaks are
    brown,
    The blue smoke rises to the low gray
    sky,   35
One leaf in the still air falls slowly down,
    A magpie's spotted feathers lie
On the black earth spread white with
    rime,
The berries redden up to Christmas-time.
    What's Christmas-time without there
    be   40

30. *leveret:* a hare during its first year.

Some other in the house than we!

She sleeps up in the attic there
Alone, poor maid. 'Tis but a stair
Betwixt us. Oh! my God! the down,

The soft young down of her, the brown,   45
The brown of her—her eyes, her hair, her hair . . .

"NOT MARBLE NOR THE GILDED MONUMENTS" *

Archibald MacLeish
(1892–   )

The praisers of women in their proud and beautiful poems
Naming the grave mouth and the hair and the eyes
Boasted those they loved should be forever remembered
These were lies

The words sound but the face in the Istrian sun is forgotten   5
The poet speaks but to her dead ears no more
The sleek throat is gone—and the breast that was troubled to listen
Shadow from door

Therefore I will not praise your knees nor your fine walking
Telling you men shall remember your name as long   10
As lips move or breath is spent or the iron of English
Rings from a tongue

I shall say you were young and your arms straight and your mouth scarlet
I shall say you will die and none will remember you
Your arms change and none remember the swish of your garments   15
Nor the click of your shoe
Not with my hand's strength not with difficult labor
Springing the obstinate words to the bones of your breast
And the stubborn line to your young stride and the breath to your breathing
And the beat to your haste   20
Shall I prevail on the hearts of unborn men to remember

(What is a dead girl but a shadowy ghost
Or a dead man's voice but a distant and vain affirmation
Like dream words most)
Therefore I will not speak of the undying glory of women   25
I will say you were young and straight and your skin fair
And you stood in the door and the sun was a shadow of leaves on your shoulders
And a leaf on your hair
I will not speak of the famous beauty of dead women
I will say the shape of a leaf lay once on your hair   30
Till the world ends and the eyes are out and the mouths broken
Look! It is there!

* Cf. Shakespeare's "Not marble, nor the gilded monuments" (Sonnet LV)

LAY YOUR SLEEPING HEAD, MY LOVE

W. H. Auden
(1907–   )

Lay your sleeping head, my love,
Human on my faithless arm;
Time and fevers burn away
Individual beauty from
Thoughtful children, and the grave   5
Proves the child ephemeral:
But in my arms till break of day
Let the living creature lie,
Mortal, guilty, but to me
The entirely beautiful.   10

Soul and body have no bonds:
To lovers as they lie upon
Her tolerant enchanted slope
In their ordinary swoon,
Grave the vision Venus sends   15
Of supernatural sympathy,
Universal love and hope;
While an abstract insight wakes
Among the glaciers and the rocks
The hermit's sensual ecstasy.   20

Certainty, fidelity
On the stroke of midnight pass
Like vibrations of a bell,
And fashionable madmen raise
Their pedantic boring cry: 25
Every farthing of the cost,
All the dreaded cards foretell,
Shall be paid, but from this night
Not a whisper, not a thought,
Not a kiss nor look be lost.   30

Beauty, midnight, vision dies:
Let the winds of dawn that blow
Softly round your dreaming head
Such a day of sweetness show

Eye and knocking heart may bless,   35
Find the mortal world enough;
Noons of dryness see you fed
By the involuntary powers,
Nights of insult let you pass
Watched by every human love.   40

■   ■   ■

A LAST CONFESSION

W. B. Yeats
(1865–1939)

What lively lad most pleasured me
Of all that with me lay?
I answer that I gave my soul
And loved in misery,
But had great pleasure with a lad   5
That I loved bodily.

Flinging from his arms I laughed
To think his passion such
He fancied that I gave a soul
Did but our bodies touch,   10
And laughed upon his breast to think
Beast gave beast as much.

I gave what other women gave
That stepped out of their clothes,
But when this soul, its body off,   15
Naked to naked goes,
He it has found shall find therein
What none other knows.

And give his own and take his own
And rule in his own right;   20
And though it loved in misery
Close and cling so tight,
There's not a bird of day that dare
Extinguish that delight.

II

THE FACES
OF VIOLENCE

FOREWORD

One individual kills a rival, another his wife, still another himself; a community lynches an intruder, individuals are destroyed in a riot; warring nations clash by night and destroy their best. These are but three of the faces of violence with which we are familiar in our century. It is these forms of violence—individual, communal, and national—that are examined in the essays, short stories, and poems included in this section.

George Orwell's account of an execution is a graphic description of legal murder and the reactions to it of a group of observers. In "Gandhi," Dwight Macdonald reflects on the meaning of the assassination of probably the most prominent advocate of nonviolence in our time. In Ernest Hemingway's short story, two men prepare to kill a third. Five poems—beginning with the ballad "Lord Randal" and ending with T. S. Eliot's "Sweeney Among the Nightingales"—express many aspects of the hate, fear, despair, and remorse that lead to and result from individual violence. In this category belongs Yeats's description of a sexual violation that has mythical overtones.

John Fischer not only delineates in his essay some types of community violence, but also suggests moral substitutes. In "The Lottery" a community employs ritualistic violence to come to terms with its own guilt. The poems by William Blake, Claude McKay, and Robinson Jeffers focus on the destructive forces inherent in any society but aggravated by man's greed, prejudice, and indifference.

Will Durant explores the causes of war. Battles result not only in physical deaths, but also spiritual deaths, as Stephen Crane demonstrates in his short story. Shakespeare has Henry V present war in its most attractive terms: patriotic duty and a test of one's strength and courage. The remaining poets in this group, however, decry the brutality and absurdity of war.

ESSAYS

A HANGING

George Orwell
(1903–1950)

It was in Burma, a sodden morning of the rains. A sickly light, like yellow tinfoil, was slanting over the high walls into the jail yard. We were waiting outside the condemned cells, a row of sheds fronted with double bars, like small animal cages. Each cell measured about ten feet by ten and was quite bare within except for a plank bed and a pot for drinking water. In some of them brown silent men were squatting at the inner bars, with their blankets draped round them. These were the condemned men, due to be hanged within the next week or two.

One prisoner had been brought out of his cell. He was a Hindu, a puny wisp of a man, with a shaven head and vague liquid eyes. He had a thick, sprouting moustache, absurdly too big for his body, rather like the moustache of a comic man on the films. Six tall Indian warders were guarding him and getting him ready for the gallows. Two of them stood by with rifles and fixed bayonets, while the others handcuffed him, passed a chain through his handcuffs and fixed it to their belts, and lashed his arms tight to his sides. They crowded very close about him, with their hands always on him in a careful, caressing grip, as though all the while feeling him to make sure he was there.

It was like men handling a fish which is still alive and may jump back into the water. But he stood quite unresisting, yielding his arms limply to the ropes, as though he hardly noticed what was happening.

Eight o'clock struck and a bugle call, desolately thin in the wet air, floated from the distant barracks. The superintendent of the jail, who was standing apart from the rest of us, moodily prodding the gravel with his stick, raised his head at the sound. He was an army doctor, with a grey toothbrush moustache and a gruff voice. "For God's sake hurry up, Francis," he said irritably. "The man ought to have been dead by this time. Aren't you ready yet?"

Francis, the head jailer, a fat Dravidian in a white drill suit and gold spectacles, waved his black hand. "Yes sir, yes sir," he bubbled. "All iss satisfactorily prepared. The hangman iss waiting. We shall proceed."

"Well, quick march, then. The prisoners can't get their breakfast till this job's over."

We set out for the gallows. Two warders marched on either side of the prisoner, with their rifles at the slope; two others marched close against him, gripping him by arm and shoulder, as though at once pushing and supporting him. The rest of us, magistrates and the like, followed behind. Suddenly, when we had gone ten yards, the procession stopped short without any order or warning. A dreadful thing had happened—a dog, come goodness knows whence, had appeared in the yard. It came bounding among us with a loud volley of barks, and leapt round us wagging its whole body, wild with glee at finding so many human beings together. It was a large woolly dog, half Airedale, half pariah. For a moment it pranced round us, and then, before anyone could stop it, it had made a dash for the prisoner and, jumping up, tried to lick his face. Everyone stood aghast, too taken aback even to grab at the dog.

"Who let that bloody brute in here?" said the superintendent angrily. "Catch it, someone!"

A warder, detached from the escort, charged clumsily after the dog, but it danced and gambolled just out of his reach, taking everything as part of the game. A young Eurasian jailer picked up a handful of gravel and tried to stone the dog away, but it dodged the stones and came after us again. Its yaps echoed from the jail walls. The prisoner, in the grasp of the two warders, looked on incuriously, as though this was another formality of the hanging. It was several minutes before someone managed to catch the dog. Then we put my handkerchief through its collar and moved off once more, with the dog still straining and whimpering.

It was about forty yards to the gallows. I watched the bare brown back of the prisoner marching in front of me. He walked clumsily with his bound arms, but quite steadily, with that bobbing gait of the Indian who never straightens his knees. At each step his muscles slid neatly into place, the lock of hair on his scalp danced up and down, his feet printed themselves on the wet gravel. And once, in spite of the men who gripped him by each shoulder, he stepped slightly aside to avoid a puddle on the path.

It is curious, but till that moment I had never realized what it means to destroy a healthy, conscious man. When I saw the prisoner step aside to avoid the puddle I saw the mystery, the unspeakable wrongness, of cutting a life short when it is in full tide. This man was not dying, he was alive just as we are alive. All the organs of his body were working—bowels digesting food, skin renewing itself, nails growing, tissues forming—all toiling away in solemn foolery. His nails would still be growing when he stood on the drop, when he was falling through the air with a tenth-of-a-second to live. His eyes saw the yellow gravel and the grey walls, and his brain still remembered, foresaw, reasoned—reasoned even about puddles. He and we were a party of men walking together, seeing, hearing, feeling, understanding the same world; and in two minutes, with a sudden snap, one of us would be gone—one mind less, one world less.

The gallows stood in a small yard, separate from the main grounds of the prison, and overgrown with tall prickly weeds. It was a brick erection like three sides of a shed, with planking on top, and above that two beams and a crossbar with the rope dangling. The hangman, a grey-haired convict in the white uniform of the prison, was waiting beside his machine. He greeted us with a servile crouch as we entered. At a word from Francis the two warders, gripping the prisoner more closely than ever, half led half pushed him to the gallows and helped him clumsily up the ladder. Then the hangman climbed up and fixed the rope round the prisoner's neck.

We stood waiting, five yards away. The warders had formed in a rough circle round the gallows. And then, when the noose was fixed, the prisoner began crying out to his god. It was a high, reiterated cry of "Ram! Ram! Ram! Ram!" not urgent and fearful like a prayer or cry for help, but steady, rhythmical, almost like the tolling of a bell. The dog answered the sound with a whine. The hangman, still standing on the gallows, produced a small cotton bag like a flour bag and drew it down over the prisoner's face. But the sound, muffled by the cloth, still persisted, over and over again: "Ram! Ram! Ram! Ram! Ram!"

The hangman climbed down and stood ready, holding the lever. Minutes seemed to pass. The steady, muffled crying from the prisoner went on and on, "Ram! Ram! "Ram!" never faltering for an instant. The superintendent, his head on his chest, was slowly poking the ground with his stick; perhaps he was counting the cries, allowing the prisoner a fixed number— fifty, perhaps, or a hundred. Everyone had changed color. The Indians had gone grey like bad coffee, and one or two of the bayonets were wavering. We looked at the lashed, hooded man on the drop, and listened to his cries—each cry another second of life; the same thought was in all our minds: oh, kill him quickly, get it over, stop that abominable noise!

Suddenly the superintendent made up his mind. Throwing up his head he made a swift motion with his stick. "Chalo!" he shouted almost fiercely.

There was a clanking noise, and then dead silence. The prisoner had vanished, and the rope was twisting on itself. I let go of the dog, and it galloped immediately to the back of the gallows; but when it got there it stopped short, barked, and then retreated into a corner of the yard, where it stood among the weeds, looking timorously out at us. We went round the gallows to inspect the prisoner's body. He was dangling with his toes pointed straight downwards, very slowly revolving, as dead as a stone.

The superintendent reached out with his stick and poked the bare brown body; it oscillated slightly. "*He's* all right," said the superintendent. He backed out from under the gallows, and blew out a deep breath. The moody look had gone out of his face quite suddenly. He glanced at his wrist-watch. "Eight minutes past eight. Well, that's all for this morning, thank God."

The warders unfixed bayonets and marched away. The dog, sobered and conscious of having misbehaved itself, slipped after them. We walked out of the gallows yard, past the condemned cells with their waiting prisoners, into the big central yard of the prison. The convicts, under the command of warders armed with lathis, were already receiving their breakfast. They squatted in long rows, each man holding a tin panikin, while two warders with buckets marched round ladling out rice; it seemed quite a homely, jolly scene, after the hanging. An enormous relief had come upon us now that the job was done. One felt an impulse to sing, to break into a run, to snigger. All at once everyone began chattering gaily.

The Eurasian boy walking beside me nodded towards the way we had come, with a knowing smile: "Do you know, sir, our friend [he meant the dead man] when he heard his appeal had been dismissed, he pissed on the floor of his cell. From fright. Kindly take one of my cigarettes, sir. Do you not admire my new silver case, sir? From the boxwalah, two rupees eight annas. Classy European style."

Several people laughed—at what, nobody seemed certain.

Francis was walking by the superintendent, talking garrulously: "Well, sir, all hass passed off with the utmost satisfactoriness. It was all finished—flick! like that. It iss not always so—oah, no! I have known cases where the doctor wass obliged to go beneath the gallows and pull the prisoner's legs to ensure decease. Most disagreeable!"

"Wriggling about, eh? That's bad," said the superintendent.

"Ach, sir, it iss worse when they become refractory! One man, I recall, clung to the bars of hiss cage when we went to take him out. You will scarcely credit, sir, that it took six warders to dislodge him, three pulling at each leg. We reasoned with him. 'My dear fellow,' we said, 'think of all the pain and trouble you are causing to us!' But no, he would not listen! Ach, he wass very troublesome!"

I found that I was laughing quite loudly. Everyone was laughing. Even the superintendent grinned in a tolerant way. "You'd better all come out and have a drink," he said quite genially. "I've got a bottle of whisky in the car. We could do with it."

We went through the big double gates of the prison into the road. "Pulling at his legs!" exclaimed a Burmese magistrate suddenly, and burst into a loud chuckling. We all began laughing again. At that moment Francis' anecdote seemed extraordinarily funny. We all had a drink together, native and European alike, quite amicably. The dead man was a hundred yards away.

GANDHI

Dwight Macdonald
(1906–   )

"A moment before he was shot, he said —some witnesses believed he was speaking to the assassin—'You are late.'"
                              —N. Y. World-Telegram,
                                  January 30, 1948

And indeed the man who killed Gandhi with three revolver shots *was* late—about two years late. The communal massacres showed that Gandhi's teaching of non-violence had not penetrated to the Indian masses. His life work had been in vain— or at least it now appeared that he had taught a "non-violence of the weak" which had been effective against the British but that the more difficult "non-violence of the strong" he had been unable to teach.

He insisted on his failure constantly, and constantly thought of death. "I am in the midst of flames," he wrote last spring. "Is it the kindness of God or His irony that the flames do not consume me?" One imagines that he experienced a dreadful joy in the split-second he saw the gun aimed at him.

Three historical events have moved me deeply of recent years: the murder of Trotsky, the atomic bombing of Hiroshima, the murder of Gandhi. That all three should be simply catastrophes— hopeless, destructive, painful—is in the style of our period. The Spanish Civil War was the last of the 19th-century type of political tragedies: the fight was lost, as in 1848 or the Paris Commune, but it had been a fight; there was hope while it was going on, and defeat might be due to some temporary relation of forces; there was a basis for a future effort.

But Trotsky and Gandhi were killed not during their great time of struggle to realize "Utopian" ideals, not while they were still fighting with a hope of success, but after their ideas—or at least their tactics—had been shown by the brutal logic of events to be inadequate. They were not shot in battle. They were executed. And their executioner was not the oppressive, conservative forces they had devoted their lives to fighting— the bourgeoisie and the British imperialists—but the scum that had frothed up from their own heroic struggle to liberate mankind: young fanatics representing a new order—of Stalinism and of Hindu nationalism—which is hopeless, deadening, corrupting and monstrous, but which is also, alas, partly the product of their own revolutionary efforts. In the 19th century, czars and governors and secret-police chiefs were assassinated by radicals; today, it is revolutionaries (out of power) like Trotsky and Gandhi who are killed by our modern Nihilists, while Stalin and Hitler and Zhdanov and Himmler and

Mussolini, and Molotov escape (unless they lose a war). *Our* Nihilists have terribly perverted Liebknecht's slogan: "The main Enemy is at Home." Or perhaps they are just more prudent than their 19th-century ancestors. Which would be in keeping, too.

Gandhi, like Trotsky, was killed after his most profound ideas and his lifelong political activity had been rebuffed by History. But, also like Trotsky, he was still alive and kicking, still throwing out imaginative concepts. The ideologue is baffled, but the human being—and by this sentimental phrase I mean the acute intelligence as much as the moralist—is not through: he has plenty of inspirations and surprises in store for us. Both men were still giving, by their personal example and still more by their unwearied experimenting with general principles, some kind of meaning, of *consciousness* to modern political life. Their assassins killed not only two men, but also two cultures. Which makes it all the more painful.

There was obvious irony in the great pacifist being killed by a gunman. But there was also an aesthetic fitness. Gandhi was the last eminent personage who insisted on dealing directly with people, reasoning with them face to face as individuals, not as crowds roped off, watched by plain-clothes men, sealed safely behind bullet-proof glass. It was a matter of principle with him not to deny anyone access to him, mentally or physically. He refused all police protection. I have heard people say he was a damn fool and got what he might expect to get. They are, of course, right. Our world is so structured that the "public man" can survive only by being private, and the most dangerous thing he can do is to meet his public face to face.

Gandhi was the last political leader in the world who was a person, not a mask or a radio voice or an institution. The last on a human scale. The last for whom I felt neither fear nor contempt nor indifference but interest and affection. He was dear to me—I realize it now better than I did when he was alive—for all kinds of reasons. He believed in love, gentleness, persuasion, simplicity of manners, and he came closer to "living up to" these beliefs than most people I know—let alone most Big Shots, on whom the pressures for the reverse must be very powerful. (To me, the wonder is not that Gandhi often resorted to sophistry or flatly went back on some of his ideas, but that he was able to put into practice as many of them as he did. I speak from personal experience.) He was dear to me because he had no respect for railroads, assembly-belt production, and other knick-knacks of liberalistic Progress, and insisted on examining their human (as against their metaphysical) value. Also because he was clever, humorous, lively, hard-headed, and never made speeches about Fascism, Democracy, the Common Man, or World Government. And because he had a keen nose for the concrete, homely "details" of living which make the real difference to people but which are usually ignored by everybody except poets. And finally because he was a good man, by which I mean not only "good" but also "man."

This leads into the next point. Many pacifists and others who have an ethical —and really admirable—attitude toward life are somewhat boring. Their point of view, their writing and conversation are wholly sympathetic but also a little on the dull side.

Intellectually, their ideas lack subtlety and logical structure. Ethically, they are *too* consistent; they don't sense the tragedy of life, the incredible difficulty of actually putting into practice an ethical concept. They have not succumbed to temptation because they have never been tempted; they are good simply because it has never occurred to them to be bad. They are, in a word, unworldly. Gandhi was not at all unworldly. He was full of humour, slyness, perversity, and—above all—practicality. Indeed, the very thing which leads people to think of him as unworldly—his ascetic ideas about diet, household economy, and sexual intercourse—seems to me to show his worldliness, or at least his imaginative grasp of The World: how could anyone be so concerned about such matters, even though in a negative sense, without a real feeling for their importance in human life, which in turn must come from a deep drive on his part *toward* gluttony, luxury, and sexual indulgence?

The Marxists, those monks of politics, were shocked by his intimacy with rich men like Birla and Tata, just as the Pharisees, the Trotskyists of their day, were shocked by Christ's sitting at table with bartenders. (The Marxist has a richer intellectual tradition than the pacifist, but his ethical sense is equally simplistic.) It is true that Gandhi "compromised" with the rich, those untouchables of the class struggle, living at their villas (though carrying on there his own ascetic regimen). But he also "compromised" with the poor, spending at least as much time in the "untouchable's" quarters (he constantly complains of the smells and lack of sanitation) as in the Birla Palace. In short, he practiced tolerance and love to such an extent that he seems to have regarded the capitalist as well as the garbage-man as his social equal.

SUBSTITUTES FOR VIOLENCE

John Fischer
(1910–   )

Scoundrels and in some cases even ruffians terrified the citizens. Young mothers had to take their babies to Central Park in armored cars. Old women went to the theater in tanks, and no pretty woman would venture forth after dark unless convoyed by a regiment of troops . . . the police wore bullet-proof underwear and were armed with mortars and fifteen-inch howitzers . . .

—James Reston
The New York Times, October 29, 1965

Like most fables, Mr. Reston's moral tale exaggerates a little. But not much; for all of us are uneasily aware that violence is becoming a central fact of American life. Year after year the official graph for crimes of violence—murder, rape, assault, robbery, and riot—inches a little higher.[1] Many of these crimes seem to be entirely senseless: a California sniper blazes away at random at passing motorists . . . Bronx youngsters pillage the Botanical Garden and wreck their own schoolrooms . . . a subway rider suddenly pulls a knife and starts slashing at his fellow passengers . . . a gang of roaming teen-agers comes across an old man drowsing on a park bench; they club and burn him to death without even bothering to rifle his pockets.

It is hardly surprising, then, that violence is becoming a dominant concern in our politics, literature, and conversation. Every campaigning candidate promises to chase the hoodlums off the city streets. Murder and mayhem—usually aimless, inexplicable, "existential"—are a growing preoccupation of American novelists: witness the recent work of Norman Mailer, Nelson Algren, and a hundred less-publicized writers. And not only the

[1] According to the annual reports of the Federal Bureau of Investigation. But its figures are based on voluntary reports by more than eight thousand local law-enforcement agencies, using different definitions of crime and widely varying statistical methods; therefore the FBI does not vouch for their accuracy. In fact, nobody knows precisely how much crime is committed in the United States, or its rate of increase, if any.

novelists; one of the most memorable nonfiction books of the past year was Truman Capote's *In Cold Blood,* a factual account of the peculiarly brutal murder of the Clutter family by two young sadists. Significantly, the scene was not a city street but a Kansas farm.

Nor is the carnage limited to the United States. As *The Economist* of London pointed out in a recent article (reprinted in the November issue of *Harper's*), rioting and hooliganism are on the rise in nearly every country, including England, Sweden, and Russia. Bloodshed in the big cities naturally gets most of the headlines, but it seems to be almost as widespread in predominantly rural areas—the Sudan, for example, India, the Congo, and Colombia, where *la violencia* has taken hundred of thousands of lives during the last two decades.

Explanations for all this are easy to come by, from nearly every clergyman, sociologist, and politician. Unfortunately they are seldom consistent. Some blame the miseries of slum life, others the breakdown of the family, or religion, or our national moral fiber. Racial and religious frictions apparently account for much free-floating hostility—in Watts and Calcutta, Capetown and Hué, even in Moscow and Peking, where African students report a lot of rough treatment from their hosts. Marxists, naturally, explain it all in terms of bourgeois decadence (although that would hardly account for the outbreaks in Prague and Novocherkassk, where the wicked bourgeoisie were liquidated long ago). While the Black Muslims decry police brutality, J. Edgar Hoover is prescribing more policemen, armed with wider powers. The Freudians suggest that sexual frustration may be the root of the trouble, while Billy Graham is just as sure that it is sexual laxity. Nearly everybody points an indignant finger at the dope peddlers, and William Buckley gets cheers whenever he proclaims that nothing will save us short of a universal moral regeneration.

Perhaps there is some truth in all these explanations. But I am beginning to wonder whether, far beneath them all, there may not lie another, more primordial reason. Just possibly the global surge of antisocial violence may result from the fact that nearly all societies—especially those we describe as "advanced"—suddenly have been forced to change a key commandment in their traditional codes of behavior; and many people, particularly the young males, have not yet been able to adjust themselves to this reversal.

That commandment was simple: "Be a fighter." Ever since human beings began to emerge as a separate species, something over a million years ago, it has been our first law of survival. For the earliest men, life was an incessant battle: against the hostile Pleistocene environment, against other mammals for food, against their own kind for a sheltering cave, a water hole, a hunting range, a mate. The fiercest, wiliest, and strongest lived to raise children. The meek, weak, slow, and stupid made an early breakfast—for a local tiger or, perhaps oftener, for a neighboring family, since archaeological evidence suggests that cannibalism was common among primeval man. The result was that "our ancestors have bred pugnacity into our bone and marrow. . . ."[2]

As civilization began to dawn, fighting became more organized—a community enterprise rather than a family one. In addition to their daily skirmishes with wolves, cattle thieves, and passing strangers, the able-bodied men of the village (or polis, kingdom, or pueblo) normally banded together at least once a year for a joint killing venture. The con-

[2] As William James put it in his classic essay, "The Moral Equivalent of War," published in 1910. His other comments on this grisly topic will be noted in a moment.

venient time for settled farming people was early fall, after the harvest was in; then they had both enough leisure and enough surplus food to mount an expedition. So it was about September when the Assyrian swept down like a wolf on the fold, when Gideon smote the Philistines, when Vikings ravaged the Kentish coast, when the Greeks shoved off for Troy, when the Dorians swept into the Argive plain, irresistibly armed with that first mass weapon, the iron sword. (Because iron ore was much more plentiful than copper, it could be used—once the secret of smelting it was learned—to equip every man in the ranks. The victims of the Dorians, still lingering in the Bronze Age, normally armed only their officers with metal blades; the rest carried flint-tipped spears and arrows.) Tribes in the preagricultural stage sometimes found other seasons more suitable for rapine. The War Moon of the Great Plains Indians, for example, came in May—since the spring grass was then just high enough to graze the horses of a raiding party, and the full moon made it easy to travel fast at night. Regardless of timing, however, warfare was for centuries the main social enterprise, absorbing virtually all of the community's surplus time, energy, and resources. "History," as William James put it, "is a bath of blood . . . war for war's sake, all the citizens being warriors. . . . To hunt a neighboring tribe, kill the males, loot the village, and possess the females was the most profitable, as well as the most exciting, way of living."

As soon as warfare became socialized, the premium on belligerence was redoubled. Always highly favored by the processes of natural selection, it was now celebrated as a prime civic virtue as well. The Great Fighter was enshrined as the universal hero. His name might be Hercules or Rustum, Beowulf or David, Kiyomori or Hiawatha, but his charac-

teristics remained the same: physical strength, reckless courage, skill with weapons, and a bottomless appetite for bloodshed. From earliest boyhood the males of the community were taught to emulate him. Their training for combat began as soon as they could lift a spear, and by eighteen they normally would be full-fledged warriors—whether in Athens or Cuzco—equally ready to defend their city's walls or to pillage a weaker neighbor. Success in battle was the basic status symbol. The best fighters were feted in victory celebrations, heaped with honors and plunder, endowed with the lushest women, both homegrown and captive. The weak and timid, on the other hand, were scorned by elders and girls alike, and in many societies cowardice was punished by death.

For nearly all of human history, then, the aggressive impulse—so deeply embedded in our genes—had no trouble in finding an outlet. This outlet was not only socially acceptable; it was encouraged and rewarded by every resource at society's disposal.

This remained true until roughly a hundred years ago. (When my grandfathers were boys, the martial virtues were still applauded about as much as ever, and both of them marched off to the Civil War with the joyous spirit of an Alcibiades bound for Syracuse.)

Then, with stunning abruptness, the rules changed. Within about a century— a mere eye-blink in terms of evolutionary development—the traditional outlet for violence closed up. Fighting, so long encouraged by society, suddenly became intolerable.

One reason, of course, was the industrialization of war. It not only made warfare ruinously expensive; it took all the fun out of it. Long before the invention of the atom bomb, farsighted men such as William James had come to see that war was no longer "the most profitable, as well as the most exciting, way of living"; and by 1918 the lesson was plain to nearly everyone. In retrospect, our Civil War seems to have been the last in which physical strength, raw courage, and individual prowess could be (sometimes, at least) decisive; perhaps that is why it is written about so much, and so nostalgically.

For there is a certain animal satisfaction (as every football player knows) in bopping another man over the head. By all accounts, our ancestors thoroughly enjoyed hammering at each other with sword and mace; it exercised the large muscles, burned up the adrenalin in the system, relieved pent-up frustrations, and demonstrated virility in the most elemental fashion. But nobody can get that kind of satisfaction out of pulling the lanyard on a cannon, pointed at an unseen enemy miles away; you might as well be pulling a light switch in a factory. Indeed, in a modern army not one man in ten ever gets near combat; the great majority of the troops are cranking mimeograph machines, driving trucks, and tending the PX far to the rear. As a consequence, warfare—aside from its other disadvantages—no longer satisfies the primitive instinct for violence as it did for uncountable thousands of years.

At about the same time—that is, roughly a century ago—the other socially approved outlets for pugnacity also began to close up. For example, so long as our society was mostly rural and small-town, a good deal of purely personal, casual brawling was easily tolerated. When Lincoln was a young man, the main public amusement seemed to be watching (and often joining in) the donnybrooks which boiled up regularly in the village street; and during his New Salem days, Abe more than held his own. Our literature of the last century, from *Huckleberry Finn* to the story of the OK Wagon Yard, is studded with this kind of spontaneous combat. And our chronicles memorialize the violent men (whether fur trappers, river boatmen, forty-niners, lumberjacks, or cowboys) in the same admiring tone as the sagas of Achilles and Roland. As recently as my own boyhood, fist-fighting was considered a normal after-school activity, like marbles and run-sheep-run; nobody thought of us as juvenile delinquents, in need of a corps of Youth Workers to hound us into docility. A tight-packed urban society, however, simply can't put up with this kind of random combat. It disturbs the peace, endangers bystanders, and obstructs traffic.

As we turned into a nation of city dwellers, we lost another traditional testing ground for masculine prowess: the struggle against nature. Since the beginning of history, when men weren't fighting each other they spent most of their time fighting the elements. To survive, they had to hack down forests, kill off predatory animals, battle with every ounce of strength and cunning against blizzards, droughts, deserts, and gales. When Richard Henry Dana came home after two years before the mast, he knew he was a man. So too with the striplings who rafted logs down rivers in a spate, drove a wagon over the Natchez Trace, pulled a fishing dory on the Grand Banks, or broke sod on the Nebraska prairies. Not long after he started shaving, my father went off alone to homestead a farm in what eventually became the state of Oklahoma. If he had been bothered by an "identity crisis"—something he couldn't even conceive—it would have evaporated long before he got his final papers.

Today of course the strenuous life, which Theodore Roosevelt thought essential for a healthy man, has all but vanished. Probably not 5 per cent of our youngsters grow up to outdoor work, in farming, forests, or fisheries; and even for them, although the work may be hard, it is rarely either exciting or dangerous. (The modern cowboy does most of his work in a pickup truck, while Captain Ahab's successor goes to sea in a floating oil factory.) This final conquest of nature has had some results both comic and a little sad. Among the Masai tribesmen, for instance, when a boy comes of age it has always been customary for him to prove his manhood by killing a lion with a spear; but according to recent reports from Africa, there are no longer enough lions to go around.

In our tamer culture, we have shown remarkable ingenuity in inventing lion-substitutes. The most fashionable surrogates for violence are the strenuous and risky sports—skiing, skin diving, surfing, mountain climbing, drag racing, sailing small boats in rough weather—which have burgeoned so remarkably in recent years. When a middle-aged Cleveland copy editor crosses the Atlantic alone in a twelve-foot sloop, nobody accuses him of suicidal impulses; on the contrary, millions of sedentary males understand all too well his yearning for at least one adventure in life, however self-imposed and unnecessary. (Women, of course, generally do not understand; most of the wives I've overheard discussing the Manry voyage wondered, not how he made it, but why Mrs. Manry ever let him try.)

But these devices serve only the middle class. For the poor, they ordinarily are too expensive. When Robert Benchley remarked that there was enough suffering in life without people tying boards on their feet and sliding down mountains, he missed the point; the real trouble with skiing is that slum kids can't afford it. Consequently, they try to get their kicks vicariously, by watching murder, football, boxing, and phony wrestling matches on television. When that palls, their next resort usually is reckless driving. That is

why access to a car (his own, his family's, or a stolen one) is as precious to the adolescent male—rich or poor—in our culture as possession of a shield was in fifth-century Athens. It is a similar badge of manhood, the equipment necessary to demonstrate that he is a fearless and dashing fellow. (It also is the reason why insurance premiums are so high on autos driven by males under twenty-five years old.)

Such games are socially useful, because they absorb in a relatively harmless way some of our pent-up aggressions. But they all have one great drawback: they are merely games. They are contrived; they are artificial adjuncts to life, rather than the core of life itself. When our ancestors harpooned a whale, pillaged a city, or held the pass at Thermopylae, they knew they were playing for keeps. When our sons break their legs on a ski slope or play "chicken" on the highway, they know that the challenge is a made-up one, and therefore never wholly satisfying. They still yearn for a genuine challenge, a chance to prove their hardihood in a way that really means something.

Lacking anything better, some of them —a growing number, apparently—turn to crimes of violence. Gang fights, vandalism, robbery are, in an important sense, more "real" than any game. And for large groups of disadvantaged people, any form of antisocial violence is a way of striking back, in blind fury, at the community which has condemned them to disappointment and frustration. This is equally true, I suspect, of the Negro rioters in Watts and the poor whites of the South, who take so readily to the murders, church burnings, and assorted barbarities of the Klan.

This sort of thing may well continue, on a rising scale, until we can discover what James called a "moral equivalent for war." He thought he had found it. He wanted to draft "the whole youthful population" into a peacetime army to serve in "the immemorial human warfare against nature." What he had in mind was a sort of gigantic Civilian Conservation Corps, in which every youngster would spend a few years at hard and dangerous labor— consigned to "coal and iron mines, to freight trains, to fishing fleets in December . . . to road-building and tunnel-making." When he wrote, a half-century ago, this idea sounded plausible, because the need for such work seemed limitless.

Today, however, his prescription is harder to apply. In many parts of the globe, the war against nature has ended, with nature's unconditional surrender. Automation, moreover, has eliminated most dangerous and physically demanding jobs; our mines and freight trains are overmanned, our roads are now built with earth-moving machines rather than pick and shovel.

Nevertheless, so far as I can see James's idea is still our best starting point. And already an encouraging number of people are groping for ways to make it work, in the different and more difficult circumstances of our time.

A few have found personal, unofficial answers. The young people who join the civil-rights movement in the South, for example, are encountering hardship, violence, and occasionally death in a cause that is obviously genuine; they aren't playing games. But The Movement can accommodate only a limited number of volunteers, and presumably it will go out of business eventually, when the white Southerners reconcile themselves to rejoining the United States. In the North, civil-rights work has often turned out to be less satisfying, emotionally, because The Enemy is harder to identify and the goals are less clear. As a result its young partisans sometimes have drifted into a kind of generalized protest, carrying placards for almost anything from SNCC to

Free Speech to World Peace: that is, they have ended up with another form of game playing.

President Kennedy, who understood thoroughly the youthful need for struggle and self-sacrifice, had the Jamesian principle in mind when he started the Peace Corps. It remains the most successful official experiment in this direction, and it led to the Job Corps and several related experiments in the domestic Antipoverty Program. How they will work out is still an open question, as William Haddad pointed out last month in *Harper's*. At least they are a public recognition that the country has to do *something*. If we don't —if we continue to let millions of young men sit around, while the adrenalin bubbles and every muscle screams for action, with no outlet in sight but a desk job at best and an unemployment check at worst —then we are asking for bad trouble. Either we can find ways to give them action, in some useful fashion, or we can look forward to a rising surge of anti-social violence. In the latter case we may, a decade from now, remember the Fort Lauderdale beach riots as a mere boyish prank.

What I am suggesting, of course, is that all of us—especially our businessmen, sociologists, and political leaders—ought to invest a good deal more effort, ingenuity, and money in the search for acceptable substitutes for violence. How many industries have really tried to create interesting and physically demanding jobs for young people? Have the paper companies, for instance, figured out how many foresters they might use, if they were to develop their timber reserves for camping, hunting, and fishing, as well as for wood pulp? And are they sure such a venture would not be profitable?

To take care of the population explosion, we are going to have to duplicate all of our present college buildings within the next twenty years. Has any university looked into the possibility of using prospective students to do some of the building? Maybe every able-bodied boy should be required to labor on the campus for six months as a bricklayer or carpenter before he is admitted to classes?

Cleaning up our polluted rivers is a task worthy of Paul Bunyan, and one we can't postpone much longer. What governor has thought of mobilizing a state Youth Corps to do part of the job? Has Ladybird Johnson calculated how many husky youngsters might be deployed, axes in hand, to chop down billboards along our highways and replace them with trees?

The possibilities aren't as easy to spot as they were in William James's day, but even in our overcrowded and overdeveloped society some of them still exist. No single one of them will provide the kind of simple, large-scale panacea that James had in mind—yet if we can discover a few hundred such projects, they might add up to a pretty fair Moral Equivalent. In any case, the search is worth a more serious try than anyone has made yet.

Why, my wife asks me, is all that necessary? Wouldn't it be simpler for you men to stop acting like savages? Since you realize that belligerence is no longer a socially useful trait, why don't you try to cultivate your gentler and more humane instincts? Are you saying that You Can't Change Human Nature?

No, that isn't quite what I'm saying. I recognize that human nature changes all the time. Cannabalism, for example, is now fairly rare, and polygamy (at least in its more open form) has been abandoned by a number of cultures. Someday (I hope and believe) the craving for violence will leach out of the human system. But the reversal of an evolutionary process takes a long time. For a good many generations, then, the Old Adam is likely to linger in our genes; and during that transitional period, probably the best we

can hope for is to keep him reasonably quiet with some variant of William James's prescription.

WHY MEN FIGHT

Will Durant
(1885–   )

I. Perspective

In the year 1830 a French customs official unearthed, in the valley of the Somme, strange implements of flint now recognized by the learned as the weapons with which the men of the Old Stone Age made war. These stones are called *coups de poing,* or "blows of the fist," for one end was rounded to be grasped in the hand, while the other end was pointed for persuasion. With these modest tools of death, it seems, Neanderthal men from what is now Germany, and Cro-Magnon men from what is now France, fought fifty thousand years ago for the mastery of the continent, and, after a day of lusty battle, left perhaps a score of dead on the field. Twenty years ago, modern Germans and modern Frenchmen fought again, in that same valley, for that same prize, with magnificent tools of death that killed ten thousand men in a day. One art alone has made indisputable progress in history, and that is the art of war.

For five hundred centuries, two thousand generations have struggled for that terrain in a calendar of wars whose beginning is as distant as its end. Our own children rest there, some of them, lured by fear or nobility into that ancient strife. Even the sophisticated mind, accustomed to magnitude and marvels, is appalled by the panorama of historic war, from the occasional brawls and raids of normally peaceful "savages," through the sanguinary annals of Sumer, Babylonia, and

Assyria, the endless fratricide of the Greek city-states, the merciful conquests of Alexander and Caesar, the brutal triumphs of Imperial Rome, the holy carnage of expanding Islam, the glorious slaughters of Genghis Khan, Tamerlane's pyramid of skulls, the destruction of Vijayanagar, the Hundred Years' War, the War of the Spanish Succession, the Seven Years' War, the English, American, French, and Russian Revolutions, the Civil Wars of England and America, the Napoleonic Wars, the War of 1812, the Crimean War, the Franco-Prussian War, the Spanish-American War, the Boer War, the Russo-Japanese War, the First World War, the suicide of Spain, the Sino-Japanese War, the Second World War. . . . This, in our pessimistic moments, seems to be the main and bloody current of history, beside which all the achievements of civilization, all the illumination of letters and the arts, all the tenderness of women and the courtesies of men, are but graceful incidents on the bank, helpless to change the course or character of the stream.

Such a chronicle of conflict exaggerates, without doubt, the rôle of war in the records of our race. Strife is dramatic, and, to most of our historians, peaceful generations appear to have no history. So our chroniclers leap from battle to battle, and unwittingly deform the past into a shambles. In our saner moments we know that it is not so; that lucid intervals of peace far outweigh, in any nation's story, the mad seizures of war and revolution; that the history of civilization—of science and invention, law and morals, religion and philosophy, literature and art—runs like hidden gold in the river bed of time. Even war cannot quite blacken the picture of man's development.

Nevertheless, war has always been. Will it always be? What are its causes in the nature of men and in the structure of societies? What are its effects, for good or evil, upon the soul, the species, and the state? Can it be prevented, or diminished in frequency, or in any measure controlled? Let us consider these questions as objectively as may be permitted to men and women standing on the brink of what may be the most brutal war that history has ever known.

II. Causes

The causes of war are psychological, biological, economic, and political—that is, they lie in the impulses of men, the competition of groups, the material needs of societies, and fluctuations of national power.

The basic causes are in ourselves, for the state is an enlarged picture of the soul. The five major instincts of mankind—food-getting, mating, parental love, fighting, and association—are the ultimate sources of war. Our inveterate habit of eating is the oldest and deepest cause of war. For thousands, perhaps millions, of years, men were uncertain of their food supply. Not knowing yet the bounty of the soil, they trusted to the fortunes of the hunt. Having captured prey, they tore or cut it to pieces, often on the spot, and gorged themselves to their cubic capacity with the raw flesh and the hot gore; how could they tell when they might eat again? Greed is eating, or hoarding, for the future; wealth is originally a hedge against starvation; war is at first a raid for food. All vices were once virtues, indispensable in the struggle for existence; they became vices only in the degree to which social order and increasing security rendered them unnecessary for survival. Once men had to chase, to kill, to grasp, to overeat, to hoard; a hundred millenniums of insecurity bred into the race those acquisitive and possessive impulses which no laws or ideals, but only centuries of security, can mitigate or destroy.

The desire for mates and the love of

children write half of the private history of mankind, but they have only rarely been the direct causes of war. The fighting instinct enters more obviously into the analysis, even if it operates most freely in persons above the military age. Nature develops it vigorously as an aid in getting or keeping food or mates; it arms every animal with organs of offense and defense, and lends to the physically weaker species the advantages of cunning and association. Since, by and large, those individuals and groups survived that excelled in food-getting, mate-getting, caring for children, and fighting, these instincts have been selected and intensified with every generation, and have budded into a hundred secondary forms of acquisition, venery, kindliness, and contention.

As the quest for food has grown into the amassing of great fortunes, so the fighting instinct has swelled into the lust for power and the waging of war. The lust for power is in most men a wholesome stimulus to ambition and creation, but in exceptional men, dressed in great and lasting authority, it becomes a dangerous disease, an elephantiasis of the soul, which goads them on to fight a thousand battles by proxy. Nietzsche, nervous and sickly and disqualified for military service, thrilled at the sight and sound of cavalry galloping along a Frankfort street, and at once composed a paean in honor of war and the "will to power." Mussolini and Hitler have read Nietzsche, and may, by replacing parliaments with supermen, and the religion of peace with the religion of war, justify the gentle maniac's prediction that the future would divide history into B.N. and A.N.—Before Nietzsche and After Nietzsche. Nothing is so improbable as the future.

The instinct of flight is hardly a source of war, though war gives it an extensive field of operations. The instinct of action enters into the picture as a love of adventure, an escape from relative and routine. A richer source is the instinct of association. Men fear solitude, and naturally seek the protection of numbers. Slowly a society develops within whose guarded frontiers men are free to live peaceably, to accumulate knowledge and goods, and to worship their gods. Since our self-love overflows into love of our parents and children, our homes and possessions, our habits and institutions, our wonted environment and transmitted faith, we form in time an emotional attachment for the nation and the civilization of which these are constituent parts; and when any of them is threatened, our instinct of pugnacity is aroused to the limit determined by the natural cowardice of mankind. Such patriotism is reasonable and necessary, for without it the group could not survive, and the individual could not survive without the groups. Prejudice is fatal to philosophy, but indispensable to a people.

Put all these passions together, gather into one force the acquisitiveness, pugnacity, egoism, egotism, affection, and lust for power of a hundred million souls, and you have the psychological sources of war. It may be that these sources are not completely instinctive, not inevitably rooted in the blood; contemporary psychology is chary of instincts, and suspects that many of them are but habits formed in early years through the imitation of corrupt adults. We need not spend ourselves on the dispute, for in any case the practical problem would remain—we should still have to change the parents before we could change the children.

The experience of Russia indicates that the business of pursuing food and mates, of fighting and gathering together, of loving children and money and power, is more deeply ingrained in human character than fashionable theory believes. Or was it that the lenience of the Ogpu allowed too many adults to survive? It is hard to build tomorrow's society with the day-after-tomorrow's men. *Historia non facit saltum:* History, like nature, makes no leaps.

These psychological impulses, taken in their social mass, become the biological sources of war. The group, too, as well as the individual, can be hungry or angry, ambitious or proud; the group, too, must struggle for existence, and be eliminated or survive. The protective fertility of organisms soon multiples mouths beyond the local food supply; the hunger of the parts, as in the body, becomes the hunger of the whole, and species wars against species, group against group, for lands or waters that may give more support to abounding life. Euripides, twenty-three hundred years ago, attributed the Trojan War to the rapid multiplication of the Greeks. "States that have a surplus population," said the ancient Stoic philosopher Chrysippus, "send great numbers out to colonies, and stir up wars against their neighbors." If that was the case when infanticide and Greek friendship were tolerated as means of controlling population, consider the results where statesmen encourage fertility. For then the birth rate must be raised to provide soldiers for war; war must be waged to conquer land for an expanding population; and population expands because the birth rate is so high: It is a very pinwheel of logic, bright and frail, a form of reasoning puzzlingly whimsical until we add its concealed premise—the will to power.

Group hunger begets group pugnacity, and pugnacity develops in the group, as in the individual, organs of protection and attack. In the group these are called armament; and when they are powerful, they may themselves, like the boy's biceptual consciousness, become a secondary source of war. On either scale some armament is necessary, for struggle is inevitable, and competition is the trade of life. The tragedy of our ideals is that we hitch them to the falling stars of equality and peace, while nature blithely bases her inescapable machinery of development upon difference and inequality of endowment and ability, upon competition and war. What chance have our ideals, nurtured in the mutual aid of the family, against that supremist court of all? Even mutual aid becomes an organ of struggle: We cooperate as individuals that we may the better compete as groups; morality and order have been developed because they strengthened the group in the inexorable competition of the world. Only when another star attacks us will the earth know internal peace; only a war of the planets can produce, for a moment, the brotherhood of man.

These psychological and biological forces are the ultimate origins of human conflict. From them flow the national rivalries that generate the proximate causes of war—those economic and political causes with which superficial analysis so readily contents itself.

The basic economic cause is rivalry for land: land to receive a designedly expanding population, land to provide material resources, land to open up new subjects to conscription and taxation. So the ancient Greeks fought their way through the Aegean isles to the coasts of Asia Minor and the Black Sea, and through the Mediterranean to Africa, Sicily, Italy, France, and Spain; so the English spread through the world in the last two centuries; so the Italians begin to spread today. There is, in history, a law of colonial expansion almost as explosive as any law of expansion in physics: Whenever a population fails to exploit the resources of its soil, it will sooner or later be conquered by a people able to exploit those resources, and to pour them into the commerce and uses of mankind.

These ancient provocations to conquest have been sharpened and magnified by the Industrial Revolution. To make war successfully a modern nation must be wealthy; to be wealthy it must develop industry; to maintain industry it must, in most cases, import food, fuel, and raw materials; to pay for these it must export manufactured goods; to sell these it must find foreign markets; to win these it must undersell its competitors or wage successful war. As likely as not, it will make war for any of the goods it must import, or for control of the routes by which it imports them.

Even in antiquity semi-industrial Athens waged war for the control of the Aegean, the Hellespont, and the Black Sea, because it was dependent upon Russian grain; Rome had to conquer Egypt because it needed corn, and Asia Minor because it needed markets for its handicrafts and fortunes for its politicians. Egyptian wheat, Near Eastern oil, and Indian cotton explain many a battle in British history; Spanish silver explains the wars of Rome with Carthage; Spanish copper, not Fascist theory, explains in our time the German help to the insurgent forces in Spain. Our sinless selves had a taste for sugar in 1898; and far back in 1853 we pointed our presents and cannon at a frightened shogun and persuaded him to allow a peaceful, agricultural, self-contained nation to transform itself into industrial, imperial, militaristic Japan. Those chickens have come home to roost.

The business cycle adds its own contribution to the causes of modern war. Since men are by nature unequal—some strong and some weak, some able and some (as they tell us) virtuous—it follows that in any society a majority of abilities will be possessed by a minority of men; from which it follows that sooner or later, in any society, a majority of goods will be possessed by a minority of men. But this natural concentration of wealth impedes the wide spread of purchasing power among the people; production, per-

petually accelerated by invention, leaps ahead of consumption; surpluses rise and generate either depression or war. For either production must stop to let consumption catch up, or foreign markets must be found to take the surplus unbought at home. Foreign markets can be secured by underselling competitors or defeating them in war. To undersell our competitors is impracticable; our standard of living is too high for that; to lower it to the level of Japan's would bring revolution; apparently the choice is between depression and war. But another major depression, possibly made worse through the increased displacement of costly labor by economical machines, might also bring revolution. What is left but war—or an unprecedented change in the behavior of men?

Add a few political causes, and our recipe for war will be complete. The first law of governments is self-preservation; their appetite grows by what they feed on, and they are seldom content. But further, the distribution of power among nations is always changing—through the discovery or development of new natural resources, through the rise or decline of population, through the weakening of religion, morals, and character, or through some other material, or biological, or psychological circumstance; and the nation that has become strong soon asserts itself over the nation that has become weak. Hence the impossibility of writing a peace pact that will perpetuate a *status quo;* hence the absurdity of Article X of the League of Nations Covenant; hence the failure of sanctions and the breakdown of the Treaty of Versailles. Excellent indeed is the peace treaty that does not generate a war.

These, then, are the causes of war. How natural it seems now, in the perspective of science and history; how ancient its source and how inscrutable its destiny!

Is it any wonder that peace is so often but invisible war, in which the nations rest only to fight again?

III. Effects

Consider briefly the effects of war. We think of these too often, too seldom of the causes. A reminding summary will suffice.

There are psychological effects. A certain exaltation of spirit may come to a country embarked upon what it believes to be a just war; the mind and heart of the people are unified, hyphens drop out, and the diverse elements of the population are more closely fused into a homogeneous nation. The citizens acquire habits of order and discipline, of courage and tenacity; if they are not destroyed, they are made stronger. Against these gains there is the silent gloom of parents and children bereaved, the disorders of demobilization, the demoralization of men new-trained to habits of violence, promiscuity, and deceit.

For a time there is a revulsion against war: pacifism flourishes so long as the evils of war are fresh in the memory; generous men like the Abbé of St. Pierre and Immanuel Kant and Woodrow Wilson offer plans for perpetual peace, and many humane resolutions are made. But as a fresh generation grows up, pacifism subsides; aged reminiscence idealizes the past, and the young are ready to believe that war is 99 per cent glory and only 1 per cent diarrhea. War loses some of its terrors; to give one's life for one's country is again sweet and beautiful; and to die in bed becomes a shameful fate reserved for noncombatants and generals.

Biologically, war reduces the pressure of population upon the means of subsistence—which is an academic way of saying that some millions of people have been killed. Probably as a result of this, the birth rate has, before our Malthusian days, risen after war; and for some unknown reason, the ratio of male to female births has increased. Dysgenic and eugenic processes go on side by side. The strong and brave go to meet their deaths; the weak remain, and the timid return, to multiply their kind. Pugnacity and brutality are diminished by the superior death rate of the pugnacious and the brutal, both in war and in peace. But usually the finer, more cultured and artistic societies are crushed out, or dominated, by the cruder and more warlike groups: Athens by Sparta, Greece by Macedonia and Rome, T'ang China by the Tatars, Sung China by the Mongols, Gupta India by the Huns, Rome by the barbarians, Renaissance Italy by France, France by Germany, Samurai Japan by the United States. History is a war between war and art, as life is a war between life and death; life and art are always defeated, and always reborn.

To most participating nations, a modern war brings complex economic results. Science and industry are occasionally advanced by researches derived from the stimulus and energy of war. Life and property are destroyed; vast sums are consumed in armament; impossible debts accumulate. Repudiation in some form becomes inevitable; currencies are depreciated or annulled, inflation relieves debtor governments and individuals, savings and investments are wiped out, and men patiently begin to save and lend again. Overexpansion in war is followed by a major depression in peace. International trade is disrupted by intensified nationalism, exalted tariffs, and the desire to develop at home all industries requisite in war. The vanquished are enslaved—physically, as in antiquity, financially and by due process of law today. The victorious masses gain little except in self-conceit; the ruling minority among the victors may gain much in conquered lands, markets, spheres of influence, supplies, and taxable population. This is the little point that Sir Norman Angell forgot.

Politically, war may bring, to the conquered, revolution; to the victors, a strengthened government, the domination of the exchequer by returning soldiers, and the transformation of good generals into bad statesmen.

The methods and institutions that won the war tend to spread abroad and to replace the methods and institutions that lost. The pride of triumph and the appetite for spoils encourage further war, until men and materials are thrown recklessly into the lap of Mars, and the victor, like Assyria and Rome, destroys itself with its victories.

IV. Nostrums

If the foregoing analysis is substantially correct, we shall be spared from any detailed examination of the usual plans for ending war; it is clear that most of these plans have ignored the multiple and tenacious roots of war in the nature of man.

William James, in his kindly way, hoped that the enrollment of the nation's youth, for a year or two, in a wide-flung "war against Nature" would give creative expression to the impulses of action, adventure, and association, and so provide a "moral equivalent of war." It is evident that such a procedure would not offer an outlet for the other and major causes of international strife.

The League of Nations, except under Briand and Stresemann, was a conspiracy of the victors to preserve the gains they had made; it had to fail as soon as the fertility and industry of the defeated had altered the balance of national power left by the Treaty of Versailles. An organization of peace designed to perpetuate the spoils of war defeats itself by definition. The life of nations cannot be strait-jacketed into immutability.

Pacifism would be a cure for war, and doubtless for sovereignty, if it could survive the call to arms or the visible peril of attack. Pacifism in England, in our time, was strong enough to endanger the British Empire through unpreparedness and timidity; but a few Fascist twists of the Lion's tail restored the latent vigor of the beast, and pacifists voted great sums for rearmament. A wise people will love peace and keep its powder dry.

Vague appeals to the conscience of mankind to put an end to war have had little effect in history, for there is no conscience of mankind. Morality is a habit of order generated by centuries of compulsion; international morality awaits international order; international order awaits international force. Conscience follows the policeman.

An effective approach to the problem of war will proceed, not by large and generous emotions but by the specific study and patient adjustment of specific causes and disputes. Peace must be planned and organized as realistically as war—with provision for every factor, and prevision for every detail. This cannot be done in an occasional moment stolen by statesmen from internal affairs; it requires the full-time attention of able minds. It should be a major function of the Department of State to wage peace vigorously and continuously on every front; to isolate the germs of war at their source and to sterilize them with understanding and negotiation. It is our good fortune that our Department of State is headed by Cordell Hull, a man who has a will, rather than merely a wish, for peace.

If now we look again at the causes of war, we shall recognize at once that, even with the best will and intelligence available, these causes can be at best mitigated, but not soon removed. We may slowly lessen the greed that breeds war, by reducing the economic insecurity of individuals and states. As the food supply becomes more secure, fear and pugnacity will decrease. As painful taxes melt back into the public mint the great fortunes generated by the contact of free ability with great natural resources, the stimulus to excessive acquisition will be reduced. Perhaps in time we shall distribute among a cabinet of first-class men appointed by and responsible to Congress, many of the burdens and powers now unbearably concentrated in the presidency; then the temptations and opportunities of the will to power will be diminished, though doubtless superior ability will still polarize power to its purposes. Possibly, the Civilian Conservation Corps can be developed as a "moral equivalent" for the impulses to action, wanderlust, adventure, and association. Conceivably, religion may achieve again the international unity and influence by which it reduced, in the Middle Ages, the frequency, extent, and barbarity of war. The slow internationalization of culture through greater ease of communication and travel, and the restoration of trade in ideas as well as goods, may diminish the egotism in patriotism, as happened in the Hellenistic world, and may win more adherents to the International of the Mind. How could a people trained to love art and music go to war with Italy or Germany, or a people matured to relish great literature make war upon England, Russia, or France?

Since the chief biological source of war is the pressure of population upon the means of life, the falling birth rate in the democratic countries is a subtle stimulus to peace. The rise of the birth rate in Germany and Russia is probably temporary; even dictators are helpless before the great tides of imitation that change the mores, or customs, of mankind. It may be possible—after the next holocaust—to organize international agreements pledging governments to refrain from artificial provocations to fertility. Such a move, however, would demand as a prerequisite the reduction of the economic incentives to war.

Those incentives are so numerous and powerful that each of them should be the major concern of an international commission specifically appointed for its consideration and adjustment. There are so many specialists, economists, and diplomats lying about—to use this verb in a purely geographical sense—that we might well distribute them into commissions severally assigned to examine the economic causes of war, to hear the disputing groups patiently, to investigate possibilities of conciliation, to do their work without the explosive excitement of publicity, and to make specific and practicable recommendations to their governments.

One such commission would study the problem of fertility, and seek territorial outlets for congested populations; another would consider the access of agriculturally limited peoples to foreign food supplies; another, the access of industrial nations to foreign or colonial raw materials and fuels; another, the breaking down of barriers to world trade; another, the opening of opportunities to investment and enterprise. It might be economical to offer to Germany and Italy access to coal and iron, copper and cotton and wheat, in return for cooperation in the reduction of armaments, imperialistic sorties, birth bonuses, and warlike orations. If the democratic nations prefer the arbitrament of battle to such tentatives of peace, it will be hard to absolve them from partial responsibility for the next world war. It is true that nations so aided would be strengthened, but they would be less dangerous in their prosperity than in their need.

Meanwhile, it is good to organize peace throughout the Western Hemisphere, and to give an example of pacific policy at home. It is good to support democracy wherever we can do it without war; for democracies are less likely to make war than nations whose powers are concentrated in a small number of irresponsible men. It may be that the growing weight and terror of rival armaments will generate, before this year passes, such secret willingness to peace as may make another world conference a practicable and hopeful thing, instead of a windy and mischievous futility. A gathering of this kind might seek, not solutions but a year's truce in arming and talking, while commissions examine the causes of conflict, explore avenues of adjustments, and prepare their reports for a reconvened conference. The more briefly such conferences sit, and the more continuously such commissions labor, the better it will be for the peace of mankind. Perhaps oratory should be added to the major causes of war.

Other proposals swarm into the imagination, but we may be sure that they involve more difficulties than are dreamt of by amiable philosophers. Many are tempted toward the idea of a federation of the English-speaking peoples of the world; here, perhaps, would be a force able to forge an international order, conscience, and peace. But, presumably, such a federation would evoke an equal and opposite federation; it would make government too powerful for the good of our public liberties; and, even if secure from without, it would not end strife within— war would merely become "civil." We do not want a crushing conformity of minds and wills to however admirable a Titan of American virtue and British order; variety and freedom are worth the price we pay for them, even the price of war.

In the end we must steel our hearts against utopias and be content, like Aristotle, with a slightly better state. We must not expect the world to improve much faster than ourselves. Perhaps, if we can broaden our borders with intelligent study, modest travel, and honest thought, if we can become conscious of the natural hunger and needs of other peoples, and sensitive to the varied beauties of many cultures and diverse lands, we shall not so readily plunge into competitive homicide, but shall find room in our hearts for a wider understanding and an almost universal sympathy. We, above all, who enjoy beyond our merits the grace of peace and unity conferred upon us by our encompassing seas, owe it as a debt of honor to see more generously the problems of nations divided by hostile frontiers, conflicting necessities, dissimilar languages, and unfamiliar ways. We shall find in all these people qualities and accomplishments from which we may learn and refresh ourselves, and by which we may enrich our inheritance and our posterity. Someday, let us hope, it will be permitted us to love our country without betraying mankind.

SHORT STORIES

THE KILLERS

Ernest Hemingway
(1898–1961)

The door of Henry's lunchroom opened and two men came in. They sat down at the counter.

"What's yours?" George asked them.

"I don't know," one of the men said. "What do you want to eat, Al?"

"I don't know," said Al. "I don't know what I want to eat."

Outside it was getting dark. The streetlight came on outside the window. The two men at the counter read the menu. From the other end of the counter Nick Adams watched them. He had been talking to George when they came in.

"I'll have a roast pork tenderloin with apple sauce and mashed potatoes," the first man said.

"It isn't ready yet."

"What the hell do you put it on the card for?"

"That's the dinner," George explained. "You can get that at six o'clock."

George looked at the clock on the wall behind the counter.

"It's five o'clock."

"The clocks says twenty minutes past five," the second man said.

"It's twenty minutes fast."

"Oh, to hell with the clock," the first man said. "What have you got to eat?"

"I can give you any kind of sandwiches," George said. "You can have ham and eggs, bacon and eggs, liver and bacon, or a steak."

"Give me chicken croquettes with green peas and cream sauce and mashed potatoes."

"That's the dinner."

"Everything we want's the dinner, eh? That's the way you work it."

"I can give you ham and eggs, bacon and eggs, liver—"

"I'll take ham and eggs," the man called Al said. He wore a derby hat and a black overcoat buttoned across the chest. His face was small and white and he had tight lips. He wore a silk muffler and gloves.

"Give me bacon and eggs," said the other man. He was about the same size as Al. Their faces were different, but they were dressed like twins. Both wore overcoats too tight for them. They sat leaning forward, their elbows on the counter.

"Got anything to drink?" Al asked.

"Silver beer, bevo, ginger-ale," George said.

"I mean you got anything to *drink?*"

"Just those I said."

"This is a hot town," said the other. "What do they call it?"

"Summit."

"Ever hear of it?" Al asked his friend.

"No," said the friend.

"What do you do here nights?" Al asked.

"They eat the dinner," his friend said. "They all come here and eat the big dinner."

"That's right," George said.

"So you think that's right?" Al asked George.

"Sure," said George.

"You're a pretty bright boy, aren't you?"

"Sure," said George.

"Well, you're not," said the other little man. "Is he, Al?"

"He's dumb," said Al. He turned to Nick. "What's your name?"

"Adams."

"Another bright boy," Al said. "Ain't he a bright boy, Max?"

"The town's full of bright boys," Max said.

George put the two platters, one of ham and eggs, the other of bacon and eggs, on the counter. He set down two side-dishes of fried potatoes and closed the wicket into the kitchen.

"Which is yours?" he asked Al.

"Don't you remember?"

"Ham and eggs."

"Just a bright boy," Max said. He leaned forward and took the ham and eggs. Both men ate with their gloves on. George watched them eat.

"What are *you* looking at?" Max looked at George.

"Nothing."

"The hell you were. You were looking at me."

"Maybe the boy meant it for a joke, Max," Al said.

George laughed.

"*You* don't have to laugh," Max said to him. "*You* don't have to laugh at all, see?"

"All right," said George.

"So he thinks it's all right." Max turned to Al. "He thinks it's all right. That's a good one."

"Oh, he's a thinker," Al said. They went on eating.

"What's the bright boy's name down the counter?" Al asked Max.

"Hey, bright boy," Max said to Nick. "You go around on the other side of the counter with your boy friend."

"What's the idea?" Nick asked.

"There isn't any idea."

"You better go around, bright boy," Al said. Nick went around behind the counter.

"What's the idea?" George asked.

"None of your damn business," Al said. "Who's out in the kitchen?"

"The nigger."

"What do you mean the nigger?"

"The nigger that cooks."

"Tell him to come in."

"What's the idea?"

"Tell him to come in."

"Where do you think you are?"

"We know damn well where we are," the man called Max said. "Do we look silly?"

"You talk silly," Al said to him. "What the hell do you argue with this kid for? Listen," he said to George, "tell the nigger to come out here."

"What are you going to do to him?"

"Nothing. Use your head, bright boy. What would we do to a nigger?"

George opened the slit that opened back into the kitchen. "Sam," he called. "Come in here a minute."

The door to the kitchen opened and the nigger came in. "What was it?" he asked. The two men at the counter took a look at him.

"All right, nigger. You stand right there," Al said.

Sam, the nigger, standing in his apron, looked at the two men sitting at the counter. "Yes, sir," he said. Al got down from his stool.

"I'm going back to the kitchen with the nigger and bright boy," he said. "Go on back to the kitchen, nigger. You go with him, bright boy." The little man walked after Nick and Sam, the cook, back into the kitchen. The door shut after them. The man called Max sat at the counter opposite George. He didn't look at George but looked in the mirror that ran along back of the counter. Henry's had been made over from a saloon into a lunch-counter.

"Well, bright boy," Max said, looking into the mirror, "why don't you say something?"

"What's it all about?"

"Hey, Al," Max called, "bright boy wants to know what it's all about."

"Why don't you tell him?" Al's voice came from the kitchen.

"What do you think it's all about?"

"I don't know."

"What do you think?"

Max looked into the mirror all the time he was talking.

"I wouldn't say."

"Hey, Al, bright boy says he wouldn't say what he thinks it's all about."

"I can hear you, all right," Al said from the kitchen. He had propped open the slit that dishes passed through into the kitchen with a catsup bottle. "Listen, bright boy," he said from the kitchen to George. "Stand a little further along the bar. You move a little to the left, Max." He was like a photographer arranging for a group picture.

"Talk to me, bright boy," Max said. "What do you think's going to happen?"

George did not say anything.

"I'll tell you," Max said. "We're going to kill a Swede. Do you know a big Swede named Ole Andreson?"

"Yes."

"He comes here to eat every night, don't he?"

"Sometimes he comes here."

"He comes here at six o'clock, don't he?"

"If he comes."

"We know all that, bright boy," Max said. "Talk about something else. Ever go to the movies?"

"Once in a while."

"You ought to go to the movies more. The movies are fine for a bright boy like you."

"What are you going to kill Ole Andreson for? What did he ever do to you?"

"He never had a chance to do anything to us. He never even seen us."

"And he's only going to see us once," Al said from the kitchen.

"What are you going to kill him for, then?" George asked.

"We're killing him for a friend. Just to oblige a friend, bright boy."

"Shut up," said Al from the kitchen. "You talk too goddam much."

"Well, I got to keep bright boy amused. Don't I, bright boy?"

"You talk too damn much," Al said. "The nigger and my bright boy are amused by themselves. I got them tied up like a couple of girl friends in the convent."

"I suppose you were in a convent."

"You never know."

"You were in a kosher convent. That's where you were."

George looked up at the clock.

"If anybody comes in you tell them the cook is off, and if they keep after it, you tell them you'll go back and cook yourself. Do you get that, bright boy?"

"All right," George said. "What you going to do with us afterward?"

"That'll depend," Max said. "That's one of those things you never know at the time."

George looked up at the clock. It was a quarter past six. The door from the street opened. A streetcar motorman came in.

"Hello, George," he said. "Can I get supper?"

"Sam's gone out," George said. "He'll be back in about half an hour."

"I'd better go up the street," the motorman said. George looked at the clock. It was twenty minutes past six.

"That was nice, bright boy," Max said. "You're a regular little gentleman."

"He knew I'd blow his head off," Al said from the kitchen.

"No," said Max. "It ain't that. Bright boy is nice. He's a nice boy. I like him."

At six-fifty-five George said: "He's not coming."

Two other people had been in the lunchroom. Once George had gone out to the kitchen and made a ham-and-egg sandwich "to go" that a man wanted to take with him. Inside the kitchen he saw Al, his derby hat tipped back, sitting on a stool beside the wicket with the muzzle of a sawed-off shotgun resting on the ledge. Nick and the cook were back to back in the corner, a towel tied in each of their mouths. George had cooked the sandwich, wrapped it up in oiled paper, put it in a bag, brought it in, and the man had paid for it and gone out.

"Bright boy can do everything," Max said. "He can cook and everything. You'd make some girl a nice wife, bright boy."

"Yes?" George said. "Your friend, Ole Andreson, isn't going to come."

"We'll give him ten minutes," Max said.

Max watched the mirror and the clock. The hands of the clock marked seven o'clock, and then five minutes past seven.

"Come on, Al," said Max. "We better go. He's not coming."

"Better give him five minutes," Al said from the kitchen.

In the five minutes a man came in, and George explained that the cook was sick.

"Why the hell don't you get another cook?" the man asked. "Aren't you running a lunch-counter?" He went out.

"Come on, Al," Max said.

"What about the two bright boys and the nigger?"

"They're all right."

"You think so?"

"Sure. We're through with it."

"I don't like it," said Al. "It's sloppy. You talk too much."

"Oh, what the hell," said Max. "We got to keep amused, haven't we?"

"You talk too much, all the same," Al said. He came out from the kitchen. The cut-off barrels of the shotgun made a slight bulge under the waist of his too tight-fitting overcoat. He straightened his coat with his gloved hands.

"So long, bright boy," he said to George. "You got a lot of luck."

"That's the truth," Max said. "You ought to play the races, bright boy."

The two of them went out the door. George watched them, through the window, pass under the arc-light and cross the street. In their tight overcoats and derby hats they looked like a vaudeville team. George went back through the swinging-door into the kitchen and untied Nick and the cook.

"I don't want any more of that," said Sam, the cook. "I don't want any more of that."

Nick stood up. He had never had a towel in his mouth before.

"Say," he said. "What the hell?" He was trying to swagger it off.

"They were going to kill Ole Andreson," George said. "They were going to shoot him when he came in to eat."

"Ole Andreson?"

"Sure."

The cook felt the corners of his mouth with his thumbs.

"They all gone?" he asked.

"Yeah," said George. "They're gone now."

"I don't like it," said the cook. "I don't like any of it at all."

"Listen," George said to Nick. "You better go see Ole Andreson."

"All right."

"You better not have anything to do with it at all," Sam, the cook, said. "You better stay way out of it."

"Don't go if you don't want to," George said.

"Mixing up in this ain't going to get you anywhere," the cook said. "You stay out of it."

"I'll go see him," Nick said to George "Where does he live?"

The cook turned away.

"Little boys always know what they want to do," he said.

"He lives up at Hirsch's rooming-house," George said to Nick.

"I'll go up there."

Outside the arc-light shone through the bare branches of a tree. Nick walked up the street beside the car-tracks and turned at the next arc-light down a side-street. Three houses up the street was Hirsch's rooming-house. Nick walked up the two steps and pushed the bell. A woman came to the door.

"Is Ole Andreson here?"

"Do you want to see him?"

"Yes, if he's in."

Nick followed the woman up a flight of stairs and back to the end of a corridor. She knocked on the door.

"Who is it?"

"It's somebody to see you, Mr. Andreson," the woman said.

"It's Nick Adams."

"Come in."

Nick opened the door and went into the room. Ole Andreson was lying on the bed with all his clothes on. He had been a heavyweight prizefighter and he was too long for the bed. He lay with his head on two pillows. He did not look at Nick.

"What was it?" he asked.

"I was up at Henry's," Nick said, "and two fellows came in and tied up me and the cook, and they said they were going to kill you."

It sounded silly when he said it. Ole Andreson said nothing.

"They put us out in the kitchen," Nick went on. "They were going to shoot you when you came in to supper."

Ole Andreson looked at the wall and did not say anything.

"George thought I better come and tell you about it."

"There isn't anything I can do about it," Ole Andreson said.

"I'll tell you what they were like."

"I don't want to know what they were like," Ole Andreson said. He looked at the wall. "Thanks for coming to tell me about it."

"That's all right."

Nick looked at the big man lying on the bed.

"Don't you want me to go and see the police?"

"No," Ole Andreson said. "That wouldn't do any good."

"Isn't there something I could do?"

"No. There ain't anything to do."

"Maybe it was just a bluff."

"No. It ain't just a bluff."

Ole Andreson rolled over toward the wall.

"The only thing is," he said, talking toward the wall, "I just can't make up my mind to go out. I been in here all day."

"Couldn't you get out of town?"

"No," Ole Andreson said. "I'm through with all that running around."

He looked at the wall.

"There ain't anything to do now."

"Couldn't you fix it up some way?"

"No. I got in wrong." He talked in the same flat voice. "There ain't anything to do. After a while I'll make up my mind to go out."

"I better go back and see George," Nick said.

"So long," said Ole Andreson. He did not look toward Nick. "Thanks for coming around."

Nick went out. As he shut the door he saw Ole Andreson with all his clothes on, lying on the bed looking at the wall.

"He's been in his room all day," the landlady said downstairs. "I guess he don't feel well. I said to him: 'Mr. Andreson, you ought to go out and take a walk on a nice fall day like this,' but he didn't feel like it."

"He doesn't want to go out."

"I'm sorry he don't feel well," the woman said. "He's an awfully nice man. He was in the ring, you know."

"I know it."

"You'd never know it except from the way his face is," the woman said. They stood talking just inside the street door. "He's just as gentle."

"Well, good-night, Mrs. Hirsch," Nick said.

"I'm not Mrs. Hirsch," the woman said. "She owns the place. I just look after it for her. I'm Mrs. Bell."

"Well, good-night, Mrs. Bell," Nick said.

"Good-night," the woman said.

Nick walked up the dark street to the corner under the arc-light, and then along the car-tracks to Henry's eating-house. George was inside, back of the counter.

"Did you see Ole?"

"Yes," said Nick. "He's in his room and he won't go out."

The cook opened the door from the kitchen when he heard Nick's voice.

"I don't even listen to it," he said and shut the door.

"Did you tell him about it?" George asked.

"Sure. I told him but he knows what it's all about."

"What's he going to do?"

"Nothing."

"They'll kill him."

"I guess they will."

"He must have got mixed up in something in Chicago."

"I guess so," said Nick.

"It's a hell of a thing."

"It's an awful thing," Nick said.

They did not say anything. George

reached down for a towel and wiped the counter.

"I wonder what he did?" Nick said.

"Double-crossed somebody. That's what they kill them for."

"I'm going to get out of this town," Nick said.

"Yes," said George. "That's a good thing to do."

"I can't stand to think about him waiting in the room and knowing he's going to get it. It's too damned awful."

"Well," said George, "you better not think about it."

THE LOTTERY

Shirley Jackson
(1916–1965)

The morning of June 27th was clear and sunny, with the fresh warmth of a full summer day; the flowers were blossoming profusely and the grass was richly green. The people of the village began to gather in the square, between the post office and the bank, around ten o'clock; in some towns there were so many people that the lottery took two days and had to be started on June 26th, but in this village, where there were only about three hundred people, the whole lottery took less than two hours, so it could begin at ten o'clock in the morning and still be through in time to allow the villagers to get home for noon dinner.

The children assembled first, of course. School was recently over for the summer, and the feeling of liberty sat uneasily on most of them; they tended to gather together quietly for a while before they broke into boisterous play, and their talk was still of the classroom and the teacher, of books and reprimands. Bobby Martin had already stuffed his pockets full of stones, and the other boys soon followed his example, selecting the smoothest and roundest stones; Bobby and Harry Jones and Dickie Delacroix—the villagers pronounced this name "Dellacroy"—eventually made a great pile of stones in one corner of the square and guarded it against the raids of the other boys. The girls stood aside, talking among themselves, looking over their shoulders at the boys, and the very small children rolled in the dust or clung to the hands of their older brothers or sisters.

Soon the men began to gather, surveying their own children, speaking of planting and rain, tractors and taxes. They stood together, away from the pile of stones in the corner, and their jokes were quiet and they smiled rather than laughed. The women, wearing faded house dresses and sweaters, came shortly after their menfolk. They greeted one another and exchanged bits of gossip as they went to join their husbands. Soon the women, standing by their husbands, began to call to their children, and the children came reluctantly, having to be called four or five times. Bobby Martin ducked under his mother's grasping hand and ran, laughing, back to the pile of stones. His father spoke up sharply, and Bobby came quickly and took his place between his father and his oldest brother.

The lottery was conducted—as were the square dances, the teen-age club, the Hallowe'en program—by Mr. Summers, who had time and energy to devote to civic activities. He was a round-faced, jovial man and he ran the coal business, and people were sorry for him, because he had no children and his wife was a scold. When he arrived in the square, carrying the black wooden box, there was a murmur of conversation among the villagers, and he waved and called, "Little late today, folks." The postmaster, Mr. Graves, followed him, carrying a three-legged stool, and the stool was put in the center of the square and Mr. Summers set the black box down on it. The villagers kept their distance, leaving a space between themselves and the stool, and when Mr. Summers said, "Some of you fellows want to give me a hand?" there was a hesitation before two men, Mr. Martin and his oldest son, Baxter, came forward to hold the box steady on the stool while Mr. Summers stirred up the papers inside it.

The original paraphernalia for the lottery had been lost long ago, and the black box now resting on the stool had been put into use even before Old Man Warner, the oldest man in town, was born. Mr. Summers spoke frequently to the villagers about making a new box, but no one liked to upset even as much tradition as was represented by the black box. There was a story that the present box had been made with some pieces of the box that had preceded it, the one that had been constructed when the first people settled down to make a village here. Every year, after the lottery, Mr. Summers began talking again about a new box, but every year the subject was allowed to fade off without anything's being done. The black box grew shabbier each year; by now it was no longer completely black but splintered badly along one side to show the original wood color, and in some places faded or stained.

Mr. Martin and his oldest son, Baxter, held the black box securely on the stool until Mr. Summers had stirred the papers thoroughly with his hand. Because so much of the ritual had been forgotten or discarded, Mr. Summers had been successful in having slips of paper substituted for the chips of wood that had been used for generations. Chips of wood, Mr. Summers had argued, had been all very well when the village was tiny, but now that the population was more than three hundred and likely to keep on growing, it was necessary to use something that would fit more easily into the black box.

The night before the lottery, Mr. Summers and Mr. Graves made up the slips of paper and put them in the box, and it was then taken to the safe of Mr. Summers' coal company and locked up until Mr. Summers was ready to take it to the square next morning. The rest of the year, the box was put away, sometimes one place, sometimes another; it had spent one year in Mr. Graves's barn and another year underfoot in the post office, and sometimes it was set on a shelf in the Martin grocery and left there.

There was a great deal of fussing to be done before Mr. Summers declared the lottery open. There were the lists to make up—of heads of families, heads of households in each family, members of each household in each family. There was the proper swearing-in of Mr. Summers by the postmaster, as the official of the lottery; at one time, some people remembered. there had been a recital of some sort, performed by the official of the lottery, a perfunctory, tuneless chant that had been rattled off duly each year; some people believed that the official of the lottery used to stand just so when he said or sang it, others believed that he was supposed to walk among the people, but years and years ago this part of the ritual had been allowed to lapse. There had been, also, a ritual salute, which the official of the lottery had to use in addressing each person who came up to draw from the box, but this also had changed with time, until now it was felt necessary only for the official to speak to each person approaching. Mr. Summers was very good at all this; in his clean white shirt and blue jeans, with one hand resting carelessly on the black box, he seemed very proper and important as he talked interminably to Mr. Graves and the Martins.

Just as Mr. Summers finally left off talking and turned to the assembled villagers, Mrs. Hutchinson came hurriedly along the path to the square, her sweater thrown over her shoulders, and slid into place in the back of the crowd. "Clean forgot what day it was," she said to Mrs. Delacroix, who stood next to her, and they both laughed softly. "Thought my old man was out back stacking wood," Mrs. Hutchinson went on, "and then I looked out the window and the kids was gone, and then I remembered it was the twenty-seventh and came a-running." She dried her hands on her apron, and Mrs. Delacroix said, "You're in time, though. They're still talking away up there."

Mrs. Hutchinson craned her neck to see through the crowd and found her husband and children standing near the front. She tapped Mrs. Delacroix on the arm as a farewell and began to make her way through the crowd. The people separated good-humoredly to let her through; two or three people said, in voices just loud enough to be heard across the crowd, "Here comes your Missus, Hutchinson," and "Bill, she made it after all." Mrs. Hutchinson reached her husband, and Mr. Summers, who had been waiting, said cheerfully, "Thought we were going to have to get on without you, Tessie." Mrs. Hutchinson said, grinning, "Wouldn't have me leave m'dishes in the sink, now, would you, Joe?" and soft laughter ran through the crowd as the people stirred back into position after Mrs. Hutchinson's arrival.

"Well, now," Mr. Summers said soberly, "guess we better get started, get this over with, so's we can go back to work. Anybody ain't here?"

"Dunbar," several people said. "Dunbar, Dunbar."

Mr. Summers consulted his list. "Clyde Dunbar," he said. "That's right. He's broke his leg, hasn't he? Who's drawing for him?"

"Me, I guess," a woman said, and Mr. Summers turned to look at her. "Wife draws for her husband," Mr. Summers said. "Don't you have a grown boy to do it for you, Janey?" Although Mr. Summers and everyone else in the village knew the answer perfectly well, it was the business of the official of the lottery to ask such questions formally. Mr. Summers waited with an expression of polite interest while Mrs. Dunbar answered.

"Horace's not but sixteen yet," Mrs. Dunbar said regretfully. "Guess I gotta fill in for the old man this year."

"Right," Mr. Summers said. He made a note on the list he was holding. Then he asked, "Watson boy drawing this year?"

A tall boy in the crowd raised his hand. "Here," he said. "I'm drawing for m'mother and me." He blinked his eyes nervously and ducked his head as several voices in the crowd said things like "Good fellow, Jack," and "Glad to see your mother's got a man to do it."

"Well," Mr. Summers said, "guess that's everyone. Old Man Warner make it?"

"Here," a voice said, and Mr. Summers nodded.

A sudden hush fell on the crowd as Mr. Summers cleared his throat and looked at the list. "All ready?" he called. "Now, I'll read the names—heads of families first—and the men come up and take a paper out of the box. Keep the paper folded in your hand without looking at it until everyone has had a turn. Everything clear?"

The people had done it so many times that they only half listened to the directions; most of them were quiet, wetting their lips, not looking around. Then Mr. Summers raised one hand high and said, "Adams." A man disengaged himself from the crowd and came forward. "Hi, Steve," Mr. Summers said, and Mr. Adams said, "Hi, Joe." They grinned at one another humorlessly and nervously. Then Mr. Adams reached into the black box and took out a folded paper. He held

it firmly by one corner as he turned and went hastily back to his place in the crowd, where he stood a little apart from his family, not looking down at his hand.

"Allen," Mr. Summers said. "Anderson. . . . Bentham."

"Seems like there's no time at all between lotteries any more," Mrs. Delacroix said to Mrs. Graves in the back row. "Seems like we got through with the last one only last week."

"Time sure goes fast," Mrs. Graves said.

"Clark. . . . Delacroix."

"There goes my old man," Mrs. Delacroix said. She held her breath while her husband went forward.

"Dunbar," Mr. Summers said, and Mrs. Dunbar went steadily to the box while one of the women said, "Go on, Janey," and another said, "There she goes."

"We're next," Mrs. Graves said. She watched while Mr. Graves came around from the side of the box, greeted Mr. Summers gravely, and selected a slip of paper from the box. By now, all through the crowd there were men holding the small folded papers in their large hands, turning them over and over nervously. Mrs. Dunbar and her two sons stood together, Mrs. Dunbar holding the slip of paper.

"Harburt. . . . Hutchinson."

"Get up there, Bill," Mrs. Hutchinson said, and the people near her laughed.

"Jones."

"They do say," Mr. Adams said to Old Man Warner, who stood next to him, "that over in the north village they're talking of giving up the lottery."

Old Man Warner snorted. "Pack of crazy fools," he said. "Listening to the young folks, nothing's good enough for *them*. Next thing you know, they'll be wanting to go back to living in caves, nobody work any more, live *that* way for a while. Used to be a saying about 'Lottery in June, corn be heavy soon.'

First thing you know, we'd all be eating stewed chickweed and acorns. There's *always* been a lottery," he added petulantly. "Bad enough to see young Joe Summers up there joking with everybody."

"Some places have already quit lotteries," Mrs. Adams said.

"Nothing but trouble in *that*," Old Man Warner said stoutly. "Pack of young fools."

"Martin." And Bobby Martin watched his father go forward. "Overdyke. . . . Percy."

"I wish they'd hurry," Mrs. Dunbar said to her older son. "I wish they'd hurry."

"They're almost through," her son said.

"You get ready to run tell Dad," Mrs. Dunbar said.

Mr. Summers called his own name and then stepped forward precisely and selected a slip from the box. Then he called, "Warner."

"Seventy-seventh year I been in the lottery," Old Man Warner said as he went through the crowd. "Seventy-seventh time."

"Watson." The tall boy came awkwardly through the crowd. Someone said, "Don't be nervous, Jack," and Mr. Summers said, "Take your time, son."

"Zanini."

After that, there was a long pause, a breathless pause, until Mr. Summers, holding his slip of paper in the air, said, "All right, fellows." For a minute, no one moved, and then all the slips of paper were opened. Suddenly, all the women began to speak at once, saying, "Who is it?," "Who's got it?," "Is it the Dunbars?," "Is it the Watsons?" Then the voices began to say, "It's Hutchinson. It's Bill." "Bill Hutchinson's got it."

"Go tell your father," Mrs. Dunbar said to her older son.

People began to look around to see the Hutchinsons. Bill Hutchinson was standing quiet, staring down at the paper in his hand. Suddenly, Tessie Hutchinson shouted to Mr. Summers, "You didn't give him time enough to take any paper he wanted. I saw you. It wasn't fair!"

"Be a good sport, Tessie," Mrs. Delacroix called, and Mrs. Graves said, "All of us took the same chance."

"Shut up, Tessie," Bill Hutchinson said.

"Well, everyone," Mr. Summers said, "that was done pretty fast, and now we've got to be hurrying a little more to get done in time." He consulted his next list. "Bill," he said, "you draw for the Hutchinson family. You got any other households in the Hutchinsons?"

"There's Don and Eva," Mrs. Hutchinson yelled. "Make *them* take their chance!"

"Daughters draw with their husbands' families, Tessie," Mr. Summers said gently. "You know that as well as anyone else."

"It wasn't *fair*," Tessie said.

"I guess not, Joe," Bill Hutchinson said regretfully. "My daughter draws with her husband's family, that's only fair. And I've got no other family except the kids."

"Then, as far as drawing for families is concerned, it's you," Mr. Summers said in explanation, "and as far as drawing for households is concerned, that's you, too. Right?"

"Right," Bill Hutchinson said.

"How many kids, Bill?" Mr. Summers asked formally.

"Three," Bill Hutchinson said. "There's Bill, Jr., and Nancy, and little Dave. And Tessie and me."

"All right, then," Mr. Summers said. "Harry, you got their tickets back?"

Mr. Graves nodded and held up the slips of paper. "Put them in the box, then," Mr. Summers directed. "Take Bill's and put it in."

"I think we ought to start over," Mrs. Hutchinson said, as quietly as she could.

"I tell you it wasn't *fair*. You didn't give him time enough to choose. *Every*body saw that."

Mr. Graves had selected the five slips and put them in the box, and he dropped all the papers but those onto the ground, where the breeze caught them and lifted them off.

"Listen, everybody," Mrs. Hutchinson was saying to the people around her.

"Ready, Bill?" Mr. Summers asked, and Bill Hutchinson, with one quick glance around at his wife and children, nodded.

"Remember," Mr. Summers said, "take the slips and keep them folded until each person has taken one. Harry, you help little Dave." Mr. Graves took the hand of the little boy, who came willingly with him up to the box. "Take a paper out of the box, Davy," Mr. Summers said. Davy put his hand into the box and laughed. "Take just *one* paper," Mr. Summers said. "Harry, you hold it for him." Mr. Graves took the child's hand and removed the folded paper from the tight fist and held it while little Dave stood next to him and looked up at him wonderingly.

"Nancy next," Mr. Summers said. Nancy was twelve, and her school friends breathed heavily as she went forward, switching her skirt, and took a slip daintily from the box. "Bill, Jr.," Mr. Summers said, and Billy, his face red and his feet overlarge, nearly knocked the box over as he got a paper out. "Tessie," Mr. Summers said. She hesitated for a minute, looking around defiantly, and then she set her lips and went up to the box. She snatched a paper out and held it behind her.

"Bill," Mr. Summers said, and Bill Hutchinson reached into the box and felt around, bringing his hand out at last with the slip of paper in it.

The crowd was quiet. A girl whispered, "I hope it's not Nancy," and the sound of the whisper reached the edges of the crowd.

"It's not the way it used to be," Old Man Warner said clearly. "People ain't the way they used to be."

"All right," Mr. Summers said. "Open the papers. Harry, you open little Dave's."

Mr. Graves opened the slip of paper and there was a general sigh through the crowd as he held it up and everyone could see that it was blank. Nancy and Bill, Jr., opened theirs at the same time, and both beamed and laughed, turning around to the crowd and holding their slips of paper above their heads.

"Tessie," Mr. Summers said. There was a pause, and then Mr. Summers looked at Bill Hutchinson, and Bill unfolded his paper and showed it. It was blank.

"It's Tessie," Mr. Summers said, and his voice was hushed. "Show us her paper, Bill."

Bill Hutchinson went over to his wife and forced the slip of paper out of her hand. It had a black spot on it, the black spot Mr. Summers had made the night before with the heavy pencil in the coal-company office. Bill Hutchinson held it up, and there was a stir in the crowd.

"All right, folks," Mr. Summers said. "Let's finish quickly."

Although the villagers had forgotten the ritual and lost the original black box, they still remembered to use stones. The pile of stones the boys had made earlier was ready; there were stones on the ground with the blowing scraps of paper that had come out of the box. Mrs. Delacroix selected a stone so large she had to pick it up with both hands and turned to Mrs. Dunbar. "Come on," she said. "Hurry up."

Mrs. Dunbar had small stones in both hands, and she said, gasping for breath, "I can't run at all. You'll have to go ahead and I'll catch up with you."

The children had stones already, and

someone gave little Davy Hutchinson a few pebbles.

Tessie Hutchinson was in the center of a cleared space by now, and she held her hands out desperately as the villagers moved in on her. "It isn't fair," she said. A stone hit her on the side of the head.

Old Man Warner was saying, "Come on, come on, everyone." Steve Adams was in the front of the crowd of villagers, with Mrs. Graves beside him.

"It isn't fair, it isn't right," Mrs. Hutchinson screamed, and then they were upon her.

A MYSTERY OF HEROISM

Stephen Crane
(1871–1900)

The dark uniforms of the men were so coated with dust from the incessant wrestling of the two armies that the regiment almost seemed a part of the clay bank which shielded them from the shells. On the top of the hill a battery was arguing in tremendous roars with some other guns, and to the eye of the infantry the artillerymen, the guns, the caissons, the horses, were distinctly outlined upon the blue sky. When a piece was fired, a red streak as round as a log flashed low in the heavens, like a monstrous bolt of lightning. The men of the battery wore white duck trousers, which somehow emphasized their legs; and when they ran and crowded in little groups at the bidding of the shouting officers, it was more impressive than usual to the infantry.

Fred Collins, of A Company, was saying: "Thunder! I wisht I had a drink. Ain't there any water round here?" Then somebody yelled: "There goes th' bugler!"

As the eyes of half the regiment swept in one machine-like movement, there was an instant's picture of a horse in a great convulsive leap of a death-wound and a rider leaning back with a crooked arm and spread fingers before his face. On the ground was the crimson terror of an exploding shell, with fibres of flame that seemed like lances. A glittering bugle swung clear of the rider's back as fell headlong the horse and the man. In the air was an odour as from a conflagration.

Sometimes they of the infantry looked down at a fair little meadow which spread at their feet. Its long green grass was rippling gently in a breeze. Beyond it was the grey form of a house half torn to pieces by shells and by the busy axes of soldiers who had pursued firewood. The line of an old fence was now dimly marked by long weeds and by an occasional post. A shell had blown the wellhouse to fragments. Little lines of grey smoke ribboning upward from some embers indicated the place where had stood the barn.

From beyond a curtain of green woods there came the sound of some stupendous scuffle, as if two animals of the size of islands were fighting. At a distance there were occasional appearances of swift-moving men, horses, batteries, flags, and with the crashing of infantry volleys were heard, often, wild and frenzied cheers. In the midst of it all Smith and Ferguson, two privates of A Company, were engaged in a heated discussion which involved the greatest questions of the national existence.

The battery on the hill presently engaged in a frightful duel. The white legs of the gunners scampered this way and that way, and the officers redoubled their shouts. The guns, with their demeanours of stolidity and courage, were typical of something infinitely self-possessed in this clamour of death that swirled around the hill.

One of a "swing" team was suddenly smitten quivering to the ground, and his maddened brethren dragged his torn body in their struggle to escape from this turmoil and danger. A young soldier astride one of the leaders swore and fumed in his saddle and furiously jerked at the bridle. An officer screamed out an order so violently that his voice broke and ended the sentence in a falsetto shriek.

The leading company of the infantry regiment was somewhat exposed, and the colonel ordered it moved more fully under the shelter of the hill. There was the clank of steel against steel.

A lieutenant of the battery rode down and passed them, holding his right arm carefully in his left hand. And it was as if this arm was not at all a part of him, but belonged to another man. His sober and reflective charger went slowly. The officer's face was grimy and perspiring, and his uniform was tousled as if he had been in direct grapple with an enemy. He smiled grimly when the men stared at him. He turned his horse toward the meadow.

Collins, of A Company, said: "I wisht I had a drink. I bet there's water in that there ol' well yonder!"

"Yes; but how you goin' to git it?"

For the little meadow which intervened was now suffering a terrible onslaught of shells. Its green and beautiful calm had vanished utterly. Brown earth was being flung in monstrous handfuls. And there was a massacre of the young blades of grass. They were being torn, burned, obliterated. Some curious fortune of the battle had made this gentle little meadow the object of the red hate of the shells, and each one as it exploded seemed like an imprecation in the face of a maiden.

The wounded officer who was riding across this expanse said to himself: "Why, they couldn't shoot any harder if the whole army was massed here!"

A shell struck the grey ruins of the house, and as, after the roar, the shattered wall fell in fragments, there was a noise which resembled the flapping of shutters during a wild gale of winter. Indeed, the infantry paused in the shelter of the bank appeared as men standing upon a shore contemplating a madness of the sea. The angel of calamity had under its glance the battery upon the hill. Fewer white-legged men laboured about the guns. A shell had smitten one of the pieces, and after the flare, the smoke, the dust, the wrath of this blow were gone, it was possible to see white legs stretched horizontally upon the ground. And at that interval to the rear where it is the business of battery horses to stand with their noses to the fight, awaiting the command to drag their guns out of the destruction, or into it, or wheresoever these incomprehensible humans demanded with whip and spur—in this line of passive and dumb spectators, whose fluttering hearts yet would not let them forget the iron laws of man's control of them—in this rank of brute-soldiers there had been relentless and hideous carnage. From the ruck of bleeding and prostrate horses, the men of the infantry could see one animal raising its stricken body with its forelegs and turning its nose with mystic and profound eloquence toward the sky.

Some comrades joked Collins about his thirst. "Well, if yeh want a drink so bad, why don't yeh go git it?"

"Well, I will in a minnet, if yeh don't shut up!"

A lieutenant of artillery floundered his horse straight down the hill with as little concern as if it were level ground. As he galloped past the colonel of the infantry, he threw up his hand in swift salute. "We've got to get out of that," he roared angrily. He was a black-bearded officer, and his eyes, which resembled beads, sparkled like those of an insane man. His jumping horse sped along the column of infantry.

The fat major, standing carelessly with his sword held horizontally behind him and with his legs far apart, looked after the receding horseman and laughed. "He wants to get back with orders pretty quick, or there'll be no batt'ry left," he observed.

The wise young captain of the second company hazarded to the lieutenant-colonel that the enemy's infantry would probably soon attack the hill, and the lieutenant-colonel snubbed him.

A private in one of the rear companies looked out over the meadow, and then turned to a companion and said, "Look there, Jim!" It was the wounded officer from the battery, who some time before had started to ride across the meadow, supporting his right arm carefully with his left hand. This man had encountered a shell, apparently, at a time when no one perceived him, and he could now be seen lying face downward with a stirruped foot stretched across the body of his dead horse. A leg of the charger extended slantingly upward, precisely as stiff as a stake. Around this motionless pair the shells still howled.

There was a quarrel in A Company. Collins was shaking his fist in the faces of some laughing comrades. "Dern yeh! I ain't afraid t' go. If yeh say much, I will go!"

"Of course, yeh will! You'll run through that there medder, won't yeh?"

Collins said, in a terrible voice: "You see now!"

At this ominous threat his comrades broke into renewed jeers.

Collins gave them a dark scowl, and went to find his captain. The latter was conversing with the colonel of the regiment.

"Captain," said Collins, saluting and standing at attention—in those days all trousers bagged at the knees—"Captain, I want t' get permission to go git some water from that there well over yonder!"

The colonel and the captain swung about simultaneously and stared across the meadow. The captain laughed. "You must be pretty thirsty, Collins?"

"Yes, sir, I am."

"Well—ah," said the captain. After a moment, he asked, "Can't you wait?"

"No, sir."

The colonel was watching Collins's face. "Look here, my lad," he said, in a pious sort of voice—"Look here, my lad"—Collins was not a lad—"don't you think that's taking pretty big risks for a little drink of water?"

"I dunno," said Collins uncomfortably. Some of the resentment toward his companions, which perhaps had forced him into this affair, was beginning to fade. "I dunno w'ether 'tis."

The colonel and the captain contemplated him for a time.

"Well," said the captain finally.

"Well," said the colonel, "if you want to go, why, go."

Collins saluted. "Much obliged t' yeh."

As he moved away the colonel called after him. "Take some of the other boys' canteens with you, an' hurry back, now."

"Yes, sir, I will."

The colonel and the captain looked at each other then, for it had suddenly occurred that they could not for the life of them tell whether Collins wanted to go or whether he did not.

They turned to regard Collins, and as they perceived him surrounded by gesticulating comrades, the colonel said: "Well, by thunder! I guess he's going."

Collins appeared as a man dreaming. In the midst of the questions, the advice, the warnings, all the excited talk of his company mates, he maintained a curious silence.

They were very busy in preparing him for his ordeal. When they inspected him carefully, it was somewhat like the examination that grooms give a horse before a race; and they were amazed, staggered, by the whole affair. Their astonishment found vent in strange repetitions.

"Are yeh sure a-goin'?" they demanded again and again.

"Certainly I am," cried Collins at last, furiously.

He strode sullenly away from them. He was swinging five or six canteens by their cords. It seemed that his cap would not remain firmly on his head, and often he reached and pulled it down over his brow.

There was a general movement in the compact column. The long animal-like thing moved slightly. Its four hundred eyes were turned upon the figure of Collins.

"Well, sir, if that ain't th' derndest thing! I never thought Fred Collins had the blood in him for that kind of business."

"What's he goin' to do, anyhow?"

"He's goin' to that well there after water."

"We ain't dyin' of thirst, are we? That's foolishness."

"Well, somebody put him up to it, an' he's doin' it."

"Say, he must be a desperate cuss."

When Collins faced the meadow and walked away from the regiment, he was vaguely conscious that a chasm, the deep valley of all prides, was suddenly between him and his comrades. It was provisional, but the provision was that he return as a victor. He had blindly been led by quaint emotions, and laid himself under an obligation to walk squarely up to the face of death.

But he was not sure that he wished to make a retraction, even if he could do so without shame. As a matter of truth, he was sure of very little. He was mainly surprised.

It seemed to him supernaturally strange that he had allowed his mind to manœuvre his body into such a situation. He understood that it might be called dramatically great.

However, he had no full appreciation of anything, excepting that he was actually conscious of being dazed. He could feel his dulled mind groping after the form and colour of this incident. He wondered why he did not feel some keen agony of fear cutting his sense like a knife. He wondered at this, because human expression had said loudly for centuries that men should feel afraid of certain things, and that all men who did not feel this fear were phenomena—heroes.

He was, then, a hero. He suffered that disappointment which we would all have if we discovered that we were ourselves capable of those deeds which we most admire in history and legend. This, then, was a hero. After all, heroes were not much.

No, it could not be true. He was not a hero. Heroes had no shames in their lives, and, as for him, he remembered borrowing fifteen dollars from a friend and promising to pay it back the next day, and then avoiding that friend for ten months. When, at home, his mother had aroused him for the early labour of his life on the farm, it had often been his fashion to be irritable, childish, diabolical; and his mother had died since he had come to the war.

He saw that, in this matter of the well, the canteens, the shells, he was an intruder in the land of fine deeds.

He was now about thirty paces from his comrades. The regiment had just turned its many faces toward him.

From the forest of terrific noises there suddenly emerged a little uneven line of men. They fired fiercely and rapidly at distant foliage on which appeared little puffs of white smoke. The spatter of skirmish firing was added to the thunder of the guns on the hill. The little line of men ran forward. A colour-sergeant fell flat with his flag as if he had slipped on ice. There was hoarse cheering from this distant field.

Collins suddenly felt that two demon

fingers were pressed into his ears. He could see nothing but flying arrows, flaming red. He lurched from the shock of this explosion, but he made a mad rush for the house, which he viewed as a man submerged to the neck in a boiling surf might view the shore. In the air little pieces of shell howled, and the earthquake explosions drove him insane with the menace of their roar. As he ran the canteens knocked together with a rhythmical tinkling.

As he neared the house, each detail of the scene became vivid to him. He was aware of some bricks of the vanished chimney lying on the sod. There was a door which hung by one hinge.

Rifle bullets called forth by the insistent skirmishes came from the far-off bank of foliage. They mingled with the shells and the pieces of shells until the air was torn in all directions by hootings, yells, howls. The sky was full of fiends who directed all their wild rage at his head.

When he came to the well, he flung himself face downward and peered into its darkness. There were furtive silver glintings some feet from the surface. He grabbed one of the canteens and, unfastening its cap, swung it down by the cord. The water flowed slowly in with an indolent gurgle.

And now, as he lay with his face turned away, he was suddenly smitten with the terror. It came upon his heart like the grasp of claws. All the power faded from his muscles. For an instant he was no more than a dead man.

The canteen filled with a maddening slowness, in the manner of all bottles. Presently he recovered his strength and addressed a screaming oath to it. He leaned over until it seemed as if he intended to try to push water into it with his hands. His eyes as he gazed down into the well shone like two pieces of metal,

and in their expression was a great appeal and a great curse. The stupid water derided him.

There was the blaring thunder of a shell. Crimson light shone through the swift-boiling smoke and made a pink reflection on part of the wall of the well. Collins jerked out his arm and canteen with the same motion that a man would use in withdrawing his head from a furnace.

He scrambled erect and glared and hesitated. On the ground near him lay the old well bucket, with a length of rusty chain. He lowered it swiftly into the well. The bucket struck the water and then, turning lazily over, sank. When, with hand reaching tremblingly over hand, he hauled it out, it knocked often against the walls of the well and spilled some of its contents.

In running with a filled bucket, a man can adopt but one kind of gait. So, through this terrible field over which screamed practical angels of death, Collins ran in the manner of a farmer chased out of a dairy by a bull.

His face went staring white with anticipation—anticipation of a blow that would whirl him around and down. He would fall as he had seen other men fall, the life knocked out of them so suddenly that their knees were no more quick to touch the ground than their heads. He saw the long blue line of the regiment, but his comrades were standing looking at him from the edge of an impossible star. He was aware of some deep wheel-ruts and hoofprints in the sod beneath his feet.

The artillery officer who had fallen in this meadow had been making groans in the teeth of the tempest of sound. These futile cries, wrenched from him by his agony, were heard only by shells, bullets. When wild-eyed Collins came running, this officer raised himself. His face contorted and blanched from pain, he was about to utter some great beseeching cry.

But suddenly his face straightened, and he called: "Say, young man, give me a drink of water, will you?"

Collins had no room amid his emotions for surprise. He was mad from the threats of destruction.

"I can't!" he screamed, and in his reply was a full description of his quaking apprehension. His cap was gone and his hair was riotous. His clothes made it appear that he had been dragged over the ground by the heels. He ran on.

The officer's head sank down, and one elbow crooked. His foot in its brass-bound stirrup still stretched over the body of his horse, and the other leg was under the steed.

But Collins turned. He came dashing back. His face had now turned grey, and in his eyes was all terror. "Here it is! here it is!"

The officer was as a man gone in drink. His arm bent like a twig. His head drooped as if his neck were of willow. He was sinking to the ground, to lie face downward.

Collins grabbed him by the shoulder. "Here it is. Here's your drink. Turn over. Turn over, man, for God's sake!"

With Collins hauling at his shoulder, the officer twisted his body and fell with his face turned toward that region where lived the unspeakable noises of the swirling missiles. There was the faintest shadow of a smile on his lips as he looked at Collins. He gave a sigh, a little primitive breath like that from a child.

Collins tried to hold the bucket steadily, but his shaking hands caused the water to splash all over the face of the dying man. Then he jerked it away and ran on.

The regiment gave him a welcoming roar. The grimed faces were wrinkled in laughter.

His captain waved the bucket away. "Give it to the men!"

The two genial, skylarking young lieutenants were the first to gain possession of it. They played over it in their fashion.

When one tried to drink, the other teasingly knocked his elbow. "Don't Billie! You'll make me spill it," said the one. The other laughed.

Suddenly there was an oath, the thud of wood on the ground, and a swift murmur of astonishment among the ranks. The two lieutenants glared at each other. The bucket lay on the ground, empty.

POEMS

LORD RANDAL

"O where hae ye been, Lord Randal, my son?
O where hae ye been, my handsome young man?"
"I hae been to the wild wood; mother, make my bed soon,
For I'm weary wi hunting, and fain wald lie down."

"Where gat ye your dinner, Lord Randal, my son?   5
Where gat ye your dinner, my handsome young man?"
"I dined wi my true-love; mother, make my bed soon,
For I'm weary wi hunting, and fain wald lie down."

"What gat ye to your dinner, Lord Randal, my son?
What gat ye to your dinner, my handsome young man?"   10
"I gat eels boiled in broo; mother, make my bed soon,
For I'm weary wi hunting, and fain wald lie down."

"What became of your bloodhounds, Lord Randal, my son?
What became of your bloodhounds, my handsome young man?"
"O they swelld and they died; mother, make my bed soon,   15
For I'm weary wi hunting, and fain wald lie down."

"O I fear ye are poisond, Lord Randal, my son!
O I fear ye are poisond, my handsome young man!"
"O yes! I am poisond; mother, make my bed soon,
For I'm sick at the heart, and I fain wald lie down."   20

4. *fain wald:* would.
11. *broo:* broth.

MY LAST DUCHESS

Robert Browning
(1812–1889)

Ferrara

That's my last Duchess painted on the wall,
Looking as if she were alive. I call
That piece a wonder, now; Frà Pandolf's hands
Worked busily a day, and there she stands.
Will't please you sit and look at her? I said   5
"Frà Pandolf" by design, for never read
Strangers like you that pictured countenance,
The depth and passion of its earnest glance,

3. *Frà Pandolf:* an imaginary painter.

But to myself they turned (since none
   puts by
The curtain I have drawn for you, but
   I)   10
And seemed as they would ask me, if they
   durst,
How such a glance came there; so, not
   the first
Are you to turn and ask thus. Sir, 'twas
   not
Her husband's presence only, called that
   spot
Of joy into the Duchess' cheek; per-
   haps   15
Frà Pandolf chanced to say, "Her mantle
   laps
Over my lady's wrist too much," or
   "Paint
Must never hope to reproduce the faint
Half-flush that dies along her throat."
   Such stuff
Was courtesy, she thought, and cause
   enough   20
For calling up that spot of joy. She had
A heart—how shall I say?—too soon
   made glad,
Too easily impressed; she liked whate'er
She looked on, and her looks went every-
   where.
Sir, 'twas all one! My favor at her
   breast,   25
The dropping of the daylight in the West,
The bough of cherries some officious
   fool
Broke in the orchard for her, the white
   mule
She rode with round the terrace—all and
   each
Would draw from her alike the approving
   speech,   30
Or blush, at least. She thanked men—
   good! but thanked
Somehow—I know not how—as if she
   ranked
My gift of a nine-hundred-years-old name
With anybody's gift. Who'd stoop to
   blame
This sort of trifling? Even had you skill 35

In speech—which I have not—to make
   your will
Quite clear to such an one, and say, "Just
   this
Or that in you disgusts me; here you miss,
Or there exceed the mark"—and if she let
Herself be lessoned so, nor plainly set   40
Her wits to yours, forsooth, and made ex-
   cuse—
E'en then would be some stooping; and I
   choose
Never to stoop. Oh, sir, she smiled, no
   doubt,
Whene'er I passed her; but who passed
   without
Much the same smile? This grew; I gave
   commands;   45
Then all smiles stopped together. There
   she stands
As if alive. Will 't please you rise? We'll
   meet
The company below, then. I repeat,
The Count your master's known munifi-
   cence
Is ample warrant that no just pretense 50
Of mine for dowry will be disallowed;
Though his fair daughter's self, as I
   avowed
At starting, is my object. Nay, we'll go
Together down, sir. Notice Neptune,
   though,
Taming a sea-horse, thought a rarity,   55
Which Claus of Innsbruck cast in bronze
   for me!

56. *Claus of Innsbruck:* a fictitious sculptor.

SOLILOQUY OF THE SPANISH CLOISTER

Robert Browning
(1812–1889)

Gr-r-r—there go, my heart's abhorrence!
   Water your damned flower-pots, do!
If hate killed men, Brother Lawrence,
   God's blood, would not mine kill you!

What? your myrtle-bush wants trim-
    ming? 5
Oh, that rose has prior claims—
Needs its leaden vase filled brimming?
    Hell dry you up with its flames!

At the meal we sit together:
    Salve tibi! I must hear 10
Wise talk of the kind of weather,
    Sort of season, time of year:
Not a plenteous cork-crop: scarcely
    Dare we hope oak-galls, I doubt:
What's the Latin name for "parsley"? 15
    What's the Greek name for Swine's
    Snout?

Whew! We'll have our platter burnished,
    Laid with care on our own shelf!
With a fire-new spoon we're furnished,
    And a goblet for ourself, 20
Rinsed like something sacrificial
    Ere 'tis fit to touch our chaps—
Marked with L for our initial!
    He-he! There his lily snaps!

Saint, forsooth! While brown Dolores 25
    Squats outside the Convent bank
With Sanchicha, telling stories,
    Steeping tresses in the tank,
Blue-black, lustrous, thick like horsehairs,
    —Can't I see his dead eye glow, 30
Bright as 'twere a Barbary corsair's?
    (That is, if he'd let it show!)

When he finishes refection,
    Knife and fork he never lays
Cross-wise, to my recollection, 35
    As do I, in Jesu's praise.
I the Trinity illustrate,
    Drinking watered orange-pulp—
In three sips the Arian frustrate;

While he drains his at one gulp. 40

Oh, those melons! If he's able
    We're to have a feast! so nice!
One goes to the Abbot's table,
    All of us get each a slice.
How go on your flowers? None double? 45
    Not one fruit-sort can you spÿ?
Strange!—And I, too, at such trouble
    Keep them close-nipped on the sly!

There's great text in Galatians,
    Once you trip on it, entails 50
Twenty-nine distinct damnations,
    One sure, if another fails:
If I trip him just a-dying,
    Sure of heaven as sure can be,
Spin him round and send him flying 55
    Off to hell, a Manichee?

Or, my scrofulous French novel
    On gray paper with blunt type!
Simply glance at it, you grovel
    Hand and foot in Belial's gripe: 60
If I double down its pages
    At the woeful sixteenth print,
When he gathers his greengages,
    Ope a sieve and slip it in't?

Or, there's Satan!—one might venture 65
    Pledge one's soul to him, yet leave
Such a flaw in the indenture
    As he'd miss till, past retrieve,
Blasted lay that rose-acacia
    We're so proud of! *Hy, Zy, Hine* . . . 70
'St, there's Vespers! *Plena gratiâ,*
    Ave, Virgo! Gr-r-r—you swine!

---

10. *Salve tibi:* Hail to thee.
14. *oak-galls:* abnormal growth on oak leaves rich in tannic acid and used in the preparation of ink.
31. *Barbary corsair:* a pirate of the Barbary coast of northern Africa.
39. *Arian:* a follower of Arius, a heretic of the fourth century who rejected the doctrine of the Trinity.

49. *text in Galatians:* in Galatians 5: 19–21 there are many passages difficult to interpret in an orthodox way. The speaker hopes to damn Brother Lawrence by catching him in a heresy.
56. *Manichee:* a follower of the Manichean heresy, which included a belief in the inherent evil of matter.
60. *Belial:* the devil.
70. *Hy, Zy, Hine:* the sounds of the vesper bells.
71–72. *Plena . . . Virgo:* "Hail, Virgin, full of grace."

THE MILL

Edwin Arlington Robinson
(1869–1935)

The miller's wife had waited long,
  The tea was cold, the fire was dead;
And there might yet be nothing wrong
  In how he went and what he said:
"There are no millers any more,"   5
  Was all that she had heard him say;
And he had lingered at the door
  So long that it seemed yesterday.

Sick with a fear that had no form
  She knew that she was there at last; 10
And in the mill there was a warm
  And mealy fragrance of the past.
What else there was would only seem
  To say again what he had meant;
And what was hanging from a beam 15
  Would not have heeded where she went.

And if she thought it followed her,
  She may have reasoned in the dark
That one way of the few there were
  Would hide her and would leave no
    mark: 20
Black water, smooth above the weir
  Like starry velvet in the night,
Though ruffled once, would soon appear
  The same as ever to the sight.

SWEENEY AMONG THE NIGHTINGALES

T. S. Eliot
(1888–1965)

ὤμοι, πέπληγμαι καιρίαν πληγὴν ἔσω. *

Apeneck Sweeney spreads his knees
Letting his arms hang down to laugh,
The zebra stripes along his jaw
Swelling to maculate giraffe.

* "Alas, I am struck deep with a mortal blow."
4. *maculate:* spotted.

The circles of the stormy moon   5
Slide westward toward the River Plate,
Death and the Raven drift above
And Sweeney guards the hornèd gate.

Gloomy Orion and the Dog
Are veiled; and hushed the shrunken
  seas;   10
The person in the Spanish cape
Tries to sit on Sweeney's knees

Slips and pulls the table cloth
Overturns a coffee cup,
Reorganized upon the floor   15
She yawns and draws a stocking up;

The silent man in mocha brown
Sprawls at the window-sill and gapes;
The waiter brings in oranges
Bananas figs and hothouse grapes; 20

The silent vertebrate in brown
Contracts and concentrates, withdraws;
Rachel *née* Rabinovitch
Tears at the grapes with murderous paws;

She and the lady in the cape   25
Are suspect, thought to be in league;
Therefore the man with heavy eyes
Declines the gambit, shows fatigue,

Leaves the room and reappears
Outside the window, leaning in,   30
Branches of wistaria
Circumscribe a golden grin;

The host with someone indistinct
Converses at the door apart,
The nightingales are singing near   35
The Convent of the Sacred Heart,

And sang within the bloody wood
When Agamemnon cried aloud,

6. *River Plate:* estuary between Uruguay and Argentina.
8. *hornèd gate:* the gates in Hades through which true dreams passed.
9. *Orion and the Dog:* constellations.

And let their liquid siftings fall
To stain the stiff dishonored shroud.   40

■ ■ ■

LONDON

William Blake
(1757–1827)

I wander through each chartered street,
Near where the chartered Thames does
    flow,
And mark in every face I meet
Marks of weakness, marks of woe.

In every cry of every man.   5
In every infant's cry of fear,
In every voice, in every ban,
The mind-forged manacles I hear:

How the chimney-sweeper's cry
Every blackening church appalls,   10
And the hapless soldier's sigh
Runs in blood down palace walls.

But most, through midnight streets I hear
How the youthful harlot's curse
Blasts the new-born infant's tear,   15
And blights with plagues the marriage
    hearse.

THE BLOODY SIRE

Robinson Jeffers
(1887–1962)

It is not bad. Let them play.
Let the guns bark and the bombing-plane
Speak his prodigious blasphemies.
It is not bad, it is high time,
Stark violence is still the sire of all the
    world's values.   5

What but the wolf's tooth whittled so fine

The fleet limbs of the antelope?
What but fear winged the birds, and hun-
    ger
Jeweled with such eyes the great gos-
    hawk's head?
Violence has been the sire of all the   10
    world's values.

Who would remember Helen's face
Lacking the terrible halo of spears?
Who formed Christ but Herod and Caesar,
The cruel and bloody victories of Caesar?
Violence, the bloody sire of all the world's
    values.   15

Never weep, let them play,
Old violence is not too old to beget new
    values.

IF WE MUST DIE

Claude McKay
(1891–1948)

If we must die—let it not be like hogs
Hunted and penned in an inglorious spot,
While round us bark the mad and hungry
    dogs,
Making their mock at our accursed lot.
If we must die—oh, let us nobly die,   5
So that our precious blood may not be
    shed
In vain; then even the monsters we defy
Shall be constrained to honor us though
    dead!
Oh, Kinsmen! We must meet the common
    foe;
Though far outnumbered, let us show us   10
    brave,
And for their thousand blows deal one
    deathblow!
What though before us lies the open
    grave?
Like men we'll face the murderous, cow-
    ardly pack,

Pressed to the wall, dying, but fighting back!

▪ ▪ ▪

"ONCE MORE UNTO THE BREACH" *

William Shakespeare
(1564–1616)

(*Henry V*, Act III, Scene i, Lines 1–34)

Once more unto the breach, dear
    friends, once more;
Or close the wall up with our English
    dead!
In peace there's nothing so becomes a
    man
As modest stillness and humility:
But when the blast of war blows in our
    ears,   5
Then imitate the action of the tiger;
Stiffen the sinews, summon up the blood,
Disguise fair nature with hard-favoured
    rage;
Then lend the eye a terrible aspect;
Let it pry through the portage of the
    head   10
Like the brass cannon; let the brow
    o'erwhelm it,
As fearfully as doth a gallèd rock
O'erhang and jutty his confounded base,
Swilled with the wild and wasteful ocean.
Now set the teeth and stretch the nostril
    wide,   15
Hold hard the breath, and bend up every
    spirit
To his full height! On, on, you noblest
    English!

* In this scene, before an important battle in
France, Henry V exhorts his troops.
10. *portage:* portholes.
12. *gallèd:* worn.
13. *jutty:* jut over.
    confounded: ruined.
14. *Swilled:* washed.

Whose blood is fet from fathers of war-
    proof;
Fathers that, like so many Alexanders,
Have in these parts from morn till even
    fought,   20
And sheathed their swords for lack of
    argument.
Dishonour not your mothers; now attest
That those whom you called fathers did
    beget you.
Be copy now to men of grosser blood,
And teach them how to war. And you,
    good yeomen,   25
Whose limbs were made in England, show
    us here
The mettle of your pasture; let us swear
That you are worth your breeding; which
    I doubt not;
For there is none of you so mean and base
That hath not noble lustre in your eyes. 30
I see you stand like greyhounds in the
    slips,
Straining upon the start. The game's afoot:
Follow your spirit; and, upon this charge
Cry "God for Harry! England and Saint
    George!"

18. *fet:* fetched.
    of war proof: proved in battle.
27. *mettle . . . pasture:* the quality of your
breeding.
31. *slips:* leashes.

CHANNEL FIRING

Thomas Hardy
(1840–1928)

That night your great guns, unawares,
Shook all our coffins as we lay,
And broke the chancel window-squares,
We thought it was the Judgment-day

And sat upright. While drearisome   5
Arose the howl of wakened hounds:
The mouse let fall the altar-crumb,
The worms drew back into the mounds,

The glebe cow drooled. Till God called,
"No;
It's gunnery practice out at sea   10
Just as before you went below;
The world is as it used to be:

"All nations striving strong to make
Red war yet redder. Mad as hatters
They do no more for Christés sake   15
Than you who are helpless in such
   matters.

"That this is not the judgment-hour
For some of them's a blessed thing,
For if it were they'd have to scour
Hell's floor for so much threaten-
   ing . . .   20

"Ha, ha. It will be warmer when
I blow the trumpet (if indeed
I ever do; for you are men,
And rest eternal sorely need)."

So down we lay again. "I wonder,   25
Will the world ever saner be,"
Said one, "than when He sent us under
In our indifferent century!"

And many a skeleton shook his head.
"Instead of preaching forty year,"   30
My neighbor Parson Thirdly said,
"I wish I had stuck to pipes and beer."

Again the guns disturbed the hour,
Roaring their readiness to avenge,
As far inland as Stourton Tower,   35
And Camelot, and starlit Stonehenge.

   9. *glebe:* land owned by a parish church.

DO NOT WEEP MAIDEN, FOR WAR IS KIND

Stephen Crane
(1871–1900)

Do not weep, maiden, for war is kind.

Because your lover threw wild hands to-
   ward the sky
And the affrighted steed ran on alone,
Do not weep.
War is kind.   5

Hoarse, booming drums of the regiment,
Little souls who thirst for fight,
These men were born to drill and die.
The unexplained glory flies above them,
Great is the battle-god, great, and his
   kingdom—   10
A field where a thousand corpses lie.

Do not weep, babe, for war is kind.
Because your father tumbled in the yellow
   trenches,
Raged at his breast, gulped and died,
Do not weep.   15
War is kind.

Swift blazing flag of the regiment,
Eagle with crest of red and gold,
These men were born to drill and die.
Point for them the virtue of slaughter,   20
Make plain to them the excellence of kill-
   ing
And a field where a thousand corpses
   lie.

Mother whose heart hung humble as a
   button
On the bright splendid shroud of your son,
Do not weep.   25
War is kind.

STRANGE MEETING

Wilfred Owen
(1893–1918)

It seemed that out of the battle I escaped
Down some profound dull tunnel, long
   since scooped

Through granites which Titanic wars had
    groined.
Yet also there encumbered sleepers
    groaned,
Too fast in thought or death to be be-
    stirred.   5
Then, as I probed them, one sprang up,
    and stared
With piteous recognition in fixed eyes,
Lifting distressful hands as if to bless.
And by his smile, I knew that sullen
    hall;
With a thousand fears that vision's face
    was grained;   10
Yet no blood reached there from the
    upper ground,
And no guns thumped, or down the flues
    made moan.
"Strange friend," I said, "here is no cause
    to mourn."
"None," said the other, "save the undone
    years,
The hopelessness. Whatever hope is
    yours,   15
Was my life also, I went hunting wild
After the wildest beauty in the world,
Which lies not calm in eyes, or braided
    hair,
But mocks the steady running of the
    hour,
And if it grieves, grieves richlier than
    here.   20
For by my glee might many men have
    laughed,
And of my weeping something had been
    left,
Which must die now. I mean the truth
    untold,
The pity of war, the pity war distilled.
Now men will go content with what we
    spoiled.   25
Or, discontent, boil bloody, and be spilled.
They will be swift with swiftness of the
    tigress,
None will break ranks, though nations
    trek from progress.
Courage was mine, and I had mystery;
Wisdom was mine, and I had mastery; 30

To miss the march of this retreating world
Into vain citadels that are not walled.
Then, when much blood had clogged their
    chariot-wheels
I would go up and wash them from sweet
    wells,
Even with truths that lie too deep for
    taint.   35
I would have poured my spirit without
    stint
But not through wounds; not on the cess
    of war.
Foreheads of men have bled where no
    wounds were.
I am the enemy you killed, my friend.
I knew you in this dark; for so you
    frowned   40
Yesterday through me as you jabbed and
    killed.
I parried; but my hands were loath and
    cold.
Let us sleep now . . ."

37. *cess:* Irish term for luck, usually used in
the negative sense.

THE DEATH OF THE BALL TURRET GUNNER

Randall Jarrell
(1914–1965)

From my mother's sleep I fell into the
    State,
And I hunched in its belly till my wet fur
    froze.
Six miles from earth, loosed from its
    dream of life,
I woke to black flak and the nightmare
    fighters.
When I died they washed me out of the
    turret with a hose.   5

■ ■ ■

LEDA AND THE SWAN *

W. B. Yeats
(1865–1939)

A sudden blow: the great wings beating still
Above the staggering girl, her thighs caressed
By the dark webs, her nape caught in his bill,
He holds her helpless breast upon his breast.

How can those terrified vague fingers push   5
The feathered glory from her loosening thighs?
And how can body, laid in that white rush,
But feel the strange heart beating where it lies?

A shudder in the loins engenders there
The broken wall, the burning roof and tower   10
And Agamemnon dead.
                          Being so caught up,
So mastered by the brute blood of the air,
Did she put on his knowledge with his power
Before the indifferent beak could let her drop?   15

* In Greek mythology Zeus, in the form of a swan, coupled with Leda. Of this union were born Helen, whose beauty led to the Trojan war, and Clytemnestra, who killed her husband, Agamemnon, the leader of the Greeks in the Trojan war.

III

DEATH

FOREWORD

Shakespeare wrote it, but all the writers in this section would agree that "Death that fell sergeant is strict in his arrest." They would definitely disagree, however, in their attitudes towards that ultimate experience.

In each of the three stories, a character's confrontation with death reveals a profound truth about life. In Katherine Mansfield's story, it is a man's reactions to a death in the past which sum up his life in the present. In Katherine Anne Porter's story, it is the stream-of-consciousness presentation of a physical death in the present that reflects another kind of death in the past. In Eudora Welty's story, it is the traveling salesman's death, a death in the future, which provides a structure both for past memories and present experiences.

The poets in this section reveal their emotions more directly and more intensely than the essayists and writers of fiction. The first six, from Donne to Dylan Thomas, welcome death as "lovely and soothing" or transcend fear of it, maintaining that death should not be proud, for it has no dominion. Emily Dickinson, W. H. Auden, and Hart Crane form the second group. They are objective, describing rather than commenting on death. The remaining poets either resent "cruel Death" (Yeats) or fear "to lie in cold obstruction and to rot" (Shakespeare).

The attitudes of the essayists more obviously, though not dogmatically, derive from such traditional doctrines as Christianity, Stoicism, and humanism. Donne's sermons are based on his Christian heritage, while Robert Louis Stevenson's stance is firmly stoic. E. B. White and Ashley Montague are basically humanists. The former, however, leavens his concern for humanity with humor, and the latter utilizes the discipline of anthropology.

ESSAYS

MEDITATION XVII

John Donne
(1573–1631)

Perchance he for whom this bell [1] tolls may be so ill, as that he knows not it tolls for him; and perchance I may think myself so much better than I am, as that they who are about me, and see my state, may have caused it to toll for me, and I know not that. The church is catholic, universal, so are all her actions; all that she does belongs to all. When she baptizes a child, that action concerns me; for that child is thereby connected to that head which is my head too, and ingrafted into that body whereof I am a member. And when she buries a man, that action concerns me: all mankind is of one author, and is one volume; when one man dies, one chapter is not torn out of the book, but translated into a better language; and every chapter must be so translated; God employs several translators; some pieces are translated by age, some by sickness, some by war, some by justice; but God's hand is in every translation, and his hand shall bind up all our scattered leaves again for that library where every book shall lie open to one another. As therefore the bell that rings to a sermon calls not upon the preacher only, but upon the congrega-

tion to come, so this bell calls us all; but how much more me, who am brought so near the door by this sickness. There was a contention as far as a suit (in which both piety and dignity, religion and estimation, were mingled), which of the religious orders should ring to prayers first in the morning; and it was determined, that they should ring first that rose earliest. If we understand aright the dignity of this bell that tolls for our evening prayer, we would be glad to make it ours by rising early, in that application, that it might be ours as well as his, whose indeed it is. The bell doth toll for him that thinks it doth; and though it intermit again, yet from that minute that that occasion wrought upon him, he is united to God. Who casts not up his eye to the sun when it rises? but who takes off his eye from a comet when that breaks out? Who bends not his ear to any bell which upon any occasion rings? but who can remove it from that bell which is passing a piece of himself out of this world? No man is an island, entire of itself; every man is a piece of the continent, a part of the main. If a clod be washed away by the sea, Europe is the less, as well as if a promontory were, as well as if a manor of thy friend's or of thine own were: any man's death diminishes me, because I am involved in mankind, and therefore never send to know for whom the bell tolls; it tolls for thee. Neither can we call this a begging of misery, or a borrowing of

[1] The author, seriously ill, hears the tolling bells of a nearby church.

115

misery, as though we were not miserable enough of ourselves, but must fetch in more from the next house, in taking upon us the misery of our neighbors. Truly it were an excusable covetousness if we did, for affliction is a treasure, and scarce any man hath enough of it. No man hath affliction enough that is not matured and ripened by it, and made fit for God by that affliction. If a man carry treasure in bullion, or in a wedge of gold, and have none coined into current money, his treasure will not defray him as he travels. Tribulation is a treasure in the nature of it, but it is not current money in the use of it, except we get nearer and nearer our home, Heaven, by it. Another man may be sick too, and sick to death, and this affliction may lie in his bowels, as gold in a mine, and be of no use to him; but this bell, that tells of his affliction, digs out and applies that gold to me: if by this consideration of another's danger I take mine own into contemplation, and so secure myself, by making my recourse to my God, who is our only security.

AES TRIPLEX

Robert Louis Stevenson (1850–1894)

The changes wrought by death are in themselves so sharp and final, and so terrible and melancholy in their consequences, that the thing stands alone in man's experience and has no parallel upon earth. It outdoes all other accidents because it is the last of them. Sometimes it leaps suddenly upon its victims, like a Thug; sometimes it lays a regular siege and creeps upon their citadel during a score of years. And when the business is done, there is sore havoc made in other people's lives, and a pin knocked out by which many subsidiary friendships hung together. There are empty chairs, solitary walks, and single beds at night. Again, in taking away our friends, death does not take them away utterly, but leaves behind a mocking, tragical, and soon intolerable residue, which must be hurriedly concealed. Hence a whole chapter of sights and customs striking to the mind, from the pyramids of Egypt to the gibbets and dule trees of mediæval Europe. The poorest persons have a bit of pageant going towards the tomb; memorial stones are set up over the least memorable; and, in order to preserve some show of respect for what remains of our old loves and friendships, we must accompany it with much grimly ludicrous ceremonial, and the hired undertaker parades before the door. All this, and much more of the same sort, accompanied by the eloquence of poets, has gone a great way to put humanity in error; nay, in many philosophies the error has been embodied and laid down with every circumstance of logic; although in real life the bustle and swiftness, in leaving people little time to think, have not left them time enough to go dangerously wrong in practice.

As a matter of fact, although few things are spoken of with more fearful whisperings than this prospect of death, few have less influence on conduct under healthy circumstances. We have all heard of cities in South America built upon the side of fiery mountains, and how, even in this tremendous neighbourhood, the inhabitants are not a jot more impressed by the solemnity of mortal conditions than if they were delving gardens in the greenest corner of England. There are serenades and suppers and much gallantry among the myrtles overhead; and meanwhile the foundation shudders underfoot, the bowels of the mountain growl, and at any moment living ruin may leap sky-high into the moonlight, and tumble man and his merry-making in the dust. In the eyes of very young people, and very dull old ones; there is something indescribably reckless and desperate in such a picture. It seems not credible that respectable married people, with umbrellas, should find appetite for a bit of supper within quite a long distance of a fiery mountain; ordinary life begins to smell of high-handed debauch when it is carried on so close to a catastrophe; and even cheese and salad, it seems, could hardly be relished in such circumstances without something like a defiance of the Creator. It should be a place for nobody but hermits dwelling in prayer and maceration, or mere born-devils drowning care in a perpetual carouse.

And yet, when one comes to think upon it calmly, the situation of these South American citizens forms only a very pale figure for the state of ordinary mankind. This world itself, travelling blindly and swiftly in overcrowded space, among a million other worlds travelling blindly and swiftly in contrary direction, may very well come by a knock that would set it into explosion like a penny squib. And what, pathologically looked at, is the human body with all its organs, but a mere bagful of petards? The least of these is as dangerous to the whole economy as the ship's powder-magazine to the ship; and with every breath we breathe, and every meal we eat, we are putting one or more of them in peril. If we clung as devotedly as some philosophers pretend we do to the abstract idea of life, or were half as frightened as they make out we are for the subversive accident that ends it all, the trumpets might sound by the hour and no one would follow them into battle—the blue-peter might fly at the truck, but who would climb into a sea-going ship? Think (if these philosophers were right) with what a preparation of spirit we should affront the daily peril of the dinner-table: a deadlier spot than any battlefield in history, where the far greater proportion of our ancestors have miserably left their bones! What woman would ever be lured into marriage, so much more dangerous than the wildest sea? And what would it be to grow old? For, after a certain distance, every step we take in life we find the ice growing thinner below our feet, and all around us and behind us we see our contemporaries going through. By the time a man gets well into the seventies, his continued existence is a mere miracle; and when he lays his old bones in bed for the night, there is an overwhelming probability that he will never see the day. Do the old men mind it, as a matter of fact? Why, no. They were never merrier; they have their grog at night, and tell the raciest stories; they hear of the death of people about their own age, or even younger, not as if it was a grisly warning, but with a simple child-like pleasure at having outlived someone else; and when a draught might puff them out like a guttering candle, or a bit of a stumble shatter them like so much glass, their old hearts keep sound and unaffrighted, and they go on bubbling with laughter, through years of man's age compared to which the valley at Balaclava was as safe and peaceful as a village cricket-green on Sunday. It may fairly be questioned (if we look to the peril only) whether it was a much more daring feat for Curtius to plunge into the gulf, than for any old gentleman of ninety to doff his clothes and clamber into bed.

Indeed, it is a memorable subject for consideration, with what unconcern and gaiety mankind pricks on along the Valley of the Shadow of Death. The whole way is one wilderness of snares, and the end of it, for those who fear the last pinch, is irrevocable ruin. And yet we go spinning through it all, like a party for the Derby. Perhaps the reader remembers one of the humorous devices of the deified Caligula: how he encouraged a vast concourse of holiday-makers on to his bridge over

Baiæ bay; and when they were in the height of their enjoyment, turned loose the Prætorian guards among the company, and had them tossed into the sea. This is no bad miniature of the dealings of nature with the transitory race of man. Only, what a chequered picnic we have of it, even while it lasts! and into what great waters, not to be crossed by any swimmer, God's pale Prætorian throws us over in the end!

We live the time that a match flickers; we pop the cork of a gingerbeer bottle, and the earthquake swallows us on the instant. Is it not odd, is it not incongruous, is it not, in the highest sense of human speech, incredible, that we should think so highly of the gingerbeer, and regard so little the devouring earthquake? The love of Life and the fear of Death are two famous phrases that grow harder to understand the more we think about them. It is a well-known fact that an immense proportion of boat accidents woud never happen if people held the sheet in their hands instead of making it fast; and yet, unless it be some martinet of a professional mariner or some landsman with shattered nerves, every one of God's creatures makes it fast. A strange instance of man's unconcern and brazen boldness in the face of death!

We confound ourselves with metaphysical phrases, which we import into daily talk with noble inappropriateness. We have no idea of what death is, apart from its circumstances and some of its consequences to others; and although we have some experience of living, there is not a man on earth who has flown so high into abstraction as to have any practical guess at the meaning of the word *life*. All literature, from Job and Omar Khayyam to Thomas Carlyle or Walt Whitman, is but an attempt to look upon the human state with such largness of view as shall enable us to rise from the consideration of living to the Definition of life. And our sages gives us about the best satisfaction in their power when they say that it is a vapour, or a show, or made out of the same stuff with dreams. Philosophy, in its more rigid sense, has been at the same work for ages; and after a myriad bald heads have wagged over the problem, and piles of words have been heaped one upon another into dry and cloudy volumes without end, philosophy has the honour of laying before us, with modest pride, her contribution towards the subject: that life is a Permanent Possibility of Sensation. Truly a fine result! A man may very well love beef, or hunting, or a woman; but surely, surely, not a Permanent Possibility of Sensation! He may be afraid of a precipice, or a dentist, or a large enemy with a club, or even an undertaker's man; but not certainly of abstract death. We may trick with the word life in its dozen senses until we are weary of tricking; we may argue in terms of all the philosophies on earth, but one fact remains true throughout—that we do not love life, in the sense that we are greatly preoccupied about its conservation; that we do not, properly speaking, love life at all, but living. Into the views of the least careful there will enter some degree of providence; no man's eyes are fixed entirely on the passing hour; but although we have some anticipation of good health, good weather, wine, active employment, love, and self-approval, the sum of these anticipations does not amount to anything like a general view of life's possibilities and issues; nor are those who cherish them most vividly at all the most scrupulous of their personal safety. To be deeply interested in the accidents of our existence, to enjoy keenly the mixed texture of human experience, rather leads a man to disregard precautions and risk his neck against a straw. For surely the love of living is stronger in an Alpine climber roping over a peril, or a hunter riding merrily at a stiff fence, than in a creature who lives upon a diet and walks a measured distance in the interest of his constitution.

There is a great deal of very vile nonsense talked upon both sides of the matter: tearing divines reducing life to the dimensions of a mere funeral procession, so short as to be hardly decent; and melancholy unbelievers yearning for the tomb as if it were a world too far away. Both sides must feel a little ashamed of their performances now and again when they draw in their chairs to dinner. Indeed, a good meal and a bottle of wine is an answer to most standard works upon the question. When a man's heart warms to his viands, he forgets a great deal of sophistry, and soars into a rosy zone of contemplation. Death may be knocking at the door, like the Commander's statue; we have something else in hand, thank God, and let him knock. Passing bells are ringing all the world over. All the world over, and every hour, someone is parting company with all his aches and ecstasies. For us also the trap is laid. But we are so fond of life that we have no leisure to entertain the terror of death. It is a honeymoon with us all through, and none of the longest. Small blame to us if we give our whole hearts to this glowing bride of ours, to the appetites, to honour, to the hungry curiosity of the mind, to the pleasure of the eyes in nature, and the pride of our own nimble bodies.

We all of us appreciate the sensations; but as for caring about the Permanence of the Possibility, a man's head is generally very bald, and his senses very dull, before he comes to that. Whether we regard life as a lane leading to a dead wall —a mere bag's end, as the French say— or whether we think of it as a vestibule or gymnasium, where we wait our turn and prepare our faculties for some more noble destiny; whether we thunder in a pulpit, or pule in little atheistic poetry-books, about its vanity and brevity;

whether we look justly for years of health and vigour, or are about to mount into a bath-chair, as a step towards the hearse; in each and all of these views and situations there is but one conclusion possible: that a man should stop his ears against paralysing terror, and run the race that is set before him with a single mind. No one surely could have recoiled with more heartache and terror from the thought of death than our respected lexicographer; and yet we know how little it affected his conduct, how wisely and boldly he walked, and in what a fresh and lively vein he spoke of life. Already an old man, he ventured on his Highland tour; and his heart, bound with triple brass, did not recoil before twenty-seven individual cups of tea. As courage and intelligence are the two qualities best worth a good man's cultivation, so it is the first part of intelligence to recognise our precarious estate in life, and the first part of courage to be not at all abashed before the fact. A frank and somewhat headlong carriage, not looking too anxiously before, not dallying in maudlin regret over the past, stamps the man who is well armoured for this world.

And not only well armoured for himself, but a good friend and a good citizen to boot. We do not go to cowards for tender dealing; there is nothing so cruel as panic; the man who has least fear for his own carcass has most time to consider others. That eminent chemist who took his walks abroad in tin shoes, and subsisted wholly upon tepid milk, had all his work cut out for him in considerable dealings with his own digestion. So soon as prudence has begun to grow up in the brain, like a dismal fungus, it finds its first expression in a paralysis of generous acts. The victim begins to shrink spiritually; he develops a fancy for parlours with a regulated temperature, and takes his morality on the principle of tin shoes and tepid milk. The care of one important body or soul becomes so engrossing, that all the noises of the outer world begin to come thin and faint into the parlour with the regulated temperature; and the tin shoes go equably forward over blood and rain. To be overwise is to ossify; and the scruple-monger ends by standing stockstill. Now the man who has his heart on his sleeve, and a good whirling weathercock of a brain, who reckons his life as a thing to be dashingly used and cheerfully hazarded, makes a very different acquaintance of the world, keeps all his pulses going true and fast, and gathers impetus as he runs, until, if he be running towards anything better than wildfire, he may shoot up and become a constellation in the end. Lord look after his health, Lord have a care for his soul, says he; and he has at the key of the position, and swashes through incongruity and peril towards his aim. Death is on all sides of him with pointed batteries, as he is on all sides of all of us; unfortunate surprises gird him round; mimouthed friends and relations hold up their hands in quite a little elegiacal synod about his path: and what cares he for all this? Being a true lover of living, a fellow with something pushing and spontaneous in his inside, he must, like any other soldier, in any other stirring, deadly warfare, push on at his best pace until he touch the goal. "A peerage or Westminster Abbey!" cried Nelson in his bright, boyish, heroic manner. These are great incentives; not for any of these, but for the plain satisfaction of living, of being about their business in some sort or other, do the brave, serviceable men of every nation tread down the nettle danger, and pass flyingly over all the stumbling-blocks of prudence. Think of the heroism of Johnson, think of that superb indifference to mortal limitation that set him upon his dictionary, and carried him through triumphantly until the end! Who, if he were wisely considerate of things at large, would ever embark upon any work much more considerable than a halfpenny postcard? Who would project a serial novel, after Thackeray and Dickens had each fallen in mid-course? Who would find heart enough to begin to live, if he dallied with the consideration of death?

And, after all, what sorry and pitiful quibbling all this is! To forego all the issues of living in a parlour with a regulated temperature—as if that were not to die a hundred times over, and for ten years at a stretch! As if it were not to die in one's own lifetime, and without even the sad immunities of death! As if it were not to die, and yet be the patient spectators of our own pitiable change! The Permanent Possibility is preserved, but the sensations carefully held at arm's length, as if one kept a photographic plate in a dark chamber. It is better to lose health like a spendthrift than to waste it like a miser. It is better to live and be done with it than to die daily in the sick-room. By all means begin your folio; even if the doctor does not give you a year, even if he hesitates about a month, make one brave push and see what can be accomplished in a week. It is not only in finished undertakings that we ought to honour useful labour. A spirit goes out of the man who means execution, which outlives the most untimely ending. All who have meant good work with their whole hearts have done good work, although they may die before they have the time to sign it. Every heart that has beat strong and cheerfully has left a hopeful impulse behind it in the world, and bettered the tradition of mankind. And even if death catch people, like an open pitfall, and in mid-career, laying out vast projects, and planning monstrous foundations, flushed with hope, and their mouths full of boastful language, they should be at once tripped up and silenced: is there not something brave and spirited in such a termination? and does not life go down with a better grace, foaming in full body over a precipice, than miserably straggling to an end in sandy deltas? When the Greeks made their fine saying that those whom the gods love die young, I cannot help believing they had this sort of death also in their eye. For surely, at whatever age it overtake the man, this is to die young. Death has not been suffered to take so much as an illusion from his heart. In the hot-fit of life, a-tiptoe on the highest point of being, he passes at a bound on to the other side. The noise of the mallet and chisel is scarcely quenched, the trumpets are hardly done blowing, when, trailing with him clouds of glory, this happy-starred, full-blooded spirit shoots into the spiritual land.

DEATH OF A PIG

E. B. White
(1899–   )

I spent several days and nights in mid-September with an ailing pig, and I feel driven to account for this stretch of time, more particularly since the pig died at last, and I lived, and things might easily have gone the other way round and none left to do the accounting. Even now, so close to the event, I cannot recall the hours sharply and am not ready to say whether death came on the third night or the fourth night. This uncertainty afflicts me with a sense of personal deterioration; if I were in decent health I would know how many nights I had sat up with a pig.

The scheme of buying a spring pig in blossomtime, feeding it through summer and fall, and butchering it when the solid cold weather arrives is a familiar scheme to me and follows an antique pattern. It is a tragedy enacted on most farms with perfect fidelity to the original script. The murder, being premeditated, is in the first degree but is quick and skillful, and the smoked bacon and ham provide a ceremonial ending whose fitness is seldom questioned.

Once in a while something slips — one of the actors goes up in his lines and the whole performance stumbles and halts. My pig simply failed to show up for a meal. The alarm spread rapidly. The classic outline of the tragedy was lost. I found myself cast suddenly in the role of pig's friend and physician—a farcical character with an enema bag for a prop. I had a presentiment, the very first afternoon, that the play would never regain its balance and that my sympathies were now wholly with the pig. This was slapstick—the sort of dramatic treatment that instantly appealed to my old dachshund, Fred, who joined the vigil, held the bag, and, when all was over, presided at the interment. When we slid the body into the grave, we both were shaken to the core. The loss we felt was not the loss of ham but the loss of pig. He had evidently become precious to me, not that he represented a distant nourishment in a hungry time, but that he had suffered in a suffering world. But I'm running ahead of my story and shall have to go back.

My pigpen is at the bottom of an old orchard below the house. The pigs I have raised have lived in a faded building that once was an icehouse. There is a pleasant yard to move about in, shaded by an apple tree that overhangs the low rail fence. A pig couldn't ask for anything better—or none has, at any rate. The sawdust in the icehouse makes a comfortable bottom in which to root, and a warm bed. This sawdust, however, came under suspicion when the pig took sick. One of my neighbors said he thought the pig would have done better on new ground—the same principle that applies in planting potatoes. He said there might be something unhealthy about that sawdust, that he never thought well of sawdust.

It was about four o'clock in the afternoon when I first noticed that there was something wrong with the pig. He failed to appear at the trough for his supper, and when a pig (or a child) refuses supper a chill wave of fear runs through any household, or ice-household. After examining my pig, who was stretched out in the sawdust inside the building, I went to the phone and cranked it four times. Mr. Dameron answered. "What's good for a sick pig?" I asked. (There is never any identification needed on a country phone; the person on the other end knows who is talking by the sound of the voice and by the character of the question.)

"I don't know, I never had a sick pig," said Mr. Dameron, "but I can find out quick enough. You hang up and I'll call Henry."

Mr. Dameron was back on the line again in five minutes. "Henry says roll him over on his back and give him two ounces of castor oil or sweet oil, and if that doesn't do the trick give him an injection of soapy water. He says he's almost sure the pig's plugged up, and even if he's wrong, it can't do any harm."

I thanked Mr. Dameron. I didn't go right down to the pig, though. I sank into a chair and sat still for a few minutes to think about my troubles, and then I got up and went to the barn, catching up on some odds and ends that needed tending to. Unconsciously I held off, for an hour, the deed by which I would officially recognize the collapse of the performance of raising a pig; I wanted no interruption in the regularity of feeding, the steadiness of growth, the even succession of days. I wanted no interruption, wanted no oil, no deviation. I just wanted to keep on raising a pig, full meal after full meal, spring into summer into fall. I didn't even know whether there were two ounces of castor oil on the place.

Shortly after five o'clock I remembered that we had been invited out to dinner that night and realized that if I were to dose a pig there was no time to lose. The dinner date seemed a familiar conflict: I move in a desultory society and often a week or two will roll by without my going to anybody's house to dinner or anyone's coming to mine, but when an occasion does arise, and I am summoned, something usually turns up (an hour or two in advance) to make all human intercourse seem vastly inappropriate. I have come to believe that there is in hostesses a special power of divination, and that they deliberately arrange dinners to coincide with pig failure or some other sort of failure. At any rate, it was after five o'clock and I knew I could put off no longer the evil hour.

When my son and I arrived at the pigyard, armed with a small bottle of castor oil and a length of clothesline, the pig had emerged from his house and was standing in the middle of his yard, listlessly. He gave us a slim greeting. I could see that he felt uncomfortable and uncertain. I had brought the clothesline thinking I'd have to tie him (the pig weighed more than a hundred pounds), but we never used it. My son reached down, grabbed both front legs, upset him quickly, and when he opened his mouth to scream I turned the oil into his throat —a pink, corrugated area I had never seen before. I had just time to read the label while the neck of the bottle was in his mouth. It said Puretest. The screams, slightly muffled by oil, were pitched in the hysterically high range of pig-sound, as though torture were being carried out, but they didn't last long: it was all over rather suddenly, and, his legs released, the pig righted himself.

In the upset position the corners of his mouth had been turned down, giving him a frowning expression. Back on his feet again, he regained the set smile that a pig wears even in sickness. He stood his ground, sucking slightly at the residue of oil; a few drops leaked out of his lips while his wicked eyes, shaded by their coy little lashes, turned on me in disgust and hatred. I scratched him gently with oily fingers and he remained quiet, as though trying to recall the satisfaction of being scratched when in health, and seeming to rehearse in his mind the indignity to which he had just been subjected. I noticed, as I stood there, four or five small dark spots on his back near the tail end, reddish brown in color, each about the size of a housefly. I could not make out what they were. They did not look troublesome but at the same time they did not look like mere surface bruises of chafe marks. Rather they seemed blemishes of internal origin. His stiff white bristles almost completely hid them and I had to part the bristles with my fingers to get a good look.

Several hours later, a few minutes before midnight, having dined well and at someone else's expense, I returned to the pighouse with a flashlight. The patient was asleep. Kneeling, I felt his ears (as you might put your hand on the forehead of a child) and they seemed cool, and then with the light made a careful examination of the yard and the house for sign that the oil had worked. I found none and went to bed.

We had been having an unseasonable spell of weather—hot, close days, with the fog shutting in every night, scaling for a few hours in midday, then creeping back again at dark, drifting in first over the trees on the point, then suddenly blowing across the fields, blotting out the world and taking possession of houses, men, and animals. Everyone kept hoping for a break, but the break failed to come. Next day was another hot one. I visited the pig before breakfast and tried to tempt him with a little milk in his trough. He just stared at it, while I made a sucking sound through my teeth to remind him of past pleasures of the feast. With very small, timid pigs, weanlings, this ruse is often quite successful and will encourage them to eat; but with a large, sick pig the ruse is senseless and the sound I made must have made him feel, if anything, more miserable. He not only did not crave food, he felt a positive revulsion to it. I found a place under the apple tree where he had vomited in the night.

At this point, although a depression had settled over me, I didn't suppose that I was going to lose my pig. From the lustiness of a healthy pig a man derives a feeling of personal lustiness; the stuff that goes into the trough and is received with such enthusiasm is an earnest of some later feast of his own, and when this suddenly comes to an end and the food lies stale and untouched, souring in the sun, the pig's imbalance becomes the man's, vicariously, and life seems insecure, displaced, transitory.

As my own spirits declined, along with the pig's, the spirits of my vile old dachshund rose. The frequency of our trips down the footpath through the orchard to the pigyard delighted him, although he suffers greatly from arthritis, moves with difficulty, and would be bedridden if he could find anyone willing to serve him meals on a tray.

He never missed a chance to visit the pig with me, and he made many professional calls on his own. You could see him down there at all hours, his white face parting the grass along the fence as he wobbled and stumbled about, his stethoscope dangling—a happy quack, writing his villainous prescriptions and grinning his corrosive grin. When the enema bag appeared, and the bucket of warm suds, his happiness was complete, and he managed to squeeze his enormous body between the two lowest rails of the yard and then assumed full charge of the irrigation. Once, when I lowered the bag to check the flow, he reached in and hurriedly drank a few mouthfuls of the suds to test their potency. I have noticed that Fred will feverishly consume any substance that is associated with trouble—the bitter flavor is to his liking. When the bag was above reach, he concentrated on the pig and was everywhere at once, a tower of strength and inconvenience. The pig, curiously enough, stood rather quietly through this colonic carnival, and the enema, though ineffective, was not as difficult as I had anticipated.

I discovered, though, that once having given a pig an enema there is no turning back, no chance of resuming one of life's more stereotyped roles. The pig's lot and mine were inextricably bound now, as though the rubber tube were the silver cord. From then until the time of his death I held the pig steadily in the bowl of my mind; the task of trying to deliver him from his misery became a strong obsession. His suffering soon became the embodiment of all earthly wretchedness. Along toward the end of the afternoon, defeated in physicking, I phoned the veterinary twenty miles away and placed the case formally in his hands. He was full of questions, and when I casually mentioned the dark spots on the pig's back, his voice changed its tone.

"I don't want to scare you," he said, "but when there are spots, erysipelas has to be considered."

Together we considered erysipelas, with frequent interruptions from the telephone operator, who wasn't sure the connection had been established.

"If a pig has erysipelas can he give it to a person?" I asked.

"Yes, he can," replied the vet.

"Have they answered?" asked the operator.

"Yes, they have," I said. Then I addressed the vet again. "You better come over here and examine this pig right away."

"I can't come myself," said the vet, "but McFarland can come this evening if that's all right. Mac knows more about pigs than I do anyway. You needn't worry too much about the spots. To indicate erysipelas they would have to be deep hemorrhagic infarcts."

"Deep hemorrhagic what?" I asked.

"Infarcts," said the vet.

"Have they answered?" asked the operator.

"Well," I said, "I don't know what you'd call these spots, except they're about the size of a housefly. If the pig has erysipelas I guess I have it, too, by this time, because we've been very close lately."

"McFarland will be over," said the vet.

I hung up. My throat felt dry and I went to the cupboard and got a bottle of whiskey. Deep hemorrhagic infarcts—the phrase began fastening its hooks in my head. I had assumed that there could be nothing much wrong with a pig during the months it was being groomed for murder; my confidence in the essential health and endurance of pigs had been strong and deep, particularly in the health of pigs that belonged to me and that were part of my proud scheme. The awakening had been violent, and I minded it all the more because I knew that what could be true of my pig could be true also of the rest of my tidy world. I tried to put this distasteful idea from me, but it kept recurring. I took a short drink of the whiskey and then, although I wanted to go down to the yard and look for fresh signs, I was scared to. I was certain I had erysipelas.

It was long after dark and the supper dishes had been put away when a car drove in and McFarland got out. He had a girl with him. I could just make her out in the darkness—she seemed young and pretty. "This is Miss Owen," he said. "We've been having a picnic supper on the shore, that's why I'm late."

McFarland stood in the driveway and stripped off his jacket, then his shirt. His stocky arms and capable hands showed up in my flashlight's gleam as I helped him find his coverall and get zipped up. The rear seat of his car contained an astonishing amount of paraphernalia, which he soon overhauled, selecting a chain, a syringe, a bottle of oil, a rubber tube, and some other things I couldn't identify. Miss Owen said she'd go along with us and see the pig. I led the way down the warm slope of the orchard, my light picking out the path for them, and we all three climbed the fence, entered the pighouse, and squatted by the pig while McFarland took a rectal reading. My flashlight picked up the glitter of an engagement ring on the girl's hand.

"No elevation," said McFarland, twisting the thermometer in the light. "You needn't worry about erysipelas." He ran his hand slowly over the pig's stomach and at one point the pig cried out in pain. "Poor piggledy-wiggledy!" said Miss Owen.

The treatment I had been giving the pig for two days was then repeated, somewhat more expertly, by the doctor, Miss Owen and I handing him things as he needed them—holding the chain that he had looped around the pig's upper jaw, holding the syringe, holding the bottle stopper, the end of the tube, all of us working in darkness and in comfort, working with the instinctive teamwork induced by emergency conditions, the pig unprotesting, the house shadowy, protecting, intimate. I went to bed tired but with a feeling of relief that I had turned over part of the responsibility of the case to a licensed doctor. I was beginning to think, though, that the pig was not going to live.

He died twenty-four hours later, or it might have been forty-eight—there is a blur in time here, and I may have lost or picked up a day in the telling and the pig one in the dying. At intervals during the last day I took cool fresh water down to him, and at such times as he found the strength to get to his feet he would stand with head in the pail and snuffle his snout around. He drank a few sips but no more; yet it seemed to comfort him to dip his nose in water and bobble it about, sucking in and blowing out through his teeth. Much of the time, now, he lay indoors half buried in sawdust. Once, near the last, while I was attending him I saw him try to make a bed for himself but he lacked the strength, and when he set his snout into the dust he was unable to plow even the little furrow he needed to lie down in.

He came out of the house to die. When I went down, before going to bed, he lay stretched in the yard a few feet from the door. I knelt, saw that he was dead, and left him there: his face had a mild look, expressive neither of deep peace nor of deep suffering, although I think he had suffered a good deal. I went back up to the house and to bed, and cried internally —deep hemorrhagic intears. I didn't wake till nearly eight the next morning, and when I looked out the open window the grave was already being dug, down beyond the dump under a wild apple. I could hear the spade strike against the small rocks that blocked the way. Never send to know for whom the grave is dug, I said to myself, it's dug for thee. Fred, I well knew, was supervising the work of digging, so I ate breakfast slowly.

It was a Saturday morning. The thicket in which I found the gravediggers at work was dark and warm, the sky overcast. Here, among alders and young hackmatacks, at the foot of the apple tree, Lennie had dug a beautiful hole, five feet long, three feet wide, three feet deep. He was standing in it, removing the last spadefuls of earth while Fred patrolled the brink in simple but impressive circles, disturbing the loose earth of the mound so that it trickled back in. There had been no rain in weeks and the soil, even three feet down, was dry and powdery. As I stood and stared, an enormous earthworm which had been partially exposed by the spade at the bottom dug itself deeper and made a slow withdrawal, seeking even remoter moistures at even lonelier depths. And just as Lennie stepped out and rested his spade against the tree and lit a cigarette, a small green apple separated itself from a branch overhead and fell into the hole. Everything about this last scene seemed overwritten—the dismal sky, the shabby woods, the imminence of rain, the worm (legendary bedfellow of the dead), the apple (conventional garnish of a pig).

But even so, there was a directness and dispatch about animal burial, I thought, that made it a more decent affair than human burial: there was no stopover in the undertaker's foul parlor, no wreath nor spray; and when we hitched a line to the pig's hind legs and dragged him swiftly from his yard, throwing our weight into the harness and leaving a wake of crushed grass and smoothed rubble over the dump, ours was a businesslike procession, with Fred, the dishonorable pallbearer, staggering along in the rear, his perverse bereavement showing in every seam in his face; and the post mortem performed handily and swiftly right at the edge of the grave, so that the inwards that had caused the pig's death preceded him into the ground and he lay at last resting squarely on the cause of his own undoing.

I threw in the first shovelful, and then we worked rapidly and without talk, until the job was complete. I picked up the rope, made it fast to Fred's collar (he is a notorious ghoul), and we all three filed back up the path to the house, Fred bringing up the rear and holding back every inch of the way, feigning unusual stiffness. I noticed that although he weighed far less than the pig, he was

harder to drag, being possessed of the vital spark.

The news of the death of my pig travelled fast and far, and I received many expressions of sympathy from friends and neighbors, for no one took the event lightly and the premature expiration of a pig is, I soon discovered, a departure which the community marks solemnly on its calendar, a sorrow in which it feels fully involved. I have written this account in penitence and in grief, as a man who failed to raise his pig, and to explain my deviation from the classic course of so many raised pigs. The grave in the woods is unmarked, but Fred can direct the mourner to it unerringly and with immense good will, and I know he and I shall often revisit it, singly and together, in seasons of reflection and despair, on flagless memorial days of our own choosing.

THE BELIEF IN IMMORTALITY IN LITERATE SOCIETIES * [1]

M. F. Ashley Montagu (1905–   )

Professor Lyman Bryson has recently remarked that scientists willingly give over any wish to speak of souls.[2] But in so far as a scientist may venture to define it, he considers the soul to be the conative aspect of the mind, the same thing as the will. As a scientist I can see no other meaning for the soul than the self, as

* This chapter appeared in *Immortality* (1955).
[1] See M. F. Ashley Montagu, *An Introduction to Physical Anthropology*, 2nd edition, C. C. Thomas, Springfield, Illinois, 1951, pp. 430–432.
[2] Lyman Bryson, *Science and Freedom*, Columbia University Press, 1947, p. 99.

Professor Bryson also realizes.[3] The theologian's conception of the soul is a very different thing. Most writers on the subject are content to say that neither the existence of the soul nor the reality of immortality can be disproved. For the matter of that, nor can the statement that the back of the moon is made of green cheese. As Charles S. Peirce remarked, most, if not all, reasoning on vitally important topics consists in finding reasons for what the heart desires. In any discussion of what contemporary men believe concerning the soul we must be careful not to confuse cordal with cerebral thinking.

With respect to immortality many men in the western world today are in the position of the churchwarden who, when buttonholed by F. W. H. Myers (one of the founders of the Society for Psychical Research) and asked what he thought would happen to him after death, after vainly trying to evade the question, burst out with "Well, I suppose I shall enter into everlasting bliss, but I do wish you would not talk about such depressing subjects."

Thinking about the future life entails thinking about death, and *that* is distinctly an unpleasant subject, any thought of which is better repressed. The late Professor F. C. S. Schiller has suggested that this explains why men have not seriously encouraged inquiries into the problem of the future life. For of the "metaphysical trinity," God, freedom of the will, and immortality, the latter is the only one that is susceptible of scientific examination, and upon which science may have something very vital to say. Professor Herbert Dingle puts the matter thus: "Can common experiences, of a kind similar to those which we used to regard as characteristic of Mr. A, come to us after the death of Mr. A? Such experiences do not normally come, but that may be because we have not established the right conditions. Psychical research, from this point of view, may therefore be a perfectly legitimate scientific procedure, although it does not follow that it is always conducted on scientific lines." And Professor Dingle adds, "Certainly, since its findings are estimated so variously by scientific men, it cannot be said that Science has at present any definite pronouncement to make on the subject. In any case, it should be noticed that while this kind of research may conceivably establish the reality of survival, it can never give a definitive answer in the negative." [4]

In spite of all claims to the contrary there has not been a single authenticated case of communication between the dead and the living.[5] If mind and body are one it is difficult to see how there could be such communication. As J. B. S. Haldane says, "No sort of atom is peculiar to life, nor is there any evidence that anything leaves the body at death. A certain pattern of chemical events comes to an end, but there is no suggestion that vital spirits escape. . . . There is nothing to suggest that any peculiar form of energy characterizes life. The balance sheet between the energy available from food and oxygen and that put out in various ways is remarkably accurate. This is notably so in man, where it might have been expected that energy would have been converted into metaphysical forms (e.g., will or thought) or derived from metaphysical sources." [6]

[3] *Ibid.*, p. 106.

[4] Herbert Dingle, *Science and Human Experience*, Macmillan, New York, 1932, p. 133.

[5] For a discussion of the whole subject from the standpoint of the student of psychical research, see G. N. M. Tyrrel's interesting book, *The Personality of Man*, Penguin Books, West Drayton, Middlesex, 1948.

[6] J. B. S. Haldane, "Interaction of Physics, Chemistry, and Biology," in *Philosophy for the Future*, Macmillan, New York, 1949, pp. 204, 205.

It has been argued by some that the proof of the existence of life after death does not depend upon the demonstration that those who have died can communicate with the living. That may be so, but if there is any other way of demonstrating the truth of this kind of immortality, I, at least, do not know of it.

In an official Catholic source, *A Catholic Dictionary,* I find immortality defined as "that attribute in virtue of which a being is free from death. A being is incorruptible if it does not contain within itself a principle of dissolution; it is indestructible if it can resist every external power tending to destroy or annihilate it. If the indestructible and incorruptible being is endowed with life it is called immortal. Annihilation is always possible to God by the mere withdrawal of his conserving act." [7]

Declarative statements prove nothing, but in this definition there are some demonstrative statements, and with these a scientist can deal. A scientist can show that every living thing contains within itself a principle of dissolution, and this is the principle of entropy. The principle of entropy states that energy is constantly becoming unavailable for use, and that when this principle reaches its limit within the organism, the organism simply ceases to function for want of energy, because it has lost the energy necessary to keep it functioning. The organism is destroyed because it is unable to resist the external powers tending to destroy it.

In the same *Dictionary* the immortality of the soul is "proven" by a number of declarative statements and some arguments. It would take more time than I have at my disposal to examine all these arguments here; most of them seem to me assumptive and circular, and prove nothing more than their author's desire to prove the immortality of the soul. But apart from purely theological arguments the author of the article goes on to say "Other arguments to establish that the soul does not perish at death can be drawn (1) from the desire of perfect happiness which is unattainable in this life, and (2) from the universal judgement of mankind in the belief of a future life, a judgement which cannot lead man into error since it springs from man's rational nature." [8]

"From the desire of perfect happiness which is unattainable in this life," as I believe we have already seen, the belief in the immortality of the soul may grow, but it would be difficult to see that such a desire proves anything other than a desire for "perfect happiness" which the desirer may wish to believe is attainable in some other life. Happiness is a condition or state which is highly valued by human beings; and if hopes and dreams of future happiness can compensate for the lack of it in the present, the present may become more bearable, and we may the more readily endure what we are called upon to suffer.

The miserable have no other medicine
But only hope.

But all this is in the realm of the psychodynamics of belief, and has nothing whatever to do with the proof of the existence either of a soul or its immortality. I have already indicated what the nature of the desire for immortality may be based on. The desire for or the belief in immortality is not a basic need, and the fact is that there are numerous persons who have never believed in or desired immortality. The belief in immortality, as we shall see, is a socially emergent need, a derived need, at most.

As for the statement that a proof of

---

[7] *A Catholic Dictionary* (edited by Donald Attwater), Macmillan, New York, 1941, p. 261.

[8] *Ibid.,* p. 261.

the fact that the soul does not perish is to be found in "the universal judgement of mankind in the belief of a future life," it may be said that if truth is to be decided by a show of hands, we leave the realm of science and enter that of the voting booth. The strength with which human beings cling to their most cherished beliefs is usually in inverse proportion to the demonstrable facts upon which they are based. Judgment originally meant critical evaluation. The universal judgment of mankind concerning immortality has hardly been that, at least no anthropologist could agree that it has been anything resembling what a scientist understands by critical evaluation. But, says the writer in the *Dictionary,* this is "a judgement that cannot lead man into error since it springs from man's rational nature."

I am not going to be so naive as to suppose that I understand what the writer means by "rational nature," but as a student of human nature I find that man's rational nature is wholly acquired. The potentialities he possesses for developing as a rational creature remain quite undeveloped in the absence of the necessary stimulation. That stimulation is the social interaction with other human beings in a particular cultural context, and it is according to the training which the growing human being receives that his rational nature will develop. That training may be such as to render him quite unfitted for the making of any critical evaluation on any issue of a fundamental nature. What the training of most human beings does for them is to enable them to make evaluations of whatever they are called upon to evaluate in terms of the training they have received. The training in the scientific evaluation of evidence seems to me the only one which fits man for the making of judgments which are as nearly as possible dispassionate and objective. A very small minority of mankind has

ever received such training, and it is a notable fact that it is among this class of men that there has appeared the largest proportion of agnostics and disbelievers with respect to immortality. The rest of mankind, it seems to me, for the most part has not been trained to think soundly. Man's mind is cut according to the cloth that is available, custom made, tailored according to the requirements of the cultural milieu into which he has been born, his rational nature is just that. Man's emotional or rational needs call into being abstractions which have no existence outside his own being, he calls those abstraction into being according to the kingdom that is within him, and the kingdom that is within him is determined by the cultural organization of his innate potentialities, and not by any inherited "essence . . . as a principle of action," which the *Catholic Dictionary* tells me that nature is.

It is to be feared that the theological interpretation of the nature of the immortality of the soul and the proof of its existence are, from the viewpoint of the scientist, quite demonstrably unsound. It is here that I differ with some scientists and philosophers who have maintained that the scientist can have nothing to say about the theological conception of immortality. I think that not only can the scientist have something to say upon that subject, but that he should also say it. "In the long run," says Freud, "nothing can withstand reason and experience. . . . We believe that it is possible for scientific work to discover something about the reality of the world through which we can increase our power and according to which we can regulate our life. . . . Science is no illusion. . . . It would be an illusion to suppose that we could get anywhere else what it cannot give us." [9]

[9] Sigmund Freud, *The Future of an Illusion,* Hogarth Press, London, 1928, pp. 94, 95, 98.

With Freud I believe it is possible to teach men how to live more effectively, and more efficiently than any religion has yet done. Humanity usually reaches the truth through a long succession of errors, fruitful errors. Has the belief in immortality been a valuable fiction, a fruitful error? We shall attempt an answer to this question in our next lecture.

With Ernest Renan (1823–1892) I believe that "the aim of humanity is not repose; it is intellectual and moral perfection. How can people talk of repose, I should like to know, when they have the infinite to traverse and the perfect to reach? Humanity will only repose when it has reached the perfect. It would be too strange if a few profane persons could, from mercenary motives or personal interest, arrest the progress of the mind, the true religious progress. The most dangerous state of humanity would be that in which the majority, finding itself quite at ease and not wishing to be disturbed, should retain its repose at the cost of thought and of an oppressed minority." [10]

"The end of humanity, and therefore the aim which political conduct should keep before it, is to realize the highest human culture possible, that is to say the most perfect religion, by science, philosophy, art and morality: in a word by all the means of attaining the ideal which are in the nature of man." [11]

"To realize the highest human culture possible, that is to say the most perfect religion," in freedom to pursue his inquiries is a desirable end that man may yet achieve; if and when he does so he will not have dispensed with the belief in immortality, but transformed it into a nobler form than men have yet given it. A form from which the supernatural and the supernormal elements shall have been removed, and the maintenance of the principle of the eternal goodness of man installed in its stead.

I do not forsee an age when man shall be without religion. I do forsee a time when men will bring the gods down from the heavens and naturalize them among themselves on earth, *not* as supernatural personifications of their own projections, but as the symbols of those noble ideals which make for the perfection of human character and personality; the attainable ideals which lead to mental and moral health, inner harmony, creativeness, and peace and goodwill. A state in which it will be unnecessary to say that a man's grasp should be beyond his reach or what's a heaven for; in which a man's grasp will be educated to function within his reach, and heaven will be on earth, and men will endure:

> Their going hence, even as their
> coming hither:
> Ripeness is all.

[10] Ernest Renan, *The Future of Science,* Chapman and Hall, London, 1891, p. 403.
[11] *Ibid.,* p. 342.

SHORT STORIES

THE FLY

Katherine Mansfield
(1888–1923)

"Y'are very snug in here," piped old Mr. Woodifield, and he peered out of the great, green leather armchair by his friend the boss's desk as a baby peers out of its pram. His talk was over; it was time for him to be off. But he did not want to go. Since he had retired, since his . . . stroke, the wife and girls kept him boxed up in the house every day of the week except Tuesday. On Tuesday he was dressed up and brushed and allowed to cut back to the City for the day. Though what he did there the wife and girls couldn't imagine. Made a nuisance of himself to his friends, they supposed. . . . Well, perhaps so. All the same, we cling to our last pleasures as the tree clings to its last leaves. So there sat old Woodifield, smoking a cigar and staring almost greedily at the boss, who rolled in his office chair, stout, rosy, five years older than he, and still going strong, still at the helm. It did one good to see him.

Wistfully, admiringly, the old voice added, "It's snug in here, upon my word!"

"Yes, it's comfortable enough," agreed the boss, and he flipped the *Financial Times* with a paperknife. As a matter of fact he was proud of his room; he liked to have it admired, especially by old Woodifield. It gave him a feeling of deep, solid satisfaction to be planted there in the midst of it in full view of that frail old figure in the muffler.

"I've had it done up lately," he explained, as he had explained for the past —how many?—weeks. "New carpet," and he pointed to the bright red carpet with a pattern of large white rings. "New furniture," and he nodded towards the massive bookcase and the table with legs like twisted treacle. "Electric heating!" He waved almost exultantly towards the five transparent, pearly sausages glowing so softly in the tilted copper pan.

But he did not draw old Woodifield's attention to the photograph over the table of a grave-looking boy in uniform standing in one of those spectral photographers' parks with photographers' storm-clouds behind him. It was not new. It had been there for over six years.

"There was something I wanted to tell you," said old Woodifield, and his eyes grew dim remembering. "Now what was it? I had it in my mind when I started out this morning." His hands began to tremble, and patches of red showed above his beard.

Poor old chap, he's on his last pins, thought the boss. And, feeling kindly, he winked at the old man, and said jokingly, "I tell you what. I've got a little drop of something here that'll do you good before you go out into the cold again. It's beautiful stuff. It wouldn't hurt a child." He took a key off his watch-chain, unlocked a cupboard below his desk, and drew forth a dark, squat bottle. "That's the medicine," said he. "And the man from whom I got it told me on the strict Q.T. it came from the cellars at Windsor Castle."

Old Woodifield's mouth fell open at the sight. He couldn't have looked more surprised if the boss had produced a rabbit.

"It's whisky, ain't it?" he piped, feebly.

The boss turned the bottle and lovingly showed him the label. Whisky it was.

"D'you know," said he, peering up at the boss wonderingly, "they won't let me touch it at home." And he looked as though he was going to cry.

"Ah, that's where we know a bit more than the ladies," cried the boss, swooping across for two tumblers that stood on the table with the water-bottle, and pouring a generous finger into each. "Drink it down. It'll do you good. And don't put any water with it. It's sacrilege to tamper with stuff like this. Ah!" He tossed off his, pulled out his handkerchief, hastily wiped his moustaches, and cocked an eye at old Woodifield, who was rolling his in his chaps.

The old man swallowed, was silent a moment, and then said faintly, "It's nutty!"

But it warmed him; it crept into his chill old brain—he remembered.

"That was it," he said, heaving himself out of his chair. "I thought you'd like to know. The girls were in Belgium last week having a look at poor Reggie's grave, and they happened to come across your boy's. They're quite near each other, it seems."

Old Woodifield paused, but the boss made no reply. Only a quiver in his eyelids showed that he heard.

"The girls were delighted with the way the place is kept," piped the old voice. "Beautifully looked after. Couldn't be

better if they were at home. You've not been across, have yer?"

"No, no!" For various reasons the boss had not been across.

"There's miles of it," quavered old Woodifield, "and it's all as neat as a garden. Flowers growing on all the graves. Nice broad paths." It was plain from his voice how much he liked a nice broad path.

The pause came again. Then the old man brightened wonderfully.

"D'you know what the hotel made the girls pay for a pot of jam?" he piped. "Ten francs! Robbery, I call it. It was a little pot, so Gertrude says, no bigger than a half-crown. And she hadn't taken more than a spoonful when they charged her ten francs. Gertrude brought the pot away with her to teach 'em a lesson. Quite right, too; it's trading on our feelings. They think because we're over there having a look around we're ready to pay anything. That's what it is." And he turned towards the door.

"Quite right, quite right!" cried the boss, though what was quite right he hadn't the least idea. He came around by his desk, followed the shuffling footsteps to the door, and saw the old fellow out. Woodifield was gone.

For a long moment the boss stayed, staring at nothing, while the grey-haired office messenger, watching him, dodged in and out of his cubbyhole like a dog that expects to be taken for a run. Then: "I'll see nobody for half an hour, Macey," said the boss. "Understand? Nobody at all."

"Very good, sir."

The door shut, the firm heavy steps recrossed the bright carpet, the fat body plumped down in the spring chair, and leaning forward, the boss covered his face with his hands. He wanted, he intended, he had arranged to weep. . . .

It had been a terrible shock to him when old Woodifield sprang that remark upon him about the boy's grave. It was exactly as though the earth had opened and he had seen the boy lying there with Woodifield's girls staring down at him. For it was strange. Although over six years had passed away, the boss never thought of the boy except as lying unchanged, unblemished in his uniform, asleep for ever. "My son!" groaned the boss. But no tears came yet. In the past, in the first months and even years after the boy's death, he had only to say those words to be overcome by such grief that nothing short of a violent fit of weeping could relieve him. Time, he had declared then, he had told everybody, could make no difference. Other men perhaps might recover, might live their loss down, but not he. How was it possible? His boy was an only son. Ever since his birth the boss had worked at building up this business for him; it had no other meaning if it was not for the boy. Life itself had come to have no other meaning. How on earth could he have slaved, denied himself, kept going all those years without the promise for ever before him of the boy's stepping into his shoes and carrying on where he left off?

And that promise had been so near being fulfilled. The boy had been in the office learning the ropes for a year before the war. Every morning they had started off together; they had come back by the same train. And what congratulations he had received as the boy's father! No wonder; he had taken to it marvelously. As to his popularity with the staff, every man jack of them down to old Macey couldn't make enough of the boy. And he wasn't in the least spoilt. No, he was just his bright, natural self, with the right word for everybody, with that boyish look and his habit of saying, "Simply splendid!"

But all that was over and done with as though it never had been. The day had come when Macey had handed him the telegram that brought the whole place crashing about his head. "Deeply regret to inform you . . ." And he had left the office a broken man, with his life in ruins.

Six years ago, six years . . . How quickly time passed! It might have happened yesterday. The boss took his hands from his face; he was puzzled. Something seemed to be wrong with him. He wasn't feeling as he wanted to feel. He decided to get up and have a look at the boy's photograph. But it wasn't a favorite photograph of his; the expression was unnatural. It was cold, even stern-looking. The boy had never looked like that.

At that moment the boss noticed that a fly had fallen into his broad inkpot, and was trying feebly but desperately to clamber out again. Help! help! said those struggling legs. But the sides of the inkpot were wet and slippery; it fell back again and began to swim. The boss took up a pen, picked the fly out of the ink, and shook it on to a piece of blotting-paper. For a fraction of a second it lay still on the dark patch that oozed round it. Then the front legs waved, took hold, and, pulling its small sodden body up it began the immense task of cleaning the ink from its wings. Over and under, over and under, went a leg along a wing, as the stone goes over and under the scythe. Then there was a pause, while the fly, seeming to stand on the tips of its toes, tried to expand first one wing and then the other. It succeeded at last, and, sitting down, it began, like a minute cat, to clean its face. Now one could imagine that the little front legs rubbed against each other lightly, joyfully. The horrible danger was over; it had escaped; it was ready for life again.

But just then the boss had an idea. He plunged his pen back into the ink, leaned his thick wrist on the blotting-paper, and as the fly tried its wings down came a great heavy blot. What would it make of that? What indeed! The little beggar seemed absolutely cowed, stunned, and afraid to move because of what would happen next. But then, as if painfully, it dragged itself forward. The front legs waved, caught hold, and, more slowly this time, the task began from the beginning.

He's a plucky little devil, thought the boss, and he felt a real admiration for the fly's courage. That was the way to tackle things; that was the right spirit. Never say die; it was only a question of . . . But the fly had again finished its laborious task, and the boss had just time to refill his pen, to shake fair and square on the new-cleaned body yet another dark drop. What about it this time? A painful moment of suspense followed. But behold, the front legs were again waving; the boss felt a rush of relief. He leaned over the fly and said to it tenderly. "You artful little b . . ." And he actually had the brilliant notion of breathing on it to help the drying process. All the same, there was something timid and weak about its efforts now, and the boss decided that this time should be the last, as he dipped the pen into the inkpot.

It was. The last blot on the soaked blotting-paper, and the draggled fly lay in it and did not stir. The back legs were stuck to the body; the front legs were not to be seen.

"Come on," said the boss. "Look sharp!" And he stirred it with his pen—in vain. Nothing happened or was likely to happen. The fly was dead.

The boss lifted the corpse on the end of the paper-knife and flung it into the waste-paper basket. But such a grinding feeling of wretchedness seized him that he felt positively frightened. He started forward and pressed the bell for Macey.

"Bring me some fresh blotting-paper," he said, sternly, "and look sharp about it." And while the old dog padded away he fell to wondering what it was he had been thinking about before. What was it? It was . . . He took out his handkerchief and passed it inside his collar. For the life of him he could not remember.

THE JILTING OF GRANNY WEATHERALL

Katherine Anne Porter
(1894–   )

She flicked her wrist neatly out of Doctor Harry's pudgy careful fingers and pulled the sheet up to her chin. The brat ought to be in knee breeches. Doctoring around the country with spectacles on his nose! "Get along now, take your schoolbooks and go. There's nothing wrong with me."

Doctor Harry spread a warm paw like a cushion on her forehead where the forked green vein danced and made her eyelids twitch. "Now, now, be a good girl, and we'll have you up in no time."

"That's no way to speak to a woman nearly eighty years old just because she's down. I'd have you respect your elders, young man."

"Well, Missy, excuse me." Doctor Harry patted her cheek. "But I've got to warn you, haven't I? You're a marvel, but you must be careful or you're going to be good and sorry."

"Don't tell me what I'm going to be. I'm on my feet now, morally speaking. It's Cornelia. I had to go to bed to get rid of her."

Her bones felt loose, and floated around in her skin, and Doctor Harry floated like a balloon around the foot of the bed. He floated and pulled down his waistcoat and swung his glasses on a cord. "Well, stay where you are, it certainly can't hurt you."

"Get along and doctor your sick," said Granny Weatherall. "Leave a well woman alone. I'll call for you when I want you. . . . Where were you forty years ago when I pulled through milk-leg and double pneumonia? You weren't even born. Don't let Cornelia lead you on," she shouted, because Doctor Harry appeared to float up to the ceiling and out. "I pay my own bills, and I don't throw my money away on nonsense!"

She meant to wave good-by, but it was too much trouble. Her eyes closed of themselves, it was like a dark curtain drawn around the bed. The pillow rose and floated under her, pleasant as a hammock in a light wind. She listened to the leaves rustling outside the window. No, somebody was swishing newspapers: no, Cornelia and Doctor Harry were whispering together. She leaped broad awake, thinking they whispered in her ear.

"She was never like this, *never* like this!" "Well, what can we expect?" "Yes, eighty years old. . . ."

Well, and what if she was? She still had ears. It was like Cornelia to whisper around doors. She always kept things secret in such a public way. She was always being tactful and kind. Cornelia was dutiful; that was the trouble with her. Dutiful and good: "So good and dutiful," said Granny, "that I'd like to spank her." She saw herself spanking Cornelia and making a fine job of it.

"What'd you say, Mother?"

Granny felt her face tying up in hard knots.

"Can't a body think, I'd like to know?"

"I thought you might want something."

"I do. I want a lot of things. First off, go away and don't whisper."

She lay and drowsed, hoping in her sleep that the children would keep out and let her rest a minute. It had been a long day. Not that she was tired. It was always pleasant to snatch a minute now and then. There was always so much to be done, let me see: tomorrow.

Tomorrow was far away and there was nothing to trouble about. Things were finished somehow when the time came; thank God there was always a little margin over for peace: then a person could spread out the plan of life and tuck in the edges orderly. It was good to have every-

thing clean and folded away, with the hair brushes and tonic bottles sitting straight on the white embroidered linen: the day started without fuss and the pantry shelves laid out with rows of jelly glasses and brown jugs and white stonechina jars with blue whirligigs and words painted on them: coffee, tea, sugar, ginger, cinnamon, allspice: and the bronze clock with the lion on top nicely dusted off. The dust that lion could collect in twenty-four hours! The box in the attic with all those letters tied up, well, she'd have to go through that tomorrow. All those letters—George's letters and John's letters and her letters to them both— lying around for the children to find afterwards made her uneasy. Yes, that would be tomorrow's business. No use to let them know how silly she had been once.

While she was rummaging around she found death in her mind and it felt clammy and unfamiliar. She had spent so much time preparing for death there was no need for bringing it up again. Let it take care of itself now. When she was sixty she had felt very old, finished, and went around making farewell trips to see her children and grandchildren, with a secret in her mind: This is the very last of your mother, children! Then she made her will and came down with a long fever. That was all just a notion like a lot of other things, but it was lucky too, for she had once for all got over the idea of dying for a long time. Now she couldn't be worried. She hoped she had better sense now. Her father had lived to be one hundred and two years old and had drunk a noggin of strong hot toddy on his last birthday. He told the reporters it was his daily habit, and he owed his long life to that. He had made quite a scandal and was very pleased about it. She believed she'd just plague Cornelia a little.

"Cornelia! Cornelia!" No footsteps, but a sudden hand on her cheek. "Bless you, where have you been?"

"Here, mother."

"Well, Cornelia, I want a noggin of hot toddy."

"Are you cold, darling?"

"I'm chilly, Cornelia. Lying in bed stops the circulation. I must have told you that a thousand times."

Well, she could just hear Cornelia telling her husband that Mother was getting a little childish and they'd have to humor her. The thing that most annoyed her was that Cornelia thought she was deaf, dumb, and blind. Little hasty glances and tiny gestures tossed around her and over her head saying, "Don't cross her, let her have her way, she's eighty years old," and she sitting there as if she lived in a thin glass cage. Sometimes Granny almost made up her mind to pack up and move back to her own house where nobody could remind her every minute that she was old. Wait, wait, Cornelia, till your own children whisper behind your back!

In her day she had kept a better house and had got more work done. She wasn't too old yet for Lydia to be driving eighty miles for advice when one of the children jumped the track, and Jimmy still dropped in and talked things over: "Now, Mammy, you've a good business head, I want to know what you think of this? . . ." Old. Cornelia couldn't change the furniture around without asking. Little things, little things! They had been so sweet when they were little. Granny wished the old days were back again with the children young and everything to be done over. It had been a hard pull, but not too much for her. When she thought of all the food she had cooked, and all the clothes she had cut and sewed, and all the gardens she had made—well, the children showed it. There they were, made out of her, and they couldn't get away from that. Sometimes she wanted to see John again and point to them and say, Well, I didn't do so badly, did I? But that would have to wait. That was for tomorrow. She used to think of

him as a man, but now all the children were older than their father, and he would be a child beside her if she saw him now. It seemed strange and there was something wrong in the idea. Why, he couldn't possibly recognize her. She had fenced in a hundred acres once, digging the post holes herself and clamping the wires with just a negro boy to help. That changed a woman. John would be looking for a young woman with the peaked Spanish comb in her hair and the painted fan. Digging post holes changed a woman. Riding country roads in the winter when women had their babies was another thing: sitting up nights with sick horses and sick negroes and sick children and hardly ever losing one. John, I hardly ever lose one of them! John would see that in a minute, that would be something he could understand, she wouldn't have to explain anything!

It made her feel like rolling up her sleeves and putting the whole place to rights again. No matter if Cornelia was determined to be everywhere at once, there were a great many things left undone on this place. She would start tomorrow and do them. It was good to be strong enough for everything, even if all you made melted and changed and slipped under your hands, so that by the time you finished you almost forgot what you were working for. What was it I set out to do? she asked herself intently, but she could not remember. A fog rose over the valley, she saw it marching across the creek swallowing the trees and moving up the hill like an army of ghosts. Soon it would be at the near edge of the orchard, and then it was time to go in and light the lamps. Come in, children, don't stay out in the night air.

Lighting the lamps had been beautiful. The children huddled up to her and breathed like little calves waiting at the bars in the twilight. Their eyes followed the match and watched the flame rise and settle in a blue curve, then they moved away from her. The lamp was lit, they didn't have to be scared and hang on to mother any more. Never, never, never more. God, for all my life I thank Thee. Without Thee, my God, I could never have done it. Hail, Mary, full of grace.

I want you to pick all the fruit this year and see that nothing is wasted. There's always someone who can use it. Don't let good things rot for want of using. You waste life when you waste good food. Don't let things get lost. It's bitter to lose things. Now, don't let me get to thinking, not when I am tired and taking a little nap before supper. . . .

The pillow rose about her shoulders and pressed against her heart and the memory was being squeezed out of it: oh, push down the pillow, somebody: it would smother her if she tried to hold it. Such a fresh breeze blowing and such a green day with no threats in it. But he had not come, just the same. What does a woman do when she has put on the white veil and set out the white cake for a man and he doesn't come? She tried to remember. No, I swear he never harmed me but in that. He never harmed me but in that . . . and what if he did? There was the day, the day, but a whirl of dark smoke rose and covered it, crept up and over into the bright field where everything was planted so carefully in orderly rows. That was hell, she knew hell when she saw it. For sixty years she had prayed against remembering him and against losing her soul in the deep pit of hell, and now the two things were mingled in one and the thought of him was a smoky cloud from hell that moved and crept in her head when she had just got rid of Doctor Harry and was trying to rest a minute. Wounded vanity, Ellen, said a sharp voice in the top of her mind. Don't let your wounded vanity get the upper hand of you. Plenty of girls get jilted. You were jilted, weren't you? Then stand up to it. Her eyelids wavered and let in streamers

of blue-gray light like tissue paper over her eyes. She must get up and pull the shades down or she'd never sleep. She was in bed again and the shades were not down. How could that happen? Better turn over, hide from the light, sleeping in the light gave you nightmares. "Mother, how do you feel now?" and a stinging wetness on her forehead. But I don't like having my face washed in cold water!

Hapsy? George? Lydia? Jimmy? No, Cornelia, and her features were swollen and full of little puddles. "They're coming, darling, they'll all be here soon." Go wash your face, child, you look funny.

Instead of obeying, Cornelia knelt down and put her head on the pillow. She seemed to be talking but there was no sound. "Well, are you tongue-tied? Whose birthday is it? Are you going to give a party?"

Cornelia's mouth moved urgently in strange shapes. "Don't do that, you bother me, daughter."

"Oh, no, Mother. Oh, no. . . ."

Nonsense. It was strange about children. They disputed your every word. "No what, Cornelia?"

"Here's Doctor Harry."

"I won't see that boy again. He just left five minutes ago."

"That was this morning, Mother. It's night now. Here's the nurse."

"This is Doctor Harry, Mrs. Weatherall. I never saw you look so young and happy!"

"Ah, I'll never be young again—but I'd be happy if they'd let me lie in peace and get rested."

She thought she spoke up loudly, but no one answered. A warm weight on her forehead, a warm bracelet on her wrist, and a breeze went on whispering, trying to tell her something. A shuffle of leaves in the everlasting hand of God, He blew on them and they danced and rattled. "Mother, don't mind, we're going to give you a little hypodermic." "Look here, daughter, how do ants get in this bed? I saw sugar ants yesterday." Did you send for Hapsy too?

It was Hapsy she really wanted. She had to go a long way back through a great many rooms to find Hapsy standing with a baby on her arm. She seemed to herself to be Hapsy also, and the baby on Hapsy's arm was Hapsy and himself and herself, all at once, and there was no surprise in the meeting. Then Hapsy melted from within and turned flimsy as gray gauze and the baby was a gauzy shadow, and Hapsy came up close and said, "I thought you'd never come," and looked at her very searchingly and said, "You haven't changed a bit!" They leaned forward to kiss, when Cornelia began whispering from a long way off, "Oh, is there anything you want to tell me? Is there anything I can do for you?"

Yes, she had changed her mind after sixty years and she would like to see George. I want you to find George. Find him and be sure to tell him I forgot him. I want him to know I had my husband just the same and my children and my house like any other woman. A good house too and a good husband that I loved and fine children out of him. Better than I hoped for even. Tell him I was given back everything he took away and more. Oh, no, oh, God, no, there was something else besides the house and the man and the children. Oh, surely they were not all? What was it? Something not given back. . . . Her breath crowded down under her ribs and grew into a monstrous frightening shape with cutting edges; it bored up into her head, and the agony was unbelievable: Yes, John, get the doctor now, no more talk, my time has come.

When this one was born it should be the last. The last. It should have been born first, for it was the one she had truly wanted. Everything came in good time. Nothing left out, left over. She was strong, in three days she would be as well as ever. Better. A woman needed milk in her to have her full health.

"Mother, do you hear me?"

"I've been telling you—"

"Mother, Father Connolly's here."

"I went to Holy Communion only last week. Tell him I'm not so sinful as all that."

"Father just wants to speak to you."

He could speak as much as he pleased. It was like him to drop in and inquire about her soul as if it were a teething baby, and then stay on for a cup of tea and a round of cards and gossip. He always had a funny story of some sort, usually about an Irishman who made his little mistakes and confessed them, and the point lay in some absurd thing he would blurt out in the confessional showing his struggles between native piety and original sin. Granny felt easy about her soul. Cornelia, where are your manners? Give Father Connolly a chair. She had her secret comfortable understanding with a few favorite saints who cleared a straight road to God for her. All as surely signed and sealed as the papers for the new Forty Acres. Forever . . . heirs and assigns forever. Since the day the wedding cake was not cut, but thrown out and wasted. The whole bottom dropped out of the world, and there she was blind and sweating with nothing under her feet and the walls falling away. His hand had caught her under the breast, she had not fallen, there was the freshly polished floor with the green rug on it, just as before. He had cursed like a sailor's parrot and said, "I'll kill him for you." Don't lay a hand on him, for my sake leave something to God. "Now, Ellen, you must believe what I tell you. . . ."

So there was nothing, nothing to worry about any more, except sometimes in the night one of the children screamed in a nightmare, and they both hustled out shaking and hunting for the matches and calling, "There, wait a minute, here we are!" John, get the doctor now, Hapsy's time has come. But there was Hapsy standing by the bed in a white cap. "Cornelia, tell Hapsy to take off her cap. I can't see her plain."

Her eyes opened very wide and the room stood out like a picture she had seen somewhere. Dark colors with the shadows rising towards the ceiling in long angles. The tall black dresser gleamed with nothing on it but John's picture, enlarged from a little one, with John's eyes very black when they should have been blue. You never saw him, so how do you know how he looked? But the man insisted the copy was perfect, it was very rich and handsome. For a picture, yes, but it's not my husband. The table by the bed had a linen cover and a candle and a crucifix. The light was blue from Cornelia's silk lampshades. No sort of light at all, just frippery. You had to live forty years with kerosene lamps to appreciate honest electricity. She felt very strong and she saw Doctor Harry with a rosy nimbus around him.

"You look like a saint, Doctor Harry, and I vow that's as near as you'll ever come to it."

"She's saying something."

"I heard you, Cornelia. What's all this carrying-on?"

"Father Connolly's saying—"

Cornelia's voice staggered and bumped like a cart in a bad road. It rounded corners and turned back again and arrived nowhere. Granny stepped up in the cart very lightly and reached for the reins, but a man sat beside her and she knew him by his hands, driving the cart. She did not look in his face, for she knew without seeing, but looked instead down the road where the trees leaned over and bowed to each other and a thousand birds were singing a Mass. She felt like singing too, but she put her hand in the bosom of her dress and pulled out a rosary, and Father Connolly murmured Latin in a very solemn voice and tickled her feet. My God, will you stop that nonsense? I'm a married woman. What if he did run away and leave me to face the priest by myself? I found another a whole world better. I wouldn't have exchanged my husband for anybody except St. Michael himself, and you may tell him that for me with a thank you in the bargain.

Light flashed on her closed eyelids, and a deep roaring shook her. Cornelia, is that lightning? I hear thunder. There's going to be a storm. Close all the windows. Call the children in. . . . "Mother, here we are, all of us." "Is that you, Hapsy?" "Oh, no, I'm Lydia. We drove as fast as we could." Their faces drifted above her, drifted away. The rosary fell out of her hands and Lydia put it back. Jimmy tried to help, their hands fumbled together, and Granny closed two fingers around Jimmy's thumb. Beads wouldn't do, it must be something alive. She was so amazed her thoughts ran round and round. So, my dear Lord, this is my death and I wasn't even thinking about it. My children have come to see me die. But I can't, it's not time. Oh, I always hated surprises. I wanted to give Cornelia the amethyst set—Cornelia, you're to have the amethyst set, but Hapsy's to wear it when she wants, and, Doctor Harry, do shut up. Nobody sent for you. Oh, my dear Lord, do wait a minute. I meant to do something about the Forty Acres, Jimmy doesn't need it and Lydia will later on, with that worthless husband of hers. I meant to finish the altar cloth and send six bottles of wine to Sister Borgia for her dyspepsia. I want to send six bottles of wine to Sister Borgia, Father Connolly, now don't let me forget.

Cornelia's voice made short turns and tilted over and crashed. "Oh, Mother, oh, Mother, oh, Mother. . . ."

"I'm not going, Cornelia. I'm taken by surprise. I can't go."

You'll see Hapsy again. What about

her? "I thought you'd never come." Granny made a long journey outward, looking for Hapsy. What if I don't find her? What then? Her heart sank down and down, there was no bottom to death, she couldn't come to the end of it. The blue light from Cornelia's lampshade drew into a tiny point in the center of her brain, it flickered and winked like an eye, quietly it fluttered and dwindled. Granny lay curled down within herself, amazed and watchful, staring at the point of light that was herself; her body was now only a deeper mass of shadow in an endless darkness and this darkness would curl around the light and swallow it up. God, give a sign!

For the second time there was no sign. Again no bridegroom and the priest in the house. She could not remember any other sorrow because this grief wiped them all away. Oh, no, there's nothing more cruel than this—I'll never forgive it. She stretched herself with a deep breath and blew out the light.

DEATH OF A TRAVELING SALESMAN

Eudora Welty
(1909–   )

R. J. Bowman, who for fourteen years had traveled for a shoe company through Mississippi, drove his Ford along a rutted dirt path. It was a long day! The time did not seem to clear the noon hurdle and settle into soft afternoon. The sun, keeping its strength here even in winter, stayed at the top of the sky, and every time Bowman stuck his head out of the dusty car to stare up the road, it seemed to reach a long arm down and push against the top of his head, right through his hat—like the practical joke of an old drummer,

long on the road. It made him feel all the more angry and helpless. He was feverish, and he was not quite sure of the way.

This was his first day back on the road after a long siege of influenza. He had had very high fever, and dreams, and had become weakened and pale, enough to tell the difference in the mirror, and he could not think clearly. . . . All afternoon, in the midst of his anger, and for no reason, he had thought of his dead grandmother. She had been a comfortable soul. Once more Bowman wished he could fall into the big feather bed that had been in her room. . . . Then he forgot her again.

This desolate hill country! And he seemed to be going the wrong way—it was as if he were going back, far back. There was not a house in sight. . . . There was no use wishing he were back in bed, though. By paying the hotel doctor his bill he had proved his recovery. He had not even been sorry when the pretty trained nurse said good-by. He did not like illness, he distrusted it, as he distrusted the road without signposts. It angered him. He had given the nurse a really expensive bracelet, just because she was packing up her bag and leaving.

But now—what if in fourteen years on the road he had never been ill before and never had an accident? His record was broken, and he had even begun almost to question it. . . . He had gradually put up at better hotels, in the bigger towns, but weren't they all, eternally, stuffy in summer and drafty in winter? Women? He could only remember little rooms within little rooms, like a nest of Chinese paper boxes, and if he thought of one woman he saw the worn loneliness that the furniture of that room seemed built of. And he himself—he was a man who always wore rather wide-brimmed black hats, and in the wavy hotel mirrors had looked something like a bullfighter, as he paused for that inevitable instant on the landing, walking downstairs to supper.

. . . He leaned out of the car again, and once more the sun pushed at his head.

Bowman had wanted to reach Beulah by dark, to go to bed and sleep off his fatigue. As he remembered, Beulah was fifty miles away from the last town, on a graveled road. This was only a cow trail. How had he ever come to such a place? One hand wiped the sweat from his face, and he drove on.

He had made the Beulah trip before. But he had never seen this hill or this petering-out path before—or that cloud, he thought shyly, looking up and then down quickly—any more than he had seen this day before. Why did he not admit he was simply lost and had been for miles? . . . He was not in the habit of asking the way of strangers, and these people never knew where the very roads they lived on went to; but then he had not even been close enough to anyone to call out. People standing in the fields now and then, or on top of the haystacks, had been too far away, looking like leaning sticks or weeds, turning a little at the solitary rattle of his car across their countryside, watching the pale sobered winter dust where it chunked out behind like big squashes down the road. The stares of these distant people had followed him solidly like a wall, impenetrable, behind which they turned back after he had passed.

The cloud floated there to one side like the bolster on his grandmother's bed. It went over a cabin on the edge of a hill, where two bare chinaberry trees clutched at the sky. He drove through a heap of dead oak leaves, his wheels stirring their weightless sides to make a silvery melancholy whistle as the car passed through their bed. No car had been along this way ahead of him. Then he saw that he was on the edge of a ravine that fell away, a red erosion, and that this was indeed the road's end.

He pulled the brake. But it did not hold, though he put all his strength into it. The car, tipped toward the edge, rolled a little. Without doubt, it was going over the bank.

He got out quietly, as though some mischief had been done him and he had his dignity to remember. He lifted his bag and sample case out, set them down, and stood back and watched the car roll over the edge. He heard something—not the crash he was listening for, but a slow, unuproarious crackle. Rather distastefully he went to look over, and he saw that his car had fallen into a tangle of immense grapevines as thick as his arm, which caught it and held it, rocked it like a grotesque child in a dark cradle, and then, as he watched, concerned somehow that he was not still inside it, released it gently to the ground.

He sighed.

Where am I? He wondered with a shock. Why didn't I do something? All his anger seemed to have drifted away from him. There was the house, back on the hill. He took a bag in each hand and with almost childlike willingness went toward it. But his breathing came with difficulty, and he had to stop to rest.

It was a shotgun house, two rooms and an open passage between, perched on the hill. The whole cabin slanted a little under the heavy heaped-up vine that covered the roof, light and green, as though forgotten from summer. A woman stood in the passage.

He stopped still. Then all of a sudden his heart began to behave strangely. Like a rocket set off, it began to leap and expand into uneven patterns of beats which showered into his brain, and he could not think. But in scattering and falling it made no noise. It shot up with great power, almost elation, and fell gently, like acrobats into nets. It began to pound profoundly, then waited irresponsibly, hitting in some sort of inward mockery first at his ribs, then against his eyes, then under his shoulder blades, and against the roof of his mouth when he tried to say, "Good afternoon, madam." But he could not hear his heart—it was as quiet as ashes falling. This was rather comforting; still, it was shocking to Bowman to feel his heart beating at all.

Stock-still in his confusion, he dropped his bags, which seemed to drift in slow bulks gracefully through the air and to cushion themselves on the gray prostrate grass near the doorstep.

As for the woman standing there, he saw at once that she was old. Since she could not possibly hear his heart, he ignored the pounding and now looked at her carefully, and yet in his distraction dreamily, with his mouth open.

She had been cleaning the lamp, and held it, half blackened, half clear, in front of her. He saw her with the dark passage behind her. She was a big woman with a weather-beaten but unwrinkled face; her lips were held tightly together, and her eyes looked with a curious dulled brightness into his. He looked at her shoes, which were like bundles. If it were summer she would be barefoot. . . . Bowman, who automatically judged a woman's age on sight, set her age at fifty. She wore a formless garment of some gray coarse material, rough-dried from a washing, from which her arms appeared pink and unexpectedly round. When she never said a word, and sustained her quiet pose of holding the lamp, he was convinced of the strength in her body.

"Good afternoon, madam," he said.

She stared on, whether at him or at the air around him he could not tell, but after a moment she lowered her eyes to show that she would listen to whatever he had to say.

"I wonder if you would be interested—" He tried once more. "An accident—my car . . ."

Her voice emerged low and remote, like a sound across a lake. "Sonny he ain't here."

"Sonny?"

"Sonny ain't here now."

Her son—a fellow able to bring my car up, he decided in blurred relief. He pointed down the hill. "My car's in the bottom of the ditch. I'll need help."

"Sonny ain't here, but he'll be here."

She was becoming clearer to him and her voice stronger, and Bowman saw that she was stupid.

He was hardly surprised at the deepening postponement and tedium of his journey. He took a breath, and heard his voice speaking over the silent blows of his heart. "I was sick. I am not strong yet. . . . May I come in?"

He stooped and laid his big black hat over the handle on his bag. It was a humble motion, almost a bow, that instantly struck him as absurd and betraying of all his weakness. He looked up at the woman, the wind blowing his hair. He might have continued for a long time in this unfamiliar attitude; he had never been a patient man, but when he was sick he had learned to sink submissively into the pillows, to wait for his medicine. He waited on the woman.

Then she, looking at him with blue eyes, turned and held open the door, and after a moment Bowman, as if convinced in his action, stood erect and followed her in.

Inside, the darkness of the house touched him like a professional hand, the doctor's. The woman set the half-cleaned lamp on a table in the center of the room and pointed, also like a professional person, a guide, to a chair with a yellow cowhide seat. She herself crouched on the hearth, drawing her knees up under the shapeless dress.

At first he felt hopefully secure. His heart was quieter. The room was enclosed in the gloom of yellow pine boards. He could see the other room, with the foot of an iron bed showing, across the passage. The bed had been made up with a red-and-yellow pieced quilt that looked like a map or a picture, a little like his grandmother's girlhood painting of Rome burning.

He had ached for coolness, but in this room it was cold. He stared at the hearth with dead coals lying on it and iron pots in the corners. The hearth and smoked chimney were of the stone he had seen ribbing the hills, mostly slate. Why is there no fire? he wondered.

And it was so still. The silence of the fields seemed to enter and move familiarly through the house. The wind used the open hall. He felt that he was in a mysterious, quiet, cool danger. It was necessary to do what? . . . To talk.

"I have a nice line of women's low-priced shoes . . ." he said.

But the woman answered, "Sonny'll be here. He's strong. Sonny'll move your car."

"Where is he now?"

"Farms for Mr. Redmond."

Mr. Redmond. Mr. Redmond. That was someone he would never have to encounter, and he was glad. Somehow the name did not appeal to him. . . . In a flare of touchiness and anxiety, Bowman wished to avoid even mention of unknown men and their unknown farms.

"Do you two live here alone?" He was surprised to hear his old voice, chatty, confidential, inflected for selling shoes, asking a question like that—a thing he did not even want to know.

"Yes. We are alone."

He was surprised at the way she answered. She had taken a long time to say that. She had nodded her head in a deep way too. Had she wished to affect him with some sort of premonition? he wondered unhappily. Or was it only that she would not help him, after all, by talking with him? For he was not strong enough

to receive the impact of unfamiliar things without a little talk to break their fall. He had lived a month in which nothing had happened except in his head and his body —an almost inaudible life of heartbeats and dreams that came back, a life of fever and privacy, a delicate life which had left him weak to the point of—what? Of begging. The pulse in his palm leapt like a trout in a brook.

He wondered over and over why the woman did not go ahead with cleaning the lamp. What prompted her to stay there across the room, silently bestowing her presence upon him? He saw that with her it was not a time for doing little tasks. Her face was grave; she was feeling how right she was. Perhaps it was only politeness. In docility he held his eyes stiffly wide; they fixed themselves on the woman's clasped hands as though she held the cord they were strung on.

Then, "Sonny's coming," she said.

He himself had not heard anything, but there came a man passing the window and then plunging in at the door, with two hounds beside him. Sonny was a big enough man, with his belt slung low about his hips. He looked at least thirty. He had a hot, red face that was yet full of silence. He wore muddy blue pants and an old military coat stained and patched. World War? Bowman wondered. Great God, it was a Confederate coat. On the back of his light hair he had a wide filthy black hat which seemed to insult Bowman's own. He pushed down the dogs from his chest. He was strong, with dignity and heaviness in his way of moving. . . . There was the resemblance to his mother.

They stood side by side. . . . He must account again for his presence here.

"Sonny, this man, he had his car to run off over the prec'pice an' wants to know if you will git it out for him," the woman said after a few minutes.

Bowman could not even state his case.

Sonny's eyes lay upon him.

He knew he should offer explanations and show money—at least appear either penitent or authoritative. But all he could do was to shrug slightly.

Sonny brushed by him going to the window, followed by the eager dogs, and looked out. There was effort even in the way he was looking, as if he could throw his sight out like a rope. Without turning Bowman felt that his own eyes could have seen nothing: it was too far.

"Got me a mule out there an' got me a block an' tackle," said Sonny meaningfully. "I *could* catch me my mule an' git me my ropes, an' before long I'd git your car out the ravine."

He looked completely around the room, as if in meditation, his eyes roving in their own distance. Then he pressed his lips firmly and yet shyly together, and with the dogs ahead of him this time, he lowered his head and strode out. The hard earth sounded, cupping to his powerful way of walking—almost a stagger.

Mischievously, at the suggestion of those sounds, Bowman's heart leapt again. It seemed to walk about inside him.

"Sonny's goin' to do it," the woman said. She said it again, singing it almost, like a song. She was sitting in her place by the hearth.

Without looking out, he heard some shouts and the dogs barking and the pounding of hoofs in short runs on the hill. In a few minutes Sonny passed under the window with a rope, and there was a brown mule with quivering, shining, purple-looking ears. The mule actually looked in the window. Under its eyelashes it turned target-like eyes into his. Bowman averted his head and saw the woman looking serenely back at the mule, with only satisfaction in her face.

She sang a little more, under her breath. It occurred to him, and it seemed quite marvelous, that she was not really talking to him, but rather following the thing that came about with words that were unconscious and part of her looking.

So he said nothing, and this time when he did not reply he felt a curious and strong emotion, not fear, rise up in him.

This time, when his heart leapt, something—his soul—seemed to leap too, like a little colt invited out of a pen. He stared at the woman while the frantic nimbleness of his feeling made his head sway. He could not move; there was nothing he could do, unless perhaps he might embrace this woman who sat there growing old and shapeless before him.

But he wanted to leap up, to say to her, I have been sick and I found out then, only then, how lonely I am. Is it too late? My heart puts up a struggle inside me, and you may have heard it, protesting against emptiness. . . . It should be full, he would rush on to tell her, thinking of his heart now as a deep lake, it should be holding love like other hearts. It should be flooded with love. There would be a warm spring day . . . Come and stand in my heart, whoever you are, and a whole river would cover your feet and rise higher and take your knees in whirlpools, and draw you down to itself, your whole body, your heart too.

But he moved a trembling hand across his eyes, and looked at the placid crouching woman across the room. She was still as a statue. He felt ashamed and exhausted by the thought that he might, in one more moment, have tried by simple words and embraces to communicate some strange thing—something which seemed always to have just escaped him . . .

Sunlight touched the furthest pot on the hearth. It was late afternoon. This time tomorrow he would be somewhere on a good graveled road, driving his car past things that happened to people, quicker than their happening. Seeing ahead to the next day, he was glad, and knew that this was no time to embrace an old woman. He could feel in his pounding temples the readying of his blood for motion and for hurrying away.

"Sonny's hitched up your car by now," said the woman. "He'll git it out the ravine right shortly."

"Fine!" he cried with his customary enthusiasm.

Yet it seemed a long time that they waited. It began to get dark. Bowman was cramped in his chair. Any man should know enough to get up and walk around while he waited. There was something like guilt in such stillness and silence.

But instead of getting up, he listened. . . . His breathing restrained, his eyes powerless in the growing dark, he listened uneasily for a warning sound, forgetting in wariness what it would be. Before long he heard something—soft, continuous, insinuating.

"What's that noise?" he asked, his voice jumping into the dark. Then wildly he was afraid it would be his heart beating so plainly in the quiet room, and she would tell him so.

"You might hear the stream," she said grudgingly.

Her voice was closer. She was standing by the table. He wondered why she did not light the lamp. She stood there in the dark and did not light it.

Bowman would never speak to her now, for the time was past. I'll sleep in the dark, he thought, in his bewilderment pitying himself.

Heavily she moved on to the window. Her arm, vaguely white, rose straight from her full side and she pointed out into the darkness.

"That white speck's Sonny," she said, talking to herself.

He turned unwillingly and peered over her shoulder; he hesitated to rise and stand beside her. His eyes searched the dusky air. The white speck floated smoothly toward her finger, like a leaf on a river, growing whiter in the dark. It was as if she had shown him something secret, part of her life, but had offered no explanation. He looked away. He was moved almost to tears, feeling for no reason that she had made a silent declaration equivalent to his own. His hand waited upon his chest.

Then a step shook the house, and Sonny was in the room. Bowman felt how the woman left him there and went to the other man's side.

"I done got your car out, mister," said Sonny's voice in the dark. "She's settin' a-waitin' in the road, turned to go back where she come from."

"Fine!" said Bowman, projecting his own voice to loudness. "I'm surely much obliged—I could never have done it myself—I was sick. . . ."

"I could do it easy," said Sonny.

Bowman could feel them both waiting in the dark, and he could hear the dogs panting out in the yard, waiting to bark when he should go. He felt strangely helpless and resentful. Now that he could go, he longed to stay. From what was he being deprived? His chest was rudely shaken by the violence of his heart. These people cherished something here that he could not see, they withheld some ancient promise of food and warmth and light. Between them they had a conspiracy. He thought of the way she had moved away from him and gone to Sonny, she had flowed toward him. He was shaking with cold, he was tired, and it was not fair. Humbly and yet angrily he stuck his hand into his pocket.

"Of course I'm going to pay you for everything—"

"We don't take money for such," said Sonny's voice belligerently.

"I want to pay. But do something more . . . Let me stay—tonight. . . ." He took another step toward them. If only they could see him, they would know his sincerity, his real need! His voice went on, "I'm not very strong yet, I'm not able to walk far, even back to my car, maybe, I don't know—I don't know exactly where I am—"

He stopped. He felt as if he might burst into tears. What would they think of him!

Sonny came over and put his hands on him. Bowman felt them pass (they were professional too) across his chest, over his hips. He could feel Sonny's eyes upon him in the dark.

"You ain't no revenuer come sneakin' here, mister, ain't got no gun?"

To this end of nowhere! And yet *he* had come. He made a grave answer. "No."

"You can stay."

"Sonny," said the woman, "you'll have to borry some fire."

"I'll go git it from Redmond's," said Sonny.

"What?" Bowman strained to hear their words to each other.

"Our fire, it's out, and Sonny's got to borry some, because it's dark an' cold," she said.

"But matches—I have matches—"

"We don't have no need for 'em," she said proudly. "Sonny's goin' after his own fire."

"I'm goin' to Redmond's," said Sonny with an air of importance, and he went out.

After they had waited a while, Bowman looked out the window and saw a light moving over the hill. It spread itself out like a little fan. It zigzagged along the field, darting and swift, not like Sonny at all. . . . Soon enough, Sonny staggered in, holding a burning stick behind him in tongs, fire flowing in his wake, blazing light into the corners of the room.

"We'll make a fire now," the woman said, taking the brand.

When that was done she lit the lamp.

It showed its dark and light. The whole room turned golden-yellow like some sort of flower, and the walls smelled of it and seemed to tremble with the quiet rushing of the fire and the waving of the burning lampwick in its funnel of light.

The woman moved among the iron pots. With the tongs she dropped hot coals on top of the iron lids. They made a set of soft vibrations, like the sound of a bell far away.

She looked up and over at Bowman, but he could not answer. He was trembling. . . .

"Have a drink, mister?" Sonny asked. He had brought in a chair from the other room and sat astride it with his folded arms across the back. Now we are all visible to one another, Bowman thought, and cried, "Yes sir, you bet, thanks!"

"Come after me and do just what I do," said Sonny.

It was another excursion into the dark. They went through the hall, out to the back of the house, past a shed and a hooded well. They came to a wilderness of thicket.

"Down on your knees," said Sonny.

"What?" Sweat broke out on his forehead.

He understood when Sonny began to crawl through a sort of tunnel that the bushes made over the ground. He followed, startled in spite of himself when a twig or a thorn touched him gently without making a sound, clinging to him and finally letting him go.

Sonny stopped crawling and, crouched on his knees, began to dig with both his hands into the dirt. Bowman shyly struck matches and made a light. In a few minutes Sonny pulled up a jug. He poured out some of the whisky into a bottle from his coat pocket, and buried the jug again. "You never know who's liable to knock at your door," he said, and laughed. "Start back," he said, almost formally. "Ain't no need for us to drink outdoors, like hogs."

At the table by the fire, sitting opposite each other in their chairs, Sonny and Bowman took drinks out of the bottle, passing it across. The dogs slept; one of them was having a dream.

"This is good," said Bowman. "This is what I needed." It was just as though he were drinking the fire off the hearth.

"He makes it," said the woman with quiet pride.

She was pushing the coals off the pots, and the smells of corn bread and coffee circled the room. She set everything on the table before the men, with a bone-handled knife stuck into one of the potatoes, splitting out its golden fiber. Then she stood for a minute looking at them, tall and full above them where they sat. She leaned a little toward them.

"You all can eat now," she said, and suddenly smiled.

Bowman had just happened to be looking at her. He set his cup back on the table in unbelieving protest. A pain pressed at his eyes. He saw that she was not an old woman. She was young, still young. He could think of no number of years for her. She was the same age as Sonny, and she belonged to him. She stood with the deep dark corner of the room behind her, the shifting yellow light scattering over her head and her gray formless dress, trembling over her tall body when it bent over them in its sudden communication. She was young. Her teeth were shining and her eyes glowed. She turned and walked slowly and heavily out of the room, and he heard her sit down on the cot and then lie down. The pattern on the quilt moved.

"She's goin' to have a baby," said Sonny, popping a bite into his mouth.

Bowman could not speak. He was shocked with knowing what was really in this house. A marriage, a fruitful marriage. That simple thing. Anyone could have had that.

Somehow he felt unable to be indignant or protest, although some sort of joke had certainly been played upon him. There was nothing remote or mysterious here—only something private. The only secret was the ancient communication between two people. But the memory of the woman's waiting silently by the cold hearth, of the man's stubborn journey a mile away to get fire, and how they finally brought out their food and drink and filled the room proudly with all they had to show, was suddenly too clear and too enormous within him for response. . . .

"You ain't as hungry as you look," said Sonny.

The woman came out of the bedroom as soon as the men had finished, and ate her supper while her husband stared peacefully into the fire.

Then they put the dogs out, with the food that was left.

"I think I'd better sleep here by the fire, on the floor," said Bowman.

He felt that he had been cheated, and that he could afford now to be generous. Ill though he was, he was not going to ask them for their bed. He was through with asking favors in this house, now that he understood what was there.

"Sure, mister."

But he had not known yet how slowly he understood. They had not meant to give him their bed. After a little interval they both rose and looking at him gravely went into the other room.

He lay stretched by the fire until it grew low and dying. He watched every tongue of blaze lick out and vanish. "There will be special reduced prices on all footwear during the month of January," he found himself repeating quietly, and then he lay with his lips tight shut.

How many noises the night had! He

heard the stream running, the fire dying, and he was sure now that he heard his heart beating, too, the sound it made under his ribs. He heard breathing, round and deep, of the man and his wife in the room across the passage. And that was all. But emotion swelled patiently within him, and he wished that the child were his.

He must get back to where he had been before. He stood weakly before the red coals and put on his overcoat. It felt too heavy on his shoulders. As he started out he looked and saw that the woman had never got through with cleaning the lamp. On some impulse he put all the money from his billfold under its fluted glass base, almost ostentatiously.

Ashamed, shrugging a little, and then shivering, he took his bags and went out. The cold of the air seemed to lift him bodily. The moon was in the sky.

On the slope he began to run, he could not help it. Just as he reached the road, where his car seemed to sit in the moonlight like a boat, his heart began to give off tremendous explosions like a rifle, bang bang bang.

He sank in fright onto the road, his bags falling about him. He felt as if all this had happened before. He covered his heart with both hands to keep anyone from hearing the noise it made.

But nobody heard it.

POEMS

DEATH, BE NOT PROUD

John Donne
(1573–1631)

Death, be not proud, though some have
    calléd thee
Mighty and dreadful, for thou art not so;
For those whom thou think'st thou dost
    overthrow
Die not, poor Death; nor yet canst thou
    kill me.
From rest and sleep, which but thy picture
    be,   5
Much pleasure; then from thee much
    more must flow;
And soonest our best men with thee do
    go—
Rest of their bones and souls' delivery!
Thou'rt slave to fate, chance, kings, and
    desperate men,
And dost with poison, war, and sickness
    dwell;   10
And poppy or charms can make us sleep
    as well
And better than thy stroke. Why swell'st
    thou then?
One short sleep past, we wake eternally,
And Death shall be no more: Death, thou
    shalt die!

LYCIDAS

John Milton
(1608–1674)

*In this Monody the Author bewails a
learned Friend, * unfortunately drowned
in his passage from Chester on the Irish
Seas. 1637; and by occasion, foretells the
ruin of our corrupted Clergy, then in
their height.*

Yet once more, O ye laurels, and once
    more,
Ye myrtles brown, with ivy never sear,
I come to pluck your berries harsh and
    crude,
And with forced fingers rude
Shatter your leaves before the mellowing
    year.
Bitter constraint and sad occasion dear
Compels me to disturb your season due;
For Lycidas is dead, dead ere his prime,
Young Lycidas, and hath not left his peer.
Who would not sing for Lycidas? He
    knew   10

* Edward King, a fellow student of Milton at
Cambridge, was drowned in the Irish Sea.
  1–2. *laurels, myrtles, ivy:* evergreens which are
emblems of poetic inspiration.
  3. *crude:* unripe.

Himself to sing, and build the lofty rime.
He must not float upon his watery bier
Unwept, and welter to the parching wind,
Without the meed of some melodious
    tear.
    Begin, then, Sisters of the sacred
    well,   15
That from beneath the seat of Jove doth
    spring;
Begin, and somewhat loudly sweep the
    string.
Hence with denial vain and coy excuse;
So may some gentle muse
With lucky words favor my destined
    urn,   20
And as he passes turn
And bid fair peace be to my sable shroud!
    For we were nursed upon the self-
    same hill,
Fed the same flock, by fountain, shade,
    and rill;
Together both, ere the high lawns ap-
    peared   25
Under the opening eyelids of the Morn,
We drove afield, and both together heard
What time the gray-fly winds her sultry
    horn,
Battening our flocks with the fresh dews
    of night,
Oft till the star that rose at evening,
    bright,   30
Toward heaven's descent had sloped his
    westering wheel.
Meanwhile the rural ditties were not
    mute,
Tempered to the oaten flute;
Rough Satyrs danced, and Fauns with
    cloven heel
From the glad sound would not be absent
    long;   35
And old Damoetas loved to hear our song.
    But, oh! the heavy change, now thou
    art gone,

Now thou art gone, and never must
    return!
Thee, Shepherd, thee the woods and desert
    caves,
With wild thyme and the gadding vine
    o'ergrown,   40
And all their echoes, mourn.
The willows, and the hazel copses green,
Shall now no more be seen
Fanning their joyous leaves to thy soft
    lays.
As killing as the canker to the rose,   45
Or taint-worm to the weanling herds that
    graze,
Or frost to flowers, that their gay ward-
    robe wear,
When first the white-thorn blows—
Such, Lycidas, thy loss to shepherd's ear.
    Where were ye, Nymphs, when the
    remorseless deep   50
Closed o'er the head of your loved
    Lycidas?
For neither were ye playing on the steep
Where your old bards, the famous Druids,
    lie,
Nor on the shaggy top of Mona high,
Nor yet where Deva spreads her wizard
    stream.   55
Aye me! I fondly dream
"Had ye been there"—for what could that
    have done?
What could the Muse herself that Orpheus
    bore,
The Muse herself, for her enchanting son,
Whom universal nature did lament,   60
When, by the rout that made the hideous
    roar,
His gory visage down the stream was sent,
Down the swift Hebrus to the Lesbian
    shore?
    Alas! what boots it with uncessant
    care

14. *meed:* reward.
15. *Sisters of the sacred well:* the Nine Muses.
29. *Battening:* feeding.
36. *Damoetas:* a stock name in classical poetry for an elderly shepherd. Here Milton probably is alluding to a Cambridge tutor.

52–55. All the places mentioned are near where King drowned.
58–63. *What could the Muse . . . Lesbian shore?:* The musician Orpheus was dismembered by the Thracian women, and his head, cast into the river Hebrus, floated to the isle of Lesbos. Even though his mother, Calliope, was the Muse of Poetry, she could not protect or save him.

To tend the homely, slighted shepherd's
   trade,   65
And strictly meditate the thankless Muse?
Were it not better done as others use,
To sport with Amaryllis in the shade,
Or with the tangles of Neaera's hair?
Fame is the spur that the clear spirit doth
   raise   70
(That last infirmity of noble mind)
To scorn delights, and live laborious days;
But, the fair guerdon when we hope to
   find,
And think to burst out into sudden blaze,
Comes the blind Fury with the abhorréd
   shears,   75
And slits the thin-spun life. "But not the
   praise,"
Phoebus replied, and touched my trem-
   bling ears;
"Fame is no plant that grows on mortal
   soil,
Nor in the glistering foil
Set off to the world, nor in broad rumor
   lies,   80
But lives and spreads aloft by those pure
   eyes
And perfect witness of all-judging Jove;
As he pronounces lastly on each deed,
Of so much fame in heaven expect thy
   meed."
   O fountain Arthuse, and thou hon-
   ored flood.   85
Smooth-sliding Mincius, crowned with
   vocal reeds,

That strain I heard was of a higher mood.
But now my oat proceeds,
And listens to the Herald of the Sea
That came in Neptune's plea.   90
He asked the waves, and asked the felon
   winds,
What hard mishaps hath doomed this
   gentle swain!
And questioned every gust of rugged
   wings
That blows from off each beakéd prom-
   ontory.
They knew not of his story;   95
And sage Hippotades their answer brings,
That not a blast was from his dungeon
   strayed;
The air was calm, and on the level brine
Sleek Panope with all her sisters played.
It was that fatal and perfidious bark, 100
Built in the eclipse, and rigged with curses
   dark,
That sunk so low that sacred head of
   thine.
   Next, Camus, reverend sire, went
   footing slow,
His mantle hairy, and his bonnet sedge,
Inwrought with figures dim, and on the
   edge   105
Like to that sanguine flower inscribed
   with woe.
"Ah! who hath reft," quoth he, "my
   dearest pledge?"
Last came, and last did go,
The Pilot of the Galilean Lake;
Two massy keys he bore of metals
   twain   110
(The golden opes, the iron shuts amain).

65–66. *To tend . . . thankless Muse?:* to write
poetry.
68–69. *Amaryllis, Neaera:* conventional names
for nymphs in Greek pastoral poetry.
73. *guerdon:* reward.
75. *the blind Fury:* in Greek myth Atropos,
the third of the three Fates, who cut the thread
of human life, was blind.
77. *Phoebus:* Apollo, the god of poetic inspiration.
   touched my trembling ears: a symbolic
act thought in classic times to enhance memory.
85. *Arethuse:* a fountain in Sicily associated
with the pastorals of Theocritus. According to
legend, Arethuse was a nymph pursued by the
river god, Alpheus, from Greece to Sicily, where
Artemis transformed her into a fountain.
86. *Mincius:* a river in Italy celebrated by
Virgil.

88. *oat:* pipe, a symbol of pastoral song.
89. *Herald of the Sea:* Triton, the messenger
of Neptune.
96. *Hippotades:* Aeolus, god of the winds.
99. *Panope:* the chief sea nymph.
101. *in the eclipse:* an unlucky time.
103. *Camus:* God of the river Cam, in Cambridge.
106. *sanguine flower:* purple hyacinth; the
markings on the hyacinth resemble the Greek
word for "alas."
109. *Pilot of the Galilean Lake:* St. Peter, originally a fisherman, who, given the keys to heaven
and hell, became the first Christian bishop.

He shook his mitered locks, and stern
  bespake:
"How well could I have spared for thee,
  young swain,
Enow of such as, for their bellies' sake,
Creep, and intrude, and climb into the
  fold!   115
Of other care they little reckoning make
Than how to scramble at the shearers'
  feast,
And shove away the worthy bidden guest.
Blind mouths! that scarce themselves
  know how to hold
A sheep-hook, or have learned aught else
  the least   120
That to the faithful herdman's art belongs!
What recks it them? What need they?
  They are sped;
And, when they list, their lean and flashy
  songs
Grate on their scrannel pipes of wretched
  straw;
The hungry sheep look up, and are not
  fed,   125
But, swoln with wind and the rank mist
  they draw,
Rot inwardly, and foul contagion spread;
Besides what the grim wolf with privy paw
Daily devours apace, and nothing said.
But that two-handed engine at the
  door   130
Stands ready to smite once, and smite no
  more."
  Return, Alpheus, the dread voice is
  past
That shrunk thy streams; return, Sicilian
  Muse,

112. *mitered locks:* the bishop's headdress.
114. *Enow:* enough.
120. *A sheep-hook:* allusion to the bishop's
pastoral staff.
122. *sped:* taken care of.
123. *list:* wish.
124. *scrannel:* harsh.
128. *the grim wolf with privy paw:* Roman
Catholicism, which operated in secret.
130. *that two-handed engine:* an obscure figure
probably referring to some instrument of revenge.
132. *Alpheus:* see footnote for line 85.
133. *Sicilian Muse:* pastoral poetry.

And call the vales, and bid them hither
  cast
Their bells and flowerets of a thousand
  hues.   135
Ye valleys low, where the mild whispers
  use
Of shades, and wanton winds, and gushing
  brooks,
On whose fresh lap the swart star sparely
  looks,
Throw hither all your quaint enameled
  eyes,
That on the green turf suck the honeyed
  showers,   140
And purple all the ground with vernal
  flowers.
Bring the rathe primrose that forsaken
  dies,
The tufted crow-toe, and pale jessa-
  mine,
The white pink, and the pansy freaked
  with jet,
The glowing violet,   145
The musk-rose, and the well-attired wood-
  bine,
With cowslips wan that hang the pensive
  head,
And every flower that sad embroidery
  wears;
Bid amaranthus all his beauty shed,
And daffodillies fill their cups with
  tears,   150
To strew the laureate hearse where Lycid
  lies.
For so, to interpose a little ease,
Let our frail thoughts dally with false
  surmise.
Aye me! Whilst thee the shores and
  sounding seas
Wash far away, where'er thy bones are
  hurled   155
Whether beyond the stormy Hebrides,
Where thou perhaps under the whelming
  tide

138. *the swart star:* Sirius, the Dog Star,
thought to wither vegetation.
142. *rathe:* early.
144. *freaked:* spotted.

Visit'st the bottom of the monstrous world;
Or whether thou, to our moist vows denied,
Sleep'st by the fable of Bellerus old, 160
Where the great Vision of the guarded mount
Looks toward Namancos and Bayona's hold.
Look homeward, Angel, now, and melt with ruth;
And, O ye dolphins, waft the hapless youth.
    Weep no more, woeful shepherds, weep no more, 165
For Lycidas, your sorrow, is not dead,
Sunk though he be beneath the watery floor;
So sinks the day-star in the ocean bed,
And yet anon repairs his drooping head,
And tricks his beams, and with new-spangled ore 170
Flames in the forehead of the morning sky.
So Lycidas sunk low, but mounted high,
Through the dear might of Him that walked the waves,
Where, other groves and other streams along,
With nectar pure his oozy locks he laves, 175
And hears the unexpressive nuptial song,
In the blest kingdoms meek of joy and love.
There entertain him all the Saints above,
In solemn troops, and sweet societies,
That sing, and singing in their glory move, 180
And wipe the tears forever from his eyes.

160. *Bellerus:* a giant who was supposed to lie buried on Land's End in Cornwall.
161. *the guarded mount:* St. Michael's Mount, an island in Cornwall.
162. *Namancos and Bayona:* two towns on the north coast of Spain.
163. *Angel:* St. Michael.
    ruth: pity.
170. *tricks:* adorns.
176. *unexpressive:* inexpressibly beautiful.

Now, Lycidas, the shepherds weep no more;
Henceforth thou art the Genius of the shore,
In thy large recompense, and shalt be good
To all that wander in that perilous flood. 185
    Thus sang the uncouth swain to the oaks and rills,
While the still morn went out with sandals gray;
He touched the tender stops of various quills,
With eager thought warbling his Doric lay.
And now the sun had stretched out all the hills, 190
And now was dropped into the western bay.
At last he rose, and twitched his mantle blue;
Tomorrow to fresh woods and pastures new.

183. *Genius:* guardian spirit.
188. *quills:* reeds in his pastoral flute.
189. *Doric lay:* pastoral poetry.

ODE TO A NIGHTINGALE

John Keats
(1795–1821)

My heart aches, and a drowsy numbness pains
    My sense, as though of hemlock I had drunk,
Or emptied some dull opiate to the drains
    One minute past, and Lethe-wards had sunk:
'Tis not through envy of thy happy lot, 5
    But being too happy in thine happiness—

4. *Lethe:* a river in Hades whose waters caused forgetfulness.

That thou, light-wingéd Dryad of
  the trees,
  In some melodious plot
Of beechen green, and shadows numberless,
Singest of summer in full-throated
  ease.   10

O, for a draught of vintage! that hath
  been
Cooled a long age in the deep-delvéd
  earth,
Tasting of Flora and the country green,
Dance, and Provençal song, and sun-
  burnt mirth!
O for a beaker full of the warm South, 15
Full of the true, the blushful Hippo-
  crene,
  With beaded bubbles winking at the
    brim,
    And purple-stainéd mouth;
That I might drink, and leave the world
  unseen,
  And with thee fade away into the
    forest dim: 20

Fade far away, dissolve, and quite forget
  What thou among the leaves hast never
    known,
The weariness, the fever, and the fret
  Here, where men sit and hear each
    other groan;
Where palsy shakes a few, sad, last gray
  hairs,   25
  Where youth grows pale, and specter-
    thin, and dies;
  Where but to think is to be full of
    sorrow
    And leaden-eyed despairs,
  Where Beauty cannot keep her lustrous
    eyes,
  Or new Love pine at them beyond to-
    morrow.   30

Away! away! for I will fly to thee,
  Not charioted by Bacchus and his
    pards,
But on the viewless wings of Poesy,
  Though the dull brain perplexes and re-
    tards:
Already with thee! tender is the night,   35
  And haply the Queen-Moon is on her
    throne,
    Clustered around by all her starry
      Fays;
    But here there is no light,
  Save what from heaven is with the
    breezes blown
  Through verdurous glooms and
    winding mossy ways.   40

I cannot see what flowers are at my feet,
  Nor what soft incense hangs upon the
    boughs,
But, in embalméd darkness, guess each
  sweet
  Wherewith the seasonable month en-
    dows
The grass, the thicket, and the fruit-tree
  wild;   45
  White hawthorn, and the pastoral
    eglantine;
    Fast fading violets covered up in
      leaves;
    And mid-May's eldest child.
The coming musk-rose, full of dewy wine,
  The murmurous haunt of flies on sum-
    mer eves.   50

Darkling I listen; and, for many a time,
  I have been half in love with easeful
    Death,
Called him soft names in many a muséd
  rime,
  To take into the air my quiet breath;
Now more than ever seems it rich to die, 55

---

7. *Dryad:* tree nymph.
13. *Flora:* Roman goddess of flowers.
14. *Provençal:* a province in France, home of
the troubadours.
16. *Hippocrene:* sacred fountain of the Muses.

32. *Bacchus:* Roman god of wine.
  pards: leopards.
33. *viewless:* invisible.
37. *Fays:* fairies.
43. *embalméd:* fragrant.
51. *Darkling:* in the dark.

To cease upon the midnight with no
   pain,
  While thou art pouring forth thy soul
    abroad
      In such an ecstasy!
Still wouldst thou sing, and I have ears in
   vain—
    To thy high requiem become a
      sod.   60

Thou wast not born for death, immortal
   Bird!
  No hungry generations tread thee
    down;
The voice I hear this passing night was
   heard
In ancient days by emperor and clown:
Perhaps the self-same song that found a
   path   65
  Through the sad heart of Ruth, when,
    sick for home,
    She stood in tears amid the alien
      corn;
      The same that oft-times hath
  Charmed magic casements, opening on
    the foam
    Of perilous seas, in faery lands for-
      lorn.   70

Forlorn! the very word is like a bell
  To toll me back from thee to my sole
    self,
Adieu! the fancy cannot cheat so well
  As she is famed to do, deceiving elf.
Adieu! adieu! thy plaintive anthem
   fades   75
  Past the near meadows, over the still
    stream,
    Up the hillside; and now 'tis buried
      deep
      In the next valley glades:
Was it a vision, or a waking dream?
  Fled is that music—Do I wake or
    sleep?   80

66–67. see Ruth 2.
70. *forlorn:* now passed.

BY NIGHT WE LINGERED ON THE LAWN *

Alfred, Lord Tennyson
(1809–1892)

(From *In Memoriam A. H. H.*)

By night we lingered on the lawn,
  For underfoot the herb was dry;
  And genial warmth; and o'er the sky
The silver haze of summer drawn;

And calm that let the tapers burn   5
  Unwavering. Not a cricket chirred;
  The brook alone far-off was heard,
And on the board the fluttering urn.

And bats went round in fragrant skies,
  And wheeled or lit the filmy shapes 10
  That haunt the dusk, with ermine capes
And woolly breasts and beaded eyes;

While now we sang old songs that pealed
  From knoll to knoll, where, couched at
    ease,
  The white kine glimmered, and the
    trees   15
Laid their dark arms about the field.

But when those others, one by one,
  Withdrew themselves from me and
    night,
  And in the house light after light
Went out, and I was all alone,   20

A hunger seized my heart; I read
  Of that glad year which once had been,
  In those fallen leaves which kept their
    green,
The noble letters of the dead.

And strangely on the silence broke   25

* This is Poem 95 of Tennyson's elegiac cycle
dedicated to his close friend, Arthur Hallam
(A. H. H.).
  8. *fluttering urn:* the boiling tea urn.
  10. *filmy shapes:* night moths.

The silent-speaking words, and strange
Was love's dumb cry defying change
To test his worth; and strangely spoke

The faith, the vigor, bold to dwell
    On doubts that drive the coward
        back,   30
    And keen through wordy snares to track
Suggestion to her inmost cell.

So word by word, and line by line,
    The dead man touched me from the
        past,
    And all at once it seemed at last   35
The living soul was flashed on mine,

And mine in his was wound, and whirled
    About empyreal heights of thought,
    And came on that which is, and caught
The deep pulsations of the world,   40

Aeonian music measuring out
    The steps of Time—the shocks of
        Chance—
    The blows of Death. At length my
        trance

36. *The living soul:* "His living soul" (Hallam's) was the original reading.
41. *Aeonian music:* harmony of the ages.

Was canceled, stricken through with
    doubt.

Vague words! but ah, how hard to
    frame   45
    In matter-molded forms of speech,
    Or even for intellect to reach
Through memory that which I became;

Till now the doubtful dusk revealed
    The knolls once more where, couched
        at ease,   50
    The white kine glimmered, and the
        trees
Laid their dark arms about the field;

And sucked from out the distant gloom
    A breeze began to tremble o'er
    The large leaves of the sycamore,   55
And fluctuate all the still perfume,

And gathering freshlier overhead,
    Rocked the full-foliaged elms, and
        swung
    The heavy-folded rose, and flung
The lilies to and fro, and said,   60

"The dawn, the dawn," and died away;
    And East and West, without a breath,
    Mixed their dim lights, like life and
        death,
To broaden into boundless day.

"COME LOVELY AND SOOTHING DEATH"

Walt Whitman
(1819–92)

(From *When Lilacs Last in the Dooryard Bloom'd*)

Come lovely and soothing death,
Undulate round the world, serenely arriving, arriving,
In the day, in the night, to all, to each,
Sooner or later delicate death.

Prais'd be the fathomless universe,   5
For life and joy, and for objects and knowledge curious,

And for love, sweet love—but praise! praise! praise!
For the sure-enwinding arms of cool-enfolding death.

Dark mother always gliding near with soft feet,
Have none chanted for thee a chant of fullest welcome?   10
Then I chant it for thee, I glorify thee above all,
I bring thee a song that when thou must indeed come, come unfalteringly.

Approach strong deliveress,
When it is so, when thou hast taken them I joyously sing the dead,
Lost in the loving floating ocean of thee,   15
Laved in the flood of thy bliss O death.

From me to thee glad serenades,
Dances for thee I propose saluting thee, adornments and feastings for thee,
And the sights of the open landscape and the high-spread sky are fitting,
And life and the fields, and the huge and thoughtful night.   20

The night in silence under many a star,
The ocean shore and the husky whispering wave whose voice I know,
And the soul turning to thee O vast and well-veil'd death,
And the body gratefully nestling close to thee.

Over the tree-tops I float thee a song,   25
Over the rising and sinking waves, over the myriad fields and the prairies wide,
Over the dense-pack'd cities all and the teeming wharves and ways,
I float this carol with joy, with joy to thee O death.

AND DEATH SHALL HAVE NO DOMINION

Dylan Thomas
(1914–1953)

And death shall have no dominion.
Dead men naked they shall be one
With the man in the wind and the west moon;
When their bones are picked clean and the clean bones gone,
They shall have stars at elbow and foot;   5
Though they go mad they shall be sane,
Though they sink through the sea they shall rise again;
Though lovers be lost love shall not;
And death shall have no dominion.

And death shall have no dominion.   10
Under the windings of the sea
They lying long shall not die windily;

Twisting on racks when sinews give way,
Strapped to a wheel, yet they shall not break;
Faith in their hands shall snap in two,   15
And the unicorn evils run them through;
Split all ends up they shan't crack;
And death shall have no dominion.

And death shall have no dominion.
No more may gulls cry at their ears   20
Or waves break loud on the seashores;
Where blew a flower may a flower no more
Lift its head to the blows of the rain;
Though they be mad and dead as nails,
Heads of the characters hammer through daisies;   25
Break in the sun till the sun breaks down,
And death shall have no dominion.

■ ■ ■

THE LAST NIGHT THAT SHE LIVED

Emily Dickinson
(1830–1886)

The last night that she lived,
It was a common night,
Except the dying; this to us
Made nature different.

We noticed smallest things,—   · 5
Things overlooked before,
By this great light upon our minds
Italicized, as 'twere.

As we went out and in
Between her final room   10
And rooms where those to be alive
Tomorrow were, a blame

That others could exist
While she must finish quite,
A jealousy for her arose   15
So nearly infinite.

We waited while she passed;
It was a narrow time,
Too jostled were our souls to speak,

At length the notice came.   20

She mentioned, and forgot;
Then lightly as a reed
Bent to the water, shivered scarce,
Consented, and was dead.

And we, we placed the hair,   25
And drew the head erect;
And then an awful leisure was,
Our faith to regulate.

AT MELVILLE'S TOMB

Hart Crane
(1899–1932)

Often beneath the wave, wide from this
     ledge
The dice of drowned men's bones he saw
     bequeath
An embassy. Their numbers as he watched,
Beat on the dusty shore and were ob-
     scured.

And wrecks passed without sound of
     bells,   5
The calyx of death's bounty giving back
A scattered chapter, livid hieroglyph,

The portent wound in corridors of shells.

Then in the circuit calm of one vast coil,
Its lashings charmed and malice recon-
ciled,   10
Frosted eyes there were that lifted altars;
And silent answers crept across the stars.

Compass, quadrant and sextant contrive
No farther tides . . . High in the azure
steeps
Monody shall not wake the mariner.   15
This fabulous shadow only the sea keeps.

MUSEE DES BEAUX ARTS

W. H. Auden
(1907–   )

About suffering they were never wrong,
The Old Masters: how well they under-
stood
Its human position; how it takes place
While someone else is eating or opening
a window or just walking dully along;
How, when the aged are reverently, pas-
sionately waiting   5
For the miraculous birth, there always
must be
Children who did not specially want it to
happen, skating
On a pond at the edge of the wood:
They never forgot
That even the dreadful martyrdom must
run its course   10
Anyhow in a corner, some untidy spot
Where the dogs go on with their doggy
life and the torturer's horse
Scratches its innocent behind on a tree.

In Breughel's *Icarus,* for instance: how
everything turns away
Quite leisurely from the disaster; the
ploughman may   15
Have heard the splash, the forsaken cry,

But for him it was not an important failure; the sun shone
As it had to on the white legs disappearing into the green
Water; and the expensive delicate ship
that must have seen
Something amazing, a boy falling out of
the sky,   20
Had somewhere to get to and sailed
calmly on.

■   ■   ■

"AY, BUT TO DIE, AND GO WE KNOW NOT WHERE" *

William Shakespeare
(1564–1616)

(From *Measure for Measure,* III, i, 118–
131)

Claudio.   Ay, but to die, and go we
know not where;
To lie in cold obstruction and to rot;
This sensible warm motion to become
A kneaded clod; and the delighted
spirit   120
To bathe in fiery floods, or to reside
In thrilling region of thick-ribbed ice,
To be imprison'd in the viewless winds,
And blown with restless violence round
about
The pendent world; or to be worse than
worst   125
Of those that lawless and incertain
thought
Imagine howling: 'tis too horrible!
The weariest and most loathed worldly
life
That age, ache, penury and imprisonment

* In this scene, Claudio, who expects soon to
be executed, gives voice to his fear of death.
118. *obstruction:* the vital processes no longer
function.
122. *thrilling:* causing one to shiver.

Can lay on nature is a paradise 130
To what we fear of death.

WHAT IS OUR LIFE?

Sir Walter Raleigh
(1552–1618)

What is our life? a play of passion;
Our mirth, the music of division;
Our mothers' wombs the tiring-house be
Where we are dressed for this short
    comedy.
Heaven the judicious sharp spectator is, 5
That sits and marks still who doth act
    amiss;
Our graves that hide us from the search-
    ing sun
Are like drawn curtains when the play is
    done.
Thus march we playing to our latest rest;
Only we die in earnest—that's no jest. 10

2. *music of division:* rapid variations on a
theme.
   3. *tiring-houses:* dressing rooms.
   6. *still:* continually.

DARK HOUSE, BY WHICH ONCE MORE I STAND *

Alfred, Lord Tennyson
(1809–1892)

(From *In Memoriam A. H. H.*)

Dark house, by which once more I stand
    Here in the long unlovely street,
    Doors, where my heart was used to
      beat
So quickly, waiting for a hand,

A hand that can be clasped no more— 5

* This is Poem 7 of Tennyson's elegiac cycle
dedicated to his close friend, Arthur Hallam
(A. H. H.).

Behold me, for I cannot sleep,
    And like a guilty thing I creep
At earliest morning to the door.

He is not here; but far away
    The noise of life begins again, 10
    And ghastly thro' the drizzling rain
On the bald street breaks the blank day.

DIRGE WITHOUT MUSIC

Edna St. Vincent Millay
(1892–1950)

I am not resigned to the shutting away of
    loving hearts in the hard ground.
So it is, and so it will be, for so it has
    been, time out of mind:
Into the darkness they go, the wise and
    the lovely. Crowned
With lilies and with laurel they go; but I
    am not resigned.

Lovers and thinkers, into the earth with
    you. 5
Be one with the dull, the indiscriminate
    dust.
A fragment of what you felt, of what you
    knew,
A formula, a phrase remains,—but the
    best is lost.

The answers quick and keen, the honest
    look, the laughter, the love,—
They are gone. They are gone to feed the
    roses. Elegant and curled 10
Is the blossom. Fragrant is the blossom. I
    know. But I do not approve.
More precious was the light in your eyes
    than all the roses of the world.

Down, down, down into the darkness of
    the grave
Gently they go, the beautiful, the tender,
    the kind;

Quietly they go, the intelligent, the witty,
    the brave.   15
I know. But I do not approve. And I am
    not resigned.

THE EMPEROR OF ICE-CREAM

Wallace Stevens
(1879–1955)

Call the roller of big cigars,
The muscular one, and bid him whip
In kitchen cups concupiscent curds.
Let the wenches dawdle in such dress
As they are used to wear, and let the
    boys   5
Bring flowers in last month's newspapers.
Let be be finale of seem.
The only emperor is the emperor of ice-
    cream.

Take from the dresser of deal,
Lacking the three glass knobs, that sheet 10
On which she embroidered fantails once
And spread it so as to cover her face.
If her horny feet protrude, they come
To show how cold she is, and dumb.
Let the lamp affix its beam.   15
The only emperor is the emperor of ice-
    cream.

    9. *deal:* fir or pine.

THE GROUNDHOG

Richard Eberhart
(1904–   )

In June, amid the golden fields,
I saw a groundhog lying dead.
Dead lay he; my senses shook,
And mind outshot our naked frailty.
There lowly in the vigorous summer   5

His form began its senseless change,
And made my senses waver dim
Seeing nature ferocious in him.
Inspecting close his maggots' might
And seething cauldron of his being,   10
Half with loathing, half with a strange
    love,
I poked him with an angry stick.
The fever arose, became a flame
And Vigour circumscribed the skies,
Immense energy in the sun,   15
And through my frame a sunless trem-
    bling.
My stick had done nor good nor harm.
Then stood I silent in the day
Watching the object, as before;
And kept my reverence for knowledge 20
Trying for control, to be still,
To quell the passion of the blood;
Until I had bent down on my knees
Praying for joy in the sight of decay.
And so I left; and I returned   25
In Autumn strict of eye, to see
The sap gone out of the groundhog,
But the bony sodden hulk remained.
But the year had lost its meaning,
And in intellectual chains   30
I lost both love and loathing,
Mured up in the wall of wisdom.
Another summer took the fields again
Massive and burning, full of life,
But when I chanced upon the spot   35
There was only a little hair left,
And bones bleaching in the sunlight
Beautiful as architecture;
I watched them like a geometer,
And cut a walking stick from a birch.   40
It has been three years, now.
There is no sign of the groundhog.
I stood there in the whirling summer,
My hand capped a withered heart,
And thought of China and of Greece,   45
Of Alexander in his tent;
Of Montaigne in his tower,
Of Saint Theresa in her wild lament.

■   ■   ■

THREE THINGS

W. B. Yeats
(1865–1939)

"O cruel Death, give three things back,"
Sang a bone upon the shore;
"A child found all a child can lack,
Whether of pleasure or of rest,
Upon the abundance of my breast":   5
*A bone wave-whitened and dried in the
   wind.*

"Three dear things that women know,"
Sang a bone upon the shore;
"A man if I but held him so
When my body was alive   10
Found all the pleasure that life gave":
*A bone wave-whitened and dried in the
   wind.*

"The third thing that I think of yet,"
Sang a bone upon the shore;
"Is that morning when I met   15
Face to face my rightful man
And did after stretch and yawn":
*A bone wave-whitened and dried in the
   wind.*

IV

SOME VARIETIES OF RELIGIOUS BELIEF

FOREWORD

Religious belief has been defined as the relationship of the individual to the "Other." Christianity, pantheism, and skepticism are three of the many forms of that relationship reflected in literature. It should be kept in mind, however, that religious belief is so personal that any significant writer's vision will have a unique quality.

Simone Weil's essay, though it might be characterized as Christian mysticism, is an example of just such label-defying individuality. D. H. Lawrence makes significant qualifications, yet his position is fundamentally a pantheistic view of the "Other" as Nature. William Stace's skepticism leads him to conclude, no matter how regretfully, that man must accept "the death of God" and of religion. Julian Huxley's essay provides an objective counterpoint to the more doctrinaire approach of the other essayists.

Tolstoi's moving story is essentially Christian in theme. Once again Lawrence represents the pantheistic world-view. The tale by Kafka is intriguingly ambiguous, but it can be considered as a fable of skepticism.

Herbert, Donne, Hopkins, and Eliot are among the most profoundly Christian poets in the English language. The next two categories (four poems each) represent respectively individual versions of pantheism and skepticism.

ESSAYS

A WAR OF RELIGIONS

Simone Weil
(1909–1943)

Men have often dreamed of abolishing the religious problem. Lucretius for one: "So many crimes has religion counselled!" The Encyclopedists thought they had succeeded, and their influence was indeed effectively felt in all countries all over the world.

Nevertheless, there is perhaps not one human being on earth today who is not suffering intimately, in his daily life, from the repercussions of a single religious drama whose theatre is the whole world.

The reason why man cannot evade the religious problem is because he finds the opposition of good and evil an intolerable burden. It makes an atmosphere in which he cannot breathe.

According to an Albigensian tradition, the devil seduced men by telling them: "With God you are unfree, because you can do only good. Follow me and you will have the power to do good or evil as you choose." And this is confirmed by experience, for men lose their innocence every day far more often to the lure of knowledge and experiment than to the lure of pleasure.

Man followed the devil. He got what the devil promised. But once he possessed good and evil he was as happy as a child who has picked up a red-hot coal. He would like to drop it; but he finds it is not so easy.

There are three ways of doing it. The first is an irreligious way. It consists in denying the reality of the opposition between good and evil. It has been attempted in this century. Blake's horrible words have been widely echoed by our contemporaries: "Sooner murder an infant in its cradle than nurse unacted desires."

But effort is not directed by desire but by its objective. The very essence of man is directed effort; both movements of the mind and movements of the body are examples of it. When direction ceases man becomes mad in the literal, medical sense. So this method, being based on the principle that all objectives are equal, leads to madness. It imposes no constraint, and yet it condemns man to a tedium like that of a prisoner in solitary confinement, where the worst torture is having nothing to do.

Europe fell into this tedium after the First World War. That is why she made hardly any effort to escape the concentration camps.

In prosperity, when our resources are abundant, we try to cheat this tedium by playing games. Not the games of children, who believe in their play. The games of grown-up men in prison.

But in affliction our resources are too weak for our needs. There is no longer any problem of how to direct our energies. There is nothing left to direct but hope. The hope of the afflicted is no material for games. The emptiness now becomes unbearable. The theory that all objectives are equal is repelled with horror.

That is what has happened in Europe. The reaction of horror has been felt by each nation in turn, as misfortune overtook it.

The second method of evasion is idolatry. It is a religious method, if one gives to the word religion the meaning given to it by French sociologists, that is to say, the adoration of the social under various divine names. This was compared by Plato to the cult of a great beast.

The method consists in delimiting a social area into which the pair of contradictories, good and evil, may not enter. In so far as he is contained within this area, man is freed from the two contradictories.

This method is frequently employed. Scientists and artists often make science and art a closed area within which there is no place for virtue or vice, whence they conclude that in their capacity of scientist or artist they are absolved from all moral responsibility. Soldiers and priests sometimes do the same, and in this way they justify the devastation of cities or the Inquisition. In general, throughout history this art of delimiting special areas has enabled men who did not appear to be monsters to perpetrate innumerable monstrous crimes.

But the method is not completely successful unless the special area is comprehensive. A scientist is not free from good and evil in his capacity of father, husband, or citizen. For complete freedom, the area from which good and evil are banished must be such that it can contain the whole man.

A nation can do this. In antiquity both Rome and Israel were such nations. Once a Roman had divested himself in his own eyes of every quality except that of being a Roman he was emancipated from good and evil. He was controlled by no law except the purely animal urge to expansion and had no duty except to rule other nations as absolute master, with more or less of leniency towards the obedient and utter ruthlessness towards the proud. The means to be employed were judged solely from the point of view of their efficacy.

A church, too, can perform this role. The emergence of the Inquisition in the Middle Ages shows that a strain of totalitarianism had found its way into Christianity. Fortunately it did not triumph; but it probably blighted that Christian civilization which the Middle Ages were on the point of bringing to flower.

At the present time the role is only played by nations, and not directly but through the intermediary of a party of the State and its associated organs. In the countries with a single party the party member who has renounced every quality except that of party membership can no longer sin. He may be clumsy, like a servant who breaks a plate; but whatever he does he can never sin, because he is nothing but a member of a body—of the Party, the Nation—which can do no wrong.

He never loses this immunity, this armour, unless he suddenly turns back into a creature of flesh and blood, or a man with a soul, that is to say, into something other than a piece of the great body. Yet so precious is the privilege of emancipation from good and evil that many men and women, having chosen once for all, can stand firm against love, friendship, physical suffering, and death.

But they pay a high price for this immunity and it is not surprising that by way of compensation they should enjoy torturing the weak. Their unrestricted licence has been purchased so dearly that they must assure themselves by experiment of its reality.

Like those who are indifferent to good and evil, these idolaters become in the end the victims of a kind of madness. But the two kinds of madness are very different. Germany suffered a more exaggerated form of the first kind than any other European nation, and her reaction from it was proportionately violent. But in plunging into the idolater's madness she retained a great deal of the former kind. The resulting product of the two has been for several years the horror and terror of the world.

Nevertheless, we ought not to hide from ourselves, we people of the twentieth century, that Germany is a mirror for all of us. What looks to us so hideous is our own features, but magnified. This thought, however, ought not to weaken our fighting spirit, but the opposite.

Idolatry is degrading. Fortunately, it is also precarious, because the idol is perishable. Rome was sacked in the end and reduced to servitude. In folklore there are many stories of giants who are invulnerable because they have hidden their soul inside an egg inside a fish in a far distant lake which is guarded by dragons. But one day a young man discovers the secret and gets possession of the egg and kills the giant. The mistake of the giant was to put his soul in an earthly hiding-place, in this world. Hitler's young S.S. men make the same mistake. To be safe, one must hide the soul elsewhere.

The third method consists in doing this. It is the mystical way. Mysticism means passing beyond the sphere where good and evil are in opposition, and this is achieved by the union of the soul with the absolute good. Absolute good is different from the good which is the opposite and correlative of evil, although it is its pattern and its source.

This union is an operation that is real and effective. Just as a young girl is no longer virgin after she has had a husband or a lover, so the soul which has experienced such a union is changed for ever.

The transformation is the opposite of what took place when men followed the devil. It is therefore a very difficult operation—much more so even than the conversion of heat into movement—it is even an impossible one; it is contrary to the law of entropy. But the impossible is possible for God. In a sense, indeed, it is only the impossible that is possible for God. He has given over the possible to the mechanics of matter and the autonomy of his creatures.

The process and the effects of this transformation were the subject of the most minute experimental study in antiquity, by the Egyptians, the Greeks, the Hindus, the Chinese, and probably many others, and in the Middle Ages by several Buddhist sects, by Mahommedans, and by Christians. For several centuries now they have been more or less forgotten in all countries.

The very nature of such a transformation makes it impossible to hope for its accomplishment by a whole people. But the whole life of a people may be permeated by a religion entirely oriented towards mysticism. It is only by this orientation that religion is distinguished from idolatry.

The French school of sociology is very nearly right in its social explanation of religion. It only fails to explain one infinitely small thing; but this infinitely small thing is the grain of mustard seed, the buried pearl, the leaven, the salt. This infinitely small thing is God; it is infinitely more than everything.

All that is needed is to place it at the centre of life, whether of a people or of an individual soul. Everything that is not directly in contact with it should be, as it were, impregnated by it through the mediation of beauty. This very nearly came to pass in the Romanesque Middle Ages, that amazing epoch when men's eyes and ears were refreshed every day by a beauty which was perfect in simplicity and purity.

The difference is infinitely small between a system of labour which leads men to discover the beauty of the world and one which hides it from them. But this infinitely small difference is real, and no effort of the imagination can bridge it.

Speaking in a general way it would not be far from the truth to say that always and everywhere until quite recent times work has been organized on the basis of guilds or corporations. Institutions like slavery, serfdom, or a proletariat were parasitic growths upon the corporative system, like a cancer that attacks an organ. For several centuries now the cancer has replaced the organ.

When fascism flaunts the corporative ideal it is no more sincere than when it talks of peace. And in any case, what is called a corporative régime nowadays has nothing at all in common with the ancient guilds or corporations. Anti-fascism, too, may one day adopt the same slogan and, under cover of it, lapse into a totalitarian form of State capitalism. A true corporative régime will only develop in a social soil that is spiritually prepared for it.

Affliction came to Germany in the form of an economic crisis; it drove her violently from the moral desert into a frenzy of idolatry. Affliction came to France in the form of conquest; a conquered people cannot indulge in nationalistic idolatry.

None of the three methods of emancipation from good and evil is available to slaves or enslaved peoples. On the other hand, evil enters into them day after day through the pains and humiliations they suffer, and it awakens evil within them in the form of fear and hatred. They can neither forget evil nor can they escape from it, and so they live in the best possible imitation of hell on earth.

But not all of the three methods are equally inaccessible. Two of them are impossible. The supernatural one is only difficult. The sole access to it is through spiritual poverty. Just as the virtue of spiritual poverty is indispensable for the rich, to save them from the defilement of riches, so it is indispensable for the afflicted, to save them from disintegrating in affliction. It is equally difficult for both. Enslaved and oppressed Europe will not see better days, when she is liberated, unless spiritual poverty has first taken root in her.

The masses are impotent to create civilization unless they are inspired by a genuine *élite*. What is needed today is an *élite* to inspire the virtue of spiritual poverty among the ill-used masses; and for this it is necessary that the *élite* shall be poor not only in spirit but in fact. This *élite* must experience every day, both in the spirit and in the flesh, the pains and humiliations of poverty.

There is no need of a new Franciscan order. The monk's habit and the convent are a barrier. The new *élite* must be a part of the mass and in direct contact with it. And, further, they must do something which is harder than enduring poverty, they must renounce all compensations; in their contacts with the people around them they must sincerely practise the humility of a naturalized citizen in the country that has received him.

Anyone who had understood that this war was going to be a religious drama could have foreseen many years ago which nations would play an active role and which would be passive victims. The nations which lived without religion could be nothing but passive victims. This was the case with almost the whole of Europe. But Germany lives by an idolatry. Russia lives by another idolatry, and it may even be that it contains some not quite extinguished life from a rejected past. And although England is wasted by the sickness of the age she has such continuity of history and such a living tradition that some of her roots are still nourished by a past which was bathed in the light of mysticism.

There was a moment when England confronted Germany like a defenceless child in face of a brute with a gun in each hand. In such a situation there is not much that a child can do. But if it coldly looks the brute in the eye it is certain that the brute will hesitate for a moment.

And that is what happened. To disguise from herself that she had hesitated, and to find an alibi, Germany fell upon Russia and broke the best of her strength there. The oceans of blood sacrificed by Russian soldiers have made us almost forget what happened before. And yet that moment when England stood silent and unshaken is even more worthy, by far, to be eternally remembered. That halting of the German troops at the Channel is the supernatural point in this war. As always, it is negative, invisible, infinitely small, and decisive. The waves of the sea roll a long way, but something limits their range. It was known in antiquity that God is the assigner of limits.

At one time all the walls in France were covered with posters announcing: 'We shall win because we are the stronger.' It was the silliest word spoken in this war. The decisive moment came when our strength was almost non-existent. The enemy forces were halted because force, not being divine, has its limits.

The War has spread to other continents. Idolatry is perhaps more violent in Japan than in any other country. In the United States the belief in democracy is still alive—in contrast to France, for example, where it was already almost dead before the War, even before Munich. But ours is an age of idolatry and faith, not of mere belief. For America the War is still new, and distance deadens its impact; but it is almost certain, if prolonged, to bring about some profound changes.

Europe remains at the centre of the drama. From the fire scattered over the world by Christ—the same fire, perhaps, that Prometheus brought—there were still a few live embers in England. It was enough to prevent the worst. But it was only a respite. We are still lost unless those embers and the flickering sparks on the Continent can be fanned into a flame to kindle the whole of Europe.

If we are only saved by American money and machines we shall fall back, one way or another, into a new servitude like the one which we now suffer. It must be remembered that Europe was not subjugated by invading hordes from another continent, or from Mars, who have only to be driven out again. She is wasted by an internal malady. She needs to be cured.

She cannot survive unless she is saved, at least in great measure, by her own exertions. Fortunately, she is not in a position to oppose the conqueror's idolatry with one of her own, because it is impossible for enslaved nations to be turned into idols. The conquered peoples can only oppose the conqueror with a religion.

If a faith were to arise in this unhappy continent, victory would be rapid, certain, and secure. That is obvious even on the strategic level. Our line of communication is the sea, and can be defended by submarines, whereas the enemy's communications are on land, among the oppressed peoples, and they would be destroyed if all the land were set ablaze by a true faith.

But we cannot foster the growth of a true faith by broadcasting descriptions of our latest bombers or promises of clothing and food packets. For the afflicted the one and only road to faith is through the virtue of spiritual poverty. But this is a cryptic truth. For spiritual poverty appears to resemble resignation to slavery. And it is indeed almost identical with it, except for an infinitely small difference. We are always brought back to something infinitely small, which is infinitely more than everything.

Affliction is not in itself a school of spiritual poverty; but it offers almost the only opportunity of learning it. And although affliction is much less fleeting than happiness, it does pass away; so we need to make haste.

Are we going to take this opportunity? From the military point of view this question is perhaps more important than strategy, and from the economic point of view more important than statistics and distribution tables. Hitler has taught us, if we are capable of learning, that a truly realistic policy takes account first and foremost of thoughts.

He hopes for the triumph of evil; his material is the mass, the dough. We hope for the triumph of good; our material is the yeast. The difference of material calls for different methods.

Translated by *Richard Rees.*

NEW MEXICO

D. H. Lawrence
(1885–1930)

Superficially, the world has become small and known. Poor little globe of earth, the tourists trot round you as easily as they trot round the Bois or round Central Park. There is no mystery left, we've been there, we've seen it, we know all about it. We've done the globe, and the globe is done.

This is quite true, superficially. On the superficies, horizontally, we've been everywhere and done everything, we know all about it. Yet the more we know, superficially, the less we penetrate, vertically. It's all very well skimming across the surface of the ocean, and saying you know all about the sea. There still remain

the terrifying under-deeps, of which we have utterly no experience.

The same is true of land travel. We skim along, we get there, we see it all, we've done it all. And as a rule, we never once go through the curious film which railroads, ships, motor-cars, and hotels stretch over the surface of the whole earth. Peking is just the same as New York, with a few different things to look at; rather more Chinese about, etc. Poor creatures that we are, we crave for experience, yet we are like flies that crawl on the pure and transparent mucous-paper in which the world like a bon-bon is wrapped so carefully that we can never get at it, though we see it there all the time as we move about it, apparently in contact, yet actually as far removed as if it were the moon.

As a matter of fact, our great-grand-fathers, who never went anywhere, in actuality had more experience of the world than we have, who have seen everything. When they listened to a lecture with lantern-slides, they really held their breath before the unknown, as they sat in the village school-room. We, bowling along in a rickshaw in Ceylon, say to ourselves: "It's very much what you'd expect." We really know it all.

We are mistaken. The know-it-all state of mind is just the result of being outside the mucous-paper wrapping of civilization. Underneath is everything we don't know and are afraid of knowing.

I realized this with shattering force when I went to New Mexico.

New Mexico, one of the United States, part of the U. S. A. New Mexico, the picturesque reservation and playground of the eastern states, very romantic, old Spanish, Red Indian, desert mesas, pueblos, cowboys, penitentes, all that film-stuff. Very nice, the great South-West, put on a sombrero and knot a red kerchief round your neck, to go out in the great free spaces!

That is New Mexico wrapped in the absolutely hygienic and shiny mucous-paper of our trite civilization. That is the New Mexico known to most of the Americans who know it at all. But break through the shiny sterilized wrapping, and actually *touch* the country, and you will never be the same again.

I think New Mexico was the greatest experience from the outside world that I have ever had. It certainly changed me for ever. Curious as it may sound, it was New Mexico that liberated me from the present era of civilization, the great era of material and mechanical development. Months spent in holy Kandy, in Ceylon, the holy of holies of southern Buddhism, had not touched the great psyche of materialism and idealism which dominated me. And years, even in the exquisite beauty of Sicily, right among the old Greek paganism that still lives there, had not shattered the essential Christianity on which my character was established. Australia was a sort of dream or trance, like being under a spell, the self remaining unchanged, so long as the trance did not last too long. Tahiti, in a mere glimpse, repelled me: and so did California, after a stay of a few weeks. There seemed a strange brutality in the spirit of the western coast, and I felt: O, let me get away!

But the moment I saw the brilliant, proud morning shine high up over the deserts of Santa Fé, something stood still in my soul, and I started to attend. There was a certain magnificence in the high-up day, a certain eagle-like royalty, so different from the equally pure, equally pristine and lovely morning of Australia, which is so soft, so utterly pure in its softness, and betrayed by green parrot flying. But in the lovely morning of Australia one went into a dream. In the magnificent fierce morning of New Mexico one sprang awake, a new part of the soul woke up

suddenly, and the old world gave way to a new.

There are all kinds of beauty in the world, thank God, though ugliness is homogeneous. How lovely is Sicily, with Calabria across the sea like an opal, and Etna with her snow in a world above and beyond! How lovely is Tuscany, with little red tulips wild among the corn: or bluebells at dusk in England, or mimosa in clouds of pure yellow among the grey-green dun foliage of Australia, under a soft, blue, unbreathed sky! But for a *greatness* of beauty I have never experienced anything like New Mexico. All those mornings when I went with a hoe along the ditch to the Cañon, at the ranch, and stood, in the fierce, proud silence of the Rockies, on their foot-hills, to look far over the desert to the blue mountains away in Arizona, blue as chalcedony, with the sage-brush desert sweeping grey-blue in between, dotted with tiny cube-crystals of houses, the vast amphitheatre of lofty, indomitable desert, sweeping round to the ponderous Sangre de Cristo, mountains on the east, and coming up flush at the pine-dotted foot-hills of the Rockies! What splendour! Only the tawny eagle could really sail out into the splendour of it all. Leo Stein once wrote to me: It is the most æsthetically-satisfying landscape I know. To me it was much more than that. It had a splendid silent terror, and a vast far-and-wide magnificence which made it way beyond mere æsthetic appreciation. Never is the light more pure and overweening than there, arching with a royalty almost cruel over the hollow, uptilted world. For it is curious that the land which has produced modern political democracy at its highest pitch should give one the greatest sense of overweening, terrible proudness and mercilessness: but so beautiful, God! so beautiful! Those that have spent morning after morning alone there pitched among the pines above the great proud world of desert will know, almost unbearably how beautiful it is, how clear and unquestioned is the might of the day. Just day itself is tremendous there. It is so easy to understand that the Aztecs gave hearts of men to the sun. For the sun is not merely hot or scorching, not at all. It is of a brilliant and unchallengeable purity and haughty serenity which would make one sacrifice the heart to it. Ah, yes, in New Mexico the heart is sacrificed to the sun and the human being is left stark, heartless, but undauntedly religious.

And that was the second revelation out there. I had looked over all the world for something that would strike *me* as religious. The simple piety of some English people, the semi-pagan mystery of some Catholics in southern Italy, the intensity of some Bavarian peasants, the semi-ecstasy of Buddhists or Brahmins: all this had seemed religious all right, as far as the parties concerned were involved, but it didn't involve me. I looked on at their religiousness from the outside. For it is still harder too feel religion at will than to love at will.

I had seen what I felt was a hint of wild religion in the so-called devil dances of a group of naked villagers from the far-remote jungle in Ceylon, dancing at midnight under the torches, glittering wet with sweat on their dark bodies as if they had been gilded, at the celebration of the Pera-hera, in Kandy, given to the Prince of Wales. And the utter dark absorption of these naked men, as they danced with their knees wide apart suddenly affected me with a *sense* of religion, I *felt* religion for a moment. For religion is an experience, an uncontrollable sensual experience, even more so than love: I use sensual to mean an experience deep down in the senses, inexplicable and inscrutable.

But this experience was fleeting, gone in the curious turmoil of the Pera-hera, and I had no permanent feeling of re-ligion till I came to New Mexico and penetrated into the old human race-experience there. It is curious that it should be in America, of all places, that a European should really experience religion, after touching the old Mediterranean and the East. It is curious that one should get a sense of living religion from the Red Indians, having failed to get it from Hindus or Sicilian Catholics or Cingalese.

Let me make a reservation. I don't stand up to praise the Red Indian as he reveals himself in contact with white civilization. From that angle, I am forced to admit he *may* be thoroughly objectionable. Even my small experience knows it. But also I know he *may* be thoroughly nice, even in his dealings with white men. It's a question of individuals, a good deal, on both sides.

But in this article, I don't want to deal with the everyday or superficial aspect of New Mexico, outside the mucous-paper wrapping, I *want* to go beneath the surface. But therefore the American Indian in his behaviour as an American citizen doesn't really concern me. What concerns me is what he is—or what he seems to me to be, in his ancient, ancient race-self and religious-self.

For the Red Indian seems to me much older than Greeks, or Hindus or any Europeans or even Egyptians. The Red Indian, as a civilized and truly religious man, civilized beyond taboo and totem, as he is in the south, is religious in perhaps the oldest sense, and deepest, of the word. That is to say, he is a remnant of the most deeply religious race still living. So it seems to me.

But again let me protect myself. The Indian who sells you baskets on Albuquerque station or who slinks around Taos plaza may be an utter waster and an indescribably low dog. Personally he may be even less religious than a New York sneak-thief. He may have broken with his tribe, or his tribe itself may have collapsed finally from its old religious integrity, and ceased, really to exist. Then he is only fit for rapid absorption into white civilization, which must make the best of him.

But while a tribe retains its religion and keeps up its religious practices, and while any member of the tribe shares in those practices, then there is a tribal integrity and a living tradition going back far beyond the birth of Christ, beyond the pyramids, beyond Moses. A vast old religion which once swayed the earth lingers in unbroken practice there in New Mexico, older, perhaps, than anything in the world save Australian aboriginal taboo and totem, and that is not yet religion.

You can feel it, the atmosphere of it, around the pueblos. Not, of course, when the place is crowded with sight-seers and motor-cars. But go to Taos pueblo on some brilliant snowy morning and see the white figure on the roof: or come riding through at dusk on some windy evening, when the black skirts of the silent women blow around the white wide boots, and you will feel the old, old root of human consciousness still reaching down to depths we know nothing of: and of which, only too often, we are jealous. It seems it will not be long before the pueblos are uprooted.

But never shall I forget watching the dancers, the men with the fox-skin swaying down from their buttocks, file out at San Geronimo, and the women with seed rattles following. The long, streaming, glistening black hair of the men. Even in ancient Crete long hair was sacred in a man, as it is still in the Indians. Never shall I forget the utter absorption of the dance, so quiet, so steadily, timelessly rhythmic, and silent, with the ceaseless down-tread, always to the earth's centre, the very reverse of the upflow of Dionysiac or Christian ecstasy. Never shall I forget the deep singing of the men at the drum, swelling and sinking, the deep-

est sound I have heard in all my life, deeper than thunder, deeper than the sound of the Pacific Ocean, deeper than the roar of a deep waterfall: the wonderful deep sound of men calling to the unspeakable depths.

Never shall I forget coming into the little pueblo of San Filipi one sunny morning in spring, unexpectedly, when bloom was on the trees in the perfect little pueblo more old, more utterly peaceful and idyllic than anything in Theocritus, and seeing a little casual dance. Not impressive as a spectacle, only, to me, profoundly moving because of the truly terrifying religious absorption of it.

Never shall I forget the Christmas dances at Taos, twilight, snow, the darkness coming over the great wintry mountains and the lonely pueblo, then suddenly, again, like dark calling to dark, the deep Indian cluster-singing around the drum, wild and awful, suddenly rousing on the last dusk as the procession starts. And then the bonfires leaping suddenly in pure spurts of high flame, columns of sudden flame forming an alley for the procession.

Never shall I forget the khiva of birch-trees, away in the Apaché country, in Arizona this time, the tepees and flickering fires, the neighing of horses unseen under the huge dark night, and the Apaches all abroad, in their silent moccasined feet: and in the khiva, beyond a little fire, the old man reciting, reciting in the unknown Apache speech, in the strange wild Indian voice that re-echoes away back to before the Flood, reciting apparently the traditions and legends of the tribe, going on and on, while the young men, the *braves* of today, wandered in, listened, and wandered away again, overcome with the power and majesty of that utterly old tribal voice, yet uneasy with their half-adherence to the modern civilization, the two things in contact. And one of these *braves* shoved his face under my hat, in the night, and stared with his glittering eyes close to mine. He'd have killed me then and there, had he dared. He didn't dare: and I knew it: and he knew it.

Never shall I forget the Indian races, when the young men, even the boys, run naked, smeared with white earth and stuck with bits of eagle fluff for the swiftness of the heavens, and the old men brush them with eagle feathers, to give them power. And they run in the strange hurling fashion of the primitive world, hurled forward, not making speed deliberately. And the race is not for victory. It is not a contest. There is no competition. It is a great cumulative effort. The tribe this day is adding up its male energy and exerting it to the utmost—for what? To get power, to get strength: to come, by sheer cumulative, hurling effort of the bodies of men, into contact with the great cosmic source of vitality which gives strength, power, energy to the men who can grasp it, energy for the zeal of attainment.

It was a vast old religion, greater than anything we know: more starkly and nakedly religious. There is no God, no conception of a god. All is god. But it is not the pantheism we are accustomed to, which expresses itself as "God is everywhere, God is in everything." In the oldest religion, everything was alive, not supernaturally but naturally alive. There were only deeper and deeper streams of life, vibrations of life more and more vast. So rocks were alive, but a mountain had a deeper, vaster life than a rock, and it was much harder for a man to bring his spirit, or his energy, into contact with the life of the mountain, and so draw strength from the mountain, as from a great standing well of life, than it was to come into contact with the rock. And he had to put forth a great religious effort. For the whole life-effort of man was to get his life into direct contact with the elemental life of the cosmos, mountain-life, cloud-life, thunder-life, air-life, earth-life, sun-life. To come into immediate *felt* contact, and so derive energy, power, and a dark sort of joy. This effort into sheer naked contact, *without an intermediary or mediator,* is the root meaning of religion, and at the sacred races the runners hurled themselves in a terrible cumulative effort, through the air, to come at last into naked contact with the very life of the air, which is the life of the clouds, and so of the rain.

It was a vast and pure religion, without idols or images, even mental ones. It is the oldest religion, a cosmic religion the same for all peoples, not broken up into specific gods or saviours or systems. It is the religion which precedes the god-concept, and is therefore greater and deeper than any god-religion.

And it lingers still, for a little while, in New Mexico: but long enough to have been a revelation to me. And the Indian, however objectionable he may be on occasion, has still some of the strange beauty and pathos of the religion that brought him forth and is now shedding him away into oblivion. When Trinidad, the Indian boy, and I planted corn at the ranch, my soul paused to see his brown hands softly moving the earth over the maize in pure ritual. He was back in his old religious self, and the ages stood still. Ten minutes later he was making a fool of himself with the horses. Horses were never part of the Indian's religious life, never would be. He hasn't a tithe of the feeling for them that he has for a bear, for example. So horses don't like Indians.

But there it is: the newest democracy ousting the oldest religion! And once the oldest religion is ousted, one feels the democracy and all its paraphernalia will collapse, and the oldest religion, which comes down to us from man's pre-war days, will start again. The sky-scraper will scatter on the winds like thistledown, and the genuine America, the America of New

Mexico, will start on its course again. This is an interregnum.

MAN AGAINST DARKNESS

W. T. Stace
(1886–1967)

1

The Catholic bishops of America recently issued a statement in which they said that the chaotic and bewildered state of the modern world is due to man's loss of faith, his abandonment of God and religion. For my part I believe in no religion at all. Yet I entirely agree with the bishops. It is no doubt an oversimplification to speak of *the* cause of so complex a state of affairs as the tortured condition of the world today. Its causes are doubtless multitudinous. Yet allowing for some element of oversimplification, I say that the bishops' assertion is substantially true.

M. Jean-Paul Sartre, the French existentialist philosopher, labels himself an atheist. Yet his views seem to me plainly to support the statement of the bishops. So long as there was believed to be a God in the sky, he says, men could regard him as the source of their moral ideals. The universe, created and governed by a fatherly God, was a friendly habitation for man. We could be sure that, however great the evil in the world, good in the end would triumph and the forces of evil would be routed. With the disappearance of God from the sky all this has changed. Since the world is not ruled by a spiritual being, but rather by blind forces, there cannot be any ideals, moral or otherwise, in the universe outside us. Our ideals, therefore, must proceed only from our own minds; they are our own inventions. Thus the world which surrounds us is

nothing but an immense spiritual emptiness. It is a dead universe. We do not live in a universe which is on the side of our values. It is completely indifferent to them.

Years ago Mr. Bertrand Russell, in his essay *A Free Man's Worship*, said much the same thing.

> Such in outline, but even more purposeless, more void of meaning, is the world which Science presents for our belief. Amid such a world, if anywhere, our ideals henceforward must find a home. . . . Blind to good and evil, reckless of destruction, omnipotent matter rolls on its relentless way; for man, condemned today to lose his dearest, tomorrow himself to pass through the gate of darkness, it remains only to cherish, ere yet the blow falls, the lofty thoughts that ennoble his little day; . . . to worship at the shrine his own hands have built; . . . to sustain alone, a weary but unyielding Atlas, the world that his own ideals have fashioned despite the trampling march of unconscious power.

It is true that Mr. Russell's personal attitude to the disappearance of religion is quite different from either that of M. Sartre or the bishops or myself. The bishops think it a calamity. So do I. M. Sartre finds it "very distressing." And he berates as shallow the attitude of those who think that without God the world can go on just the same as before, as if nothing had happened. This creates for mankind, he thinks, a terrible crisis. And in this I agree with him. Mr. Russell, on the other hand, seems to believe that religion has done more harm than good in the world, and that its disappearance will be a blessing. But his picture of the world, and of the modern mind, is the same as that of M. Sartre. He stresses the *purposelessness* of the universe, the facts that man's ideals are his own creations, that the universe outside him in no way supports them, that man is alone and friendless in the world.

Mr. Russell notes that it is science which has produced this situation. There is no doubt that this is correct. But the way in which it has come about is not generally understood. There is a popular belief that some particular scientific discoveries or theories, such as the Darwinian theory of evolution, or the views of geologists about the age of the earth, or a series of such discoveries, have done the damage. It would be foolish to deny that these discoveries have had a great effect in undermining religious dogmas. But this account does not at all go to the root of the matter. Religion can probably outlive any scientific discoveries which could be made. It can accommodate itself to them. The root cause of the decay of faith has not been any particular discovery of science, but rather the general spirit of science and certain basic assumptions upon which modern science, from the seventeenth century onwards, has proceeded.

2

It was Galileo and Newton—notwithstanding that Newton himself was a deeply religious man—who destroyed the old comfortable picture of a friendly universe governed by spiritual values. And this was effected, not by Newton's discovery of the law of gravitation nor by any of Galileo's brilliant investigations, but by the general picture of the world which these men and others of their time made the basis of the science, not only of their own day, but of all succeeding generations down to the present. That is why the century immediately following Newton, the eighteenth century, was notoriously an age of religious skepticism. Skepticism did not have to wait for the discoveries of Darwin and the geologists in the nineteenth century. It flooded the world immediately after the age of the rise of science.

Neither the Copernican hypothesis nor any of Newton's or Galileo's particular discoveries were the real causes. Religious faith might well have accommodated itself to the new astronomy. The real turning point between the medieval age of faith and the modern age of unfaith came when the scientists of the seventeenth century turned their backs upon what used to be called "final causes." The final cause of a thing or event meant the purpose which it was supposed to serve in the universe, its cosmic purpose. What lay back of this was the presupposition that there is a cosmic order or plan and that everything which exists could in the last analysis be explained in terms of its place in this cosmic plan, that is, in terms of its purpose.

Plato and Aristotle believed this, and so did the whole medieval Christian world. For instance, if it were true that the sun and the moon were created and exist for the purpose of giving light to man, then this fact would explain why the sun and the moon exist. We might not be able to discover the purpose of everything, but everything must have a purpose. Belief in final causes thus amounted to a belief that the world is governed by purposes, presumably the purposes of some overruling mind. This belief was not the invention of Christianity. It was basic to the whole of Western civilization, whether in the ancient pagan world or in Christendom, from the time of Socrates to the rise of science in the seventeenth century.

The founders of modern science—for instance, Galileo, Kepler, and Newton—were mostly pious men who did not doubt God's purposes. Nevertheless they took the revolutionary step of consciously and deliberately expelling the idea of purpose as controlling nature from their new science of nature. They did this on the ground that inquiry into purposes is useless for what science aims at: namely, the prediction and control of events. To predict an eclipse, what you have to know is not its purpose but its causes. Hence science from the seventeenth century onwards became exclusively an inquiry into causes. The conception of purpose in the world was ignored and frowned on. This, though silent and almost unnoticed, was the greatest revolution in human history, far outweighing in importance any of the political revolutions whose thunder has reverberated through the world.

For it came about in this way that for the past three hundred years there has been growing up in men's minds, dominated as they are by science, a new imaginative picture of the world. The world, according to this new picture, is purposeless, senseless, meaningless. Nature is nothing but matter in motion. The motions of matter are governed, not by any purpose, but by blind forces and laws. Nature on this view, says Whitehead—to whose writings I am indebted in this part of my paper—is "merely the hurrying of material, endlessly, meaninglessly." You can draw a sharp line across the history of Europe dividing it into two epochs of very unequal length. The line passes through the lifetime of Galileo. European man before Galileo—whether ancient pagan or more recent Christian—thought of the world as controlled by plan and purpose. After Galileo European man thinks of it as utterly purposeless. This is the great revolution of which I spoke.

It is this which has killed religion. Religion could survive the discoveries that the sun, not the earth, is the center; that men are descended from simian ancestors; that the earth is hundreds of millions of years old. These discoveries may render out of date some of the details of older theological dogmas, may force their restatement in new intellectual frameworks. But they do not touch the essence of the religious

vision itself, which is the faith that there is plan and purpose in the world, that the world is a moral order, that in the end all things are for the best. This faith may express itself through many different intellectual dogmas, those of Christianity, of Hinduism, of Islam. All and any of these intellectual dogmas may be destroyed without destroying the essential religious spirit. But that spirit cannot survive destruction of belief in a plan and purpose of the world, for that is the very heart of it. Religion can get on with any sort of astronomy, geology, biology, physics. But it cannot get on with a purposeless and meaningless universe.

If the scheme of things is purposeless and meaningless, then the life of man is purposeless and meaningless too. Everything is futile, all effort is in the end worthless. A man may, of course, still pursue disconnected ends, money, fame, art, science, and may gain pleasure from them. But his life is hollow at the center. Hence the dissatisfied, disillusioned, restless, spirit of modern man.

The picture of a meaningless world, and a meaningless human life, is, I think, the basic theme of much modern art and literature. Certainly it is the basic theme of modern philosophy. According to the most characteristic philosophies of the modern period from Hume in the eighteenth century to the so-called positivists of today, the world is just what it is, and that is the end of all inquiry. There is no reason for its being what it is. Everything might just as well have been quite different, and there would have been no reason for that either. When you have stated what things are, what things the world contains, there is nothing more which could be said, even by an omniscient being. To ask any question about *why* things are thus, or what purpose their being so serves, is to ask a senseless question, because they serve no purpose at all. For instance, there is for modern philosophy no such thing as the ancient problem of evil. For this once famous question presupposes that pain and misery, though they seem so inexplicable and irrational to us, must ultimately subserve some rational purpose, must have their places in the cosmic plan. But this is nonsense. There is no such overruling rationality in the universe. Belief in the ultimate irrationality of everything is the quintessence of what is called the modern mind.

It is true that, parallel with these philosophies which are typical of the modern mind, preaching the meaninglessness of the world, there has run a line of idealistic philosophies whose contention is that the world is after all spiritual in nature and that moral ideals and values are inherent in its structure. But most of these idealisms were simply philosophical expressions of romanticism, which was itself no more than an unsuccessful counter-attack of the religious against the scientific view of things. They perished, along with romanticism in literature and art, about the beginning of the present century, though of course they still have a few adherents.

At the bottom these idealistic systems of thought were rationalizations of man's wishful thinking. They were born of the refusal of men to admit the cosmic darkness. They were comforting illusions within the warm glow of which the more tender-minded intellectuals sought to shelter themselves from the icy winds of the universe. They lasted a little while. But they are shattered now, and we return once more to the vision of a purposeless world.

3

Along with the ruin of the religious vision there went the ruin of moral principles and indeed of all values. If there is a cosmic purpose, if there is in the nature of things a drive towards goodness, then our moral systems will derive their validity from this. But if our moral rules do not proceed from something outside us in the nature of the universe—whether we say it is God or simply the universe itself—then they must be our own inventions. Thus it came to be believed that moral rules must be merely an expression of our own likes and dislikes. But likes and dislikes are notoriously variable. What pleases one man, people, or culture displeases another. Therefore morals are wholly relative.

This obvious conclusion from the idea of a purposeless world made its appearance in Europe immediately after the rise of science, for instance in the philosophy of Hobbes. Hobbes saw at once that if there is no purpose in the world there are no values either. "Good and evil," he writes, "are names that signify our appetites and aversions; which in different tempers, customs, and doctrines of men are different. . . . Every man calleth that which pleaseth him, good; and that which displeaseth him, evil."

This doctrine of the relativity of morals, though it has recently received an impetus from the studies of anthropologists, was thus really implicit in the whole scientific mentality. It is disastrous for morals because it destroys their entire traditional foundation. That is why philosophers who see the danger signals, from the time at least of Kant, have been trying to give to morals a new foundation, that is, a secular or nonreligious foundation. This attempt may very well be intellectually successful. Such a foundation, independent of the religious view of the world, might well be found. But the question is whether it can ever be a *practical* success, that is whether apart from its logical validity and its influence with intellectuals, it can ever replace among the masses of men the lost religious foundation. On that question hangs perhaps the future of civilization. But meanwhile disaster is overtaking us.

The widespread belief in "ethical relativity" among philosophers, psychologists, ethnologists, and sociologists is the theoretical counterpart of the repudiation of principle which we see all around us, especially in international affairs, the field in which morals have always had the weakest foothold. No one any longer effectively believes in moral principles except as the private prejudices either of individual men or of nations or cultures. This is the inevitable consequence of the doctrine of ethical relativity, which in turn is the inevitable consequence of believing in a purposeless world.

Another characteristic of our spiritual state is loss of belief in the freedom of the will. This also is a fruit of the scientific spirit, though not of any particular scientific discovery. Science has been built up on the basis of determinism, which is the belief that every event is completely determined by a chain of causes and is therefore theoretically predictable beforehand. It is true that recent physics seems to challenge this. But so far as its practical consequences are concerned, the damage has long ago been done. A man's actions, it was argued, are as much events in the natural world as is an eclipse of the sun. It follows that men's actions are as theoretically predictable as an eclipse. But if it is certain now that John Smith will murder Joseph Jones at 2:15 P.M. on January 1, 1963, what possible meaning can it have to say that when that time comes John Smith will be *free* to choose whether he will commit the murder or not? And if he is not free, how can he be held responsible?

It is true that the whole of this argument can be shown by a competent philosopher to be a tissue of fallacies—or at least I claim that it can. But the point is that the analysis required to show this is much too subtle to be understood by the

average entirely unphilosophical man. Because of this, the argument against free will is generally swallowed whole by the unphilosophical. Hence the thought that man is not free, that he is the helpless plaything of forces over which he has no control, has deeply penetrated the modern mind. We hear of economic determinism, cultural determinism, historical determinism. We are not responsible for what we do because our glands control us, or because we are the products of environment or heredity. Not moral self-control, but the doctor, the psychiatrist, the educationist, must save us from doing evil. Pills and injections in the future are to do what Christ and the prophets have failed to do. Of course I do not mean to deny that doctors and educationists can and must help. And I do not mean in any way to belittle their efforts. But I do wish to draw attention to the weakening of moral controls, the greater or less repudiation of personal responsibility which, in the popular thinking of the day, result from these tendencies of thought.

4

What, then, is to be done? Where are we to look for salvation from the evils of our time? All the remedies I have seen suggested so far are, in my opinion, useless. Let us look at some of them.

Philosophers and intellectuals generally can, I believe, genuinely do something to help. But it is extremely little. What philosophers can do is to show that neither the relativity of morals nor the denial of free will really follows from the grounds which have been supposed to support them. They can also try to discover a genuine secular basis for morals to replace the religious basis which has disappeared. Some of us are trying to do these things. But in the first place philosophers unfortunately are not agreed about these matters, and their disputes are utterly confusing to non-philosophers. And in the second place their influence is practically negligible because their analyses necessarily take place on a level on which the masses are totally unable to follow them.

The bishops, of course, propose as remedy a return to belief in God and in the doctrines of the Christian religion. Others think that a new religion is what is needed. Those who make these proposals fail to realize that the crisis in man's spiritual condition is something unique in history for which there is no sort of analogy in the past. They are thinking perhaps of the collapse of the ancient Greek and Roman religions. The vacuum then created was easily filled by Christianity, and it might have been filled by Mithraism if Christianity had not appeared. By analogy they think that Christianity might now be replaced by a new religion, or even that Christianity itself, if revivified, might bring back health to men's lives.

But I believe that there is no analogy at all between our present state and that of the European peoples at the time of the fall of paganism. Men had at that time lost their belief only in particular dogmas, particular embodiments of the religious view of the world. It had no doubt become incredible that Zeus and the other gods were living on the top of Mount Olympus. You could go to the top and find no trace of them. But the imaginative picture of a world governed by purpose, a world driving towards the good —which is the inner spirit of religion— had at that time received no serious shock. It had merely to re-embody itself in new dogmas, those of Christianity or some other religion. Religion itself was not dead in the world, only a particular form of it.

But now the situation is quite different. It is not merely that particular dogmas, like that of the virgin birth, are unacceptable to the modern mind. That is true, but it constitutes a very superficial diagnosis of the present situation of religion. Modern skepticism is of a wholly different order from that of the intellectuals of the ancient world. It has attacked and destroyed not merely the outward forms of the religious spirit, its particularized dogmas, but the very essence of that spirit itself, belief in a meaningful and purposeful world. For the founding of a new religion a new Jesus Christ or Buddha would have to appear, in itself a most unlikely event and one for which in any case we cannot afford to sit and wait. But even if a new prophet and a new religion did appear, we may predict that they would fail in the modern world. No one for long would believe in them, for modern men have lost the vision, basic to all religion, of an ordered plan and purpose of the world. They have before their minds the picture of a purposeless universe, and such a world-picture must be fatal to any religion at all, not merely to Christianity.

We must not be misled by occasional appearances of a revival of the religious spirit. Men, we are told, in their disgust and disillusionment at the emptiness of their lives, are turning once more to religion, or are searching for a new message. It may be so. We must expect such wistful yearnings of the spirit. We must expect men to wish back again the light that is gone, and to try to bring it back. But however they may wish and try, the light will not shine again,—not at least in the civilization to which we belong.

Another remedy commonly proposed is that we should turn to science itself, or the scientific spirit, for our salvation. Mr. Russell and Professor Dewey both make this proposal, though in somewhat different ways. Professor Dewey seems to believe that discoveries in sociology, the application of scientific method to social and political problems, will rescue us. This seems to me to be utterly naïve. It is not likely that science, which is basically the cause of our spiritual troubles, is likely also to produce the cure for them.

Also it lies in the nature of science that, though it can teach us the best means for achieving our ends, it can never tell us what ends to pursue. It cannot give us any ideals. And our trouble is about ideals and ends, not about the means for reaching them.

5

No civilization can live without ideals, or to put it in another way, without a firm faith in moral ideas. Our ideals and moral ideas have in the past been rooted in religion. But the religious basis of our ideals has been undermined, and the superstructure of ideals is plainly tottering. None of the commonly suggested remedies on examination seems likely to succeed. It would therefore look as if the early death of our civilization were inevitable.

Of course we know that it is perfectly possible for individual men, very highly educated men, philosophers, scientists, intellectuals in general, to live moral lives without any religious convictions. But the question is whether a whole civilization, a whole family of peoples, composed almost entirely of relatively uneducated men and women, can do this.

It follows, of course, that if we could make the vast majority of men as highly educated as the very few are now, we might save the situation. And we are already moving slowly in that direction through the techniques of mass education. But the critical question seems to concern the time-lag. Perhaps in a few hundred years most of the population will, at the present rate, be sufficiently highly educated and civilized to combine high ideals with an absence of religion. But long before we reach any such stage, the collapse of our civilization may have come about. How are we to live through the intervening period?

I am sure that the first thing we have to do is to face the truth, however bleak it may be, and then next we have to learn to live with it. Let me say a word about each of these two points. What I am urging as regards the first is complete honesty. Those who wish to resurrect Christian dogmas are not, of course, consciously dishonest. But they have that kind of unconscious dishonesty which consists in lulling oneself with opiates and dreams. Those who talk of a new religion are merely hoping for a new opiate. Both alike refuse to face the truth that there is, in the universe outside man, no spirituality, no regard for values, no friend in the sky, no help or comfort for man of any sort. To be perfectly honest in the admission of this fact, not to seek shelter in new or old illusions, not to indulge in wishful dreams about this matter, this is the first thing we shall have to do.

I do not urge this course out of any special regard for the sanctity of truth in the abstract. It is not self-evident to me that truth is the supreme value to which all else must be sacrificed. Might not the discoverer of a truth which would be fatal to mankind be justified in suppressing it, even in teaching men a falsehood? Is truth more valuable than goodness and beauty and happiness? To think so is to invent yet another absolute, another religious delusion in which Truth with a capital T is substituted for God. The reason why we must now boldly and honestly face the truth that the universe is non-spiritual and indifferent to goodness, beauty, happiness, or truth is not that it would be wicked to suppress it, but simply that it is too late to do so, so that in the end we cannot do anything else but face it. Yet we stand on the brink, dreading the icy plunge. We need courage. We need honesty.

Now about the other point, the necessity of learning to live with the truth. This means learning to live virtuously and happily, or at least contentedly, without illusions. And this is going to be extremely difficult because what we have now begun dimly to perceive is that human life in the past, or at least human happiness, has almost wholly depended upon illusions. It has been said that man lives by truth, and that the truth will make us free. Nearly the opposite seems to me to be the case. Mankind has managed to live only by means of lies, and the truth may very well destroy us. If one were a Bergsonian one might believe that nature deliberately puts illusions into our souls in order to induce us to go on living.

The illusions by which men have lived seem to be of two kinds. First, there is what one may perhaps call the Great Illusion—I mean the religious illusion that the universe is moral and good, that it follows a wise and noble plan, that it is gradually generating some supreme value, that goodness is bound to triumph in it. Secondly, there is a whole host of minor illusions on which human happiness nourishes itself. How much of human happiness notoriously comes from the illusions of the lover about his beloved? Then again we work and strive because of the illusions connected with fame, glory, power, or money. Banners of all kinds, flags, emblems, insignia, ceremonials, and rituals are invariably symbols of some illusion or other. The British Empire, the connection between mother country and dominions, is partly kept going by illusions surrounding the notion of kingship. Or think of the vast amount of human happiness which is derived from the illusion of supposing that if some nonsense syllable, such as "sir" or "count" or "lord" is pronounced in conjunction with our names, we belong to a superior order of people.

There is plenty of evidence that human happiness is almost wholly based upon illusions of one kind or another. But the scientific spirit, or the spirit of truth, is the enemy of illusions and therefore the enemy of human happiness. That is why it is going to be so difficult to live with the truth.

There is no reason why we should have to give up the host of minor illusions which render life supportable. There is no reason why the lover should be scientific about the loved one. Even the illusions of fame and glory may persist. But without the Great Illusion, the illusion of a good, kindly, and purposeful universe, we shall *have* to learn to live. And to ask this is really no more than to ask that we become genuinely civilized beings and not merely sham civilized beings.

I can best explain the difference by a reminiscence. I remember a fellow student in my college days, an ardent Christian, who told me that if he did not believe in a future life, in heaven and hell, he would rape, murder, steal, and be a drunkard. That is what I call being a sham civilized being. On the other hand, not only could a Huxley, a John Stuart Mill, a David Hume, live great and fine lives without any religion, but a great many others of us, quite obscure persons, can at least live decent lives without it.

To be genuinely civilized means to be able to walk straightly and to live honorably without the props and crutches of one or another of the childish dreams which have so far supported men. That such a life is likely to be ecstatically happy I will not claim. But that it can be lived in quiet content, accepting resignedly what cannot be helped, not expecting the impossible, and thankful for small mercies, this I would maintain. That it will be difficult for men in general to learn this lesson I do not deny. But that it will be impossible I would not admit since so many have learned it already.

Man has not yet grown up. He is not adult. Like a child he cries for the moon and lives in a world of fantasies. And the race as a whole has perhaps reached the great crisis of its life. Can it grow up as a race in the same sense as individual men grow up? Can man put away childish things and adolescent dreams? Can he grasp the real world as it actually is, stark and bleak, without its romantic or religious halo, and still retain his ideals, striving for great ends and noble achievements? If he can, all may yet be well. If he cannot, he will probably sink back into the savagery and brutality from which he came, taking a humble place once more among the lower animals.

RELIGION AS AN OBJECTIVE PROBLEM

Julian Huxley
(1887–   )

Religion, like any other subject, can be treated as an objective problem, and studied by the method of science. The first step is to make a list of the ideas and practices associated with different religions—gods and demons, sacrifice, prayer, belief in a future life, taboos and moral rules in this life. This, however, is but a first step. It is like making a collection of animals and plants, or a catalogue of minerals or other substances, with their properties and uses. Science always begins in this way, but it cannot stop at this level: it inevitably seeks to penetrate deeper and to make an analysis.

This analysis may take two directions. It may seek for a further understanding of religion as it now exists, or it may adopt the historical method and search for an explanation of the present in the past.

With regard to the historical approach, it is clear that religion, like other social activities, evolves. Further, its evolution is determined by two main kinds of factors. One is its own emotional and intellectual momentum, its inner logic: the other is the influence of the material and social conditions of the period. As an example of the first, take the tendency from polytheism towards monotheism: granted the theistic premise, this tendency seems almost inevitably to declare itself in the course of time. As examples of the second, we have the fact of propitiatory sacrifice related to helplessness in face of external nature.

The comparative evolutionary study of religion brings out two or three main points. For instance, we have the original prevalence of magical ideas, and their application first to the practical activities of communal existence such as food-getting and war, and only later to the problems of personal salvation: and these in their turn come gradually to be dominated more by moral ideas and less by magic. In the sphere of theology we have the early prevalence of rambling myth, and its gradual crystallization into a fully-rationalized system. In this domain too we see an interesting evolution from an early stage in which certain objects, acts, and persons are supposed to be imbued with an impersonal sacred influence or *mana,* and a later stage at which this sacred influence is pushed back a stage and attributed to supernatural beings behind objects.

Finally, there is the important fact that religious beliefs and practices have a very strong time-lag—a high degree of hysteresis, if you prefer a physical metaphor.

We next have to ask ourselves what is the result of our other type of analysis of the nature of religion. In the most general terms, it is that religion is the product of a certain type of interaction between man and his environment. It always involves an emotional component—the sense of sacredness. It always involves a more than intellectual belief—a sense of compulsive rightness. It is always concerned with human destiny, and with a way of life. It always brings the human being into some sort of felt relation with powers or agencies outside his personal self. It always involves some sort of escape from inner conflict. These different components may be very unequally developed, but they are always present.

Pushing the analysis a stage further, religion is seen as an attempt to come to terms with the irrational forces that affect man—some cosmic, some social, some personal. These terms may be terms of capitulation or of victory, of compromise or of escape. Here once more there is immense variety.

A very important further point is this —that there is no single function of religion. We may class religious functions by their external points of reference or by their internal origins. Externally, the first religious function is to place man in a satisfactory emotional relation with his non-human environment, regarded as outer destiny or fate. The second is to do the same for his social environment; the third, to do the same for his personal actions.

Looked at from the point of view of internal origin, the matter is much more complicated. One very important religious function is that of rationalization—giving coherent explanations in rational terms for acts and feelings which arise from instinctive and therefore irrational sources. Another is that which we have already mentioned, the desire for unity. These two between them provide the theological side of religions.

More fundamental—since they provide the raw materials on which the rationalizing and unifying urges act—are the purely emotional components. These fall under two main heads—the functions arising from conflict or reaction between the self and the outer world, and those arising from conflict or reaction between parts of the self.

Among the former we may mention the need to escape from frustration and limitations; and need for enhancement of the actual, the gilding of the imperfect. At length we come to relations between parts of the self, which are the most potent of all in generating religious reactions. Here we must take account of several basic facts of the human mind. First there is the inevitability of conflict—a necessary consequence of man's mental make-up. Then there is the illimitable nature of desire and aspiration. Analogous to this last, but in the intellectual instead of the emotional sphere, is man's concept-forming activity, which inevitably gives rise to abstract terms like justice, truth, and beauty. These, being abstract, are empty; but illimitable desire perennially fills them with its imaginations. Then there is the fact of childhood repression, with its consequences, only now beginning to be realized by the world, of a burden of (often unconscious) guilt. Closely linked with this is the obsession of certitude. The mechanism of repression is an all-or-none mechanism: and the conscious accompaniment of such a mechanism is a subjective sense of certitude.

Another very important function is to provide something which is felt as eternal and unchanging (even though in reality it may merely be long-range and slow-changing) over against the limitations and changes of ordinary existence.

But I must not spend too much time on mere analysis. The next question is whether the scientific approach can throw any light on the present crisis in religion and its possible future solution.

The particular situation that confronts the religion of Western civilization is this. The concept of God has reached the limits of its usefulness: it cannot evolve further. Supernatural powers were created by man to carry the burden of religion. From diffuse magic *mana* to personal spirits; from spirits to gods; from gods to God— so crudely speaking, the evolution has gone. The particular phase of that evolution which concerns us is that of gods. In one period of our Western civilization the gods were necessary fictions, useful hypotheses by which to live.

But the gods are only necessary or useful in a certain phase of evolution. For gods to be of value to man, three things are necessary. The disasters of the outer world must still be sufficiently uncomprehended and uncontrolled to be mysteriously alarming. Or else the beastliness and hopelessness of common life must be such as to preclude any pinning of faith to the improvement in this world: then God can, and social life cannot, provide the necessary escape-mechanism. The belief in magical power must still be current, even if it be in a refined or sublimated form. And the analytic exploration of his own mind by man must not be so advanced that he can no longer project and personify the unconscious forces of his Super-ego and his Id as beings external to himself.

The advance of natural science, logic, and psychology have brought us to a stage at which God is no longer a useful hypothesis. Natural science has pushed God into an ever greater remoteness, until his function as ruler and dictator disappears and he becomes a mere first cause or vague general principle. The realization that magic is a false principle, and that control is to be achieved by science and its application, has removed the meaning from sacrificial ritual and petitionary prayer. The analysis of the human mind, with the discovery of its powers of projection and wish-fulfilment, its hidden subconsciousness and realized repressions, makes it unnecessary to believe that conversion and the like are due to any external spiritual power and unscientific to ascribe inner certitude to guidance by God.

And theological logic, inevitably tending to unify and to universalize its ideas of the Divine, has resulted in a monotheism which is self-contradictory and incomprehensible, and in some respects of less practical value than the polytheism which it replaced.

If you grant theism of any sort, the logical outcome is monotheism. But why theism at all? Why a belief in supernatural beings who stand in some relation to human destiny and human aspirations? Theistic belief depends on man's projection of his own ideas and feelings into nature: it is a personification of non-personal phenomena. Personification is God's major premise. But it is a mere assumption, and one which, while serviceable enough in earlier times, is now seen not only to be unwarranted, but to raise more difficulties than it solves. Religion, to continue as an element of first-rate importance in the life of the community, must drop the idea of God or at least relegate it to a subordinate position, as has happened to the magical element in the past. God, equally with gods, angels, demons, spirits, and other small spiritual fry, is a human product, arising inevitably from a certain kind of ignorance and a certain degree of helplessness with regard to man's external environment.

With the substitution of knowledge for ignorance in this field, and the growth of control, both actually achieved and realized by thought as possible, God is simply fading away, as the Devil has faded before him, and the pantheons of the ancient world, and the nymphs and the local spirits.

> Peor and Baalim
> Forsake their temples dim . . .

Milton wrote of the fading of all the pagan gods; and Milton's God too is joining them in limbo. God has become more remote and more incomprehensible, and, most important of all, of less practical use to men and women who want guidance and consolation in living their lives. A faint trace of God, half metaphysical and half magic, still broods over our world, like the smile of a cosmic Cheshire Cat. But the growth of psychological knowledge will rub even that from the universe.

However—and this is vital—the fading of God does not mean the end of religion. God's disappearance is in the strictest sense of the word a theological process: and while theologies change, the religious impulses which gave them birth persist.

The disappearance of God means a recasting of religion, and a recasting of a fundamental sort. It means the shouldering by man of ultimate responsibilities which he had previously pushed off on to God.

What are these responsibilities which man must now assume? First, responsibility for carrying on in face of the world's mystery and his own ignorance. In previous ages that burden was shifted on to divine inscrutability: "God moves in a mysterious way.". . . Now we lay it to the account of our own ignorance, and face the possibility that ignorance of ultimates may, through the limitations of our nature, be permanent.

Next, responsibility for the long-range control of destiny. That we can no longer shift on to God the Ruler. Much that theistic religion left to divine guidance remains out of our hands: but our knowledge gives us power of controlling our fate and that of the planet we inhabit, within wide limits. In a phrase, we are the trustees of the evolutionary process and, like all trustees, responsible for our trust.

Thirdly and most urgently, responsibility for the immediate health and happiness of the species, for the enhancement of life on this earth, now and in the immediate future. Poverty, slavery, ill-health, social misery, democracy, kingship, this or that economic or political system—they do not inhere inevitably in a divinely appointed order of thing: they are phenomena to be understood and con-

trolled in accordance with our desire, just as much as the phenomena of chemistry or electricity.

Finally, there is the question of the immediate future of religion. Can science make any prophecy or offer any guidance in regard to this? I think that within limits, it can. In the first place, by analysing the reasons for the breakdown of the traditional supernatural religious systems of the West, it can point out that, unless the trend of history is reversed, the breakdown is an irremediable one. For it is due to the increase of our knowledge and control, the decrease of our ignorance and fear, in relation to man's external environment—machinery, crop-production, physical and chemical invention, floods, disease-germs—and unless science and technology disappear in a new Dark Age, this will persist.

The collapse of supernaturalist theology has been accompanied by the collapse, first of supernatural moral sanctions, and then of any absolute basis for morals. This too must be regarded as a process which, in the event of the continuance of civilization, is irreversible.

We can, however, go further. We have seen that the breakdown of traditional religion has been brought about by the growth of man's knowledge and control over his environment. But biologists distinguish between the external and the internal environment. Our blood provides our tissues with an internal environment regulated to a nicety both as regards its temperature and its chemical constitution, whereas the blood of a sea-urchin affords no such constancy. The organization of an ants' nest provides for the species an internal environment of a social nature. And in contrast with the rapid increase of man's knowledge of and control over his external environment, there has been little or no corresponding progress as regards the internal environment of his species. This is equally true in regard to the structure of society which provides the social environment for the individual and the race, and for the complex of feelings and ideas which provide the psychological environment in which the personal life of the individual is bathed.

These two aspects of man's internal environment of course interact and at points indeed unite—witness the field of social psychology: but for the most part they can be best considered from two very different angles—on the one side from the angle of economics, politics, law and sociology, on the other from the angle of psychological science. Not only have we as yet no adequate scientific knowledge or control over these phenomena, but our absence of control is causing widespread bewilderment. The common man to-day is distressed not only over his own sufferings, but at the spectacle of the helplessness of those in responsible positions in face of the maladjustments of the world's economic and political machinery.

In this field the fear of the uncomprehended, banished elsewhere, has once more entered human life. The fear is all the more deadly because the forces feared are of man's own making. No longer can we blame the gods. The modern Prometheus has chained himself to the rock, and himself fostered the vulture which now gnaws his vitals: his last satisfaction, of defying the Olympian tyrant, is gone.

The distress and the bewilderment are experienced as yet mainly in the more tangible realm of social and economic organization: the mental stresses and distortions arising from the social maladjustment remain for the time being in the background of public consciousness.

With the aid of our analysis of the nature and functions of religion, we can accordingly make certain definite assertions as to its future. The prophesy of science about the future of religion is that the religious impulses will become progressively more concerned with the

organization of society—which, in the immediate future, will mean the organization of society on the basis of the nation or the regional group of nations.

The process, of course, has already begun. Many observers have commented on the religious elements in Russian communism—the fanaticism, the insistence on orthodoxy, the violent "theological" disputes, the "worship" of Lenin, the spirit of self-dedication, the persecutions, the common enthusiasm, the puritan element, the mass-emotions, the censorship. A very similar set of events is to be seen in Nazi Germany. In that country, of especial interest to the scientist and the student of comparative religion are such phenomena as the falsification of history and anthropological theory in the interest of a theory of the State and of the Germanic race which serves as the necessary "theological" rationalization of the emotions underlying the Nazi movement, and the dragooning of the Protestant churches to fit them into the Nazi scheme of things. The modern persecution of the Jews, which has its real basis in economic and social dislike, is justified on the basis of this new religiously-felt Germanism, just as the medieval persecutions of the Jews, which equally sprang from economic and social dislike, was justified on the basis of Christianity.

These are the first gropings of the human mind after a social embodiment of the religious impulse. They are as crude and in some respects as nasty as its first gropings, millennia previously, after a theistic embodiment of religion. The beast-headed gods and goddesses of those earlier times, the human sacrifice, the loss of self-criticism in the flood of emotional certitude, the sinister power of a privileged hierarchy, the justification of self and the vilification of critics and the violence toward opponents—these and other primitive phenomena of early God-religion have their counterparts in today's dawn of social religion. And the general unrest and the widespread preoccupation with emotionally-based group movements such as Fascism and Communism, is in many ways comparable with the religious unrest that swept the Mediterranean world in the centuries just before and after the beginning of the Christian Era.

To achieve some real understanding and control of the forces and processes operating in human societies is the next great task for science; and the applications of scientific discovery in this field will have as their goal what we may call the Socialized State. The religious impulse, itself one of the social forces to be more fully comprehended and controlled, will increasingly find its outlet in the promotion of the ideals of the Socialized State.

Exactly how all this will happen no one can say—whether the religious impulse will again crystallize into a definite religious system with its own organization, or will find its outlets within the bounds of other organizations, as it does for instance in the Communist party in Russia. We can, however, on the basis of the past history of religion, make a further prophecy. We can be reasonably sure that the inner momentum of logic and moral feelings, combined with the outer momentum derived from increasing comprehension and control, will lead to an improvement in the expression of this socialized religion comparable to the progress of theistic religion from its crude beginnings toward developed monotheism.

Accordingly, we can prophesy that in the long run the nationalistic element in socialized religion will be subordinated or adjusted to the internationalist: that the persecution of minorities will give place to toleration; that the subtler intellectual and moral virtues will find a place and will gradually oust the cruder from their present preeminence in the religiously-conceived social organism.

We can also assert with fair assurance that this process of improvement will be a slow one, and accompanied by much violence and suffering.

Finally we can make the prophecy that part of this process will come about through interaction between two expressions of the religious spirit—one which strives to identify itself with the Socialized State, and the other which reacts against the limitations thus imposed and strives to assert and uphold values that are felt to be more permanent and more universal. The cruder and more violent is the socialized religion, the more will it encourage such reactions. Already in Nazi Germany such a reaction has taken place among certain elements of the Protestant churches, who feel that their principles embody something higher, more lasting, and more general than anything, however intense, which is at the basis of a nationalist and racialist conception of social aims.

This is the one domain in which traditional religion, with its universalist monotheism, will in the near future have a real advantage over socialized religion, which for some time will inevitably be bound up with nationalist states.

It is probable, however, that a universalist Humanism (and probably Communism too) will soon become a strong rival of the old theistic systems in this field. It is also probable that with the growth of intolerant socialized feelings, both in Communistic and Fascist societies, the pioneers of such a Humanism will be those most exposed to religious persecution, but also those who will be doing most for their form of socialized religion and for religious progress in general.

One final prophecy, and I have done. It seems evident that as the religious impulse comes to create these new outlets of expression, whether by way of the Socialized State or by way of Humanism, it will be increasingly confronted by psychological problems—as indeed will the Socialized State itself. Men will realize that economic and social planning will not solve their problems so long as ignorance and absence of control obtain in regard to their own minds. Psychological science will then come into its own, with social psychology as its dominant branch. And this will mean a new understanding of religious phenomena, and new possibilities of integrating them with the life of the community.

To sum up, I would say first that the so-called "conflict between science and religion" has been a conflict between one aspect of science and one aspect of religion. These aspects have both been concerned with man's relation to his *external* environment. The systems of religion which are in danger of collapse grew out of man's ignorance and helplessness in face of external nature; the aspect of science which is endangering those religious systems is that which has provided knowledge and control in this same domain.

In the near future, the religious impulse will find its main outlet in relation to the internal environment of the human species —social, economic, and psychological— for it is the forces of this internal en-

vironment that are now causing distress and bewilderment and are being felt as Destiny to be propitiated or otherwise manipulated. Meanwhile science will find its main scope for new endeavour in this same field, since it is here that our ignorance and our lack of control are now most glaring.

There will again be a race between the effects of ignorance and those of knowledge; but with several new features. For one thing the growth of science in the new field will this time not lag by many centuries behind that of the new modes of religious expression; and for another, the facts concerning the religious impulse and its expression will themselves fall within the scope of the new scientific drive. The probable result will be that in the Socialized State the relation between religion and science will gradually cease to be one of conflict and will become one of co-operation. Science will be called on to advise what expressions of the religious impulse are intellectually permissible and socially desirable, if that impulse is to be properly integrated with other human activities and harnessed to take its share in pulling the chariot of man's destiny along the path of progress.

SHORT STORIES

WHAT MEN LIVE BY

Lev Tolstoi
(1828–1910)

"We know that we have passed out of death unto life, because we love the brethren. He that loveth not abideth in death."—1 Epistle St. John iii. 14.

"Whoso hath the world's goods, and beholdeth his brother in need, and shutteth up his compassion from him, how doth the love of God abide in him? My little children, let us not love in word, neither with the tongue; but in deed and truth."—iii. 17–18.

"Love is of God; and every one that loveth is begotten of God, and knoweth God. He that loveth not knoweth not God; for God is love."—iv. 7–8.

"No man hath beheld God at any time; if we love one another, God abideth in us."—iv. 12.

"God is love; and he that abideth in love abideth in God, and God abideth in him."—iv. 16.

"If a man say, I love God, and hateth his brother, he is a liar; for he that loveth not his brother whom he hath seen, how can he love God whom he hath not seen?"—iv. 20.

A shoemaker named Simon, who had neither house nor land of his own, lived with his wife and children in a peasant's hut and earned his living by his work. Work was cheap but bread was dear, and what he earned he spent for food. The man and his wife had but one sheep-skin coat between them for winter wear, and even that was worn to tatters, and this was the second year he had been wanting to buy sheepskins for a new coat. Before winter Simon saved up a little money: a three-rúble note lay hidden in his wife's box, and five rúbles and twenty kopéks were owed him by customers in the village.

So one morning he prepared to go to the village to buy the sheep-skins. He put on over his shirt his wife's wadded nankeen jacket, and over that he put his own cloth coat. He took the three-rúble note in his pocket, cut himself a stick to serve as a staff, and started off after breakfast. "I'll collect the five rúbles that are due to me," thought he, "add the three I have got, and that will be enough to buy sheepskins for the winter coat."

He came to the village and called at a peasant's hut, but the man was not at home. The peasant's wife promised that the money should be paid next week, but she would not pay it herself. Then Simon called on another peasant, but this one swore he had no money, and would only pay twenty kopéks which he owed for a pair of boots Simon had mended. Simon then tried to buy the sheep-skins on credit, but the dealer would not trust him.

"Bring your money," said he, "then you may have your pick of the skins. We know what debt-collecting is like."

So all the business the shoemaker did was to get the twenty kopéks for boots he had mended, and to take a pair of felt boots a peasant gave him to sole with leather.

Simon felt downhearted. He spent the twenty kopéks on vódka, and started homewards without having bought any skins. In the morning he had felt the frost; but now, after drinking the vódka, he felt warm even without a sheep-skin coat. He trudged along, striking his stick on the frozen earth with one hand, swinging the felt boots with the other, and talking to himself.

"I'm quite warm," said he, "though I have no sheep-skin coat. I've had a drop and it runs through all my veins. I need no sheep-skins. I go along and don't worry about anything. That's the sort of man I am! What do I care? I can live without sheep-skins. I don't need them. My wife will fret, to be sure. And, true enough, it *is* a shame; one works all day long and then does not get paid. Stop a bit! If you don't bring that money along, sure enough I'll skin you, blessed if I don't. How's that? He pays twenty kopéks at a time! What can I do with twenty kopéks? Drink it—that's all one can do! Hard up, he says he is! So he may be—but what about me? You have house, and cattle, and everything; I've only what I stand up in! You have corn of your own growing, I have to buy every grain. Do what I will, I must spend three rúbles every week for bread alone. I come home and find the bread all used up and I have to fork out another rúble and a half. So just you pay up what you owe, and no nonsense about it!"

By this time he had nearly reached the shrine at the bend of the road. Looking up, he saw something whitish behind the shrine. The daylight was fading, and the shoemaker peered at the thing without being able to make out what it was. "There was no white stone here before.

Can it be an ox? It's not like an ox. It has a head like a man, but it's too white; and what could a man be doing there?"

He came closer, so that it was clearly visible. To his surprise it really was a man, alive or dead, sitting naked, leaning motionless against the shrine. Terror seized the shoemaker, and he thought, "Some one has killed him, stripped him, and left him here. If I meddle I shall surely get into trouble."

So the shoemaker went on. He passed in front of the shrine so that he could not see the man. When he had gone some way he looked back, and saw that the man was no longer leaning aginst the shrine, but was moving as if looking towards him. The shoemaker felt more frightened than before, and thought, "Shall I go back to him or shall I go on? If I go near him something dreadful may happen. Who knows who the fellow is? He has not come here for any good. If I go near him he may jump up and throttle me, and there will be no getting away. Or if not, he'd still be a burden on one's hands. What could I do with a naked man? I couldn't give him my last clothes. Heaven only help me to get away!"

So the shoemaker hurried on, leaving the shrine behind him—when suddenly his conscience smote him and he stopped in the road.

"What are you doing, Simon?" said he to himself. "The man may be dying of want, and you slip past afraid. Have you grown so rich as to be afraid of robbers? Ah, Simon, shame on you!"

So he turned back and went up to the man.

II

Simon approached the stranger, looked at him, and saw that he was a young man, fit, with no bruises on his body, but evidently freezing and frightened, and he sat there leaning back without looking up at Simon, as if too faint to lift his eyes. Simon went close to him and then the man seemed to wake up. Turning his head, he opened his eyes and looked into Simon's face. That one look was enough to make Simon fond of the man. He threw the felt boots on the ground, undid his sash, laid it on the boots, and took off his cloth coat.

"It's not a time for talking," said he. "Come, put this coat on at once!" And Simon took the man by the elbows and helped him to rise. As he stood there, Simon saw that his body was clean and in good condition, his hands and feet shapely, and his face good and kind. He threw his coat over the man's shoulders, but the latter could not find the sleeves. Simon guided his arms into them, and drawing the coat well on, wrapped it closely about him, tying the sash round the man's waist.

Simon even took off his torn cap to put it on the man's head, but then his own head felt cold and he thought: "I'm quite bald, while he has long curly hair." So he put his cap on his own head again. "It will be better to give him something for his feet," thought he; and he made the man sit down and helped him to put on the felt boots, saying, "There, friend, now move about and warm yourself. Other matters can be settled later on. Can you walk?"

The man stood up and looked kindly at Simon, but could not say a word.

"Why don't you speak?" said Simon. "It's too cold to stay here, we must be getting home. There now, take my stick, and if you're feeling weak lean on that. Now step out!"

The man started walking and moved easily, not lagging behind.

As they went along, Simon asked him, "And where do you belong to?"

"I'm not from these parts."

"I thought as much. I know the folks hereabouts. But how did you come to be there by the shrine?"

"I cannot tell."

"Has some one been ill-treating you?"

"No one has ill-treated me. God has punished me."

"Of course God rules all. Still, you'll have to find food and shelter somewhere. Where do you want to go?"

"It is all the same to me."

Simon was amazed. The man did not look like a rogue, and he spoke gently, but yet he gave no account of himself. Still Simon thought, "Who knows what may have happened?" And he said to the stranger: "Well then, come home with me and at least warm yourself awhile."

So Simon walked towards his home, and the stranger kept up with him, walking at his side. The wind had risen and Simon felt it cold under his shirt. He was getting over his tipsiness by now and began to feel the frost. He went along sniffling and wrapping his wife's jacket round him, and he thought to himself: "There now—talk about sheep-skins! I went out for sheep-skins and come home without even a coat to my back, and what is more, I'm bringing a naked man along with me. Matréna won't be pleased!" And when he thought of his wife he felt sad; but when he looked at the stranger and remembered how he had looked up at him at the shrine, his heart was glad.

III

Simon's wife had everything ready early that day. She had cut wood, brought water, fed the children, eaten her own meal, and now she sat thinking. She wondered when she ought to make bread: now or to-morrow? There was still a large piece left.

"If Simon has had some dinner in town," thought she, "and does not eat much for supper, the bread will last out another day."

She weighed the piece of bread in her hand again and again, and thought: "I won't make any more to-day. We have only enough flour left to bake one batch. We can manage to make this last out till Friday."

So Matrëna put away the bread, and sat down at the table to patch her husband's shirt. While she worked she thought how her husband was buying skins for a winter coat.

"If only the dealer does not cheat him. My good man is much too simple; he cheats nobody, but any child can take him in. Eight rúbles is a lot of money—he should get a good coat at that price. Not tanned skins, but still a proper winter coat. How difficult it was last winter to get on without a warm coat. I could neither get down to the river nor go out anywhere. When he went out he put on all we had, and there was nothing left for me. He did not start very early to-day, but still it's time he was back. I only hope he has not gone on the spree!"

Hardly had Matrëna thought this than steps were heard on the threshold and some one entered. Matrëna stuck her needle into her work and went out into the passage. There she saw two men: Simon, and with him a man without a hat and wearing felt boots.

Matrëna noticed at once that her husband smelt of spirits. "There now, he has been drinking," thought she. And when she saw that he was coatless, had only her jacket on, brought no parcel, stood there silent, and seemed ashamed, her heart was ready to break with disappointment. "He has drunk the money," thought she, "and has been on the spree with some good-for-nothing fellow whom he has brought home with him."

Matrëna let them pass into the hut, followed them in, and saw that the stranger was a young, slight man, wearing her husband's coat. There was no shirt to be seen under it, and he had no hat.

Having entered, he stood neither moving nor raising his eyes, and Matrëna thought: "He must be a bad man—he's afraid."

Matrëna frowned, and stood beside the stove looking to see what they would do.

Simon took off his cap and sat down on the bench as if things were all right.

"Come, Matrëna; if supper is ready, let us have some."

Matrëna muttered something to herself and did not move, but stayed where she was, by the stove. She looked first at the one and then at the other of them and only shook her head. Simon saw that his wife was annoyed, but tried to pass it off. Pretending not to notice anything, he took the stranger by the arm.

"Sit down, friend," said he, "and let us have some supper."

The stranger sat down on the bench.

"Haven't you cooked anything for us?" said Simon.

Matrëna's anger boiled over. "I've cooked, but not for you. It seems to me you have drunk your wits away. You went to buy a sheep-skin coat, but come home without so much as the coat you had on, and bring a naked vagabond with you. I have no supper for drunkards like you."

"That's enough, Matrëna. Don't wag your tongue without reason! You had better ask what sort of man—"

"And you tell me what you've done with the money?"

Simon found the pocket of the jacket, drew out the three-rúble note, and unfolded it.

"Here is the money. Trifonov did not pay, but promises to pay soon."

Matrëna got still more angry; he had bought no sheep-skins, but had put his only coat on some naked fellow and had even brought him to their house.

She snatched up the note from the table, took it to put away in safety, and said: "I have no supper for you. We can't feed all the naked drunkards in the world."

"There now, Matrëna, hold your tongue a bit. First hear what a man has to say—!"

"Much wisdom I shall hear from a drunken fool. I was right in not wanting to marry you—a drunkard. The linen my mother gave me you drank; and now you've been to buy a coat—and have drunk it too!"

Simon tried to explain to his wife that he had only spent twenty kopéks; tried to tell how he had found the man—but Matrëna would not let him get a word in. She talked nineteen to the dozen, and dragged in things that had happened ten years before.

Matrëna talked and talked, and at last she flew at Simon and seized him by the sleeve.

"Give me my jacket. It is the only one I have, and you must needs take it from me and wear it yourself. Give it here, you mangy dog, and may the devil take you."

Simon began to pull off the jacket, and turned a sleeve of it inside out; Matrëna seized the jacket and it burst its seams. She snatched it up, threw it over her head and went to the door. She meant to go out, but stopped undecided—she wanted to work off her anger, but she also wanted to learn what sort of a man the stranger was.

IV

Matrëna stopped and said: "If he were a good man he would not be naked. Why, he hasn't even a shirt on him. If he were all right, you would say where you came across the fellow."

"That's just what I am trying to tell you," said Simon. "As I came to the shrine I saw him sitting all naked and frozen. It isn't quite the weather to sit about naked! God sent me to him or he would have perished. What was I to do?

How do we know what may have happened to him? So I took him, clothed him, and brought him along. Don't be so angry, Matrëna. It is a sin. Remember, we must all die one day."

Angry words rose to Matrëna's lips, but she looked at the stranger and was silent. He sat on the edge of the bench, motionless, his hands folded on his knees, his head drooping on his breast, his eyes closed, and his brows knit as if in pain. Matrëna was silent, and Simon said: "Matrëna, have you no love of God?"

Matrëna heard these words, and she looked at the stranger, suddenly her heart softened towards him. She came back from the door, and going to the stove she got out the supper. Setting a cup on the table, she poured out some *kvas*.[1] Then she brought out the last piece of bread and set out a knife and spoons.

'Eat, if you want to," said she.

Simon drew the stranger to the table.

"Take your place, young man," said he.

Simon cut the bread, crumbled it into the broth, and they began to eat. Matrëna sat at the corner of the table, resting her head on her hand and looking at the stranger.

And Matrëna was touched with pity for the stranger and began to feel fond of him. And at once the stranger's face lit up; his brows were no longer bent, he raised his eyes and smiled at Matrëna.

When they had finished supper, the woman cleared away the things and began questioning the stranger. "Where are you from?" said she.

"I am not from these parts."

"But how did you come to be on the road?"

"I may not tell."

"Did some one rob you?"

"God punished me."

"And you were lying there naked?"

"Yes, naked and freezing. Simon saw

[1] A non-intoxicating drink usually made from rye-malt and rye-flour. [Translator's note.]

me and had pity on me. He took off his coat, put it on me, and brought me here. And you have fed me, given me drink, and shown pity on me. God will reward you!"

Matrëna rose, took from the window Simon's old shirt she had been patching, and gave it to the stranger. She also brought out a pair of trousers for him.

"There," said she, "I see you have no shirt. Put this on, and lie down where you please, in the loft or on the stove." [2]

The stranger took off the coat, put on the shirt, and lay down in the loft. Matrëna put out the candle, took the coat, and climbed to where her husband lay on the stove.

Matrëna drew the skirts of the coat over her and lay down but could not sleep; she could not get the stranger out of her mind.

When she remembered that he had eaten their last piece of bread and that there was none for to-morrow, and thought of the shirt and trousers she had given away, she felt grieved; but when she remembered how he had smiled, her heart was glad.

Long did Matrëna lie awake, and she noticed that Simon also was awake—he drew the coat towards him.

"Simon!"

"Well?"

"You have had the last of the bread and I have not put any to rise. I don't know what we shall do to-morrow. Perhaps I can borrow some of neighbor Martha."

"If we're alive we shall find something to eat."

The woman lay still awhile, and then said, "He seems a good man, but why does he not tell us who he is?"

[2] The brick stove, including the oven, in a Russian peasant's hut is usually built so as to leave a flat top, large enough to lie on, for those who want to sleep in a warm place. [Translator's note.]

"I suppose he has his reasons."

"Simon!"

"Well?"

"We give; but why does nobody give us anything?"

Simon did not know what to say; so he only said, "Let us stop talking," and turned over and went to sleep.

V

In the morning Simon awoke. The children were still asleep; his wife had gone to the neighbor's to borrow some bread. The stranger alone was sitting on the bench, dressed in the old shirt and trousers, and looking upwards. His face was brighter than it had been the day before.

Simon said to him, "Well, friend; the belly wants bread and the naked body clothes. One has to work for a living. What work do you know?"

"I do not know any."

This surprised Simon, but he said, "Men who want to learn can learn anything."

"Men work and I will work also."

"What is your name?"

"Michael."

"Well, Michael, if you don't wish to talk about yourself, that is your own affair; but you'll have to earn a living for yourself. If you will work as I tell you, I will give you food and shelter."

"May God reward you! I will learn. Show me what to do."

Simon took yarn, put it round his thumb and began to twist it.

"It is easy enough—see!"

Michael watched him, put some yarn round his own thumb in the same way, caught the knack, and twisted the yarn also.

Then Simon showed him how to wax the thread. This also Michael mastered. Next Simon showed him how to twist the bristle in, and how to sew, and this, too, Michael learned at once.

Whatever Simon showed him he understood at once, and after three days he worked as if he had sewn boots all his life. He worked without stopping and ate little. When work was over he sat silently, looking upwards. He hardly went into the street, spoke only when necessary, and neither joked nor laughed. They never saw him smile, except that first evening when Matrëna gave them supper.

VI

Day by day and week by week the year went round. Michael lived and worked with Simon. His fame spread till people said that no one sewed boots so neatly and strongly as Simon's workman, Michael; from all the district round people came to Simon for their boots, and he began to be well off.

One winter day, as Simon and Michael sat working, a carriage on sledge-runners, with three horses and with bells, drove up to the hut. They looked out of the window; the carriage stopped at their door, a fine servant jumped down from the box and opened the door. A gentleman in a fur coat got out and walked up to Simon's hut. Up jumped Matrëna and opend the door wide. The gentleman stooped to enter the hut, and when he drew himself up again his head nearly reached the ceiling and he seemed quite to fill his end of the room.

Simon rose, bowed, and looked at the gentleman with astonishment. He had never seen any one like him. Simon himself was lean, Michael was thin, and Matrëna was dry as a bone, but this man was like some one from another world: red-faced, burly, with a neck like a bull's, and looking altogether as if he were cast in iron.

The gentleman puffed, threw off his fur coat, sat down on the bench, and said,

"Which of you is the master bootmaker?"

"I am, your Excellency," said Simon coming forward.

Then the gentleman shouted to his lad, "Hey, Fédka, bring the leather!"

The servant ran in, bringing a parcel. The gentleman took the parcel and put it on the table.

"Untie it," said he. The lad untied it.

The gentleman pointed to the leather.

"Look here, shoemaker," said he, "do you see this leather?"

"Yes, your Honor."

"But do you know what sort of leather it is?"

Simon felt the leather and said, "It is good leather."

"Good, indeed! Why, you fool, you never saw such leather before in your life. It's German, and cost twenty rúbles."

Simon was frightened, and said, "Where should I ever see leather like that?"

"Just so! Now, can you make it into boots for me?"

"Yes, your Excellency, I can."

Then the gentleman shouted at him: "You *can,* can you? Well, remember whom you are to make them for, and what the leather is. You must make me boots that will wear for a year, neither losing shape nor coming unsewn. If you can do it, take the leather and cut it up; but if you can't, say so. I warn you now, if your boots come unsewn or lose shape within a year I will have you put in prison. If they don't burst or lose shape for a year, I will pay you ten rúbles for your work."

Simon was frightened and did not know what to say. He glanced at Michael and, nudging him with his elbow, whispered: "Shall I take the work?"

Michael nodded his head as if to say, "Yes, take it."

Simon did as Michael advised and undertook to make boots that would not lose shape or split for a whole year.

Calling his servant, the gentleman told

him to pull the boot off his left leg, which he stretched out.

"Take my measure!" said he.

Simon stitched a paper measure seventeen inches long, smoothed it out, knelt down, wiped his hands well on his apron so as not to soil the gentleman's sock, and began to measure. He measured the sole, and round the instep, and began to measure the calf of the leg, but the paper was too short. The calf of the leg was as thick as a beam.

"Mind you don't make it too tight in the leg."

Simon stitched on another strip of paper. The gentleman twitched his toes about in his sock looking round at those in the hut, and as he did so he noticed Michael.

"Whom have you there?" asked he.

"That is my workman. He will sew the boots."

"Mind," said the gentleman to Michael, "remember to make them so that they will last me a year."

Simon also looked at Michael, and saw that Michael was not looking at the gentleman, but was gazing into the corner behind the gentleman, as if he saw some one there. Michael looked and looked, and suddenly he smiled, and his face became brighter.

"What are you grinning at, you fool?" thundered the gentleman. "You had better look to it that the boots are ready in time."

"They shall be ready in good time," said Michael.

"Mind it is so," said the gentleman, and put on his boots and his fur coat, wrapped the latter round him, and went to the door. But he forgot to stoop, and struck his head against the lintel.

He swore and rubbed his head. Then he took his seat in the carriage and drove away.

When he had gone, Simon said: "There's a figure of a man for you! You could not kill him with a mallet. He almost knocked out the lintel, but little harm it did him."

And Matrēna said: "Living as he does, how should he not grow strong? Death itself can't touch such a rock as that."

VII

Then Simon said to Michael: "Well, we have taken the work, but we must see we don't get into trouble over it. The leather is dear, and the gentleman hot-tempered. We must make no mistakes. Come, your eye is truer and your hands have become nimbler than mine, so you take this measure and cut out the boots. I will finish off the sewing of the vamps."

Michael did as he was told. He took the leather, spread it out on the table, folded it in two, took a knife and began to cut out.

Matrēna came and watched him cutting, and was surprised to see how he was doing it. Matrēna was accustomed to seeing boots made, and she looked and saw that Michael was not cutting the leather for boots, but was cutting it round.

She wished to say something, but she thought to herself: "Perhaps I do not understand how gentlemen's boots should be made. I suppose Michael knows more about it—and I won't interfere."

When Michael had cut up the leather he took a thread and began to sew not with two ends, as boots are sewn, but with a single end, as for soft slippers.

Again Matrēna wondered, but again she did not interfere. Michael sewed on steadily till noon. Then Simon rose for dinner, looked around, and saw that Michael had made slippers out of the gentleman's leather.

"Ah!" groaned Simon, and he thought, "How is it that Michael, who has been with me a whole year and never made a mistake before, should do such a dreadful thing? The gentleman ordered high boots, welted, with whole fronts, and Michael has made soft slippers with single soles, and has wasted the leather. What am I to say to the gentleman? I can never replace leather such as this."

And he said to Michael, "What are you doing, friend? You have ruined me! You know the gentleman ordered high boots, but see what you have made!"

Hardly had he begun to rebuke Michael when "rat-tat" went the iron ring that hung at the door. Some one was knocking. They looked out of the window; a man had come on horseback and was fastening his horse. They opened the door, and the servant who had been with the gentleman came in.

"Good day," said he.

"Good day," replied Simon. "What can we do for you?"

"My mistress has sent me about the boots."

"What about the boots?"

"Why, my master no longer needs them. He is dead."

"Is it possible?"

"He did not live to get home after leaving you, but died in the carriage. When we reached home and the servants came to help him alight, he rolled over like a sack. He was dead already, and so stiff that he could hardly be got out of the carriage. My mistress sent me here, saying: 'Tell the bootmaker that the gentleman who ordered boots of him and left the leather for them no longer needs the boots, but that he must quickly make soft slippers for the corpse. Wait till they are ready and bring them back with you.' That is why I have come."

Michael gathered up the remnants of the leather; rolled them up, took the soft slippers he had made, slapped them together, wiped them down with his apron, and handed them and the roll of leather to the servant, who took them and said: "Good-bye, masters, and good day to you!"

VIII

Another year passed, and another, and Michael was now living his sixth year with Simon. He lived as before. He went nowhere, only spoke when necessary, and had only smiled twice in all those years —once when Matrëna gave him food, and a second time when the gentleman was in their hut. Simon was more than pleased with his workman. He never now asked him where he came from, and only feared lest Michael should go away.

They were all at home one day. Matrëna was putting iron pots in the oven; the children were running along the benches and looking out of the window; Simon was sewing at one window and Michael was fastening on a heel at the other.

One of the boys ran along the bench to Michael, leant on his shoulder, and looked out of the window.

"Look, Uncle Michael! There is a lady with little girls! She seems to be coming here. And one of the girls is lame."

When the boy said that, Michael dropped his work, turned to the window, and looked out into the street.

Simon was surprised. Michael never used to look out into the street, but now he pressed against the window, staring at something. Simon also looked out and saw that a well-dressed woman was really coming to his hut, leading by the hand two little girls in fur coats and woolen shawls. The girls could hardly be told one from the other, except that one of them was crippled in her left leg and walked with a limp.

The woman stepped into the porch and entered the passage. Feeling about for the entrance she found the latch, which she lifted and opened the door. She let the two girls go in first, and followed them into the hut.

"Good day, good folk!"

"Pray come in," said Simon. "What can we do for you?"

The woman sat down by the table. The two little girls pressed close to her knees, afraid of the people in the hut.

"I want leather shoes made for these two little girls, for spring."

"We can do that. We never have made such small shoes, but we can make them; either welted or turnover shoes, linen-lined. My man, Michael, is a master at the work."

Simon glanced at Michael and saw that he had left his work and was sitting with his eyes fixed on the little girls. Simon was surprised. It was true the girls were pretty, with black eyes, plump, and rosy-cheeked, and they wore nice kerchiefs and fur coats, but still Simon could not understand why Michael should look at them like that—just as if he had known them before. He was puzzled, but went on talking with the woman and arranging the price. Having fixed it, he prepared the measure. The woman lifted the lame girl on to her lap and said: "Take two measures from this little girl. Make one shoe for the lame foot and three for the sound one. They both have the same-sized feet. They are twins."

Simon took the measure and, speaking of the lame girl, said: "How did it happen to her? She is such a pretty girl. Was she born so?"

"No, her mother crushed her leg."

Then Matrëna joined in. She wondered who this woman was and whose the children were, so she said: "Are not you their mother, then?"

"No, my good woman; I am neither their mother nor any relation to them. They were quite strangers to me, but I adopted them."

"They are not your children and yet you are so fond of them?"

"How can I help being fond of them? I fed them both at my own breasts. I had a child of my own, but God took him.

I was not so fond of him as I now am of these."

"Then whose children are they?"

IX

The woman, having begun talking, told them the whole story.

"It is about six years since their parents died, both in one week: their father was buried on the Tuesday, and their mother died on the Friday. These orphans were born three days after their father's death, and their mother did not live another day. My husband and I were then living as peasants in the village. We were neighbors of theirs, our yard being next to theirs. Their father was a lonely man, a wood-cutter in the forest. When felling trees one day they let one fall on him. It fell across his body and crushed his bowels out. They hardly got him home before his soul went to God; and that same week his wife gave birth to twins—these little girls. She was poor and alone; she had no one, young or old, with her. Alone she gave them birth, and alone she met her death.

"The next morning I went to see her, but when I entered the hut, she, poor thing, was already stark and cold. In dying she had rolled on to this child and crushed her leg. The village folk came to the hut, washed the body, laid her out, made a coffin, and buried her. They were good folk. The babies were left alone. What was to be done with them? I was the only woman there who had a baby at the time. I was nursing my first-born—eight weeks old. So I took them for a time. The peasants came together, and thought and thought what to do with them; and at last they said to me: 'For the present, Mary, you had better keep the girls, and later on we will arrange what to do for them.' So I nursed the sound one at my breast, but at first I did not feed this crippled one. I did not suppose she would live. But then I thought to myself, why should the poor innocent suffer? I pitied her and began to feed her. And so I fed my own boy and these two—the three of them—at my own breast. I was young and strong and had good food, and God gave me so much milk that at times it even overflowed. I used sometimes to feed two at a time, while the third was waiting. When one had had enough I nursed the third. And God so ordered it that these grew up, while my own was buried before he was two years old. And I had no more children, though we prospered. Now my husband is working for the corn merchant at the mill. The pay is good and we are well off. But I have no children of my own, and how lonely I should be without these little girls! How can I help loving them! They are the joy of my life!"

She pressed the lame little girl to her with one hand, while with the other she wiped the tears from her cheeks.

And Matrëna sighed, and said: "The proverb is true that says, 'One may live without father or mother, but one cannot live without God.'"

So they talked together, when suddenly the whole hut was lighted up as though by summer lightning from the corner where Michael sat. They all looked towards him and saw him sitting, his hands folded on his knees, gazing upwards and smiling.

X

The woman went away with the girls. Michael rose from the bench, put down his work, and took off his apron. Then, bowing low to Simon and his wife, he said: "Farewell, masters. God has forgiven me. I ask your forgiveness, too, for anything done amiss."

And they saw that a light shone from Michael. And Simon rose, bowed down to Michael, and said: "I see, Michael, that you are no common man, and I can neither keep you nor question you. Only tell me this: how is it that when I found you and brought you home, you were gloomy, and when my wife gave you food you smiled at her and became brighter? Then when the gentleman came to order the boots, you smiled again and became brighter still? And now, when this woman brought the little girls, you smiled a third time and have become as bright as day? Tell me, Michael, why does your face shine so, and why did you smile those three times?"

And Michael answered: "Light shines from me because I have been punished, but now God has pardoned me. And I smiled three times, because God sent me to learn three truths, and I have learnt them. One I learnt when your wife pitied me, and that is why I smiled the first time. The second I learnt when the rich man ordered the boots, and then I smiled again. And now, when I saw those little girls, I learnt the third and last truth, and I smiled the third time."

And Simon said, "Tell me, Michael, what did God punish you for? And what were the three truths—that I, too, may know them?"

And Michael answered: "God punished me for disobeying Him. I was an angel in heaven and disobeyed God. God sent me to fetch a woman's soul. I flew to earth, and saw a sick woman lying alone who had just given birth to twin girls. They moved feebly at their mother's side but she could not lift them to her breast. When she saw me, she understood that God had sent me for her soul, and she wept and said: 'Angel of God! My husband has just been buried, killed by a falling tree. I have neither sister, nor aunt, nor mother: no one to care for my orphans. Do not take my soul! Let me nurse my babes, feed them, and set them on their feet before I die. Children cannot live without father or mother.' And I hearkened to her. I placed one child at her breast and gave the other into her arms, and returned to the Lord in heaven. I flew to the Lord, and said: 'I could not take the soul of the mother. Her husband was killed by a tree; the woman has twins and prays that her soul may not be taken. She says: "Let me nurse and feed my children, and set them on their feet. Children cannot live without father or mother." I have not taken her soul.' And God said: 'Go—take the mother's soul, and learn three truths: Learn *What dwells in man, What is not given to man,* and *What men live by.* When thou hast learnt these things, thou shalt return to heaven.' So I flew again to earth and took the mother's soul. The babes dropped from her breasts. Her body rolled over on the bed and crushed one babe, twisting its leg. I rose above the village, wishing to take her soul to God, but a wind seized me and my wings drooped and dropped off. Her soul rose alone to God, while I fell to earth by the roadside."

XI

And Simon and Matrëna understood who it was that had lived with them, and whom they had clothed and fed. And they wept with awe and with joy. And the angel said: "I was alone in the field, naked. I had never known human needs, cold and hunger, till I became a man. I was famished, frozen, and did not know what to do. I saw, near the field I was in, a shrine built for God, and I went to it hoping to find shelter. But the shrine was locked and I could not enter. So I sat down behind the shrine to shelter myself at least from the wind. Evening drew on, I was hungry, frozen, and in pain. Suddenly I heard a man coming along the road. He carried a pair of boots and was talking to himself. For the first time since I became a man I saw the mortal face of a man, and his face seemed terrible to me

and I turned from it. And I heard the man talking to himself of how to cover his body from the cold in winter, and how to feed wife and children. And I thought: 'I am perishing of cold and hunger and here is a man thinking only of how to clothe himself and his wife, and how to get bread for themselves. He cannot help me.' When the man saw me he frowned and became still more terrible, and passed me by on the other side. I despaired; but suddenly I heard him coming back. I looked up and did not recognize the same man: before, I had seen death in his face; but now he was alive and I recognized in him the presence of God. He came up to me, clothed me, took me with him, and brought me to his home. I entered the house; a woman came to meet us and began to speak. The woman was still more terrible than the man had been; the spirit of death came from her mouth; I could not breathe for the stench of death that spread around her. She wished to drive me out into the cold, and I knew that if she did so she would die. Suddenly her husband spoke to her of God, and the woman changed at once. And when she brought me food and looked at me, I glanced at her and saw that death no longer dwelt in her; she had become alive, and in her too I saw God.

"Then I remembered the first lesson God had set me: *'Learn what dwells in man.'* And I understood that in man dwells Love! I was glad that God had already begun to show me what He had promised, and I smiled for the first time. But I had not yet learnt all. I did not yet know *What is not given to man,* and *What men live by.*

"I lived with you and a year passed. A man came to order boots that should wear for a year without losing shape or cracking. I looked at him, and suddenly, behind his shoulder, I saw my comrade—the angel of death. None but me saw that angel; but I knew him, and knew that before the sun set he would take that rich man's soul. And I thought to myself, 'The man is making preparations for a year and does not know that he will die before evening.' And I remembered God's second saying, '*Learn what is not given to man.*'

"What dwells in man I already knew. Now I learnt what is not given him. It is not given to man to know his own needs. And I smiled for the second time. I was glad to have seen my comrade angel— glad also that God had revealed to me the second saying.

"But I still did not know all. I did not know *What men live by*. And I lived on, waiting till God should reveal to me the last lesson. In the sixth year came the girl-twins with the woman; and I recognized the girls and heard how they had been kept alive. Having heard the story, I thought, 'Their mother besought me for the children's sake, and I believed her when she said that children cannot live without father or mother; but a stranger has nursed them, and has brought them up.' And when the woman showed her love for the children that were not her own, and wept over them, I saw in her the living God, and understood *What men live by*. And I knew that God had revealed to me the last lesson, and had forgiven my sin. And then I smiled for the third time."

XII

And the angel's body was bared, and he was clothed in light so that eye could not look on him; and his voice grew louder, as though it came not from him but from heaven above. And the angel said:

"I have learnt that all men live not by care for themselves, but by love.

"It was not given to the mother to know what her children needed for their life. Nor was it given to the rich man to know what he himself needed. Nor is it given to any man to know whether, when evening comes, he will need boots for his body or slippers for his corpse.

"I remained alive when I was a man, not by care of myself but because love was present in a passer-by, and because he and his wife pitied and loved me. The orphans remained alive not because of their mother's care, but because there was love in the heart of a woman, a stranger to them, who pitied and loved them. And all men live not by the thought they spend on their own welfare, but because love exists in man.

"I knew before that God gave life to men and desires that they should live; now I understand more than that.

"I understood that God does not wish men to live apart, and therefore he does not reveal to them what each one needs for himself; but he wishes them to live united, and therefore reveals to each of them what is necessary for all.

"I have now understood that though it seems to men that they live by care for themselves, in truth it is love alone by which they live. He who has love, is in God, and God is in him, for God is love."

And the angel sang praise to God, so that the hut trembled at his voice. The roof opened, and a column of fire rose from earth to heaven. Simon and his wife and children fell to the ground. Wings appeared upon the angel's shoulders and he rose into the heavens.

And when Simon came to himself the hut stood as before, and there was no one in it but his own family.

Translated by *Louise* and *Aylmer Maude*.

SUN

D. H. Lawrence
(1885–1930)

I

"Take her away, into the sun," the doctors said.

She herself was sceptical of the sun, but she permitted herself to be carried away, with her child, and a nurse, and her mother, over the sea.

The ship sailed at midnight. And for two hours her husband stayed with her, while the child was put to bed, and the passengers came on board. It was a black night, the Hudson swayed with heavy blackness, shaken over with spilled dribbles of light. She leaned on the rail, and looking down thought: This is the sea; it is deeper than one imagines, and fuller of memories. At that moment the sea seemed to heave like the serpent of chaos that has lived forever.

"These partings are no good, you know," her husband was saying, at her side. "They're no good. I don't like them."

His tone was full of apprehension, misgiving, and there was a certain note of clinging to the last straw of hope.

"No, neither do I," she responded in a flat voice.

She remembered how bitterly they had wanted to get away from one another, he and she. The emotion of parting gave a slight tug at her emotions, but only caused the iron that had gone into her soul to gore deeper.

So, they looked at their sleeping son, and the father's eyes were wet. But it is not the wetting of the eyes which counts, it is the deep iron rhythm of habit, the year-long, life-long habits; the deep-set stroke of power.

And in their two lives, the stroke of power was hostile, his and hers. Like two engines running at variance, they shattered one another.

"All ashore! All ashore!"

"Maurice, you must go!"

And she thought to herself: For him it is *All ashore!* For me it is *Out to sea!*

Well, he waved his hanky on the midnight dreariness of the pier, as the boat inched away; one among a crowd. One among a crowd! *C'est ça!*

The ferry-boats, like great dishes piled with rows of lights, were still slanting across the Hudson. That black mouth must be the Lackawanna Station.

The ship ebbed on, the Hudson seemed interminable. But at last they were round the bend, and there was the poor harvest of lights at the Battery. Liberty flung up her torch in a tantrum. There was the wash of the sea.

And though the Atlantic was grey as lava, she did come at last into the sun. Even she had a house above the bluest of seas, with a vast garden, or vineyard, all vines and olives dropping steeply, terrace after terrace, to the strip of coast-plain; and the garden full of secret places, deep groves of lemon far down in the cleft of earth, and hidden, pure green reservoirs of water; then a spring issuing out of a little cavern, where the old Sicules had drunk before the Greeks came; and a grey goat bleating, stabled in an ancient tomb, with all the niches empty. There was the scent of mimosa, and beyond, the snow of the volcano.

She saw it all, and in a measure it was soothing. But it was all external. She didn't really care about it. She was herself, just the same, with all her anger and frustration inside her, and her incapacity to feel anything real. The child irritated her, and preyed on her peace of mind. She felt so horribly, ghastly responsible for him: as if she must be responsible for every breath he drew. And that was torture to her, to the child, and to everybody else concerned.

"You know, Juliet, the doctor told you to lie in the sun, without your clothes. Why don't you?" said her mother.

"When I am fit to do so, I will. Do you want to kill me?" Juliet flew at her.

"To kill you, no! Only to do you good."

"For God's sake, leave off wanting to do me good."

The mother at last was so hurt and incensed, she departed.

The sea went white—and then invisible. Pouring rain fell. It was cold, in the house built for the sun.

Again a morning when the sun lifted himself naked and molten, sparkling over the sea's rim. The house faced southwest. Juliet lay in her bed and watched him rise. It was as if she had never seen the sun rise before. She had never seen the naked sun stand up pure upon the sea-line, shaking the night off himself.

So the desire sprang secretly in her, to go naked in the sun. She cherished her desire like a secret.

But she wanted to go away from the house—away from people. And it is not easy, in a country where every olive tree has eyes, and every slope is seen from afar, to go hidden.

But she found a place: a rocky bluff, shoved out to the sea and sun and overgrown with large cactus, the flat-leaved cactus called prickly pear. Out of this blue-grey knoll of cactus rose one cypress tree, with a pallid, thick trunk, and a tip that leaned over, flexible, up in the blue. It stood like a guardian looking to sea; or a low, silvery candle whose huge flame was darkness against light: earth sending up her proud tongue of gloom.

Juliet sat down by the cypress tree, and took off her clothes. The contorted cactus made a forest, hideous yet fascinating, about her. She sat and offered her bosom to the sun, sighing, even now, with a certain hard pain, against the cruelty of having to give herself.

But the sun marched in blue heaven and sent down his rays as he went. She felt the soft air of the sea on her breasts, that seemed as if they would never ripen. But she hardly felt the sun. Fruits that would wither and not mature, her breasts.

Soon, however, she felt the sun inside them, warmer than ever love had been, warmer than milk or the hands of her baby. At last, at last her breasts were like long white grapes in the hot sun.

She slid off all her clothes and lay naked in the sun, and as she lay she looked up through her fingers at the central sun, his blue pulsing roundness, whose outer edges streamed brilliance. Pulsing with marvellous blue, and alive, and streaming white fire from his edges, the sun! He faced down to her with his look of blue fire, and enveloped her breasts and her face, her throat, her tired belly, her knees, her thighs and her feet.

She lay with shut eyes, the colour of rosy flame through her lids. It was too much. She reached and put leaves over her eyes. Then she lay again, like a long white gourd in the sun, that must ripen to gold.

She could feel the sun penetrating even into her bones; nay, further, even into her emotions and her thoughts. The dark tensions of her emotion began to give way, the cold dark clots of her thoughts began to dissolve. She was beginning to feel warm right through. Turning over, she let her shoulders dissolve in the sun, her loins, the backs of her thighs, even her heels. And she lay half stunned with wonder at the thing that was happening to her. Her weary, chilled heart was melting, and, in melting, evaporating.

When she was dressed again she lay once more and looked up at the cypress tree, whose crest, a flexible filament, fell this way and that in the breeze. Meanwhile, she was conscious of the great sun roaming in heaven.

So, dazed, she went home, only halfseeing, sun-blinded and sun-dazed. And her blindness was like a richness to her, and her dim, warm, heavy half-consciousness was like wealth.

"Mummy! Mummy!" her child came running towards her, calling in that peculiar bird-like little anguish of want, always wanting her. She was surprised that her drowsed heart for once felt none of the anxious love-anguish in return. She caught the child up in her arms, but she thought:

He should not be such a lump! If he were in the sun, he would spring up.

She resented, rather, his little hands clutching at her, especially at her neck. She pulled her throat away. She did not want to be touched. She put the child gently down.

"Run!" she said. "Run in the sun!"

And there and then she took off his clothes and set him naked on the warm terrace.

"Play in the sun!" she said.

He was frightened and wanted to cry. But she, in the warm indolence of her body, and the complete indifference of her heart, rolled him an orange across the red tiles, and with his soft, unformed little body he toddled after it. Then immediately he had it, he dropped it because it felt strange against his flesh. And he looked back at her, querulous, wrinkling his face to cry, frightened because he was stark.

"Bring me the orange," she said, amazed at her own deep indifference to his trepidation. "Bring Mummy the orange."

"He shall not grow up like his father," she said to herself. "Like a worm that the sun has never seen."

II

She had had the child so much on her mind, in a torment of responsibility, as if, having borne him, she had to answer for his whole existence. Even if his nose were running, it had been repulsive and a goad in her vitals, as if she must say to herself: Look at the thing you brought forth!

Now a change took place. She was no longer vitally interested in the child, she took the strain of her anxiety and her will from off him. And he thrived all the more for it.

She was thinking inside herself, of the sun in his splendour, and her mating with him. Her life was now a whole ritual. She lay always awake, before dawn, watching for the grey to colour to pale gold, to know if clouds lay on the sea's edge. Her joy was when he rose all molten in his nakedness, and threw off blue-white fire, into the tender heaven.

But sometimes he came ruddy, like a big, shy creature. And sometimes slow and crimson red, with a look of anger, slowly pushing and shouldering. Sometimes again she could not see him, only the level cloud threw down gold and scarlet from above, as he moved behind the wall.

She was fortunate. Weeks went by, and though the dawn was sometimes clouded, and afternoon was sometimes grey, never a day passed sunless, and most days, winter though it was, streamed radiant. The thin little wild crocuses came up mauve and striped, the wild narcissi hung their winter stars.

Every day she went down to the cypress tree, among the cactus grove on the knoll with yellowish cliffs at the foot. She was wiser and subtler now, wearing only a dove-grey wrapper, and sandals. So that in an instant, in any hidden niche, she was naked to the sun. And the moment she was covered again she was grey and invisible.

Every day, in the morning towards noon, she lay at the foot of the powerful, silver-pawed cypress tree, while the sun rode jovial in heaven. By now she knew the sun in every thread of her body, there was not a cold shadow left. And her heart, that anxious, straining heart, had disappeared altogether, like a flower that falls in the sun, and leaves only a ripe seed-case.

She knew the sun in heaven, blue-molten with his white fire edges, throwing off fire. And though he shone on all the world, when she lay unclothed he focused on her. It was one of the wonders of the sun, he could shine on a million people and still be the radiant, splendid, unique sun, focused on her alone.

With her knowledge of the sun, and her conviction that the sun *knew* her, in the cosmic carnal sense of the word, came over her a feeling of detachment from people, and a certain contempt for human beings altogether. They were so unelemental, so unsunned. They were so like graveyard worms.

Even the peasants passing up the rocky, ancient little road with their donkeys, sun-blackened as they were, were not sunned right through. There was a little soft white core of fear, like a snail in a shell, where the soul of the man cowered in fear of death, and in fear of the natural blaze of life. He dared not quite emerge: always innerly cowed. All men were like that.

Why admit men!

With her indifference to people, to men, she was not now so cautious about being unseen. She had told Marinina, who went shopping for her in the village, that the doctor had ordered sun-baths. Let that suffice.

Marinina was a woman over sixty, tall, thin, erect, with curling dark-grey hair, and dark-grey eyes that had the shrewdness of thousands of years in them, with the laugh that underlies all long experience. Tragedy is lack of experience.

"It must be beautiful to go unclothed in the sun," said Marinina, with a shrewd laugh in her eyes, as she looked keenly at the other woman. Juliet's fair, bobbed hair curled in a little cloud at her temple. Marinina was a woman of Magna Græcia, and had far memories. She looked again at Juliet. "But you have to be beautiful yourself, if you're not going to give offence to the sun? Isn't it so?" she added, with that queer, breathless little laugh of the women of the past.

"Who knows if I am beautiful!" said Juliet.

But beautiful or not, she felt that by the sun she was appreciated. Which is the same.

When, out of the sun at noon, sometimes she stole down over the rocks and past the cliff-edge, down to the deep gully where the lemons hung in cool eternal shadow; and in the silence slipped off her wrapper to wash herself quickly at one of the deep, clear green basins, she would notice, in the bare green twilight under the lemon leaves, that all her body was rosy, rosy and turning to gold. She was like another person. She was another person.

So she remembered that the Greeks had said, a white, unsunned body was fishy and unhealthy.

And she would rub a little olive oil in her skin, and wander a moment in the dark underworld of the lemons, balancing a lemon flower in her navel, laughing to herself. There was just a chance some peasant might see her. But if he did he would be more afraid of her than she of him. She knew the white core of fear in the clothed bodies of men.

She knew it even in her little son. How he mistrusted her, now that she laughed at him, with the sun in her face! She insisted on his toddling naked in the sunshine, every day. And now his little body was pink, too, his blond hair was pushed thick from his brow, his cheeks had a pomegranate scarlet, in the delicate gold of the sunny skin. He was bonny and healthy, and the servants, loving his red and gold and blue, called him an angel from heaven.

But he mistrusted his mother: she laughed at him. And she saw in his wide blue eyes, under the little frown, that centre of fear, misgiving, which she believed was at the centre of all male eyes, now. She called it fear of the sun.

"He fears the sun," she would say to herself, looking down into the eyes of the child.

And as she watched him toddling, swaying, tumbling in the sunshine, making his little, bird-like noises, she saw that he held himself tight and hidden from the sun, inside himself. His spirit was like a snail in a shell, in a damp, cold crevice inside himself. It made her think of his father. She wished she could make him come forth, break out in a gesture of recklessness and salutation.

She determined to take him with her, down to the cypress tree among the cactus. She would have to watch him, because of the thorns. But surely in that place he would come forth from that little shell, deep inside him. That little civilized tension would disappear off his brow.

She spread a rug for him and sat him down. Then she slid off her wrapper and lay down herself, watching a hawk high in the blue, and the tip of the cypress hanging over.

The boy played with stones on the rug. When he got up to toddle away, she sat up too. He turned and looked at her. Almost, from his blue eyes, it was the challenging, warm look of the true male. And he was handsome, with the scarlet in the golden blond of his skin. He was not really white. His skin was gold-dusky.

"Mind the thorns, darling," she said.

"Thorns!" re-echoed the child, in a birdy chirp, still looking at her over his shoulder, like some naked cherub in a picture, doubtful.

"Nasty prickly thorns."

" 'Ickly thorns!"

He staggered in his little sandals over the stones, pulling at the dry wild mint. She was quick as a serpent, leaping to him, when he was going to fall against the prickles. It surprised even herself. "What a wild cat I am, really!" she said to herself.

She brought him every day, when the sun shone, to the cypress tree.

"Come!" she said. " Let us go to the cypress tree."

And if there was a cloudy day, with the tramontana blowing, so that she could not go down, the child would chirp incessantly: "Cypress tree! Cypress tree!"

He missed it as much as she did.

It was not just taking sun-baths. It was much more than that. Something deep inside her unfolded and relaxed, and she was given. By some mysterious power inside her, deeper than her known consciousness and will, she was put into connection with the sun, and the stream flowed of itself, from her womb. She herself, her conscious self, was secondary, a secondary person, almost an onlooker. The true Juliet was this dark flow from her deep body to the sun.

She had always been mistress of herself, aware of what she was doing, and held tense for her own power. Now she felt inside her quite another sort of power, something greater than herself, flowing by itself. Now she was vague, but she had a power beyond herself.

III

The end of February was suddenly very hot. Almond blossom was falling like pink snow, in the touch of the smallest breeze. The mauve, silky little anemones were out, the asphodels tall in bud, and the sea was cornflower blue.

Juliet had ceased to trouble about anything. Now, most of the day, she and the child were naked in the sun, and it was all she wanted. Sometimes she went down to the sea to bathe: often she wandered in the gullies where the sun shone in, and she was out of sight. Sometimes she saw a peasant with an ass, and he saw her. But she went so simply and quietly with her child; and the fame of the sun's healing power, for the soul as well as for the body, had already spread among the people; so that there was no excitement.

The child and she were now both tanned with a rosy-golden tan, all over. "I am another being!" she said to herself, as she looked at her red-gold breasts and thighs.

The child, too, was another creature, with a peculiar quiet, sun-darkened absorption. Now he played by himself in silence, and she hardly need notice him. He seemed no longer to know, when he was alone.

There was not a breeze, and the sea was ultramarine. She sat by the great silver paw of the cypress tree, drowsed in the sun, but her breasts alert, full of sap. She was becoming aware that an activity was rousing in her, an activity which would carry her into a new way of life. Still she did not want to be aware. She knew well enough the vast cold apparatus of civilization, so difficult to evade.

The child had gone a few yards down the rocky path, round the great sprawling of a cactus. She had seen him, a real gold-brown infant of the winds, with burnt gold hair and red cheeks, collecting the speckled pitcher-flowers and laying them in rows. He could balance now, and was quick for his own emergencies, like an absorbed young animal playing silent.

Suddenly she heard him speaking: *"Look, Mummy! Mummy, look!"* A note in his bird-like voice made her lean forward sharply.

Her heart stood still. He was looking over his naked little shoulder at her, and pointing with a loose little hand at a snake which had reared itself up a yard away from him, and was opening its mouth so that its forked, soft tongue flickered black like a shadow, uttering a short hiss.

"Look, Mummy!"

"Yes, darling, it's a snake!" came the slow, deep voice.

He looked at her, his wide blue eyes uncertain whether to be afraid or not. Some stillness of the sun in her reassured him.

"Snake!" he chirped.

"Yes, darling! Don't touch it, it can bite."

The snake had sunk down, and was reaching away from the coils in which it had been basking asleep, and slowly was easing its long, gold-brown body into the rocks, with slow curves. The boy turned and watched it in silence. Then he said:

"Snake going!"

"Yes! Let it go. It likes to be alone."

He still watched the slow, easing length as the creature drew itself apathetic out of sight.

"Snake gone back," he said.

"Yes, it's gone back. Come to Mummy a moment."

He came and sat with his plump, naked little body on her naked lap, and she smoothed his burnt, bright hair. She said nothing, feeling that everything was passed. The curious soothing power of the sun filled her, filled the whole place like a charm, and the snake was part of the place, along with her and the child.

Another day, in the dry stone wall of one of the olive terraces, she saw a black snake horizontally creeping.

"Marinina," she said, "I saw a black snake. Are they harmful?"

"Ah, the black snakes, no! But the yellow ones, yes! If the yellow ones bite you, you die. But they frighten me, they frighten me, even the black ones, when I see one."

Juliet still went to the cypress tree with the child. But she always looked carefully round before she sat down, examining everywhere where the child might go. Then she would lie and turn to the sun again, her tanned, pear-shaped breasts pointing up. She would take no thought for the morrow. She refused to think outside her garden, and she could not write letters. She would tell the nurse to write.

IV

It was March, and the sun was growing very powerful. In the hot hours she would lie in the shade of the trees, or she would even go down to the depths of the cool lemon grove. The child ran in the distance, like a young animal absorbed in life.

One day she was sitting in the sun on the steep slope of the gully, having bathed in one of the great tanks. Below, under the lemons, the child was wading among the yellow oxalis flowers of the shadow, gathering fallen lemons, passing with his tanned little body into flecks of light, moving all dappled.

Suddenly, high over the land's edge, against the full-lit pale-blue sky, Marinina appeared, a black cloth tied round her head, calling quietly: *"Signora! Signora Giulietta!"*

Juliet faced round, standing up. Marinina paused a moment, seeing the naked woman standing alert, her sun-faded fair hair in a little cloud. Then the swift old woman came on down the slant of the steep track.

She stood a few steps, erect, in front of the sun-coloured woman, and eyed her shrewdly.

"But how beautiful you are, you!" she said coolly, almost cynically. "There is your husband."

"My husband!" cried Juliet.

The old woman gave a shrewd bark of a little laugh, the mockery of the women of the past.

"Haven't you got one, a husband, you?" she taunted.

"But where is he?" cried Juliet.

The old woman glanced over her shoulder.

"He was following me," she said. "But he will not have found the path." And she gave another little bark of a laugh.

The paths were all grown high with grass and flowers and nepitella, till they were like bird-trails in an eternally wild place. Strange, the vivid wildness of the old places of civilization, a wildness that is not gaunt.

Juliet looked at her serving-woman with meditating eyes.

"Oh, very well!" she said at last. "Let him come."

"Let him come here? Now?" asked Marinina, her laughing, smoke-grey eyes looking with mockery into Juliet's. Then she gave a little jerk of her shoulders.

"All right, as you wish. But for him it is a rare one!"

She opened her mouth in a laugh of noiseless joy. Then she pointed down to the child, who was heaping lemons against his little chest. "Look how beautiful the child is! That, certainly, will please him, poor thing. Then I'll bring him."

"Bring him," said Juliet.

The old woman scrambled rapidly up the track again. Maurice was standing grey-faced, in his grey felt hat and his dark-grey suit, at a loss among the vine terraces. He looked pathetically out of place, in that resplendent sunshine and the grace of the old Greek world; like a blot of ink on the pale, sun-growing slope.

"Come!" said Marinina to him. "She is down here."

And swiftly she led the way, striding with a rapid stride, making her way through the grasses. Suddenly she stopped on the brow of the slope. The tops of the lemon trees were dark, away below.

"You, you go down here," she said to him, and he thanked her, looking up at her swiftly.

He was a man of forty, clean-shaven, grey-faced, very quiet and really shy. He managed his own business carefully, without startling success, but efficiently. And he confided in nobody. The old woman of Magna Græcia saw him at a glance: he is good, she said to herself, but not a man, poor thing.

"Down there is the Signora!" said Marinina, pointing like one of the Fates.

And again he said "Thank you! Thank

you!" without a twinkle, and stepped carefully into the track. Marinina lifted her chin with a joyful wickedness. Then she strode off towards the house.

Maurice was watching his step, through the tangle of Mediterranean herbage, so he did not catch sight of his wife till he came round a little bend, quite near her. She was standing erect and nude by the jutting rock, glistening with the sun and with warm life. Her breasts seemed to be lifting up, alert, to listen, her thighs looked brown and fleet. Her glance on his, as he came like ink on blotting-paper, was swift and nervous.

Maurice, poor fellow, hesitated, and glanced away from her. He turned his face aside.

"Hello, Julie!" he said, with a little nervous cough—"Splendid! Splendid!"

He advanced with his face averted, shooting further glances at her, as she stood with the peculiar satiny gleam of the sun on her tanned skin. Somehow she did not seem so terribly naked. It was the golden-rose tan of the sun that clothed her.

"Hello, Maurice!" she said, hanging back from him. "I wasn't expecting you so soon."

"No," he said. "No! I managed to slip away a little earlier."

And again he coughed awkwardly.

They stood several yards away from one another, and there was silence.

"Well!" he said, "er—this is splendid, splendid! You are—er—splendid! Where is the boy?"

"There he is," she said, pointing down to where a naked urchin in the deep shade was piling fallen lemons together.

The father gave an odd little laugh.

"Ah, yes! there he is! So there's the little man! Fine!" he said. He really was thrilled in his suppressed, nervous soul. "Hello, Johnny!" he called, and it sounded rather feeble. "Hello, Johnny!"

The child looked up, spilling lemons from his chubby arms, but did not respond.

"I guess we'll go down to him," said Juliet, as she turned and went striding down the path. Her husband followed, watching the rosy, fleet-looking lifting and sinking of her quick hips, as she swayed a little in the socket of her waist. He was dazed with admiration, but also, at a deadly loss. What should he do with himself? He was utterly out of the picture, in his dark-grey suit and pale-grey hat, and his grey, monastic face of a shy business man.

"He looks all right, doesn't he?" said Juliet, as they came through the deep sea of yellow-flowering oxalis, under the lemon trees.

"Ah!—yes! yes! Splendid! Splendid!—Hello, Johnny! Do you know Daddy? Do you know Daddy, Johnny?"

He crouched down and held out his hands.

"Lemons!" said the child, birdily chirping. "Two lemons!"

"Two lemons!" replied the father. "Lots of lemons."

The infant came and put a lemon in each of his father's open hands. Then he stood back to look.

"Two lemons!" repeated the father. "Come, Johnny! Come and say 'Hello' to Daddy."

"Daddy going back?" said the child.

"Going back? Well—well—not to-day."

And he gathered his son in his arms.

"Take a coat off! Daddy take a coat off!" said the boy, squirming debonair away from the cloth.

"All right, son! Daddy take a coat off."

He took off his coat and laid it carefully aside, then again took his son in his arms. The naked woman looked down at the naked infant in the arms of the man in his shirt sleeves. The boy had pulled off the father's hat, and Juliet looked at the sleek, black-and-grey hair of her husband, not a hair out of place. And utterly,

utterly indoors. She was silent for a long time, while the father talked to the child, who was fond of his Daddy.

"What are you going to do about it, Maurice?" she said, suddenly.

He looked at her swiftly, sideways.

"Er—about what, Julie?"

"Oh, everything! About this! I can't go back into East Forty-Seventh."

"Er—" he hesitated, "no, I suppose not —not just now at least."

"Never," she said, and there was a silence.

"Well—er—I don't know," he said.

"Do you think you can come out here?" she said.

"Yes!—I can stay for a month. I think I can manage a month," he hesitated. Then he ventured a complicated, shy peep at her, and hid his face again.

She looked down at him, her alert breasts lifted with a sigh, as if a breeze of impatience shook them.

"I can't go back," she said slowly. "I can't go back on this sun. If you can't come here—"

She ended on an open note. He glanced at her again and again, furtively, but with growing admiration and lessening confusion.

"No!" he said. "This kind of thing suits you. You are splendid! No, I don't think you can go back."

He was thinking of her in the New York flat, pale, silent, oppressing him terribly. He was the soul of gentle timidity, in his human relations, and her silent, awful hostility, after the baby was born, had frightened him deeply. Because he had realized she couldn't help it. Women were like that. Their feelings took a reverse direction, even against their own selves, and it was awful—awful! Awful, awful to live in the house with a woman like that, whose feelings were reversed even against herself! He had felt himself ground down under the millstone of her helpless enmity. She had ground even her-

self down to the quick, and the child as well. No, anything rather than that.

"But what about *you?*" she asked.

"I? Oh, I!—I can carry on the business, and—er—come over here for the holidays—as long as you like to stay. You stay as long as you wish." He looked a long time down at the earth, then glanced up at her with a touch of supplication in his uneasy eyes.

"Even forever?"

"Well—er—yes, if you like. Forever is a long time. One can't set a date."

"And I can do anything I like?" She looked him straight in the eyes, challenging. And he was powerless against her rosy, wind-hardened nakedness.

"Er—yes!—I suppose so! So long as you don't make yourself unhappy—or the boy."

Again he looked up at her with a complicated, uneasy appeal—thinking of the child, but hoping for himself.

"I won't," she said quickly.

"No!" he said. "No! I don't think you will."

There was a pause. The bells of the village were hastily clanging midday. That meant lunch.

She slipped into her grey crêpe kimono, and fastened a broad green sash round her waist. Then she slipped a little blue shirt over the boy's head, and they went up to the house.

At table she watched her husband, his grey city face, his fixed, black-grey hair, his very precise table manners, and his extreme moderation in eating and drinking. Sometimes he glanced at her, furtively, from under his black lashes. He had the gold-grey eyes of an animal that has been caught young, and reared completely in captivity.

They went on to the balcony for coffee. Below, beyond, on the next podere across the steep little gully, a peasant and his wife were sitting under an almond tree, near the green wheat, eating their midday meal from a little white cloth spread on the ground. There was a huge piece of bread, and glasses with dark wine.

Juliet put her husband with his back to this picture: she sat facing. Because, the moment she and Maurice had come out on the balcony, the peasant had glanced up.

V

She knew him, in the distance, perfectly. He was a rather fat, very broad fellow of about thirty-five, and he chewed large mouthfuls of bread. His wife was stiff and dark-faced, handsome, sombre. They had no children. So much Juliet had learned.

The peasant worked a great deal alone, on the opposite podere. His clothes were always very clean and cared-for, white trousers and a coloured shirt, and an old straw hat. Both he and his wife had that air of quiet superiority which belongs to individuals, not to a class.

His attraction was in his vitality, the peculiar quick energy which gave a charm to his movements, stout and broad as he was. In the early days before she took to the sun, Juliet had met him suddenly, among the rocks, when she had scrambled over to the next podere. He had been aware of her before she saw him, so that, when she did look up, he took off his hat, gazing at her with shyness and pride, from his big blue eyes. His face was broad, sunburnt, he had a cropped brown moustache, and thick brown eyebrows, nearly as thick as his moustache, meeting under his low, wide brow.

"Oh!" she said. "Can I walk here?"

"Surely!" he replied, with that peculiar hot haste which characterized his movement. "My padrone would wish you to walk wherever you like on his land."

And he pressed back his head in the quick, vivid, shy generosity of his nature.

She had gone on quickly. But instantly she had recognized the violent generosity of his blood, and the equally violent *farouche* shyness.

Since then she had seen him in the distance every day, and she came to realize that he was one who lived a good deal to himself, like a quick animal, and that his wife loved him intensely, with a jealousy that was almost hate; because, probably, he wanted to give himself still, still further, beyond where she could take him.

One day, when a group of peasants sat under a tree, she had seen him dancing quick and gay with a child—his wife watching darkly.

Gradually Juliet and he had become intimate, across the distance. They were aware of one another. She knew, in the morning, the moment he arrived with his ass. And the moment she went out on the balcony he turned to look. But they never saluted. Yet she missed him when he did not come to work on the podere.

Once, in the hot morning when she had been walking naked, deep in the gully between the two estates, she had come upon him, as he was bending down, with his powerful shoulders, picking up wood to pile on his motionless, waiting donkey. He saw her as he lifted his flushed face, and she was backing away. A flame went over his eyes, and a flame flew over her body, melting her bones. But she backed away behind the bushes, silently, and retreated whence she had come. And she wondered a little resentfully over the silence in which he could work, hidden in the bushy places. He had that wild animal faculty.

Since then there had been a definite pain of consciousness in the body of each of them, though neither would admit it, and they gave no sign of recognition. But the man's wife was instinctively aware.

And Juliet had thought: Why shouldn't

I meet this man for an hour, and bear his child? Why should I have to identify my life with a man's life? Why not meet him for an hour, as long as the desire lasts, and no more? There is already the spark between us.

But she had never made any sign. And now she saw him looking up, from where he sat by the white cloth, opposite his black-clad wife, looking up at Maurice. The wife turned and looked, too, saturnine.

And Juliet felt a grudge come over her. She would have to bear Maurice's child again. She had seen it in her husband's eyes. And she knew it from his answer, when she spoke to him.

"Will you walk about in the sun, too, without your clothes?" she asked him.

"Why—er—yes! Yes, I should like to, while I'm here—I suppose it's quite private?"

There was a gleam in his eyes, a desperate kind of courage of his desire, and a glance at the alert lifting of her breasts in her wrapper. In this way, he was a man, too, he faced the world and was not entirely quenched in his male courage. He would dare to walk in the sun, even ridiculously.

But he smelled of the world, and all its fetters and its mongrel cowering. He was branded with the brand that is not a hallmark.

Ripe now, and brown-rosy all over with the sun, and with a heart like a fallen rose, she had wanted to go down to the hot, shy peasant and bear his child. Her sentiments had fallen like petals. She had seen the flushed blood in the burnt face, and the flame in the southern blue eyes, and the answer in her had been a gush of fire. He would have been a procreative sun-bath to her, and she wanted it.

Nevertheless, her next child would be Maurice's. The fatal chain of continuity would cause it.

THE JUDGMENT

Franz Kafka
(1883–1924)

(An excerpt from *The Trial*)

"In the writings which preface the Law that particular delusion is described thus: before the Law stands a doorkeeper. To this doorkeeper there comes a man from the country who begs for admittance to the Law. But the doorkeeper says that he cannot admit the man at the moment. The man, on reflection, asks if he will be allowed, then, to enter later. 'It is possible,' answers the doorkeeper, 'but not at this moment.' Since the door leading into the Law stands open as usual and the doorkeeper steps to one side, the man bends down to peer through the entrance. When the doorkeeper sees that, he laughs and says: 'If you are so strongly tempted, try to get in without my permission. But note that I am powerful. And I am only the lowest doorkeeper. From hall to hall, keepers stand at every door, one more powerful than the other. And the sight of the third man is already more than even I can stand.' These are difficulties which the man from the country has not expected to meet, the Law, he thinks, should be accessible to every man and at all times, but when he looks more closely at the doorkeeper in his furred robe, with his huge pointed nose and long thin Tartar beard, he decides that he had better wait until he gets permission to enter. The doorkeeper gives him a stool and lets him sit down at the side of the door. There he sits waiting for days and years. He makes many attempts to be allowed in and wearies the doorkeeper with his importunity. The doorkeeper often engages him in brief conversation, asking him about his home and about other matters, but the questions are put quite impersonally, as great men put questions, and always conclude with the statement that the man cannot be allowed to enter yet. The man, who has equipped himself with many things for his journey, parts with all he has, however valuable, in the hope of bribing the doorkeeper. The doorkeeper accepts it all, saying, however, as he takes each gift: 'I take this only to keep you from feeling that you have left something undone.' During all these long years the man watches the doorkeeper almost incessantly. He forgets about the other doorkeepers, and this one seems to him the only barrier between himself and the Law. In the first years he curses his evil fate aloud; later, as he grows old, he only mutters to himself. He grows childish, and since in his prolonged study of the doorkeeper he has learned to know even the fleas in his fur collar, he begs the very fleas to help him and to persuade the doorkeeper to change his mind. Finally his eyes grow dim and he does not know whether the world is really darkening around him or whether his eyes are only deceiving him. But in the darkness he can now perceive a radiance that streams inextinguishably from the door of the Law. Now his life is drawing to a close. Before he dies, all that he has experienced during the whole time of his sojourn condenses in his mind into one question, which he has never yet put to the doorkeeper. He beckons the doorkeeper, since he can no longer raise his stiffening body. The doorkeeper has to bend far down to hear him, for the difference in size between them has increased very much to the man's disadvantage. 'What do you want to know now?' asks the doorkeeper, 'you are insatiable.' 'Everyone strives to attain the Law,' answers the man, 'how does it come about, then, that in all these years no one has come seeking admittance but me?' The doorkeeper perceives that the man is nearing his end and his hearing is failing, so he bellows in his ear: 'No one but you could gain admittance through this door, since this door was intended for you. I am now going to shut it.' "

"So the doorkeeper deceived the man," said K. immediately, strongly attracted by the story. "Don't be too hasty," said the priest, "don't take over someone else's opinion without testing it. I have told you the story in the very words of the scriptures. There's no mention of deception in it." "But it's clear enough," said K., "and your first interpretation of it was quite right. The doorkeeper gave the message of salvation to the man only when it could no longer help him." "He was not asked the question any earlier," said the priest, "and you must consider, too, that he was only a doorkeeper, and as such fulfilled his duty." "What makes you think he fulfilled his duty?" asked K. "He didn't fulfill it. His duty might have been to keep all strangers away, but this man, for whom the door was intended, should have been let in." "You have not enough respect for the written word and you are altering the story," said the priest. "The story contains two important statements made by the doorkeeper about admission to the Law, one at the beginning, the other at the end. The first statement is: that he cannot admit the man at the moment, and the other is: that this door was intended only for the man. If there were a contradiction between the two, you would be right and the doorkeeper would have deceived the man. But there is no contradiction. The first statement, on the contrary, even implies the second. One could almost say that in suggesting to the man the possibility of future admittance the doorkeeper is exceeding his duty. At that time his apparent duty is only to refuse admittance and indeed many commentators are surprised that the suggestion should be made at all, since the doorkeeper appears to be a precisian with a stern regard for duty. He does not once leave his post during these many years, and he does not shut the door until the very last minute; he is conscious of the importance of his office, for he says: 'I am powerful'; he is respectful to his superiors, for he says: 'I am only the lowest doorkeeper'; he is not garrulous, for during all these years he puts only what are called 'impersonal questions'; he is not to be bribed, for he says in accepting a gift: 'I take this only to keep you from feeling that you have left something undone'; where his duty is concerned he is to be moved neither by pity nor rage, for we are told that the man 'wearied the doorkeeper with his importunity'; and finally even his external appearance hints at a pedantic character, the large, pointed nose and the long, thin, black, Tartar beard. Could one imagine a more faithful doorkeeper? Yet the doorkeeper has other elements in his character which are likely to advantage anyone seeking admittance and which make it comprehensible enough that he should somewhat exceed his duty in suggesting the possibility of future admittance. For it cannot be denied that he is a little simple-minded and consequently a little conceited. Take the statements he makes about his power and the power of the other doorkeepers and their dreadful aspect which even he cannot bear to see —I hold that these statements may be true enough, but that the way in which he brings them out shows that his perceptions are confused by simpleness of mind and conceit. The commentators note in this connection: 'The right perception of any matter and a misunderstanding of the same matter do not wholly exclude each other.' One must at any rate assume that such simpleness and conceit, however sparingly manifest, are likely to weaken his defense of the door; they are breaches in the character of the doorkeeper. To this must be added the fact that the doorkeeper seems to be a friendly creature by nature, he is by no means always on his official dignity. In the very first moments he allows himself the jest of inviting the man to enter in spite of the strictly maintained veto against entry; then he does not, for instance, send the man away, but gives him, as we are told, a stool and lets him sit down beside the door. The patience with which he endures the man's appeals during so many years, the brief conversations, the acceptance of the gifts, the politeness with which he allows the man to curse loudly in his presence the fate for which he himself is responsible —all this lets us deduce certain feelings of pity. Not every doorkeeper would have acted thus. And finally, in answer to a gesture of the man's he bends down to give him the chance of putting a last question. Nothing but mild impatience— the doorkeeper knows that this is the end of it all—is discernible in the words: 'You are insatiable.' Some push this mode of interpretation even further and hold that these words express a kind of friendly admiration, though not without a hint of condescension. At any rate the figure of the doorkeeper can be said to come out very differently from what you fancied." "You have studied the story more exactly and for a longer time than I have," said K. They were both silent for a little while. Then K. said: "So you think the man was not deceived?" "Don't misunderstand me," said the priest, "I am only showing you the various opinions concerning that point. You must not pay too much attention to them. The scriptures are unalterable and the comments often enough merely express the commentators' despair. In this case there even exists an interpretation which claims that the deluded person is really the doorkeeper." "That's a far-fetched interpretation," said K. "On what is it based?" "It is based," answered the priest, "on the simple-mindedness of the doorkeeper. The argument is that he does not know the Law from inside, he knows only the way that leads to it, where he patrols up and down. His ideas of the interior are assumed to be childish, and it is supposed that he himself is afraid of the other guardians whom he holds up as bogies before the man. Indeed, he fears them more than the man does, since the man is determined to enter after hearing about the dreadful guardians of the interior, while the doorkeeper has no desire to enter, at least not so far as we are told. Others again say that he must have been in the interior already, since he is after all engaged in the service of the Law and can only have been appointed from inside. This is countered by arguing that he may have been appointed by a voice calling from the interior, and that anyhow he cannot have been far inside, since the aspect of the third doorkeeper is more than he can endure. Moreover, no indication is given that during all these years he ever made any remarks showing a knowledge of the interior, except for the one remark about the doorkeepers. He may have been forbidden to do so, but there is no mention of that either. On these grounds the conclusion is reached that he knows nothing about the aspect and significance of the interior, so that he is in a state of delusion. But he is deceived also about his relation to the man from the country, for he is inferior to the man and does not know it. He treats the man instead as his own subordinate, as can be recognized from many details that must be still fresh in your mind. But, according to this view of the story, it is just as clearly indicated that he is really subordinated to the man. In the first place, a bondman is always subject to a free man. Now the man from the country is really free, he can go where he likes, it is only the Law that is closed to him, and access to the Law is forbidden him only by one individual, the doorkeeper. When he sits down on the stool by the side of the door and stays there for the rest of his life, he does it of his own free will; in the story there is no mention

of any compulsion. But the doorkeeper is bound to his post by his very office, he does not dare go out into the country, nor apparently may he go into the interior of the Law, even should he wish to. Besides, although he is in the service of the Law, his service is confined to this one entrance; that is to say, he serves only this man for whom alone the entrance is intended. On that ground too he is inferior to the man. One must assume that for many years, for as long as it takes a man to grow up to the prime of life, his service was in a sense an empty formality, since he had to wait for a man to come, that is to say someone in the prime of life, and so he had to wait a long time before the purpose of his service could be fulfilled, and, moreover, had to wait on the man's pleasure, for the man came of his own free will. But the termination of his service also depends on the man's term of life, so that to the very end he is subject to the man. And it is emphasized throughout that the doorkeeper apparently realizes nothing of all this. That is not in itself remarkable, since according to this interpretation the doorkeeper is deceived in a much more important issue, affecting his very office. At the end, for example, he says regarding the entrance to the Law: 'I am now going to shut it,' but at the beginning of the story we are told that the door leading into the Law always stands open, and if it always stands open, that is to say at all times, without reference to the life or death of the man, then the doorkeeper cannot close it. There is some difference of opinion about the motive behind the doorkeeper's statement, whether he said he was going to close the door merely for the sake of giving an answer, or to emphasize his devotion to duty, or to bring the man into a state of grief and regret in his last moments. But there is no lack of agreement that the doorkeeper will not be able to shut the door. Many indeed profess to find that he is subordinate to the man even in knowledge, toward the end, at least, for the man sees the radiance that issues from the door of the Law while the doorkeeper in his official position must stand with his back to the door, nor does he say anything to show that he has perceived the change." "That is well argued," said K., after repeating to himself in a low voice several passages from the priest's exposition. "It is well argued, and I am inclined to agree that the doorkeeper is deceived. But that has not made me abandon my former opinion, since both conclusions are to some extent compatible. Whether the doorkeeper is clear-sighted or deceived does not dispose of the matter. I said the man is deceived. If the doorkeeper is clear-sighted, one might have doubts about that, but if the doorkeeper himself is deceived, then his deception must of necessity be communicated to the man. That makes the doorkeeper not, indeed, a deceiver, but a creature so simple-minded that he ought to be dismissed at once from his office. You mustn't forget that the doorkeeper's deceptions do himself no harm but do infinite harm to the man." "There are objections to that," said the priest "Many aver that the story confers no right on anyone to pass judgment on the doorkeeper. Whatever he may seem to us, he is yet a servant of the Law; that is, he belongs to the Law and as such is beyond human judgment. In that case one must not believe that the doorkeeper is subordinate to the man. Bound as he is by his service even only at the door of the Law, he is incomparably greater than anyone at large in the world. The man is only seeking the Law, the doorkeeper is already attached to it. It is the Law that has placed him at his post; to doubt his dignity is to doubt the Law itself." "I don't agree with that point of view," said K., shaking his head, "for if one accepts it, one must accept as true everything the doorkeeper says. But you yourself have sufficiently proved how impossible it is to do that." "No," said the priest, "it is not necessary to accept everything as true, one must only accept it as necessary." "A melancholy conclusion," said K. "It turns lying into a universal principle."

Translated by *Willa* and *Edwin Muir.*

POEMS

BATTER MY HEART, THREE-PERSONED GOD

John Donne
(1573–1631)

Batter my heart, three-personed God; for, you
As yet but knock, breathe, shine, and seek to mend;
That I may rise and stand, o'erthrow me, and bend
Your force, to break, blow, burn, and make me new.
I, like an usurped town, to another due,   5
Labor to admit you, but oh, to no end,
Reason, your viceroy in me, me should defend,
But is captived, and proves weak or untrue.
Yet dearly I love you, and would be lovèd fain,
But am betrothed unto your enemy: 10
Divorce me, untie, or break that knot again,
Take me to you, imprison me, for I
Except you enthrall me, never shall be free,
Nor ever chaste, except you ravish me.

9. *fain:* gladly.

THE COLLAR *

George Herbert
(1593–1633)

I struck the board, and cried, "No more;
    I will abroad!

* Meant both literally (a clerical collar) and metaphorically (a symbol of submission).

What! shall I ever sigh and pine?
My lines and life are free; free as the road,
    Loose as the wind, as large as store.
    Shall I be still in suit?   5
Have I no harvest but a thorn
To let me blood, and not restore
What I have lost with cordial fruit?
    Sure there was wine
Before my sighs did dry it; there was corn   10
    Before my tears did drown it;
Is the year only lost to me?
    Have I no bays to crown it,
No flowers, no garlands gay? all blasted,
    All wasted?   15
Not so, my heart, but there is fruit,
    And thou hast hands.
    Recover all thy sigh-blown age
On double pleasures; leave thy cold dispute
Of what is fit and not; forsake thy cage,   20
    Thy rope of sands
Which petty thoughts have made, and made to thee
    Good cable, to enforce and draw,
    And be thy law,
While thou didst wink and wouldst not see.   25
    Away! take heed;
    I will abroad.
Call in thy death's head there, tie up thy fears;
    He that forbears
    To suit and serve his need   30
    Deserves his load."

4. *as large as store:* plentiful.
    5. *in suit:* waiting for a favor.
8. *cordial:* restorative.
    13. *bays:* poet's wreath.

But as I raved, and grew more fierce and
wild
    At every word,
Methought I heard one calling, "Child";
    And I replied, "My Lord."   35

GOD'S GRANDEUR

Gerard Manley Hopkins
(1844–1889)

The world is charged with the grandeur
    of God.
  It will flame out, like shining from
    shook foil;
  It gathers to a greatness, like the ooze
    of oil
Crushed. Why do men then now not reck
    his rod?
Generations have trod, have trod, have
    trod;   5
  And all is seared with trade; bleared,
    smeared with toil;
  And wears man's smudge and shares
    man's smell: the soil
Is bare now, nor can foot feel, being shod.

And for all this, nature is never spent;
  There lives the dearest freshness deep
    down things;   10
And though the last lights off the black
    West went
  Oh, morning, at the brown brink east-
    ward, springs—
Because the Holy Ghost over the bent
  World broods with warm breast and
    with ah! bright wings.

2. *foil:* as in tinfoil or goldfoil.
3–4. *ooze of oil/ Crushed:* from olives.
4. *reck:* heed.

THOU ART INDEED JUST, LORD

Gerard Manley Hopkins
(1844–1889)

*Justus quidem tu es, Domine, si dispu-
tecum: verum-tamen justa loquar ad te:*

Quare via impiorum prosperatur? &c.*
Thou art indeed just, Lord, if I contend
With thee; but, sir, so what I plead is just.
Why do sinners' ways prosper? and why
    must
Disappointment all I endeavour end?
  Wert thou my enemy, O thou my
    friend,   5
How wouldst thou worse, I wonder, than
    thou dost
Defeat, thwart me? Oh, the sots and
    thralls of lust
Do in spare hours more thrive than I that
    spend,
Sir, life upon thy cause. See, banks and
    brakes
Now, leavèd how thick! lacèd they are
    again   10
With fretty chervil, look, and fresh wind
    shakes
Them; birds build—but not I build; no,
    but strain,
Time's eunuch, and not breed one work
    that wakes.
Mine, O thou lord of life, send my roots
    rain.

JOURNEY OF THE MAGI

T. S. Eliot
(1888–1965)

'A cold coming we had of it,
Just the worst time of the year
For a journey, and such a long journey:
The ways deep and the weather sharp,
The very dead of winter.'   5
And the camels galled, sore-footed, re-
    fractory,
Lying down in the melting snow.

* "Righteous art thou, O Lord, when I plead
with thee: yet let me talk with thee of thy judgments: Wherefore doth the way of the wicked
prosper etc." Jeremiah xii, 1 (King James). The
Latin is from the Vulgate.
1–5. *'A cold coming . . . dead of winter,':*
adapted from a sermon by Lancelot Andrewes
in 1622.

There were times we regretted
The summer palaces on slopes, the ter-
　races,
And the silken girls bringing sherbet.　10
Then the camel men cursing and grum-
　bling
And running away, and wanting their liq-
　uor and women,
And the night-fires going out, and the lack
　of shelters,
And the cities hostile and the towns un-
　friendly
And the villages dirty and charging high
　prices:　　　　　　　　　　　　15
A hard time we had of it.
At the end we preferred to travel all night,
Sleeping in snatches,
With the voices singing in our ears, saying
That this was all folly.　　　　　　20

Then at dawn we came down to a temper-
　ate valley,
Wet, below the snow line, smelling of
　vegetation;
With a running stream and a water-mill
　beating the darkness,
And three trees on the low sky,
And an old white horse galloped away in
　the meadow.　　　　　　　　25
Then we came to a tavern with vine-leaves
　over the lintel,
Six hands at an open door dicing for
　pieces of silver,
And feet kicking the empty wine-skins.
But there was no information, and so we
　continued
And arrived at evening, not a moment too
　soon　　　　　　　　　　　30
Finding the place, it was (you may say)
　satisfactory.

All this was a long time ago, I remember,
And I would do it again, but set down
This set down
This: were we led all that way for　　35

24. *three trees:* an allusion to the three crosses
on Calvary.

Birth or Death? There was a Birth, cer-
　tainly,
We had evidence and no doubt. I had
　seen birth and death,
But had thought they were different; this
　Birth was
Hard and bitter agony for us, like Death,
　our death.
We returned to our places, these King-
　doms,　　　　　　　　　　　40
But no longer at ease here, in the old dis-
　pensation,
With an alien people clutching their gods.
I should be glad of another death.

　　　■　　■　　■

UNIVERSAL HUMANITY
(From *VALA*)

William Blake
(1757–1827)

And as the seed waits eagerly watching
　for its flower and fruit,
Anxious its little soul looks out into the
　clear expanse
To see if hungry winds are abroad with
　their invisible array;
So Man looks out in tree, and herb, and
　fish, and bird, and beast,
Collecting up the scattered portions of his
　immortal body　　　　　　　5
Into the elemental forms of everything
　that grows.
He tries the sullen North wind, riding on
　its angry furrows,
The sultry South when the sun rises, and
　the angry East
When the sun sets, and the clods harden,
　and the cattle stand
Drooping, and the birds hide in their
　silent nests. He stores his thoughts　10
As in store-houses in his memory. He reg-
　ulates the forms

Of all beneath and all above, and in the
    gentle West
Reposes where the sun's heat dwells. He
    rises to the sun,
And to the planets of the night, and to the
    stars that gild
The zodiacs, and the stars that sullen
    stand to North and South,   15
He touches the remotest pole, and in the
    centre weeps
That Man should labour and sorrow, and
    learn and forget, and return
To the dark valley whence he came, and
    begin his labours anew.
In pain he sighs, in pain he labours in his
    universe;
Sorrowing in birds over the deep, or howl-
    ing in the wolf   20
Over the slain, and moaning in the cattle,
    and in the winds,
And weeping over Orc and Urizen in
    clouds and dismal fires,
And in cries of birth and in the groans of
    death his voice
Is heard throughout the universe. Wher-
    ever a grass grows
Or a leaf buds the Eternal Man is seen, is
    heard, is felt,   25
And all his sorrows, till he reassumes his
    ancient bliss.

22. *Orc:* for Blake the symbol of rebellious
anarchy, the opponent of restrictive morality,
which was in turn symbolized by Urizen.

LINES COMPOSED A FEW
MILES ABOVE TINTERN ABBEY
ON REVISITING THE BANKS
OF THE WYE DURING A TOUR,
JULY 13, 1798

William Wordsworth
(1770–1850)

Five years have past; five summers, with
    the length

Of five long winters! and again I hear
These waters, rolling from their moun-
    tain-springs
With a soft inland murmur.—Once again
Do I behold these steep and lofty
    cliffs,   5
That on a wild secluded scene impress
Thoughts of more deep seclusion; and
    connect
The landscape with the quiet of the sky.
The day is come when I again repose
Here, under this dark sycamore, and
    view   10
These plots of cottage-ground, these
    orchard-tufts,
Which at this season, with their unripe
    fruits,
Are clad in one green hue, and lose them-
    selves
Mid groves and copses. Once again I see
These hedgerows, hardly hedgerows,
    little lines   15
Of sportive wood run wild: these pastoral
    farms,
Green to the very door; and wreaths of
    smoke
Sent up, in silence, from among the trees!
With some uncertain notice, as might
    seem
Of vagrant dwellers in the houseless
    woods,   20
Or of some Hermit's cave, where by his
    fire
The Hermit sits alone.
                These beauteous forms,
Through a long absence, have not been
    to me
As is a landscape to a blind man's eye:
But oft, in lonely rooms, and 'mid the
    din   25
Of towns and cities, I have owed to
    them,
In hours of weariness, sensations sweet,
Felt in the blood, and felt along the heart;
And passing even into my purer mind,
With tranquil restoration—feelings too 30
Of unremembered pleasure: such, per-
    haps,

As have no slight or trivial influence
On that best portion of a good man's life,
His little, nameless, unremembered acts
Of kindness and of love. Nor less, I
   trust,   35
To them I may have owed another gift,
Of aspect more sublime; that blessèd
   mood,
In which the burthen of the mystery,
In which the heavy and the weary weight
Of all this unintelligible world,   40
Is lightened—that serene and blessèd
   mood,
In which the affections gently lead us
   on—
Until, the breath of this corporeal frame
And even the motion of our human
   blood
Almost suspended, we are laid asleep 45
In body, and become a living soul:
While with an eye made quiet by the
   power
Of harmony, and the deep power of
   joy,
We see into the life of things.
                   If this
Be but a vain belief, yet, oh! how
   oft—   50
In darkness and amid the many shapes
Of joyless daylight; when the fretful stir
Unprofitable, and the fever of the world,
Have hung upon the beatings of my
   heart—
How oft, in spirit, have I turned to
   thee,   55
O sylvan Wye! thou wanderer through the
   woods,
How often has my spirit turned to thee!
   And now, with gleams of half-ex-
   tinguished thought,
With many recognitions dim and faint,
And somewhat of a sad perplexity,   60
The picture of the mind revives again:
While here I stand, not only with the
   sense
Of present pleasure, but with pleasing
   thoughts

That in this moment there is life and
   food
For future years. And so I dare to
   hope,   65
Though changed, no doubt, from what I
   was when first
I came among these hills; when like a
   roe
I bounded o'er the mountains, by the
   sides
Of the deep rivers, and the lonely
   streams,
Wherever nature led: more like a man 70
Flying from something that he dreads
   than one
Who sought the thing he loved. For
   nature then
(The coarser pleasures of my boyish
   days,
And their glad animal movements all
   gone by)
To me was all in all.—I cannot paint 75
What then I was. The sounding cataract
Haunted me like a passion: the tall rock,
The mountain, and the deep and gloomy
   wood,
Their colors and their forms, were then
   to me
An appetite; a feeling and a love,   80
That had no need of a remoter charm,
By thought supplied, nor any interest
Unborrowed from the eye.—That time
   is past,
And all its aching joys are now no more,
And all its dizzy raptures. Not for this 85
Faint I, nor mourn nor murmur; other
   gifts
Have followed; for such loss, I would
   believe,
Abundant recompense. For I have
   learned
To look on nature, not as in the hour
Of thoughtless youth; but hearing often-
   times   90
The still, sad music of humanity,
Nor harsh nor grating, though of ample
   power

To chasten and subdue. And I have felt
A presence that disturbs me with the joy
Of elevated thoughts; a sense sublime 95
Of something far more deeply interfused,
Whose dwelling is the light of setting
  suns,
And the round ocean and the living air,
And the blue sky, and in the mind of
  man:
A motion and a spirit, that impels   100
All thinking things, all objects of all
  thought,
And rolls through all things. Therefore
  am I still
A lover of the meadows and the woods,
And mountains; and of all that we
  behold
From this green earth; of all the mighty
  world   105
Of eye, and ear—both what they half
  create,
And what perceive; well pleased to recog-
  nize
In nature and the language of the sense
The anchor of my purest thoughts, the
  nurse,
The guide, the guardian of my heart, and
  soul   110
Of all my moral being.
                        Nor perchance,
If I were not thus taught, should I the
  more
Suffer my genial spirits to decay:
For thou art with me here upon the
  banks
Of this fair river; thou my dearest
  Friend,   115
My dear, dear Friend; and in thy voice I
  catch
The language of my former heart, and
  read
My former pleasures in the shooting
  lights
Of thy wild eyes. Oh! yet a little while
May I behold in thee what I was once, 120

115. *my dearest Friend:* Dorothy, his sister.

My dear, dear Sister! and this prayer I
  make,
Knowing that Nature never did betray
The heart that loved her; 'tis her
  privilege,
Through all the years of this our life, to
  lead
From joy to joy: for she can so in-
  form   125
The mind that is within us, so impress
With quietness and beauty, and so feed
With lofty thoughts, that neither evil
  tongues,
Rash judgments, nor the sneers of selfish
  men,
Nor greetings where no kindness is, nor
  all   130
The dreary intercourse of daily life,
Shall e'er prevail against us, or disturb
Our cheerful faith, that all which we
  behold
Is full of blessings. Therefore let the
  moon
Shine on thee in thy solitary walk;   135
And let the misty mountain-winds be
  free
To blow against thee: and, in after years,
When these wild ecstasies shall be ma-
  tured
Into a sober pleasure; when thy mind
Shall be a mansion for all lovely
  forms,   140
Thy memory be as a dwelling-place
For all sweet sounds and harmonies; oh!
  then,
If solitude, or fear, or pain, or grief,
Should be thy portion, with what healing
  thoughts
Of tender joy wilt thou remember me, 145
And these my exhortations! Nor, per-
  chance—
If I should be where I no more can hear
Thy voice, nor catch from thy wild eyes
  these gleams
Of past existence—wilt thou then forget
That on the banks of this delightful
  stream   150

We stood together; and that I, so long
A worshiper of Nature, hither came
Unwearied in that service: rather say
With warmer love—oh! with far deeper zeal
Of holier love. Nor wilt thou then forget 155
That after many wanderings, many years
Of absence, these steep woods and lofty cliffs,
And this green pastoral landscape, were to me
More dear, both for themselves and for thy sake!

SONG OF MYSELF—STANZA 6

Walt Whitman
(1819–1892)

A child said, What is the grass? fetching it to me with full hands;
How could I answer the child? . . . . I do not know what it is any more than he.

I guess it must be the flag of my disposition, out of hopeful green stuff woven.

Or I guess it is the handkerchief of the Lord,   5
A scented gift and remembrancer designedly dropped,
Bearing the owner's name someway in the corners, that we may see and remark,
    and say Whose?

Or I guess the grass is itself a child . . . . the produced babe of the vegetation.

Or I guess it is a uniform hieroglyphic,
And it means, Sprouting alike in broad zones and narrow zones,
Growing among black folks as among white,   10
Kanuck, Tuchahoe, Congressman, Cuff, I give them the same, I receive them the
    same.

And now it seems to me the beautiful uncut hair of graves.

Tenderly will I use you curling grass,
It may be you transpire from the breasts of young men,
It may be if I had known them I would have loved them;   15
It may be you are from old people and from women, and from offspring taken
    soon out of their mothers' laps,
And here you are the mothers' laps.

This grass is very dark to be from the white heads of old mothers,
Darker than the colorless beards of old men,
Dark to come from under the faint red roofs of mouths.   20

O I perceive after all so many uttering tongues!
And I perceive they do not come from the roofs of mouths for nothing.

I wish I could translate the hints about the dead young men and women,
And the hints about old men and mothers, and the offspring taken soon out of
   their laps.

What do you think has become of the young and old men?   25
And what do you think has become of the women and children?

They are alive and well somewhere;
The smallest sprout shows there is really no death,
And if ever there was it led forward life, and does not wait at the end to arrest it,
And ceased the moment life appeared.   30

All goes onward and outward . . . . and nothing collapses,
And to die is different from what any one supposed, and luckier.

SONG OF MYSELF—STANZA 31

Walt Whitman
(1819–1892)

I believe a leaf of grass is no less than the journeywork of the stars,
And the pismire is equally perfect, and a grain of sand, and the egg of the wren,
And the tree-toad is a chef-d'œuvre for the highest,
And the running blackberry would adorn the parlors of heaven,
And the narrowest hinge in my hand puts to scorn all machinery,   5
And the cow crunching with depressed head surpasses any statue,
And a mouse is miracle enough to stagger sextillions of infidels.
And I could come every afternoon of my life to look at the farmer's girl boiling
   her iron tea-kettle and baking shortcake.

I find I incorporate gneiss and coal and long-threaded moss and fruits and grains
   and esculent roots,
And am stucco'd with quadrupeds and birds all over,   10
And have distanced what is behind me for good reasons,
And call any thing close again when I desire it.

In vain the speeding or shyness,
In vain the plutonic rocks send their old heat against my approach,
In vain the mastodon retreats beneath its own powdered bones,   15
In vain objects stand leagues off and assume manifold shapes,
In vain the ocean settling in hollows and the great monsters lying low,
In vain the buzzard houses herself with the sky,
In vain the snake slides through the creepers and logs,
In vain the elk takes to the inner passes of the woods,   20
In vain the razorbilled auk sails far north to Labrador,
I follow quickly . . . . I ascend to the nest in the fissure of the cliff.

9. *gneiss:* a laminated or foliated rock, corresponding to granite or some other plutonic rock.

THE FORCE THAT THROUGH THE GREEN FUSE DRIVES THE FLOWER

Dylan Thomas
(1914–1953)

The force that through the green fuse
  drives the flower
Drives my green age; that blasts the roots
  of trees
Is my destroyer.
And I am dumb to tell the crooked rose
My youth is bent by the same wintry
  fever.   5

The force that drives the water through
  the rocks
Drives my red blood; that dries the
  mouthing streams
Turns mine to wax.
And I am dumb to mouth unto my veins
How at the mountain spring the same
  mouth sucks.   10

The hand that whirls the water in the
  pool
Stirs the quicksand; that ropes the blow-
  ing wind
Hauls my shroud sail.
And I am dumb to tell the hanging man
How of my clay is made the hangman's
  lime.   15

The lips of time leech to the fountain
  head;
Love drips and gathers, but the fallen
  blood
Shall calm her sores.
And I am dumb to tell a weather's wind
How time has ticked a heaven round the
  stars.   20

And I am dumb to tell the lover's tomb
How at my sheet goes the same crooked
  worm.

■ ■ ■

DOVER BEACH

Matthew Arnold
(1822–1888)

The sea is calm tonight,
The tide is full, the moon lies fair
Upon the straits;—on the French coast
  the light
Gleams and is gone; the cliffs of England
  stand,
Glimmering and vast, out in the tranquil
  bay.   5
Come to the window, sweet is the night-
  air!

Only, from the long line of spray
Where the sea meets the moon-blanched
  land,
Listen! you hear the grating roar
Of pebbles which the waves draw back,
  and fling,   10
At their return, up the high strand,
Begin, and cease, and then again begin,
With tremulous cadence slow, and bring
The eternal note of sadness in.

Sophocles long ago   15
Heard it on the Aegean, and it brought
Into his mind the turbid ebb and flow
Of human misery; we
Find also in the sound a thought,
Hearing it by this distant northern sea. 20

The Sea of Faith
Was once, too, at the full, and round
  earth's shore
Lay like the folds of a bright girdle
  furled.
But now I only hear
Its melancholy, long, withdrawing roar, 25
Retreating, to the breath
Of the night-wind, down the vast edges
  drear

15–18. See Sophocles' *Antigone*, ll. 583 ff.

And naked shingles of the world.

Ah, love, let us be true
To one another! for the world, which
    seems   30
To lie before us like a land of dreams,
So various, so beautiful, so new,

28. *shingles:* pebbled beaches.

Hath really neither joy, nor love, nor
    light,
Nor certitude, nor peace, nor help for
    pain;
And we are here as on a darkling plain 35
Sweet with confused alarms of struggle
    and flight,
Where ignorant armies clash by night.

NATURE'S QUESTIONING

Thomas Hardy
(1840–1928)

When I look forth at dawning, pool,
    Field, flock, and lonely tree,
    All seem to gaze at me
Like chastened children sitting silent in a school;

Their faces dulled, constrained, and worn,   5
    As though the master's ways
    Through the long teaching days
Had cowed them till their early zest was overborne.

Upon them stirs in lippings mere
    (As if once clear in call,   10
    But now scarce breathed at all)—
"We wonder, ever wonder, why we find us here!

"Has some Vast Imbecility,
    Mighty to build and blend,
    But impotent to tend,   15
Framed us in jest, and left us now to hazardry?

"Or come we of an Automaton
    Unconscious of our pains? . . .
    Or are we live remains
Of Godhead dying downwards, brain and eye now gone?   20

"Or is it that same high Plan betides,
    As yet not understood,
    Of Evil stormed by Good,
We the Forlorn Hope over which Achievement strides?"

Thus things around. No answerer I . . .   25
    Meanwhile the winds, and rains,
    And Earth's old glooms and pains
Are still the same, and Life and Death are neighbours nigh.

THE CHESTNUT CASTS HIS FLAMBEAUX *

A. E. Housman
(1859–1936)

The chestnut casts his flambeaux, and
    the flowers
  Stream from the hawthorn on the wind
    away,
The doors clap to, the pane is blind with
    showers.
  Pass me the can, lad; there's an end of
    May.

There's one spoilt spring to scant our
    mortal lot,   5
  One season ruined of our little store.
May will be fine next year as like as not:
  Oh ay, but then we shall be twenty-
    four.

We for a certainty are not the first
  Have sat in taverns while the tempest
    hurled   10
Their hopeful plans to emptiness, and
    cursed
  Whatever brute and blackguard made
    the world.

It is in truth iniquity on high
  To cheat our sentenced souls of aught
    they crave,
And mar the merriment as you and I   15
  Fare on our long fool's-errand to the
    grave.

Iniquity it is; but pass the can.
  My lad, no pair of kings our mothers
    bore;
Our only portion is the estate of man:
  We want the moon, but we shall get no
    more   20

* Literally, a flaming torch; figuratively, Housman is alluding to the flamelike appearance of the chestnut tree's flower clusters.

If here today the cloud of thunder lours
  Tomorrow it will hie on far behests;
The flesh will grieve on other bones than
    ours
  Soon, and the soul will mourn in other
    breasts.

The troubles of our proud and angry
    dust   25
  Are from eternity, and shall not fail.
Bear them we can, and if we can we must.
  Shoulder the sky, my lad, and drink
    your ale.

DESERT PLACES

Robert Frost
(1875–1963)

Snow falling and night falling fast, oh,
    fast
In a field I looked into going past,
And the ground almost covered smooth
    in snow,
But a few weeds and stubble showing last.

The woods around it have it—it is
    theirs.   5
All animals are smothered in their lairs.
I am too absent-spirited to count;
The loneliness includes me unawares.

And lonely as it is that loneliness
Will be more lonely ere it will be less— 10
A blanker whiteness of benighted snow
With no expression, nothing to express.

They cannot scare me with their empty
    spaces
Between stars—on stars where no human
    race is.
I have it in me so much nearer home   15
To scare myself with my own desert
    places.

THE END OF THE WORLD

Archibald MacLeish
(1892–   )

Quite unexpectedly, as Vasserot
The armless ambidextrian was lighting
A match between his great and second toe,
And Ralph the lion was engaged in biting
The neck of Madame Sossman while the
    drum   5
Pointed, and Teeny was about to cough
In waltz-time swinging Jocko by the
    thumb—
Quite unexpectedly the top blew off:

And there, there overhead, there, there
    hung over
Those thousands of white faces, those
    dazed eyes,   10
There in the starless dark the poise, the
    hover,
There with vast wings across the cancelled
    skies,
There in the sudden blackness the black
    pall
Of nothing, nothing, nothing—nothing at
    all.

▪ ▪ ▪

TWO SONGS FROM A PLAY *

W. B. Yeats
(1865–1939)

I

I saw a staring virgin stand
Where holy Dionysus died,

* Intended for Yeats's play *The Resurrection*.
2. *Dionysus:* the god of wine and procreation.

And tear the heart out of his side,
And lay the heart upon her hand
And bear that beating heart away;   5
And then did all the Muses sing
Of Magnus Annus at the spring,
As though God's death were but a play.

Another Troy must rise and set,
Another lineage feed the crow,   10
Another Argo's painted prow
Drive to a flashier bauble yet.
The Roman Empire stood appalled:
It dropped the reins of peace and war
When that fierce virgin and her Star   15
Out of the fabulous darkness called.

II

In pity for man's darkening thought
He walked that room and issued thence
In Galilean turbulence;
The Babylonian starlight brought   20
A fabulous, formless darkness in;
Odour of blood when Christ was slain
Made all Platonic tolerance vain
And vain all Doric discipline.

Everything that man esteems   25
Endures a moment or a day.
Love's pleasure drives his love away,
The painter's brush consumes his dreams;
The herald's cry, the soldier's tread
Exhaust his glory and his might: 30
Whatever flames upon the night
Man's own resinous heart has fed.

3–5. *tear . . . heart away:* according to a
Greek legend, the heart of the dismembered
Dionysus was brought to Zeus by Athena.
7–8. *at the spring . . . but a play:* Greek
drama originated in spring festivals held in
honor of the resurrection of Dionysus. Yeats is
associating this festival with Easter.
14. *It dropped . . . war:* Christ was born during the peaceful reign of the Emperor Augustus.
18. *He:* Christ.
24. *Doric:* Spartan.

V

DREAMS
AND THE
UNCONSCIOUS

FOREWORD

Man through the ages has attempted to explain the dreams that enliven or haunt his sleeping hours. They have been interpreted as omens, repressed desires, messages from God, or whisperings of the devil. In our century, they have provided a fruitful area of exploration in psychology and have offered a continuing challenge to the biological sciences.

Charles Lamb's essay captures what may well be the most familiar of dreams, that of wish fulfillment. Erich Fromm and Norman MacKenzie exhibit a present-day concern with the dynamics of dreams: the emotional and physiological forces at work when we dream.

Fromm probes the relation of the unconscious to our dreams. The article by MacKenzie is a summary of some of the more recent discoveries about the physiology of sleep.

All the stories and poems in this chapter have one element in common: each either describes a dream or suggests how dreams can reflect and influence our waking reality. The selections of fiction and poetry are not in contrast with each other, but rather, as a whole, with the world of waking existence. Even here the contrasts merge, for the dream can become a vision in which fantasy and reality become one.

ESSAYS

DREAM-CHILDREN: A REVERIE

Charles Lamb
(1775–1834)

Children love to listen to stories about their elders, when *they* were children; to stretch their imagination to the conception of a traditionary great-uncle, or grandame, whom they never saw. It was in this spirit that my little ones crept about me the other evening to hear about their great-grandmother Field, who lived in a great house in Norfolk (a hundred times bigger than that in which they and papa lived) which had been the scene— so at least it was generally believed in that part of the country—of the tragic incidents which they had lately become familiar with from the ballad of the Children in the Wood. Certain it is that the whole story of the children and their cruel uncle was to be seen fairly carved out in wood upon the chimney-piece of the great hall, the whole story down to the Robin Redbreasts, till a foolish rich person pulled it down to set up a marble one of modern invention in its stead, with no story upon it. Here Alice put out one of her dear mother's looks, too tender to be called upbraiding. Then I went on to say how religious and how good their great-grand-

mother Field was, how beloved and respected by everybody, though she was not indeed the mistress of this great house, but had only the charge of it (and yet in some respects she might be said to be the mistress of it too) committed to her by the owner, who preferred living in a newer and more fashionable mansion which he had purchased somewhere in the adjoining county; but still she lived in it in a manner as if it had been her own, and kept up the dignity of the great house in a sort while she lived, which afterwards came to decay, and was nearly pulled down, and all its old ornaments stripped and carried away to the owner's other house, where they were set up, and looked as awkward as if someone were to carry away the old tombs they had seen lately at the Abbey, and stick them up in Lady C.'s tawdry gilt drawing-room. Here John smiled, as much as to say, "that would be foolish, indeed." And then I told how, when she came to die, her funeral was attended by a concourse of all the poor, and some of the gentry too, of the neighborhood for many miles around, to show their respect for her memory, because she had been such a good and religious woman; so good indeed that she knew all the Psaltery by heart, ay, and a great part of the Testament besides. Here little Alice spread her hands. Then I told what a tall, upright, graceful person their great-grandmother Field once was; and how in her youth she was esteemed the best dancer —here Alice's little right foot played an involuntary movement, till upon my looking grave, it desisted—the best dancer, I was saying, in the county, till a cruel disease, called a cancer, came, and bowed her down with pain; but it could never bend her good spirits, or make them stoop, but they were still upright, because she was so good and religious. Then I told how she was used to sleep by herself in a lone chamber of the great lone house; and how she believed that an apparition of two infants was to be seen at midnight gliding up and down the great staircase near where she slept, but she said "those innocents would do her no harm"; and how frightened I used to be, though in those days I had my maid to sleep with me, because I was never half so good or religious as she—and yet I never saw the infants. Here John expanded all his eyebrows and tried to look courageous. Then I told how good she was to all her grandchildren, having us to the great house in the holidays, where I in particular used to spend many hours by myself, in gazing upon the old busts of the twelve Caesars, that had been emperors of Rome, till the old marble heads would seem to live again, or I to be turned into marble with them; how I never could be tired with roaming about that huge mansion, with its vast empty rooms, with their worn-out hangings, fluttering tapestry, and carved oaken panels, with the gilding almost rubbed out—sometimes in the spacious old-fashioned gardens, which I had almost to myself, unless when now and then a solitary gardening man would cross me— and how the nectarines and peaches hung upon the walls without my ever offering to pluck them, because they were forbidden fruit, unless now and then—and because I had more pleasure in strolling about among the old melancholy-looking yew-trees, or the firs, and picking up the red berries, and the fir apples, which were good for nothing but to look at—or in lying about upon the fresh grass, with all the fine garden smells around me—or basking in the orangery, till I could almost fancy myself ripening too along with the oranges and the limes in that grateful warmth—or in watching the dace that darted to and fro in the fishpond, at the bottom of the garden, with here and there a great sulky pike hanging midway down the water in silent state, as if it mocked at their impertinent friskings—I had more pleasure in these busy idle diversions than in all the sweet flavors of peaches, nectarines, oranges, and such-like common baits of children. Here John slyly deposited back upon the plate a bunch of grapes which, not unobserved by Alice, he had meditated dividing with her, and both seemed willing to relinquish them for the present as irrelevant. Then in somewhat a more heightened tone, I told how, though their great-grandmother Field loved all her grandchildren, yet in an especial manner she might be said to love their uncle, John L—— because he was so handsome and spirited a youth, and a king to the rest of us; and, instead of moping about in solitary corners, like some of us, he would mount the most mettlesome horse he could get, when but an imp no bigger than themselves, and make it carry him half over the county in a morning, and join the hunters when there were any out—and yet he loved the old great house and gardens too, but had too much spirit to be always pent up within their boundaries—and how their uncle grew up to man's estate as brave as he was handsome, to the admiration of everybody, but of their great-grandmother Field most especially; and how he used to carry me upon his back when I was a lame-footed boy—for he was a good bit older than me —many a mile when I could not walk for pain;—and how in after-life he became lame-footed too, and I did not always (I fear) make allowances enough for him when he was impatient, and in pain, nor remember sufficiently how considerate he had been to me when I was lame-footed; and how when he died, though he had not been dead an hour, it seemed as if he had died a great while ago, such a distance there is betwixt life and death; and how I bore his death as I thought pretty well at first, but afterwards it haunted and haunted me; and though I did not cry or take it to heart as some do, and as I think he would have done if I had died, yet I missed him all day long, and knew not till then how much I had loved him. I missed his kindness, and I missed his crossness, and wished him to be alive again, to be quarreling with him (for we quarreled sometimes), rather than not have him again, and was as uneasy without him, as he, their poor uncle, must have been when the doctor took off his limb. Here the children fell a-crying, and asked if their little mourning which they had on was not for Uncle John, and they looked up, and prayed me not to go on about their uncle, but to tell them some stories about their pretty dead mother. Then I told how for seven long years, in hope sometimes, sometimes in despair, yet persisting ever, I courted the fair Alice W——n; and, as much as children could understand, I explained to them what coyness, and difficulty, and denial meant in maidens—when suddenly, turning to Alice, the soul of the first Alice looked out at her eyes with such a reality of representment, that I became in doubt which of them stood there before me, or whose that bright hair was; and while I stood gazing, both the children gradually grew fainter to my view, receding, and still receding till nothing at last but two mournful features were seen in the uttermost distance, which without speech, strangely impressed upon me the effects of speech: "We are not of Alice, nor of thee; nor are we children at all. The chil-

dren of Alice call Bartrum father. We are nothing; less than nothing, and dreams. We are only what might have been, and must wait upon the tedious shores of Lethe millions of ages before we have existence and a name"—and immediately awaking, I found myself quietly seated in my bachelor armchair, where I had fallen asleep, with the faithful Bridget unchanged by my side—but John L. (or James Elia) was gone forever.

THE NATURE OF DREAMS *

Erich Fromm
(1900–   )

The views held about the nature of dreams differed vastly throughout the centuries and through various cultures. But whether one believes that dreams are real experiences of our disembodied souls, which have left the body during sleep, or whether one holds that dreams are inspired by God, or by evil spirits, whether one sees in them the expression of our irrational passions or, in contrast, of our highest and most moral powers, one idea is not controversial: the view that all dreams are meaningful and significant. Meaningful, because they contain a message which can be understood if one has the key for its translation. Significant, because we do not dream of anything that is trifling, even though it may be expressed in a language which hides the significance of the dream message behind a trifling façade.

Only in recent centuries was there a radical departure from this view. Dream interpretation was relegated to the realm

* This chapter appeared in *The Forgotten Language* (New York: Holt, Rinehart and Winston, 1951).

of superstitions, and the enlightened, educated person, layman or scientist, had no doubt that dreams were senseless and insignificant manifestations of our minds, at best mental reflexes of bodily sensations experienced during sleep.

It was Freud, who, at the beginning of the twentieth century, reaffirmed the old concept: dreams are both meaningful and significant; we do not dream anything that is not an important expression of our inner lives and all dreams can be understood provided we have the key; the interpretation of dreams is the "via regia," the main avenue leading to the understanding of the unconscious and thereby to the most powerful motivating force in pathological as well as in normal behavior. Beyond this general statement about the nature of dreams Freud emphatically and somewhat rigidly reaffirmed one of the oldest theories: the dream is the fulfillment of irrational passions, repressed during our waking life.

Instead of presenting Freud's and the older theories of the dream at this point, I shall . . . proceed now to discuss the nature of the dream as I have come to understand it, with the help of Freud's work and as the result of my own experience as a dreamer and as a dream interpreter.

In view of the fact that there is no expression of mental activity which does not appear in the dream, I believe that the only description of the nature of dreams that does not distort or narrow down the phenomenon is the broad one that *dreaming is a meaningful and significant expression of any kind of mental activity under the condition of sleep.*

Obviously this definition is too broad to be of much help for the understanding of the nature of dreams unless we can say something more definite about the "condition of sleep" and the particular effect of this condition on our mental activity.

If we can find out what the specific effect of sleeping is on our mental activity, we may discover a good deal more about the nature of dreaming.

Physiologically, sleep is a condition of chemical regeneration of the organism; energy is restored while no action takes place and even sensory perception is almost entirely shut off. Psychologically, sleep suspends the main function characteristic of waking life: man's reacting toward reality by perception and action. This difference between the biological functions of waking and of sleeping is, in fact, a difference between two states of existence.

In order to appreciate the effect of sleep existence on our mental process, we must first consider a more general problem, that of the interdependence of the kind of activity we are engaged in and our thinking process. The way we think is largely determined by what we do and what we are interested in achieving. This does not mean that our thinking is distorted by our interest but simply that it differs according to it.

What is, for example, the attitude of different people toward a forest? A painter who has gone there to paint, the owner of the forest who wishes to evaluate his business prospects, an officer who is interested in the tactical problem of defending the area, a hiker who wants to enjoy himself—each of them will have an entirely different concept of the forest because a different aspect is significant to each one. The painter's experience will be one of form and color; the businessman's of size, number, and age of the trees; the officer's of visibility and protection; the hiker's of trails and motion. While they can all agree to the abstract statement that they stand at the edge of a forest, the different kinds of activity they are set to accomplish will determine their experience of "seeing a forest."

The difference between the biological

and psychological functions of sleeping and waking is more fundamental than any difference between various kinds of activity, and accordingly the difference between the conceptual systems accompanying the two states is incomparably greater. In the waking state thoughts and feelings respond primarily to challenge—the task of mastering our environment, changing it, defending ourselves against it. Survival is the task of waking man; he is subject to the laws that govern reality. This means that he has to think in terms of time and space and that his thoughts are subject to the laws of time and space logic.

While we sleep we are not concerned with bending the outside world to our purposes. We are helpless, and sleep, therefore, has rightly been called the "brother of death." But we are also free, freer than when awake. We are free from the burden of work, from the task of attack or defense, from watching and mastering reality. We need not look at the outside world; we look at our inner world, are concerned exclusively with ourselves. When asleep we may be likened to a fetus or a corpse; we may also be likened to angels, who are not subject to the laws of "reality." In sleep the realm of necessity has given way to the realm of freedom in which "I am" is the only system to which thoughts and feelings refer.

Mental activity during sleep has a logic different from that of waking existence. Sleep experience need not pay any attention to qualities that matter only when one copes with reality. If I feel, for instance, that a person is a coward, I may dream that he changed from a man into a chicken. This change is logical in terms of what I feel about the person, illogical only in terms of my orientation to outside reality (in terms of what I could *do,* realistically, to or with the person). Sleep experience is not lacking in logic but is subject to different logical rules, which

are entirely valid in that particular experiential state.

Sleep and waking life are the two poles of human existence. Waking life is taken up with the function of action, sleep is freed from it. Sleep is taken up with the function of self-experience. When we wake from our sleep, we move into the realm of action. We are then oriented in terms of this system, and our memory operates within it: we remember what can be recalled in space-time concepts. The sleep world has disappeared. Experiences we had in it—our dreams—are remembered with the greatest difficulty.[1] The situation has been represented symbolically in many a folk tale: at night ghosts and spirits, good and evil, occupy the scene, but when dawn arrives, they disappear, and nothing is left of all the intense experience.

From these considerations certain conclusions about the nature of the unconscious follow:

It is neither Jung's mythical realm of racially inherited experience nor Freud's seat of irrational libidinal forces. It must be understood in terms of the principle: "What we think and feel is influenced by what we do."

Consciousness is the mental activity in our state of being preoccupied with external reality—with acting. The unconscious is the mental experience in a state of existence in which we have shut off communications with the outer world, are no longer preoccupied with action but with our self-experience. The unconscious is an experience related to a special mode of life—that of nonactivity; and the characteristics of the unconscious follow from the nature of this mode of existence. The qualities of consciousness, on the other hand, are determined by the nature of

[1] Cf. to the problem of memory function in its relation to dream activity the very stimulating article by Dr. Ernest G. Schnachtel, "On Memory and Childhood Amnesia," *Psychiatry,* February, 1947.

action and by the survival function of the waking state of existence.

The "unconscious" is the unconscious only in relation to the "normal" state of activity. When we speak of "unconscious" we really say only that an experience is alien to that frame of mind which exists while and as we act; it is then felt as a ghostlike, intrusive element, hard to get hold of and hard to remember. But the day world is as unconscious in our sleep experience as the night world is in our waking experience. The term "unconscious" is customarily used solely from the standpoint of day experience; and thus it fails to denote that both conscious and unconscious are only different states of mind referring to different states of existence.

It will be argued that in the waking state of existence, too, thinking and feeling are not entirely subject to the limitations of time and space; that our creative imagination permits us to think about past and future objects as if they were present, and of distant objects as if they were before our eyes; that our waking feeling is not dependent on the physical presence of the object nor on its coexistence in time; that, therefore, the absence of the space-time system is not characteristic of sleep existence in contradistinction to waking existence, but of thinking and feeling in contradistinction to acting. This welcome objection permits me to clarify an essential point in my argument.

We must differentiate between the *contents* of thought processes and the *logical categories* employed in thinking. While it is true that the contents of our waking thoughts are not subject to limitations of space and time, the categories of logical thinking are those of the space-time nature. I can, for instance, think of my father and state that his attitude in a certain situation is identical with mine. This statement is logically correct. On the other hand, if I state "I am my

father," the statement is "illogical" because it is not conceived in reference to the physical world. The sentence is logical, however, in a purely experiential realm: it expresses the experience of identity with my father. Logical thought processes in the waking state are subject to categories which are rooted in a special form of existence—the one in which we relate ourselves to reality in terms of action. In my sleep existence, which is characterized by lack of even potential action, logical categories are employed which have reference only to my self-experience. The same holds true of feeling. When I feel, in the waking state, with regard to a person whom I have not seen for twenty years, I remain aware of the fact that the person is not present. If I dream about the person, my feeling deals with the person as if he or she were present. But to say "as if he were present" is to express the feeling in logical "waking life" concepts. In sleep existence there is no "as if"; the person *is* present.

In the foregoing pages the attempt has been made to describe the conditions of sleep and to draw from this description certain conclusions concerning the quality of dream activity. We must now proceed to study one specific element among the conditions of sleep which will prove to be of great significance to the understanding of dream processes. We have said that while we are asleep we are not occupied with managing outer reality. We do not perceive it and we do not influence it, nor are we subject to the influences of the outside world on us. From this it follows that the effect of this separation from reality depends on the quality of reality itself. If the influence from the outside world is essentially beneficial, the absence of this influence during sleep would tend to lower the value of our dream activity, so that it would be inferior to our mental activities during the daytime when we are exposed to the beneficial influence of outside reality.

But are we right in assuming that the influence of reality is exclusively a beneficial one? May it not be that it is also harmful and that, therefore, the absence of its influence tends to bring forth qualities superior to those we have when we are awake?

In speaking of the reality outside ourselves, reference is not made primarily to the world of nature. Nature as such is neither good nor bad. It may be helpful to us or dangerous, and the absence of our perception of it relieves us, indeed, from our task of trying to master it or of defending ourselves against it; but it does not make us either more stupid or wiser, better or worse. It is quite different with the man-made world around us, with the culture in which we live. Its effect upon us is quite ambiguous, although we are prone to assume that it is entirely to our benefit.

Indeed, the evidence that cultural influences are beneficial to us seems almost overwhelming. What differentiates us from the world of animals is our capacity to create culture. What differentiates the higher from the lower stages of human development is the variation in cultural level. The most elementary element of culture, language, is the precondition for any human achievement. Man has been rightly called a symbol-making animal, for without our capacity to speak, we could hardly be called human. But every other human function also depends on our contact with the outside world. We learn to think by observing others and by being taught by them. We develop our emotional, intellectual artistic capacities under the influence of contact with the accumulation of knowledge and artistic achievement that created society. We learn to love and to care for others by contact with them, and we learn to curb impulses of hostility and egoism by

love for others, or at least by fear of them.

Is, then, the man-made reality outside ourselves not the most significant factor for the development of the very best in us, and must we not expect that, when deprived of contact with the outside world, we regress temporarily to a primitive, animal-like, unreasonable state of mind? Much can be said in favor of such an assumption, and the view that such a regression is the essential feature of the state of sleep, and thus of dream activity, has been held by many students of dreaming from Plato to Freud. From this viewpoint dreams are expected to be expressions of the irrational, primitive strivings in us, and the fact that we forget our dreams so easily is amply explained by our being ashamed of those irrational and criminal impulses which we express when we are not under the control of society. Undoubtedly this interpretation of dreams is true, and we shall presently turn to it and give some illustrations. But the question is whether it is exclusively true or whether the negative elements in the influence of society do not account for the paradoxical fact that *we are not only less reasonable and less decent in our dreams but that we are also more intelligent, wiser, and capable of better judgment when we are asleep than when we are awake.*

Indeed, culture has not only a beneficial but also a detrimental influence on our intellectual and moral functions. Human beings are dependent on each other, they need each other. But human history up to now has been influenced by one fact: material production was not sufficient to satisfy the legitimate needs of all men. The table was set for only a few of the many who wanted to sit down and eat. Those who were stronger tried to secure places for themselves, which meant that they had to prevent others from getting seats. If they had loved their brothers as much as Buddha or the Prophets or Jesus postulated, they would have shared their bread rather than eat meat and drink wine without them. But, love being the highest and most difficult achievement of the human race, it is no slur on man that those who could sit at the table and enjoy the good things of life did not want to share, and therefore were compelled to seek power over those who threatened their privileges. This power was often the power of the conqueror, the physical power that forced the majority to be satisfied with their lot. But physical power was not always available or sufficient. One had to have power over the minds of people in order to make them refrain from using their fists. This control over mind and feeling was a necessary element in retaining the privileges of the few. In this process, however, the minds of the few became as distorted as the minds of the many. The guard who watches a prisoner becomes almost as much a prisoner as the prisoner himself. The "elite" who have to control those who are not "chosen" become the prisoners of their own restrictive tendencies. Thus the human mind, of both rulers and ruled, becomes deflected from its essential human purpose, which is to feel and to think humanly, to use and to develop the powers of reason and love that are inherent in man and without the full development of which he is crippled.

In this process of deflection and distortion man's character becomes distorted. Aims which are in contrast to the interests of his real human self become paramount. His powers of love are impoverished, and he is driven to want power over others. His inner security is lessened, and he is driven to seek compensation by passionate cravings for fame and prestige. He loses the sense of dignity and integrity and is forced to turn himself into a commodity, deriving his self-respect from his salability, from his success. All this makes for the fact that we learn not only what is true, but also what is false. That we hear not only what is good, but are constantly under the influence of ideas detrimental to life.

This holds true for a primitive tribe in which strict laws and customs influence the mind, but it is true also for modern society with its alleged freedom from rigid ritualism. In many ways the spread of literacy and of the media of mass communication has made the influence of cultural clichés as effective as it is in a small, highly restricted tribal culture. Modern man is exposed to an almost unceasing "noise," the noise of the radio, television, headlines, advertising, the movies, most of which do not enlighten our minds but stultify them. We are exposed to rationalizing lies which masquerade as truths, to plain nonsense which masquerades as common sense or as the higher wisdom of the specialist, to double talk, intellectual laziness, or dishonesty which speaks in the name of "honor" or "realism," as the case may be. We feel superior to the superstitions of former generations and so-called primitive cultures, and we are constantly hammered at by the very same kind of superstitious beliefs that set themselves up as the latest discoveries of science. Is it surprising, then, that to be awake is not exclusively a blessing but also a curse? Is it surprising that in a state of sleep, when we are alone with ourselves, when we can look into ourselves without being bothered by the noise and nonsense that surround us in the daytime, we are better able to feel and to think our truest and most valuable feelings and thoughts?

This, then, is the conclusion at which we arrive: the state of sleep has an ambiguous function. In it the lack of contact with culture makes for the appearance both of our worst *and* of our best; therefore, if we dream, we may be less intelligent, less wise, and less decent, but we may also be better and wiser than in our waking life.

Having arrived at this point, the difficult problem arises: how do we know whether a dream is to be understood as an expression of our best or of our worst? Is there any principle which can guide us in this attempt?

To answer this question we must leave the somewhat general level of our discussion and try to get further insight by discussing a number of concrete dream illustrations.

The following dream was reported by a man who had met a "very important person" the day before he had this dream. This person had the reputation of being wise and kind, and the dreamer had come to see him, impressed by what everyone said about the old man. He had left after an hour or so with a feeling that he had met a great and kind man.

> I see Mr. X [the very important person]; his face looks quite different from what it looked yesterday. I see a cruel mouth and a hard face. He is laughingly telling someone that he has just succeeded in cheating a poor widow out of her last few cents. I feel a sense of revulsion.

When asked to tell what occurred to him about this dream, the dreamer remarked that he could remember a fleeting feeling of disappointment when he walked into Mr. X's room and had a first glimpse of his face; this feeling, however, disappeared as soon as X started an engaging and friendly conversation.

How are we to understand this dream? Perhaps the dreamer is envious of Mr. X's fame and for this reason dislikes him? In that case the dream would be the expression of the irrational hate that the dreamer harbors without being aware of it. But in the case I am reporting here, it was different. At subsequent meetings, after our dreamer had become aware of his suspicion through his dreams, he observed X carefully and discovered that there was in the man an element of ruthlessness which he had seen for the first time in his dream. His impression was corroborated by the few who dared to doubt the majority's opinion that X was such a kind man. It was corroborated by some facts in X's life which were by no means so crude as that in the dream, but which nevertheless were expressive of a similar spirit.

What we see, then, is that the dreamer's insight into the character of X was much more astute in his sleep than in his waking life. The "noise" of public opinion, which insisted that X was a wonderful man, prevented him from becoming aware of his critical feeling toward X when he saw him. It was only later, after he had this dream, that he could remember the split second of distrust and doubt he had felt. In his dream, when he was protected from this "noise" and in a position to be alone with himself and his impressions and feelings, he could make a judgment which was more accurate and true than his waking-state judgment.

In this, as in every other dream, we can decide whether the dream is expressive of irrational passion or of reason only if we consider the person of the dreamer, the mood he was in when he fell asleep, and whatever data we have on the reality aspect of the situation he has dreamed about. In this case our interpretation is corroborated by a number of factors. The dreamer could remember the initial fleeting impression of dislike. He had no reason to and did not harbor any hostile feelings against X. The data of X's life and later observations confirmed the impression the dreamer had had in his sleep. If all these factors were lacking, our interpretation would be different. For instance, if he were prone to be jealous of famous people, could not find any evidence for the dream judgment about X, could not remember the feeling of disgust when he saw him first, then, of course, we would be prone to assume that this dream was not an expression of insight but an expression of irrational hate.

Insight is closely related to prediction. To predict means to infer the future course of events from the direction and intensity of the forces that we can see at work at present. Any thorough knowledge, not of the surface but of the forces operating underneath it, will lead to making predictions, and any valuable prediction must be based on such knowledge. No wonder we often predict developments and events which are later borne out by the facts. Quite regardless of the question of telepathy, many dreams in which the dreamer forecasts future events fall into the category of rational predictions as we just defined them. One of the oldest dreams of prediction was Joseph's:

> And Joseph dreamed a dream, and he told it his brethren; and they hated him yet the more. And he said unto them, Hear, I pray you, this dream which I have dreamed: for, behold, we were binding sheaves in the field, and, lo, my sheaf arose, and also stood upright; and behold, your sheaves stood round about, and made obeisance to my sheaf. And his brethren said to him, Shalt thou indeed reign over us? Or shalt thou indeed have dominion over us? And they hated him yet the more for his dreams, and for his words.

> And he dreamed yet another dream, and told it his brethren, and said, Behold, I have dreamed a dream more; and, behold, the sun and the moon and the eleven stars made obeisance to me. And he told it to his father, and to his brethren: and his father rebuked

him, and said unto him, What is this dream that thou hast dreamed? Shall I and thy mother and thy brethren indeed come to bow down ourselves to thee to the earth?

> And his brethren envied him; but his father observed the saying.

This report in the Old Testament shows us a situation in which dreams were still understood immediately by the "layman," and one did not yet need the help of an expert dream interpreter to understand a comparatively simple dream. (That to understand a more difficult dream one needed an expert is shown in the story of Pharaoh's dreams; where, in fact, the court dream interpreters were not able to understand his dreams and Joseph had to be brought in.) The brothers understand immediately that the dream is an expression of Joseph's fantasy that one day he will become superior to his father as well as to his brothers and that they would stand in awe of him. Undoubtedly this dream is an expression of Joseph's ambition, without which he probably would not have reached the high position he attained. But it happens that this dream came true, that it was not only an expression of irrational ambition but at the same time a prediction of events which actually occurred. How could Joseph make such a prediction? His life history in the Biblical report shows that he was not only an ambitious man, but a man of unusual talent. In his dream he is more closely aware of his extraordinary gifts than he could be in his waking life, where he was impressed by the fact that he was younger and weaker than all his brothers. His dream is a blend of his passionate ambition and an insight into his gifts without which his dream could not have come true.

A prediction of a different kind occurs in the following dream: A, who has met B to discuss a future business association, was favorably impressed and decided that he would take B into his business as a partner. The night after the meeting he had this dream:

I see B sitting in our common office. He is going over the books and changing figures in them in order to cover the fact that he has embezzled large sums of money.

A wakes up and, being accustomed to paying some attention to dreams, is puzzled. Being convinced that dreams are always the expression of our irrational desires, he tells himself that this dream is an expression of his own hostility and competitiveness with other men, that this hostility and suspicion lead him to a fantasy that B is a thief. Having interpreted the dream in this fashion, he leans over backwards to rid himself of these irrational suspicions. After he started the business association with B, a number of incidents occurred which re-aroused A's suspicion. But recalling his dream and its interpretation, he was convinced that again he was under the influence of irrational suspicions and feelings of hostility and decided to pay no attention to those circumstances which had made him suspicious. After one year, however, he discovered that B had embezzled considerable sums of money and covered it by false entries in the books. His dream had come true almost literally.

The analysis of A's association showed that his dream expressed an insight into B which he had gained at the first meeting, but of which he had not been aware in his waking thought. Those many and complex observations which we make about other persons in a split second without being aware of our own thought processes had made A recognize that B was dishonest. But, since there was no "evidence" for this view and since B's manner made it difficult for A's conscious thinking to believe in B's dishonesty, he had repressed the thought completely, or rather the thought had not even registered with him while he was awake. In his dream, however, he had the clear awareness of his suspicion and had he listened to this self-communication he could have avoided a good deal of trouble. His conviction that dreams were always the expression of our irrational fantasies and desires made him misread the dream and even certain later factual observations.

A dream which expresses moral judgment is that of a writer who had been offered a job in which he would earn a great deal more money than in his present position, but where he would also be forced to write things he did not believe in and to violate his personal integrity. Nevertheless, the offer was so tempting as far as money and prestige were concerned that he was not sure that he could reject it. He went through all the typical rationalizations that most people in such a situation go through. He reasoned that, after all, he might see the situation too black and that the concessions he would have to make were of a minor nature. Furthermore, even if he could not write as he pleased, this condition would last only for a few years and then he would give up the job, and have so much money that he would be entirely independent and free to do the work that was meaningful to him. He thought of his friends and family relations and what he could do for them. In fact, he sometimes presented the problem to himself in such a way that to accept the job seemed his moral obligation, while to refuse it would be an expression of a self-indulgent, egotistical attitude. Nevertheless, none of these rationalizations really satisfied him; he continued doubting and was not able to make up his mind until one night he had the following dream:

I was sitting in a car at the foot of a high mountain where a narrow and exceedingly steep road began which led to the top of the mountain. I was doubtful whether I should drive up, since the road seemed very dangerous. But a man who stood near my car told me to drive up and not to be afraid. I listened to him and decided to follow his advice. I drove up, and the road got more and more dangerous. I could not stop, though, because there was no possibility of turning around. When I was near the top the motor stalled, the brakes would not work, the car rolled back and fell over a precipice! I woke up in terror.

One association must be reported for the full understanding of the dream. The dreamer said that the man who had encouraged him to drive up the mountain road was a former friend, a painter, who had "sold out," become a fashionable portrait painter and made a lot of money, but who at the same time had ceased to be creative. He knew that in spite of his success this friend was unhappy and suffered from the fact that he had betrayed himself. To understand the whole dream is not difficult. The steep mountain this man was to drive up is a symbolic expression of the successful career about which he has to make his choice. In his dream he knows that this path is dangerous. He is aware of the fact that if he accepts the offer he will do exactly the same thing his friend has done, something for which he had despised his friend and because of which he had broken off their friendship. In the dream he is aware that this decision can only lead to his destruction. In the dream picture the destruction is that of his physical self, symbolizing his intellectual and spiritual self that is in danger of being destroyed.

The dreamer in his sleep saw the ethical problem clearly and recognized that he had to choose between "success," on the one hand, and integrity and happiness, on the other. He recognized what his fate would be if he made the wrong decision. In his waking state he could not see the alternative clearly. He was so impressed by the "noise" that says that it is stupid not to accept the chance to have more money, power and prestige. He was so influenced by the voices that say it is childish and impractical to be "idealistic" that he was caught in the many rationalizations one uses to drown out the voice of one's conscience. This particular dreamer, being aware of the fact that we often know more in our dreams than in our waking state, was sufficiently startled by this dream that the fog in his mind lifted, he was able to see the alternative clearly and made the decision for his integrity and against the self-destructive temptation.

Not only do insight into our relation to others or theirs to us, value judgments and predictions occur in our dreams, but also intellectual operations superior to those in the waking state. This is not surprising, since penetrating thinking requires an amount of concentration which we are often deprived of in the waking state, while the state of sleep is conducive to it. The best-known example of this kind of dream is the one of the discoverer of the Benzine ring. He had been searching for the chemical formula for Benzine for quite some time, and one night the correct formula stood before his eyes in a dream. He was fortunate enough to remember it after he awoke. There are numerous examples of people who look for solutions of a problem in mathematics, engineering, philosophy, or of practical problems, and one night they dream the solution with perfect clarity.

Sometimes one finds exceedingly complicated intellectual considerations occurring in dreams. The following illustration is an example of such a dream process, although it entails at the same time a very personal element. The dreamer is an intelligent woman and this is her dream:

> I saw a cat and many mice. And I thought, I shall ask my husband tomorrow morning why one hundred mice are not stronger than one cat, and why they cannot overpower her. I know he will answer me that this is no different from the historical problem that dictators can rule over millions of people and not be overthrown by them. I knew, however, that this was a trick question and that his answer was wrong.

The morning following this dream she told her husband the first part of her dream and asked him, "What does it mean that I dreamed that the one hundred mice could not defeat one cat?" He promptly gave the answer she had anticipated in her dream. Two days later she recited to her husband a little poem she had composed. The poem dealt with a black cat who found herself on snow-covered fields surrounded by hundreds of mice. The mice were all laughing at the cat because, being black, she could be seen so clearly against the snow, and the cat wished to be white in order to be less visible. One line of the poem said, "And now I understand what puzzled me last night."

In repeating this poem to her husband, she was not aware of any connection between the poem and the dream. He saw the connection and said, "Well, so your poem gives the answer to your dream. You identified yourself not, as I had thought, with the mice, but with the cat; and in your dream you were proud that even one hundred mice could not defeat you. But at the same time you express a feeling of humiliation that the weak mice toward whom you feel so superior could laugh at you if they could see you very clearly." (The dreamer loves cats and feels sympathy and affinity with them.)

DREAMS AND DREAMING *

Norman MacKenzie (1921–   )

There is an old fable about two knights who fought a duel because they disagreed over the color of a shield. One maintained that it was silver, the other insisted that it was gold. Each claimed that he alone was right; they quarreled and eventually fought. The combat was brought to an end by a bystander, who pointed out that they were both right: the shield was silver on one side, and gold on the other.

Much of the long debate about the nature and meaning of dreams has been a disagreement of the same kind. We have seen how one school of thought—whose views can be traced back as far as the dawn of scientific thinking in classical Greece—always sought a physical explanation of dreams, attributing them to causes as simple as bad digestion or as complex as subtle changes in the chemistry of the brain cells. But we have also observed another tradition, emerging from primitive magic and religion into philosophy and modern psychology, which regarded dreams as the result of hidden but vital mental processes, revealing much about the personality of the dreamer. The antagonism between those two basic types of dream theory has persisted for centuries, and has sometimes been acrimonious. Yet it is as foolish as the dispute between the two knights in the fable. The

* This chapter appeared in *Dreams and Dreaming* (New York: Vanguard Press, 1965).

more we know about dreams, the more we must look for an explanation of them that takes account of both the physiological and the psychological evidence.

Toward the end of his life Freud complained that "the analysts behave as though they had nothing more to say about the dream, as though the whole subject of dream theory were finished and done with." His complaint had some justification, for much analytical work with dreams had been little more than detailed elaboration of ideas originally formulated by Freud himself, Jung, Stekel, and other pioneers. One of the limiting factors was the analytical obsession with dream theory as an end in itself; because Freud had insisted on the crucial significance of dreams, there was a sectarian suspicion on the part of many psychoanalysts about other paths of inquiry into unconscious mental processes. Yet dream theory could not develop in isolation and mainly on the basis of accumulating case reports, selected to make clinical or doctrinal points, any more than psychoanalysts could "prove" that their methods were "scientific" by essentially subjective evaluations of their effectiveness.

New lines of advance had to be found. One of these was the extension of clinical and experimental psychology, using laboratory techniques to test a range of theories about perception, responses, learning, and memory, about fantasy, role playing, and social behavior. (We have drawn on these without examining them in detail, for they are seldom directly concerned with the problem of dreams.) Another was the breakthrough in sleep research that took place after 1953. Both of these changes, particularly the latter, provided new and verifiable evidence against which the propositions of Freud and others could be tested and from which new conceptions might be derived. "The development of the Kleitman-Dement technique," Dr. Harry Trosman of Chicago wrote in 1963, "thus serves as a challenge for the psychoanalyst to re-examine, develop, or modify basic dream theory and to discover where discrepancies lie between empirical findings and hypothetical constructs."

Dreaming may well be one important road to the unconscious (though there are other and increasingly useful paths to the hidden parts of the mind); but there is now little doubt that it is also the outcome of distinct physical processes in the human organism. It occurs at precisely the point where the functions of mind and body fuse into the mystery of personality—and where, therefore, all the disciplines that deal with the study of man have a valuable contribution to make. Merely to write this book, for instance, it has been necessary to use material drawn from anthropology, archaeology, history, mythology, religion, philosophy, sociology, and psychology, as well as from medicine, physiology, and biochemistry.

In the search for a unified theory of dreams, however, we should on no account disparage the role played by Freud and the other pioneers of psychoanalysis in directing serious attention to the content of dreams. It was their work, after all, that taught us to regard the dream as a meaningful expression of emotions and memories of which we are consciously unaware—and thus transformed the study of dreams from a kind of occult parlor game into a reputable and profoundly rewarding occupation. Freud himself foresaw that this would happen. In the first chapter of *The Interpretation of Dreams* he wrote: "A modification of our attitude to dreams will at the same time affect our views upon the internal mechanism of mental disorders . . . we shall be working towards an explanation of the psychoses while we are endeavouring to throw some light on the mystery of dreams."

When Freud's book first appeared, it

was greeted in some quarters with ridicule. Times have changed. Psychotherapy is now a recognized and valuable means of treating mental illness; and the search for the causes and cure of psychosis is being urgently pursued as a joint endeavor by psychiatrists, neurologists, and biochemists. There are institutes of dream research and well-equipped laboratories devoted to the study of sleep, and applied psychology has given us many new insights into the orders and disorders of the mind. The old dividing line between "mental" and "physical" theories—of dreams as well as of psychosis—is fast disappearing, if in fact it has not already been wholly erased. Whether or not one accepts Freud's specific ideas about the nature of dreams, it is impossible to deny the greatest of his achievements. By studying dreams he changed man's view of himself.

We began this book with a simple question: What are dreams? We cannot yet provide a comprehensive answer. But the answers we can give to matters men have speculated about for centuries have set the dream debate in an entirely different context.

We can now say that dreaming occurs as part of a distinct and biologically determined rhythm, which appears to be as natural and necessary as breathing. This rhythm, moreover, is related to a cycle of sleep and wakefulness that can be observed even in very small infants, and it probably goes on in some form in waking hours. The imagery of the dream, that is to say, is a psychological characteristic of a definite and identifiable physical state that differs from both wakefulness and non-dreaming sleep. This state, as we have seen, can be demonstrated in various ways; there are the tracings on the EEG machine, which registers the minute electrical impulses within the brain, the onset of rapid eye movements, changes in respiration, pulse rate, and the electrical conductivity of the skin, the disappearance of certain muscle tensions, and a diminution of body movements. Most recently, Dr. Charles Fisher has added a new feature—a cycle of penile erections in the male dreamer that coincides with the dream state—and it seems likely that further research will reveal other physical and chemical changes taking place within the body whenever dreaming occurs.

It follows from this evidence that dreams are a regular, not a random, phenomenon. The normal person, in good health and enjoying adequate sleep, dreams to a timetable scarcely affected by heat, or cold, or noise, or what he eats or drinks. He dreams when he is due to dream, and his first dream starts approximately 90 minutes after he has gone to sleep. Other dreams come at similar though shorter intervals throughout the night. As the intervals decrease, however, the length of the dream period increases. The first dream has an average duration of about 10 minutes, the second may last as long as 20 minutes, while the third and fourth may go on for half an hour or more.

This dream timetable, of course, is an average. Each of us has a slightly different dream pattern; in all of us—as Dr. Dement has shown experimentally—it can be drastically modified if we are unable to get our usual quota of dreaming. One important line of research is to look for significant differences between individuals. Do men dream differently from women? Are dreams more or less frequent in the aged, who tend to have rather different sleep habits? How far is the timetable changed by mental or physical illness, or by drugs, or fatigue, or climatic factors? Do dreams in color occur to everyone, or only to some individuals? We cannot yet answer such questions, but at least we now have a scientific technique that will enable us, in time, to find the answers.

But how can such evidence be reconciled with psychological theories of the dream? How can we sustain Freud's view that dreams are due to the upwelling of instinctive desires when Dr. Dement demonstrated that they occur at regular intervals? If dreams are psychic phenomena, why should they appear like the figures on an animated clock, which emerge to strike the hours and perform other complicated maneuvers?

We still seem to be faced by a choice between the psychic and physical theories of the dream. But must we make such a choice? Can we retain much of what Freud and others have taught us about the meaning of dreams, while accepting the new theories of their cause?

One valuable idea was advanced by the Czech psychiatrist Dr. Samuel Lowy in a book published in London in 1942. In his *Psychological and Biological Foundations of Dream Interpretation,* this pupil of Stekel's suggested that the dreaming process might be a rhythmic factor, "desirable and beneficial for life"—and it might be due to excessive secretion of hormones. Lowy argued that physical stimuli (such as poor digestion or the need to urinate), and psychic excitement (hate or anxiety, for instance), were both sources of dreams. There was, therefore, a "need for a unified conception of the total dreaming process, which would consider the two kinds of dream-stimuli as having a common denominator." He then went further, suggesting "that the dreaming process, which in the absence of waking consciousness results in the dream images proper, continues operating in the waking state." Thus he saw daydreams, psychotic states, and the delusions of the intoxicated as end results of the same organic mechanism. In all these ways, Lowy's difficult and somewhat neglected book anticipates the direction in which dream research has recently moved.

In 1958 Dr. A. Ullman, an American psychiatrist, made a further contribution. He noted that dreams appeared in so-called "light" sleep, and asked whether dreaming might be related to the biological mechanism that permits man to sleep yet maintains a state of vigilance so that he can quickly arouse himself if danger threatens. This readiness to fight or flee on awakening is instinctual in man —and in other animals. It depends on the supply of adrenaline and other nerve hormones, which translate the emergency signals from the brain into rapid physical responses. This is the reason why sudden waking sometimes makes one "feel queer"; the system is given a rapid stimulus by the adrenaline released and one may feel dizzy and even a little disorientated.

[It has been] suggested that adrenaline, and other chemicals of this type, may play a very important role in causing hallucinations and even mental illness of various kinds; if there is an excess of these chemicals, some researchers believe, the body cannot easily eliminate or convert them, and fantasies arise. If for any reason the body systematically produced such an excess in sleep and needed a period of time to accomplish the complex chemical processes required to dispose of these chemicals, we might find an explanation of the regular onset of dream states.

Why should this be the case? To answer this question we must move from what we know to what, at present, we can only guess. But the theory we now put forward does take account of a great deal of the recent evidence about sleep, dreams, and the chemistry of the brain.

It is conceivable that, in the long evolution of the human race, man's sleeping habits have changed. We know that, in small children, the basic rhythm of sleep is a 60-minute cycle; every hour or so the baby is on the point of waking, and it tends to take its sleep in multiples of one hour. As we grow older, as Professor Kleitman has shown, we develop the habit of the long sleep. Within this we find the 90-minute cycle, ranging from deep sleep to the "light" sleep that precedes arousal. It seems as if, biologically, man is a creature who is prepared to wake fairly often (as do dogs and cats, for instance), and that he has acquired the technique of long sleeps comparatively recently in the evolutionary process. Even though he now sleeps for several hours, the mechanism that kept him in a state of readiness for frequent arousals may persist as an underlying rhythm—the 90-minute cycle. We can go on to suggest that, in preparation for the contingency of sudden waking, he builds up stocks of adrenaline and other necessary chemicals. When these are not required, because sleep continues, they take some time to be eliminated—and during this period man enters what is called the dream state. When the conversion of the relevant chemicals is completed—and the assumption is that some of the by-products of this process are hallucinogenic—the dreamer returns to deep sleep. If some such process is going on in sleep, there would be a regular rhythm of dreaming. Such an explanation, moreover, would account for the fact that, as the night wears on, the interval between the dream states becomes shorter and the dream periods themselves become longer. After some hours, sleep is less necessary and waking is more likely. Thus, as a man moves toward the end of his "normal" night's sleep, his body might prepare larger stocks of the chemicals it needs for arousal. If waking did not actually occur, it would then take more time (a longer dream period) for these stocks to be eliminated.

The EEG tracings . . . give some support for this hypothesis. These showed that the sleeper reaches the dream state as he emerges from deep, non-dreaming sleep; he appears to be on the verge of waking, but instead of waking he dreams. When the dreams ends, he returns to deep sleep. The dream, that is to say, becomes a substitute for waking.

Freud guessed that this was the case, even though he did not have the benefit of modern scientific equipment to reveal the electrical rhythms of the brain. He concluded from this fact that dreams were the "guardians of sleep." He assumed man had a need to sleep, that sleep was likely to be disturbed by instinctual wishes welling up in his sleeper's mind, and that the dream discharged these wishes in a fantasy form so that sleep could continue. It has been claimed that Freud's view is now untenable; after Kleitman and Dement established that there was a regular rhythm of dreams, it was asked why instinctual wishes should well up with such regularity.

It may indeed be necessary to modify Freud's theory, but need we reject its fundamental idea? If the chemicals released in the sleep cycle stimulate the "old" or instinctual areas of the brain—and . . . there is reason to suspect that this is what happens—then the feelings and memories thus aroused will appear as dream images. (This process, or something closely analogous to it, seems to occur in psychosis or under the influence of hallucinogenic drugs.) But these dreams would not arise, as Freud put it, to prevent the dreamer being awakened by uncomfortable feelings. They might express certain instinctual and emotional tensions, but they would arise because the dreamer has no immediate need to wake —and the biochemical preparations he has made for arousal are therefore diverted into a fantasy substitute for waking life. We can extend this statement. If the dream mechanism is in some way a physical preparation for a return to conscious activity, then the dream content may also be regarded as a psychological preparation for the problems of everyday existence.

On this argument, the dream has a physical cause but psychological consequences—or, to put this another way, the rhythm of dreaming is the result of a primordial physical process, which occurs even in newborn infants, while the content of dreaming is a secondary and psychically significant process. There is a similar relationship between breathing, which is a basic function of the human organism, and speech; breathing makes speech possible, and man has gradually developed his ability to speak into refined systems of communication. Long ago, perhaps, man's ancestors developed the physical rhythm of dreaming; more recently, in evolutionary terms, man came to use the ensuing dreams to release his deepest and consciously unrecognized feeling, or even to anticipate his everyday problems and to seek possible solutions for them.

This would mean that, in certain conditions, a biochemical change in the body permits our unconscious conflicts, hopes, and fears to break through the barrier that normally separates them from consciousness. Such a change, moreover, occurs regularly in sleep but may take place at any time if the human organism is subjected to unusual physical or mental stress —fatigue, sensory deprivation, withdrawal into introspection and meditation, a worrying situation, unsatisfactory relationships with other people, or the use of drugs. When this happens, the consciousness of the real world is diminished and we regress into the world of fantasy. In extreme cases, such as psychosis, the power of the fantasy becomes overwhelming and the individual loses contact with reality.

The key idea in this theory was the suggestion Dr. Ullman made in 1958, that dreaming might be related to the arousal mechanism. As has happened so often in the tortuous evolution of our ideas about dreams, a new idea is little more than a new formulation of an older and neglected one. In this case, the original source was the valuable book *Conflict and Dream,* published in 1922 by Dr. W. H. Rivers. . . .

The book, which sharply criticized Freud's emphasis on infantile sexuality and argued that dreams are attempts to solve the conflicts of everyday life, has received too little attention. For this noted anthropologist had asked, in an appendix written shortly before he died, whether dreams had a biological role. Animals, Rivers had pointed out, need some agent to awaken them and prepare them to adapt to a new situation. This agency, in his view, had been much modified in man —above all by the development of an ability to discriminate between a sensory stimulus that made waking imperative and one that could safely be disregarded. Presumably, this ability was a function of the cerebral cortex, which receives sensory impressions, evaluates them, and transmits the appropriate response to the motor areas of the brain.

The suggestion of Dr. Rivers has found support recently in the work of Dr. Ian Oswald, who has demonstrated that one of the types of cortical activity that does continue in sleep is this ability to discriminate between the stimulus that can be ignored and that which demands arousal. A mother sleeps as trains pass her window, but wakes at the first cry from her baby; sleepers will ignore many names played on a tape-recorder but respond immediately to their own names.

We have been outlining a possible theory of dreaming that could overcome the old contradiction between the physical and psychological concepts of the dream. While it goes far beyond anything that can yet be proved, it does fit much of the evidence now available. Once we recognize that the physical state of dreaming opens the door through which the fantasies of the unconscious can emerge, it will be much easier to reconcile the new scientific discoveries with the older insights of the psychologists.

We have now reached the frontier of dream research, and while we may make guesses about what lies beyond, we cannot tell what routes we shall find through the dark territory of the mind. There are too many questions that we cannot yet answer. Why, for instance, should the cerebral cortex behave in a dream as if it is receiving real sensory impressions? What stops the brain from reacting to these sensory impressions as it would to the same situations in real life? What part of the mind *knows* that the images are merely fantasy? What has gone wrong when the capacity to tell fantasy from reality fails us, or when we become somnambulists? More important, perhaps, we must ask what is happening when we are not dreaming. Is there some kind of "third thinking" that is neither conscious nor fantastic, or is there a "true" sleep in which the brain does no more than sustain the autonomic processes necessary to keep us alive? We do not know. We do not even know how to set about answering some of these questions, or many others that we could ask—or whether, in fact, they are the right questions.

The same is true of other aspects of the dream to which we have paid very little attention, though they have intrigued men for centuries. Can dreams foretell the future, or reveal events at a distance? Are dreams evidence of a different dimension of Time, as J. W. Dunne and J. B. Priestly —among others—have suggested? Can we know things about other people in our dreams that we do not consciously know about them?

The difficulty about such questions is that we can only speculate about them, as the ancients did, for we are not in a very much better position to answer them

than Aristotle or Artemidorus. But in view of modern experiments in extrasensory perception or telepathy, we should do well to keep an open mind. In view of scientific thinking about the nature of Time, we should be equally cautious about dogmatically insisting that there are no other dimensions to existence than those we know in waking consciousness. And, in the light of what we have learned about subliminal perception, we must concede that we "unconsciously" acquire a mass of information of which we are consciously unaware—including subtle assessments of the character and problems of other people—some of which later emerges in our dreams.

We need to explore all such problems, because we do not know when one of them will suddenly yield a vital piece of evidence. But the evidence at present available is so fragmentary and inconclusive, and so influenced by occult attitudes, that it would have been misleading to summarize it in this book. For the same reason, we have excluded some scientific research that is in such an early stage that its implications for dreaming are far from clear. There is, for instance, some evidence that the incidence of mental illness may increase during magnetic storms or other climatic changes, and that memory —and possibly genetic patterns—may be affected by intense magnetic fields. Before we can develop a real science of dreaming, we shall have to take account of many old guesses and new discoveries.

Nothing that has been discovered during the last few years, however, invalidates the hypothesis that dreams are meaningful and capable of interpretation —even if there is room for a good deal of controversy about what they mean and how they are best interpreted. This hypothesis, as we have seen, has persisted since antiquity, and survived every change in man's beliefs about the origins and nature of dreams.

In this century, thanks to Freud and other great psychologists, we have come to take dreams seriously, and learned to regard them as one of many fantasy states that provide clues to the hidden orders and disorders of the mind. That is a great gain. For man today needs every means to self-discovery and self-mastery, if he is to control the forces he has unleashed on the world. He needs to recognize the terrors and also the beauties that lie within him, and to confront them boldly. If he shrinks from self-examination, he cannot grow to maturity and full human responsibility; he remains a child in nature emotionally crippled, and liable to vent on others the fears and fancies he cannot admit within himself. But, to the degree that he explores what lies within him, he learns to recognize his true feelings, to relate passionately to other people, and to face the problems of his life with dignity and courage. Because the study of the dream has opened the door on man's inner world it has been one of the golden keys to human freedom.

SHORT STORIES

THE DREAM OF A RIDICULOUS MAN

Fëodor Dostoevski
(1821–1888)

I

I am a ridiculous person. Now they call me a madman. That would be a promotion if it were not that I remain as ridiculous in their eyes as before. But now I do not resent it, they are all dear to me now, even when they laugh at me— and, indeed, it is just then that they are particularly dear to me. I could join in their laughter—not exactly at myself, but through affection for them, if I did not feel so sad as I look at them. Sad because they do not know the truth and I do know it. Oh, how hard it is to be the only one who knows the truth! But they won't understand that. No, they won't understand it.

In old days I used to be miserable at seeming ridiculous. Not seeming, but being. I have always been ridiculous, and I have known it, perhaps, from the hour I was born. Perhaps from the time I was seven years old I knew I was ridiculous. Afterwards I went to school, studied at the university, and, do you know, the more I learned, the more thoroughly I understood that I was ridiculous. So that it seemed in the end as though all the sciences I studied at the university existed only to prove and make evident to me as I went more deeply into them that I was ridiculous. It was the same with life as it was with science. With every year the same consciousness of the ridiculous figure I cut in every relation grew and strengthened. Every one always laughed at me. But not one of them knew or guessed that if there were one man on earth who knew better than anybody else that I was absurd, it was myself, and what I resented most of all was that they did not know that. But that was my own fault; I was so proud that nothing would have ever induced me to tell it to any one. This pride grew in me with the years; and if it had happened that I allowed myself to confess to any one that I was ridiculous, I believe that I should have blown out my brains the same evening. Oh, how I suffered in my early youth from the fear that I might give way and confess it to my school-fellows. But since I grew to manhood, I have for some unknown reason become calmer, though I realised my awful characteristic more fully every year. I say "unknown," for to this day I cannot tell why it was. Perhaps it was owing to the terrible misery that was growing in my soul through something which was of more consequence than anything else about me: that something was the conviction that had come upon me that *nothing in the world mattered*. I had long had an inkling of it, but the full realisation came last year almost suddenly. I suddenly felt that it was all the same to me whether the world existed or whether there had never been anything at all: I began to feel with all my being that there was *nothing existing*. At first I fancied that many things had existed in the past, but afterwards I guessed that there never had been anything in the past either, but that it had only seemed so for some reason. Little by little I guessed that there would be nothing in the future either. Then I left off being angry with people and almost ceased to notice them. Indeed this showed itself even in the pettiest trifles: I used, for instance, to knock against people in the street. And not so much from being lost in thought: what had I to think about? I had almost given up thinking by that time; nothing mattered to me. If at least I had solved my problems! Oh, I had not settled one of them, and how many they were! But I gave up caring about anything, and all the problems disappeared.

And it was after that that I found out the truth. I learnt the truth last November—on the third of November, to be precise—and I remember every instant since. It was a gloomy evening, one of the gloomiest possible evenings. I was going home at about eleven o'clock and I remember that I thought that the evening could not be gloomier. Even physically. Rain had been falling all day, and it had been a cold, gloomy, almost menacing rain, with, I remember, an unmistakable spite against mankind. Suddenly between ten and eleven it had stopped, and was followed by a horrible dampness, colder and damper than the rain, and a sort of steam was rising from everything, from every stone in the street, and from every by-lane if one looked down it as far as one could. A thought suddenly occurred to me, that if all the street lamps had been put out it would have been less cheerless, that the gas made one's heart sadder because it lighted it all up. I had had scarcely any dinner that day, and had been

spending the evening with an engineer, and two other friends had been there also. I sat silent—I fancy I bored them. They talked of something rousing and suddenly they got excited over it. But they did not really care, I could see that, and only made a show of being excited. I suddenly said as much to them. "My friends," I said, "you really do not care one way or the other." They were not offended, but they all laughed at me. That was because I spoke without any note of reproach, simply because it did not matter to me. They saw it did not, and it amused them.

As I was thinking about the gas lamps in the street I looked up at the sky. The sky was horribly dark, but one could distinctly see tattered clouds, and between them fathomless black patches. Suddenly I noticed in one of these patches a star, and began watching it intently. That was because that star gave me an idea: I decided to kill myself that night. I had firmly determined to do so two months before, and poor as I was, I bought a splendid revolver that very day, and loaded it. But two months had passed and it was still lying in my drawer; I was so utterly indifferent that I wanted to seize a moment when I would not be so indifferent—why, I don't know. And so for two months every night that I came home I thought I would shoot myself. I kept waiting for the right moment. And so now this star gave me a thought. I made up my mind that it should certainly be that night. And why the star gave me the thought I don't know.

And just as I was looking at the sky, this little girl took me by the elbow. The street was empty, and there was scarcely any one to be seen. A cabman was sleeping in the distance in his cab. It was a child of eight with kerchief on her head, wearing nothing but a wretched little dress all soaked with rain, but I noticed particularly her wet broken shoes and I recall them now. They caught my eye particularly. She suddenly pulled me by the elbow and called me. She was not weeping, but was spasmodically crying out some words which she could not utter properly, because she was shivering and shuddering all over. She was in terror about something, and kept crying, "Mammy, mammy!" I turned facing her, I did not say a word and went on; but she ran, pulling at me, and there was that note in her voice which in frightened children means despair. I know that sound. Though she did not articulate the words, I understood that her mother was dying, or that something of the sort was happening to them, and that she had run out to call some one, to find something to help her mother. I did not go with her; on the contrary, I had an impulse to drive her away. I told her first to go to a policeman. But clasping her hands, she ran beside me sobbing and gasping, and would not leave me. Then I stamped my foot, and shouted at her. She called out "Sir! sir! . . ." but suddenly abandoned me and rushed headlong across the road. Some other passer-by appeared there, and she evidently flew from me to him.

I mounted up to my fifth storey. I have a room in a flat where there are other lodgers. My room is small and poor, with a garret window in the shape of a semicircle. I have a sofa covered with American leather, a table with books on it, two chairs and a comfortable arm-chair, as old as old can be, but of the good old-fashioned shape. I sat down, lighted the candle, and began thinking. In the room next to mine, through the partition wall, a perfect Bedlam was going on. It had been going on for the last three days. A retired captain lived there, and he had half a dozen visitors, gentlemen of doubtful reputation, drinking vodka and playing *stoss* with old cards. The night before there had been a fight, and I know that two of them had been for a long time engaged in dragging each other about by the hair. The landlady wanted to complain, but she was in abject terror of the captain. There was only one other lodger in the flat, a thin little regimental lady, on a visit to Petersburg, with three little children who had been taken ill since they came into the lodgings. Both she and her children were in mortal fear of the captain, and lay trembling and crossing themselves all night, and the youngest child had a sort of fit from fright. That captain, I know for a fact, sometimes stops people in the Nevsky Prospect and begs. They won't take him into the service, but strange to say (that's why I am telling this), all this month that the captain has been here his behaviour has caused me no annoyance. I have, of course, tried to avoid his acquaintance from the very beginning, and he, too, was bored with me from the first; but I never care how much they shout the other side of the partition nor how many of them there are in there: I sit up all night and forget them so completely that I do not even hear them. I stay awake till daybreak, and have been going on like that for the last year. I sit up all night in my arm-chair at the table, doing nothing. I only read by day. I sit—don't even think; ideas of a sort wander through my mind and I let them come and go as they will. A whole candle is burnt every night. I sat down quietly at the table, took out the revolver and put it down before me. When I had put it down I asked myself, I remember, "Is that so?" and answered with complete conviction, "It is." That is, I shall shoot myself. I knew that I should shoot myself that night for certain, but how much longer I should go on sitting at the table I did not know. And no doubt I should have shot myself if it had not been for that little girl.

II

You see, though nothing mattered to me, I could feel pain, for instance. If any one had struck me it would have hurt me. It was the same morally: if anything very pathetic happened, I should have felt pity just as I used to do in old days when there were things in life that did matter to me. I had felt pity that evening. I should have certainly helped a child. Why, then, had I not helped the little girl? Because of an idea that occurred to me at the time: when she was calling and pulling at me, a question suddenly arose before me and I could not settle it. The question was an idle one, but I was vexed. I was vexed at the reflection that if I were going to make an end of myself that night, nothing in life ought to have mattered to me. Why was it that all at once I did not feel that nothing mattered and was sorry for the little girl? I remember that I was very sorry for her, so much so that I felt a strange pang, quite incongruous in my position. Really I do not know better how to convey my fleeting sensation at the moment, but the sensation persisted at home when I was sitting at the table, and I was very much irritated as I had not been for a long time past. One reflection followed another. I saw clearly that so long as I was still a human being and not nothingness, I was alive and so could suffer, be angry and feel shame at my actions. So be it. But if I am going to kill myself, in two hours, say, what is the little girl to me and what have I to do with shame or with anything else in the world? I shall turn into nothing, absolutely nothing. And can it really be true that the consciousness that I shall *completely* cease to exist immediately and so everything else will cease to exist, does not in the least affect my feeling of pity for the child nor the feeling of shame after a contemptible action? I stamped and shouted at the unhappy child as though to say—not only I feel no pity, but even if I behave inhumanly and contemptibly, I am free to, for in another two hours everything will be extinguished. Do you believe that that

was why I shouted that? I am almost convinced of it now. It seemed clear to me that life and the world somehow depended upon me now. I may almost say that the world now seemed created for me alone: if I shot myself the world would cease to be at least for me. I say nothing of its being likely that nothing will exist for any one when I am gone, and that as soon as my consciousness is extinguished the whole world will vanish too and become void like a phantom, as a mere appurtenance of my consciousness, for possibly all this world and all these people are only me myself. I remember that as I sat and reflected, I turned all these new questions that swarmed one after another quite the other way, and thought of something quite new. For instance, a strange reflection suddenly occurred to me, that if I had lived before on the moon or on Mars and there had committed the most disgraceful and dishonourable action and had there been put to such shame and ignominy as one can only conceive and realise in dreams, in nightmares, and if, finding myself afterwards on earth, I were able to retain the memory of what I had done on the other planet and at the same time knew that I should never, under any circumstances, return there, then looking from the earth to the moon—*should I care or not?* Should I feel shame for that action or not? These were idle and superfluous questions for the revolver was already lying before me, and I knew in every fibre of my being that *it* would happen for certain, but they excited me and I raged. I could not die now without having first settled something. In short, the child had saved me, for I put off my pistol shot for the sake of these questions. Meanwhile the clamour had begun to subside in the captain's room: they had finished their game, were settling down to sleep, and meanwhile were grumbling and languidly winding up their quarrels. At that point I suddenly fell asleep in my chair at the table—a thing which had never happened to me before. I dropped asleep quite unawares.

Dreams, as we all know, are very queer things: some parts are presented with appalling vividness, with details worked up with the elaborate finish of jewellery, while others one gallops through, as it were, without noticing them at all as, for instance, through space and time. Dreams seem to be spurred on not by reason but by desire, not by the head but by the heart, and yet what complicated tricks my reason has played sometimes in dreams, what utterly incomprehensible things happen to it! My brother died five years ago, for instance. I sometimes dream of him; he takes part in my affairs, we are very much interested, and yet all through my dream I quite know and remember that my brother is dead and buried. How is it that I am not surprised that, though he is dead, he is here beside me and working with me? Why is it that my reason fully accepts it? But enough. I will begin about my dream. Yes, I dreamed a dream, my dream of the third of November. They tease me now, telling me it was only a dream. But does it matter whether it was a dream or reality, if the dream made known to me the truth? If once one has recognised the truth and seen it, you know that it is the truth and that there is no other and there cannot be, whether you are asleep or awake. Let it be a dream, so be it, but that real life of which you make so much I had meant to extinguish by suicide, and my dream, my dream—oh, it revealed to me a different life, renewed, grand and full of power!

Listen.

III

I have mentioned that I dropped asleep unawares and even seemed to be still reflecting on the same subjects. I suddenly dreamt that I picked up the revolver and aimed it straight at my heart—my heart, and not my head; and I had determined beforehand to fire at my head, at my right temple. After aiming at my chest I waited a second or two, and suddenly my candle, my table, and the wall in front of me began moving and heaving. I made haste to pull the trigger.

In dreams you sometimes fall from a height, or are stabbed, or are beaten, but you never feel pain unless, perhaps, you really bruise yourself against the bedstead, then you feel pain and almost always wake up from it. It was the same in my dream. I did not feel any pain, but it seemed as though with my shot everything within me was shaken and everything was suddenly dimmed, and it grew horribly black around me. I seemed to be blinded and benumbed, and I was lying on something hard, stretched on my back; I saw nothing, and could not make the slightest movement. People were walking and shouting around me, the captain bawled, the landlady shrieked—and suddenly another break and I was being carried in a closed coffin. And I felt how the coffin was shaking and reflected upon it, and for the first time the idea struck me that I was dead, utterly dead, I knew it and had no doubt of it, I could neither see nor move and yet I was feeling and reflecting. But I was soon reconciled to the position, and as one usually does in a dream, accepted the facts without disputing them.

And now I was buried in the earth. They all went away, I was left alone, utterly alone. I did not move. Whenever before I had imagined being buried the one sensation I associated with the grave was that of damp and cold. So now I felt that I was very cold, especially the tips of my toes, but I felt nothing else.

I lay still, strange to say I expected nothing, accepting without dispute that a dead man had nothing to expect. But it was damp. I don't know how long a time passed—whether an hour, or several days, or many days. But all at once a drop of water fell on my closed left eye, making its way through a coffin lid; it was followed a minute later by a second, then a minute later by a third—and so on, regularly every minute. There was a sudden glow of profound indignation in my heart, and I suddenly felt in it a pang of physical pain. "That's my wound," I thought; "that's the bullet. . . ." And drop after drop every minute kept falling on my closed eyelid. And all at once, not with my voice, but with my whole being, I called upon the power that was responsible for all that was happening to me:

"Whoever you may be, if you exist, and if anything more rational than what is happening here is possible, suffer it to be here now. But if you are revenging yourself upon me for my senseless suicide by the hideousness and absurdity of this subsequent existence, then let me tell you that no torture could ever equal the contempt which I shall go on dumbly feeling, though my martyrdom may last a million years!"

I made this appeal and held my peace. There was a full minute of unbroken silence and again another drop fell, but I knew with infinite unshakable certainty that everything would change immediately. And behold my grave suddenly was rent asunder, that is, I don't know whether it was opened or dug up, but I was caught up by some dark and unknown being and we found ourselves in space. I suddenly regained my sight. It was the dead of night, and never, never had there been such darkness. We were flying through space far away from the earth. I did not question the being who was taking me; I was proud and waited. I assured myself that I was not afraid, and was thrilled with ecstasy at the thought that I was not afraid. I do not know how long we were flying, I cannot imagine; it happened as it always does in dreams when you skip over space and time, and the laws of

thought and existence, and only pause upon the points for which the heart yearns. I remember that I suddenly saw in the darkness a star. "Is that Sirius?" I asked impulsively, though I had not meant to ask any questions.

"No, that is the star you saw between the clouds when you were coming home," the being who was carrying me replied.

I knew that it had something like a human face. Strange to say, I did not like that being, in fact I felt an intense aversion for it. I had expected complete nonexistence, and that was why I had put a bullet through my heart. And here I was in the hands of a creature not human, of course, but yet living, existing. "And so there is life beyond the grave," I thought with the strange frivolity one has in dreams. But in its inmost depth my heart remained unchanged. "And if I have got to exist again," I thought, "and live once more under the control of some irresistible power, I won't be vanquished and humiliated."

"You know that I am afraid of you and despise me for that," I said suddenly to my companion, unable to refrain from the humiliating question which implied a confession, and feeling my humiliation stab my heart as with a pin. He did not answer my question, but all at once I felt that he was not even despising me, but was laughing at me and had no compassion for me, and that our journey had an unknown and mysterious object that concerned me only. Fear was growing in my heart. Something was mutely and painfully communicated to me from my silent companion, and permeated my whole being. We were flying through dark, unknown space. I had for some time lost sight of the constellations familiar to my eyes. I knew that there were stars in the heavenly spaces the light of which took thousands or millions of years to reach the earth. Perhaps we were already flying through those spaces. I expected something with a terrible anguish that tortured my heart. And suddenly I was thrilled by a familiar feeling that stirred me to the depths: I suddenly caught sight of our sun! I knew that it could not be *our* sun, that gave life to *our* earth, and that we were an infinite distance from our sun, but for some reason I knew in my whole being that it was a sun exactly like ours, a duplicate of it. A sweet, thrilling feeling resounded with ecstasy in my heart: the kindred power of the same light which had given me light stirred an echo in my heart and awakened it, and I had a sensation of life, the old life of the past for the first time since I had been in the grave.

"But if that is the sun, if that is exactly the same as our sun," I cried, "where is the earth?"

And my companion pointed to a star twinkling in the distance with an emerald light. We were flying straight towards it.

"And are such repetitions possible in the universe? Can that be the law of Nature? . . . And if that is an earth there, can it be just the same earth as ours . . . just the same, as poor, as unhappy, but precious and beloved for ever, arousing in the most ungrateful of her children the same poignant love for her that we feel for our earth?" I cried out, shaken by irresistible, ecstatic love for the old familiar earth which I had left. The image of the poor child whom I had repulsed flashed through my mind.

"You shall see it all," answered my companion, and there was a note of sorrow in his voice.

But we were rapidly approaching the planet. It was growing before my eyes; I could already distinguish the ocean, the outline of Europe; and suddenly a feeling of a great and holy jealousy glowed in my heart.

"How can it be repeated and what for? I love and can love only that earth which I have left, stained with my blood, when, in my ingratitude, I quenched my life with a bullet in my heart. But I have never, never ceased to love that earth, and perhaps on the very night I parted from it I loved it more than ever. Is there suffering upon this new earth? On our earth we can only love with suffering and through suffering. We cannot love otherwise, and we know of no other sort of love. I want suffering in order to love. I long, I thirst, this very instant, to kiss with tears the earth that I have left, and I don't want, I won't accept life on any other!"

But my companion had already left me. I suddenly, quite without noticing how, found myself on this other earth, in the bright light of a sunny day, fair as paradise. I believe I was standing on one of the islands that make up on our globe the Greek archipelago, or on the coast of the mainland facing that archipelago. Oh, everything was exactly as it is with us, only everything seemed to have a festive radiance, the splendour of some great, holy triumph attained at last. The caressing sea, green as emerald, splashed softly upon the shore and kissed it with manifest, almost conscious love. The tall, lovely trees stood in all the glory of their blossom, and their innumerable leaves greeted me, I am certain, with their soft, caressing rustle and seemed to articulate words of love. The grass glowed with bright and fragrant flowers. Birds were flying in flocks in the air, and perched fearlessly on my shoulders and arms and joyfully struck me with their darling, fluttering wings. And at last I saw and knew the people of this happy land. They came to me of themselves, they surrounded me, kissed me. The children of the sun, the children of their sun—oh, how beautiful they were! Never had I seen on our own earth such beauty in mankind. Only perhaps in our children, in their earliest years, one might find some remote, faint reflection of this beauty. The eyes of these happy people shone with a clear brightness. Their faces were radiant with the light of reason and fulness of a serenity that comes of perfect understanding, but those faces were gay; in their words and voices there was a note of childlike joy. Oh, from the first moment, from the first glance at them, I understood it all! It was the earth untarnished by the Fall; on it lived people who had not sinned. They lived just in such a paradise as that in which, according to all the legends of mankind, our first parents lived before they sinned; the only difference was that all this earth was the same paradise. These people, laughing joyfully, thronged round me and caressed me; they took me home with them, and each of them tried to reassure me. Oh, they asked me no questions, but they seemed, I fancied, to know everything without asking, and they wanted to make haste and smooth away the signs of suffering from my face.

IV

And do you know what? Well, granted that it was only a dream, yet the sensation of the love of those innocent and beautiful people has remained with me for ever, and I feel as though their love is still flowing out to me from over there. I have seen them myself, have known them and been convinced; I loved them, I suffered for them afterwards. Oh, I understood at once even at the time that in many things I could not understand them at all; as an up-to-date Russian progressive and contemptible Petersburger, it struck me as inexplicable that, knowing so much, they had, for instance, no science like ours. But I soon realised that their knowledge was gained and fostered by intuitions different from those of us on earth, and that their aspirations, too, were quite different. They desired nothing and

were at peace; they did not aspire to knowledge of life as we aspire to understand it, because their lives were full. But their knowledge was higher and deeper than ours; for our science seeks to explain what life is, aspires to understand it in order to teach others how to live, while they without science knew how to live; and that I understood, but I could not understand their knowledge. They showed me their trees, and I could not understand the intense love with which they looked at them; it was as though they were talking with creatures like themselves. And perhaps I shall not be mistaken if I say that they conversed with them. Yes, they had found their language, and I am convinced that the trees understood them. They looked at all Nature like that—at the animals who lived in peace with them and did not attack them, but loved them, conquered by their love. They pointed to the stars and told me something about them which I could not understand, but I am convinced that they were somehow in touch with the stars, not only in thought, but by some living channel. Oh, these people did not persist in trying to make me understand them, they loved me without that, but I knew that they would never understand me, and so I hardly spoke to them about our earth. I only kissed in their presence the earth on which they lived and mutely worshipped them themselves. And they saw that and let me worship them without being abashed at my adoration, for they themselves loved much. They were not unhappy on my account when at times I kissed their feet with tears, joyfully conscious of the love with which they would respond to mine. At times I asked myself with wonder how it was they were able never to offend a creature like me, and never once to arouse a feeling of jealousy or envy in me? Often I wondered how it could be that, boastful and untruthful as I was, I never talked to them of what I knew—of which, of course, they had no notion—that I was never tempted to do so by a desire to astonish or even to benefit them.

They were as gay and sportive as children. They wandered about their lovely woods and copses, they sang their lovely songs; their fare was light—the fruits of their trees, the honey from their woods, and the milk of the animals who loved them. The work they did for food and raiment was brief and not laborious. They loved and begot children, but I never noticed in them the impulse of that *cruel* sensuality which overcomes almost every man on this earth, all and each, and is the source of almost every sin of mankind on earth. They rejoiced at the arrival of children as new beings to share their happiness. There was no quarrelling, no jealousy among them, and they did not even know what the words meant. Their children were the children of all, for they all made up one family. There was scarcely any illness among them, though there was death; but their old people died peacefully, as though falling alseep, giving blessings and smiles to those who surrounded them to take their last farewell with bright and loving smiles. I never saw grief or tears on those occasions, but only love, which reached the point of ecstasy, but a calm ecstasy, made perfect and contemplative. One might think that they were still in contact with the departed after death, and that their earthly union was not cut short by death. They scarcely understood me when I questioned them about immortality, but evidently they were so convinced of it without reasoning that it was not for them a question at all. They had no temples, but they had a real living and uninterrupted sense of oneness with the whole of the universe; they had no creed, but they had a certain knowledge that when their earthly joy had reached the limits of earthly nature, then

there would come for them, for the living and for the dead, a still greater fulness of contact with the whole of the universe. They looked forward to that moment with joy, but without haste, not pining for it, but seeming to have a foretaste of it in their hearts, of which they talked to one another.

In the evening before going to sleep they liked singing in musical and harmonious chorus. In those songs they expressed all the sensations that the parting day had given them, sang its glories and took leave of it. They sang the praises of nature, of the sea, of the woods. They liked making songs about one another, and praised each other like children; they were the simplest songs, but they sprang from their hearts and went to one's heart. And not only in their songs but in all their lives they seemed to do nothing but admire one another. It was like being in love with each other, but an all-embracing, universal feeling.

Some of their songs, solemn and rapturous, I scarcely understood at all. Though I understood the words I could never fathom their full significance. It remained, as it were, beyond the grasp of my mind, yet my heart unconsciously absorbed it more and more. I often told them that I had had a presentiment of it long before, that this joy and glory had come to me on our earth in the form of a yearning melancholy that at times approached insufferable sorrow; that I had had a foreknowledge of them all and of their glory in the dreams of my heart and the visions of my mind; that often on our earth I could not look at the setting sun without tears . . . that in my hatred for the men of our earth there was always a yearning anguish: why could I not hate them without loving them? why could I not help forgiving them? and in my love for them there was a yearning grief: why could I not love them without hating them? They listened to me, and I saw they could not conceive what I was saying, but I did not regret that I had spoken to them of it: I knew that they understood the intensity of my yearning anguish over those whom I had left. But when they looked at me with their sweet eyes full of love, when I felt that in their presence my heart, too, became as innocent and just as theirs, the feeling of the fulness of life took my breath away, and I worshipped them in silence.

Oh, every one laughs in my face now, and assures me that one cannot dream of such details as I am telling now, that I only dreamed or felt one sensation that arose in my heart in delirium and made up the details myself when I woke up. And when I told them that perhaps it really was so, my God, how they shouted with laughter in my face, and what mirth I caused! Oh, yes, of course I was overcome by the mere sensation of my dream, and that was all that was preserved in my cruelly wounded heart; but the actual forms and images of my dreams, that is, the very ones I really saw at the very time of my dream, were filled with such harmony, were so lovely and enchanting and were so actual, that on awakening I was, of course, incapable of clothing them in our poor language, so that they were bound to become blurred in my mind; and so perhaps I really was forced afterwards to make up the details, and so of course to distort them in my passionate desire to convey at least some of them as quickly as I could. But on the other hand, how can I help believing that it was all true? It was perhaps a thousand times brighter, happier and more joyful than I describe it. Granted that I dreamed it, yet it must have been real. You know, I will tell you a secret: perhaps it was not a dream at all! For then something happened so awful, something so horribly true, that it could not have been imagined in a dream. My heart may have originated the dream, but would my heart alone have been capable of originating the awful event which happened to me afterwards? How could I alone have invented it or imagined it in my dream? Could my petty heart and my fickle, trivial mind have risen to such a revelation of truth? Oh, judge for yourselves: hitherto I have concealed it, but now I will tell the truth. The fact is that I . . . corrupted them all!

V

Yes, yes it ended in my corrupting them all! How it could come to pass I do not know, but I remember it clearly. The dream embraced thousands of years and left in me only a sense of the whole. I only know that I was the cause of their sin and downfall. Like a vile trichina, like a germ of the plague infecting whole kingdoms, so I contaminated all this earth, so happy and sinless before my coming. They learnt to lie, grew fond of lying, and discovered the charm of falsehood. Oh, at first perhaps it began innocently, with a jest, coquetry, with amorous play, perhaps indeed with a germ, but that germ of falsity made its way into their hearts and pleased them. Then sensuality was soon begotten, sensuality begot jealousy, jealousy—cruelty. . . . Oh, I don't know, I don't remember; but soon, very soon the first blood was shed. They marvelled and were horrified, and began to be split up and divided. They formed into unions, but it was against one another. Reproaches, upbraidings, followed. They came to know shame, and shame brought them to virtue. The conception of honour sprang up, and every union began waving its flags. They began torturing animals, and the animals withdrew from them into the forests and became hostile to them. They began to struggle for separation, for isolation, for individuality, for mine and thine. They began to talk in different languages. They became acquainted with sorrow and loved sorrow; they thirsted for suffering, and said that truth could only be attained through suffering. Then science appeared. As they became wicked they began talking of brotherhood and humanitarianism, and understood those ideas. As they became criminal, they invented justice and drew up whole legal codes in order to observe it, and to ensure their being kept, set up a guillotine. They hardly remembered what they had lost, in fact refused to believe that they had ever been happy and innocent. They even laughed at the possibility of this happiness in the past, and called it a dream. They could not even imagine it in definite form and shape, but, strange and wonderful to relate, though they lost all faith in their past happiness and called it a legend, they so longed to be happy and innocent once more that they succumbed to this desire like children, made an idol of it, set up temples and worshipped their own idea, their own desire; though at the same time they fully believed that it was unattainable and could not be realised, yet they bowed down to it and adored it with tears! Nevertheless, if it could have happened that they had returned to the innocent and happy condition which they had lost, and if some one had shown it to them again and had asked them whether they wanted to go back to it, they would certainly have refused. They answered me:

"We may be deceitful, wicked and unjust, we *know* it and weep over it, we grieve over it; we torment and punish ourselves more perhaps than that merciful Judge Who will judge us and whose Name we know not. But we have science, and by means of it we shall find the truth and we shall arrive at it consciously. Knowledge is higher than feeling, the consciousness of life is higher than life. Science will give us wisdom, wisdom will reveal the laws, and the knowledge of the laws of happiness is higher than happiness."

That is what they said, and after saying such things every one began to love himself better than any one else, and indeed they could not do otherwise. All became so jealous of the rights of their own personality that they did their very utmost to curtail and destroy them in others, and made that the chief thing in their lives. Slavery followed, even voluntary slavery; the weak eagerly submitted to the strong, on condition that the latter aided them to subdue the still weaker. Then there were saints who came to these people, weeping, and talked to them of their pride, of their loss of harmony and due proportion, of their loss of shame. They were laughed at or pelted with stones. Holy blood was shed on the threshold of the temples. Then there arose men who began to think how to bring all people together again, so that everybody, while still loving himself best of all, might not interfere with others, and all might live together in something like a harmonious society. Regular wars sprang up over this idea. All the combatants at the same time firmly believed that science, wisdom and the instinct of self-preservation would force men at last to unite into a harmonious and rational society; and so, meanwhile, to hasten matters, "the wise" endeavoured to exterminate as rapidly as possible all who were "not wise" and did not understand their idea, that the latter might not hinder its triumph. But the instinct of self-preservation grew rapidly weaker; there arose men, haughty and sensual, who demanded all or nothing. In order to obtain everything they resorted to crime, and if they did not succeed—to suicide. There arose religions with a cult of non-existence and self-destruction for the sake of the everlasting peace of annihilation. At last these people grew weary of their meaningless toil, and signs of suffering came into their faces, and then they proclaimed that suffering was a beauty, for in suffering alone was there meaning. They glorified suffering in their songs. I moved about among them, wringing my hands and weeping over them, but I loved them perhaps more than in old days when there was no suffering in their faces and when they were innocent and so lovely. I loved the earth they had polluted even more than when it had been a paradise, if only because sorrow had come to it. Alas! I always loved sorrow and tribulation, but only for myself, for myself; but I wept over them, pitying them. I stretched out my hands to them in despair, blaming, cursing and despising myself. I told them that all this was my doing, mine alone; that it was I had brought them corruption, contamination and falsity. I besought them to crucify me, I taught them how to make a cross. I could not kill myself, I had not the strength, but I wanted to suffer at their hands. I yearned for suffering, I longed that my blood should be drained to the last drop in these agonies. But they only laughed at me, and began at last to look upon me as crazy. They justified me, they declared that they had only got what they wanted themselves, and that all that now was could not have been otherwise. At last they declared to me that I was becoming dangerous and that they should lock me up in a madhouse if I did not hold my tongue. Then such grief took possession of my soul that my heart was wrung, and I felt as though I were dying; and then . . . then I awoke.

It was morning, that is, it was not yet daylight, but about six o'clock. I woke up in the same arm-chair; my candle had burnt out; every one was asleep in the captain's room, and there was a stillness all round, rare in our flat. First of all I leapt up in great amazement: nothing like this had ever happened to me before, not even in the most trivial detail; I had never, for instance, fallen asleep like this in my arm-chair. While I was standing and coming to myself I suddenly caught sight of my revolver lying loaded, ready—but instantly I thrust it away! Oh, now, life, life! I lifted up my hands and called upon eternal truth, not with words but with tears; ecstasy, immeasurable ecstasy flooded my soul. Yes, life and spreading the good tidings! Oh, I at that moment resolved to spread the tidings, and resolved it, of course, for my whole life. I go to spread the tidings, I want to spread the tidings—of what? Of the truth, for I have seen it, have seen it with my own eyes, have seen it in all its glory.

And since then I have been preaching! Moreover I love all those who laugh at me more than any of the rest. Why that is so I do not know and cannot explain, but so be it. I am told that I am vague and confused, and if I am vague and confused now, what shall I be later on? It is true indeed: I am vague and confused, and perhaps as time goes on I shall be more so. And of course I shall make many blunders before I find out how to preach, that is, find out what words to say, what things to do, for it is a very difficult task. I see all that as clear as daylight, but, listen, who does not make mistakes? And yet, you know, all are making for the same goal, all are striving in the same direction anyway, from the sage to the lowest robber, only by different roads. It is an old truth, but this is what is new: I cannot go far wrong. For I have seen the truth; I have seen and I know that people can be beautiful and happy without losing the power of living on earth. I will not and cannot believe that evil is the normal condition of mankind. And it is just this faith of mine that they laugh at. But how can I help believing it? I have seen the truth—it is not as though I had invented it with my mind, I have seen it, seen it, and *the living image* of it has filled my soul for ever. I have seen it in such full perfection that I cannot believe that it is impossible for people to have it. And so how can I go wrong? I shall make some slips no doubt, and shall perhaps talk in second-hand language, but not for long: the living image of what I saw will always be with me and will always correct and guide me. Oh, I am full of courage and freshness, and I will go on and on if it were for a thousand years! Do you know, at first I meant to conceal the fact that I corrupted them, but that was a mistake—that was my first mistake! But truth whispered to me that I was *lying,* and preserved me and corrected me. But how establish paradise—I don't know, because I do not know how to put it into words. After my dream I lost command of words. All the chief words, anyway, the most necessary ones. But never mind, I shall go and I shall keep talking, I won't leave off, for anyway I have seen it with my own eyes, though I cannot describe what I saw. But the scoffers do not understand that. It was a dream, they say, delirium, hallucination. Oh! As though that meant so much! And they are so proud! A dream! What is a dream? And is not our life a dream? I will say more. Suppose that this paradise will never come to pass (that I understand), yet I shall go on preaching it. And yet how simple it is: in one day, *in one hour* everything could be arranged at once! The chief thing is to love others like yourself, that's the great thing, and that's everything; nothing else is wanted—you will find out at once how to arrange it all. And yet it's an old truth which has been told and retold a billion times—but it has not formed part of our lives! The consciousness of life is higher than life, the knowledge of the laws of happiness is higher than happiness—that is what one must contend against. And I shall. If only every one wants it, it can all be arranged at once.

And I tracked out that little girl . . . and I shall go on and on!

Translated by *Constance Garnett*

MR. ARCULARIS

Conrad Aiken
(1889–   )

Mr. Arcularis stood at the window of his room in the hospital and looked down at the street. There had been a light shower, which had patterned the sidewalks with large drops, but now again the sun was out, blue sky was showing here and there between the swift white clouds, a cold wind was blowing the poplar trees. An itinerant band had stopped before the building and was playing, with violin, harp, and flute, the finale of "Cavalleria Rusticana." Leaning against the window-sill—for he felt extraordinarily weak after his operation— Mr. Arcularis suddenly, listening to the wretched music, felt like crying. He rested the palm of one hand against a cold window-pane and stared down at the old man who was blowing the flute, and blinked his eyes. It seemed absurd that he should be so weak, so emotional, so like a child—and especially now that everything was over at last. In spite of all their predictions, in spite, too, of his own dreadful certainty that he was going to die, here he was, as fit as a fiddle—but what a fiddle it was, so out of tune!— with a long life before him. And to begin with, a voyage to England ordered by the doctor. What could be more delightful? Why should he feel sad about it and want to cry like a baby? In a few minutes Harry would arrive with his car to take him to the wharf; in an hour he would be on the sea, in two hours he would see the sunset behind him, where Boston had been, and his new life would be opening before him. It was many years since he had been abroad. June, the best of the year to come—England, France, the Rhine—how ridiculous that he should already be homesick!

There was a light footstep outside the door, a knock, the door opened, and Harry came in.

"Well, old man, I've come to get you. The old bus actually got here. Are you ready? Here, let me take your arm. You're tottering like an octogenarian!"

Mr. Arcularis submitted gratefully, laughing, and they made the journey slowly along the bleak corridor and down the stairs to the entrance hall. Miss Hoyle, his nurse, was there, and the Matron, and the charming little assistant with freckles who had helped to prepare him for the operation. Miss Hoyle put out her hand.

"Goodbye, Mr. Arcularis," she said, "and *bon voyage*."

"Goodbye, Miss Hoyle, and thank you for everything. You were very kind to me. And I fear I was a nuisance."

The girl with the freckless, too, gave him her hand, smiling. She was very pretty, and it would have been easy to fall in love with her. She reminded him of someone. Who was it? He tried in vain to remember while he said goodbye to her and turned to the Matron.

"And not too many latitudes with the young ladies, Mr. Arcularis!" she was saying.

Mr. Arcularis was pleased, flattered, by all this attention to a middle-aged invalid, and felt a joke taking shape in his mind, and no sooner in his mind than on his tongue.

"Oh, no latitudes," he said, laughing. "I'll leave the latitudes to the ship!"

"Oh, come now," said the Matron, "we don't seem to have hurt him much, do we?"

"I think we'll have to operate on him again and *really* cure him," said Miss Hoyle.

He was going down the front steps, between the potted palmettos, and they all laughed and waved. The wind was cold, very cold for June, and he was glad he had put on his coat. He shivered.

"Damned cold for June!" he said. "Why should it be so cold?"

"East wind," Harry said, arranging the rug over his knees. "Sorry it's an open car, but I believe in fresh air and all that sort of thing. I'll drive slowly. We've got plenty of time."

They coasted gently down the long hill toward Beacon Street, but the road was badly surfaced, and despite Harry's care Mr. Arcularis felt his pain again. He found that he could alleviate it a little by leaning to the right, against the arm-rest, and not breathing too deeply. But how glorious to be out again! How strange and vivid the world looked! The trees had innumerable green fresh leaves—they were all blowing and shifting and turning and flashing in the wind; drops of rainwater fell downward sparkling; the robins were singing their absurd, delicious little four-noted songs; even the street cars looked unusually bright and beautiful, just as they used to look when he was a child and had wanted above all things to be a motorman. He found himself smiling foolishly at everything, foolishly and weakly, and wanted to say something about it to Harry. It was no use, though—he had no strength, and the mere finding of words would be almost more than he could manage. And even if he should succeed in saying it, he would then most likely burst into tears. He shook his head slowly from side to side.

"Ain't it grand?" he said.

"I'll bet it looks good," said Harry.

"Words fail me."

"You wait till you get out to sea. You'll have a swell time."

"Oh, swell! . . . I hope not. I hope it'll be calm."

"Tut tut."

When they passed the Harvard Club Mr. Arcularis made a slow and somewhat painful effort to turn in his seat and look at it. It might be the last chance to see it for a long time. Why this sentimental longing to stare at it, though? There it was, with the great flag blowing in the wind, the Harvard seal now concealed by the swift folds and now revealed, and there were the windows in the library, where he had spent so many delightful hours reading—Plato, and Kipling, and the Lord knows what—and the balconies from which for so many years he had watched the Marathon. Old Talbot might be in there now, sleeping with a book on his knee, hoping forlornly to be interrupted by anyone, for anything.

"Goodbye to the old club," he said.

"The bar will miss you," said Harry, smiling with friendly irony and looking straight ahead.

"But let there be no moaning," said Mr. Arcularis.

"What's *that* a quotation from?"

" 'The Odyssey.' "

In spite of the cold, he was glad of the wind on his face, for it helped to dissipate the feeling of vagueness and dizziness that came over him in a sickening wave from time to time. All of a sudden everything would begin to swim and dissolve, the houses would lean their heads together, he had to close his eyes, and there would be a curious and dreadful humming noise, which at regular intervals rose to a crescendo and then drawlingly subsided again. It was disconcerting. Perhaps he still had a trace of fever. When he got on the ship he would have a glass of whisky. . . . From one of these spells he opened his eyes and found that they were on the ferry, crossing to East Boston. It must have been the ferry's engines that he had heard. From another spell he woke to find himself on the wharf, the car at a standstill beside a pile of yellow packing cases.

"We're here because we're here because we're here," said Harry.

"Because we're here," added Mr. Arcularis.

He dozed in the car while Harry—and what a good friend Harry was!—attended to all the details. He went and came with tickets and passports and baggage checks and porters. And at last he unwrapped Mr. Arcularis from the rugs and led him up the steep gangplank to the deck, and thence by devious windings to a small cold stateroom with a solitary porthole like the eye of a cyclops.

"Here you are," he said, "and now I've got to go. Did you hear the whistle?"

"No."

"Well, you're half asleep. It's sounded the all-ashore. Goodbye, old fellow, and take care of yourself. Bring me back a spray of edelweiss. And send me a picture postcard from the Absolute."

"Will you have it finite or infinite?"

"Oh, infinite. But with your signature on it. Now you'd better turn in for a while and have a nap. Cheerio!"

Mr. Arcularis took his hand and pressed it hard, and once more felt like crying. Absurd! Had he become a child again?

"Goodbye," he said.

He sat down in the little wicker chair, with his overcoat still on, closed his eyes, and listened to the humming of the air in the ventilator. Hurried footsteps ran up and down the corridor. The chair was not too comfortable, and his pain began to bother him again, so he moved, with his coat still on, to the narrow berth and fell asleep. When he woke up, it was dark, and the porthole had been partly opened. He groped for the switch and turned on the light. Then he rang for the steward.

"It's cold in here," he said. "Would you mind closing the port?"

The girl who sat opposite him at dinner was charming. Who was it she reminded him of? Why, of course, the girl at the hospital, the girl with the freckles. Her hair was beautiful, not quite red, not quite gold, nor had it been bobbed; arranged with a sort of graceful untidiness, it made him think of a Melozzo da Forli angel. Her face was freckled, she had a mouth which was both humorous and voluptuous. And she seemed to be alone.

He frowned at the bill of fare and ordered the thick soup.

"No hors d'oeuvres?" asked the steward.

"I think not," said Mr. Arcularis. "They might kill me."

The steward permitted himself to be amused and deposited the menu card on the table against the water bottle. His eyebrows were lifted. As he moved away, the girl followed him with her eyes and smiled.

"I'm afraid you shocked him," she said.

"Impossible," said Mr. Arcularis. "These stewards, they're dead souls. How could they be stewards otherwise? And they think they've seen and known everything. They suffer terribly from the *déjà vu*. Personally, I don't blame them."

"It must be a dreadful sort of life."

"It's because they're dead that they accept it."

"Do you think so?"

"I'm sure of it. I'm enough of a dead soul myself to know the signs!"

"Well, I don't know what you mean by that!"

"But nothing mysterious! I'm just out of hospital, after an operation. I was given up for dead. For six months I had given *myself* up for dead. If you've ever been seriously ill you know the feeling. You have a posthumous feeling—a mild, cynical tolerance for everything and everyone. What is there you haven't seen or done or understood? Nothing."

Mr. Arcularis waved his hands and smiled.

"I wish I could understand you," said the girl, "but I've never been ill in my life."

"Never?"

"Never."

"Good God!"

The torrent of the unexpressed and inexpressible paralyzed him and rendered him speechless. He stared at the girl, wondering who she was and then, realizing that he had perhaps stared too fixedly, averted his gaze, gave a little laugh, rolled a pill of bread between his fingers. After a second or two he allowed himself to look at her again and found her smiling.

"Never pay any attention to invalids," he said, "or they'll drag you to the hospital."

She examined him critically, with her head tilted a little to one side, but with friendliness.

"You don't *look* like an invalid," she said.

Mr. Arcularis thought her charming. His pain ceased to bother him, the disagreeable humming disappeared, or rather, it was dissociated from himself and became merely, as it should be, the sound of the ship's engines, and he began to think the voyage was going to be really delightful. The parson on his right passed him the salt.

"I fear you will need this in your soup," he said.

"Thank you. Is it as bad as that?"

The steward, overhearing, was immediately apologetic and solicitous. He explained that on the first day everything was at sixes and sevens. The girl looked up at him and asked him a question.

"Do you think we'll have a good voyage?" she said.

He was passing the hot rolls to the parson, removing the napkins from them with a deprecatory finger.

"Well, madam, I don't like to be a Jeremiah, but—"

"Oh, come," said the parson, "I hope we have no Jeremiahs."

"What do you mean?" said the girl.

Mr. Arcularis ate his soup with gusto —it was nice and hot.

"Well, maybe I shouldn't say it, but there's a corpse on board, going to Ireland; and I never yet knew a voyage with a corpse on board that we didn't have bad weather."

"Why, steward, you're just superstitious! What nonsense!"

"That's a very ancient superstition," said Mr. Arcularis. "I've heard it many times. Maybe it's true. Maybe we'll be wrecked. And what does it matter, after all?" He was very bland.

"Then let's be wrecked," said the parson coldly.

Nevertheless, Mr. Arcularis felt a shudder go through him on hearing the steward's remark. A corpse in the hold—a coffin? Perhaps it was true. Perhaps some disaster would befall them. There might be fogs. There might be icebergs. He thought of all the wrecks of which he had read. There was the *Titanic,* which he had read about in the warm newspaper room at the Harvard Club—it had seemed dreadfully real, even there. That band, playing "Nearer My God to Thee" on the afterdeck while the ship sank! It was one of the darkest of his memories. And the *Empress of Ireland*—all those poor people trapped in the smoking room, with only one door between them and life, and that door locked for the night by the deck steward, and the deck steward nowhere to be found! He shivered, feeling a draft, and turned to the parson.

"How do these strange delusions arise?" he said.

The parson looked at him searchingly, appraisingly—from chin to forehead, from forehead to chin—and Mr. Arcularis, feeling uncomfortable, straightened his tie.

"From nothing but fear," said the parson. "Nothing on earth but fear."

"How strange!" said the girl.

Mr. Arcularis again looked at her—she had lowered her face—and again tried to think of whom she reminded him. It wasn't only the little freckle-faced girl at the hospital—both of them had reminded him of someone else. Someone far back in his life: remote, beautiful, lovely. But he couldn't think. The meal came to an end, they all rose, the ship's orchestra played a feeble foxtrot, and Mr. Arcularis, once more alone, went to the bar to have his whisky. The room was stuffy, and the ship's engines were both audible and palpable. The humming and throbbing oppressed him, the rhythm seemed to be the rhythm of his own pain, and after a short time he found his way, with slow steps, holding on to the walls in his moments of weakness and dizziness, to his forlorn and white little room. The port had been—thank God!—closed for he night; it was cold enough anyway. The white and blue ribbons fluttered from the ventilator, the bottle and glasses clicked and clucked as the ship swayed gently to the long, slow motion of the sea. It was all very peculiar—it was all like something he had experienced somewhere before. What was it? Where was it? . . . He untied his tie, looking at his face in the glass, and wondered, and from time to time put his hand to his side to hold in the pain. It wasn't at Portsmouth, in his childhood, nor at Salem, nor in the rose garden at his Aunt Julia's nor in the schoolroom at

Cambridge. It was something very queer, very intimate, very precious. The jack-stones, the Sunday-school cards which he had loved when he was a child. . . . He fell asleep.

The sense of time was already hope-lessly confused. One hour was like an-other, the sea looked always the same, morning was indistinguishable from after-noon—and was it Tuesday or Wednesday? Mr. Arcularis was sitting in the smoking room, in his favorite corner, watching the parson teach Miss Dean to play chess. On the deck outside he could see the people passing and repassing in their restless round of the ship. The red jacket went by, then the black hat with the white feather, then the purple scarf, the brown tweed coat, the Bulgarian mustache, the monocle, the Scotch cap with fluttering ribbons, and in no time at all the red jacket again, dipping past the windows with its own peculiar rhythm, followed once more by the black hat and the purple scarf. How odd to reflect on the fixed little orbits of these things—as definite and profound, perhaps, as the orbits of the stars, and as important to God or the Absolute. There was a kind of tyranny in this fixedness, too—to think of it too much made one uncomfortable. He closed his eyes for a moment, to avoid seeing for the fortieth time the Bulgarian mustache and the pursuing monocle. The parson was explaining the movements of knights. Two forward and one to the side. Eight pos-sible moves, always to the opposite color from that on which the piece stands. Two forward and one to the side: Miss Dean repeated the words several times with reflective emphasis. Here, too, was the terrifying fixed curve of the infinite, the creeping curve of logic which at last must become the final signpost at the edge of nothing. After that—the deluge. The great white light of annihilation. The bright flash of death. . . . Was it merely the sea which made these abstractions so insistent, so intrusive? The mere notion of *orbit* had somehow become extraor-dinarily naked; and to rid himself of the discomfort and also to forget a little the pain which bothered his side whenever he sat down, he walked slowly and care-fully into the writing room, and exam-ined a pile of superannuated magazines and catalogues of travel. The bright colors amused him, the photographs of remote islands and mountains, savages in sampans or sarongs or both—it was all very far off and delightful, like something in a dream or a fever. But he found that he was too tired to read and was incapable of concentration. Dreams! Yes, that re-minded him. That rather alarming busi-ness—sleep-walking!

Later in the evening—at what hour he didn't know—he was telling Miss Dean about it, as he had intended to do. They were sitting in deck chairs on the sheltered side. The sea was black, and there was a cold wind. He wished they had chosen to sit in the lounge.

Miss Dean was extremely pretty—no, beautiful. She looked at him, too, in a very strange and lovely way, with some-thing of inquiry, something of sympathy, something of affection. It seemed as if, between the question and the answer, they had sat thus for a very long time, ex-changing an unspoken secret, simply look-ing at each other quietly and kindly. Had an hour or two passed? And was it at all necessary to speak?

"No," she said, "I never have."

She breathed into the low words a note of interrogation and gave him a slow smile.

"That's the funny part of it. I never had either until last night. Never in my life. I hardly ever even dream. And it really rather frightens me."

"Tell me about it, Mr. Arcularis."

"I dreamed at first that I was walking, alone, in a wide plain covered with snow.

It was growing dark, I was very cold, my feet were frozen and numb, and I was lost. I came then to a signpost—at first it seemed to me there was nothing on it. Nothing but ice. Just before it grew finally dark, however, I made out on it the one word 'Polaris.' "

"The Pole Star."

"Yes—and you see, I didn't myself know that. I looked it up only this morning. I suppose I must have seen it somewhere? And of course it rhymes with my name."

"Why, so it does!"

"Anyway, it gave me—in the dream—an awful feeling of despair, and the dream changed. This time, I dreamed I was standing *outside* my stateroom in the little dark corridor, or *cul-de-sac,* and trying to find the door-handle to let myself in. I was in my pajamas, and again I was very cold. And at this point I woke up. . . . The extraordinary thing is that's exactly where I was!"

"Good heavens. How strange!"

"Yes. And now the question is, *Where had I been?* I was frightened, when I came to—not unnaturally. For among other things I *did* have, quite definitely, the feeling that I *had been* somewhere. Somewhere it was very cold. It doesn't sound very proper. Suppose I had been seen!"

"That might have been awkward," said Miss Dean.

"Awkward! It might indeed. It's very singular. I've never done such a thing before. It's this sort of thing that reminds one—rather wholesomely, perhaps, don't you think?"—and Mr. Arcularis gave a nervous little laugh—"how extraordinarily little we know about the workings of our own minds or souls. After all, what *do* we know?"

"Nothing—nothing—nothing—nothing," said Miss Dean slowly.

"*Absolutely* nothing."

Their voices had dropped, and again they were silent; and again they looked at each other gently and sympathetically, as if for the exchange of something unspoken and perhaps unspeakable. Time ceased. The orbit—so it seemed to Mr. Arcularis—once more became pure, became absolute. And once more he found himself wondering who it was that Miss Dean—Clarice Dean—reminded him of. Long ago and far away. Like those pictures of the islands and mountains. The little freckle-faced girl at the hospital was merely, as it were, the stepping stone, the signpost, or, as in algebra, the "equals" sign. But what was it they both "equaled"? The jackstones came again into his mind and his Aunt Julia's rose garden—at sunset; but this was ridiculous. It couldn't be simply that they reminded him of his childhood! And yet why not?

They went into the lounge. The ship's orchestra, in the oval-shaped balcony among faded palms, was playing the finale of "Cavalleria Rusticana," playing it badly.

"Good God!" said Mr. Arcularis, "can't I ever escape from that damned sentimental tune? It's the last thing I heard in America, and the last thing I *want* to hear."

"But don't you like it?"

"As music? No! It moves me too much, but in the wrong way."

"What, exactly, do you mean?"

"Exactly? Nothing. When I heard it at the hospital—when was it?—it made me feel like crying. Three old Italians tootling it in the rain. I suppose, like most people, I'm afraid of my feelings."

"Are they so dangerous?"

"Now then, young woman! Are you pulling my leg?"

The stewards had rolled away the carpets, and the passengers were beginning to dance. Miss Dean accepted the invitation of a young officer, and Mr. Arcularis watched them with envy. Odd, that last exchange of remarks—very odd; in fact, everything was odd. Was it possible that they were falling in love? Was that what it was all about—all these concealed references and recollections? He had read of such things. But at his age! And with a girl of twenty-two! It was ridiculous.

After an amused look at his old friend Polaris from the open door on the sheltered side, he went to bed.

The rhythm of the ship's engines was positively a persecution. It gave one no rest, it followed one like the Hound of Heaven, it drove on, out into space and across the Milky Way and then back home by way of Betelgeuse. It was cold there, too. Mr. Arcularis, making the round trip by way of Betelgeuse and Polaris, sparkled with frost. He felt like a Christmas tree. Icicles on his fingers and icicles on his toes. He tinkled and spangled in the void, hallooed to the waste echoes, rounded the buoy on the verge of the Unknown, and tacked glitteringly homeward. The wind whistled. He was barefooted. Snowflakes and tinsel blew past him. Next time, by George, he would go farther still—for altogether it was rather a lark. Forward into the untrodden! as somebody said. Some intrepid explorer of his own backyard, probably, some middle-aged professor with an umbrella: those were the fellows for courage! But give us time, thought Mr. Arcularis, give us time, and we will bring back with us the night-rime of the Obsolute. Or was it Absolete? If only there weren't this perpetual throbbing, this iteration of sound, like a pain, these circles and repetitions of light—the feeling as of everything coiling inward to a center of misery. . . .

Suddenly it was dark, and he was lost. He was groping, he touched the cold, white, slippery woodwork with his fingernails, looking for an electric switch. The throbbing, of course, was the throbbing of the ship. But he was almost home—almost home. Another corner to round, a door to be opened, and there he would

be. Safe and sound. Safe in his father's home.

It was at this point that he woke up: in the corridor that led to the dining saloon. Such pure terror, such horror, seized him as he had never known. His heart felt as if it would stop beating. His back was toward the dining saloon; apparently he had just come from it. He was in his pajamas. The corridor was dim, all but two lights having been turned out for the night, and—thank God!—deserted. Not a soul, not a sound. He was perhaps fifty yards from his room. With luck he could get to it unseen. Holding tremulously to the rail that ran along the wall, a brown, greasy rail, he began to creep his way forward. He felt very weak, very dizzy, and his thoughts refused to concentrate. Vaguely he remembered Miss Dean—Clarice—and the freckled girl, as if they were one and the same person. But he wasn't in the hospital, he was on the ship. Of course. How absurd. The Great Circle. Here we are, old fellow . . . steady round the corner . . . hold hard to your umbrella. . . .

In his room, with the door safely shut behind him, Mr. Arcularis broke into a cold sweat. He had no sooner got into his bunk, shivering, than he heard the night watchman pass.

"But where"—he thought, closing his eyes in agony—"have I been? . . ."

A dreadful idea had occurred to him.

"It's nothing serious—how could it be anything serious? Of course, it's nothing serious," said Mr. Arcularis.

"No, it's nothing serious," said the ship's doctor urbanely.

"I knew you'd think so. But just the same—"

"Such a condition is the result of worry," said the doctor. "Are you worried—do you mind telling me—about something? Just try to think."

"Worried?"

Mr. Arcularis knitted his brows. *Was there something?* Some little mosquito of a cloud disappearing into the southwest, the northeast? Some little gnat-song of despair? But no, that was all over. All over.

"Nothing," he said, "nothing whatever."

"It's very strange," said the doctor.

"Strange! I should say so. I've come to sea for a rest, not for a nightmare! What about a bromide?"

"Well, I can give you a bromide, Mr. Arcularis—"

"Then, please, if you don't mind, give me a bromide."

He carried the little phial hopefully to his stateroom, and took a dose at once. He could see the sun through his porthole. It looked northern and pale and small, like a little peppermint, which was only natural enough, for the latitude was changing with every hour. But why was it that doctors were all alike? And all, for that matter, like his father, or that other fellow at the hospital? Smythe, his name was. Doctor Smythe. A nice, dry little fellow, and they said he was a writer. Wrote poetry, or something like that. Poor fellow—disappointed. Like everybody else. Crouched in there, in his cabin, night after night, writing blank verse or something—all about the stars and flowers and love and death; ice and the sea and the infinite; time and tide—well, every man to his own taste.

"But it's nothing serious," said Mr. Arcularis, later, to the parson. "How could it be?"

"Why, of course not, my dear fellow," said the parson, patting his back. "How could it be?"

"I know it isn't and yet I worry about it."

"It would be ridiculous to think it serious," said the parson. Mr. Arcularis shivered; it was colder than ever. It was said that they were near icebergs. For a few hours in the morning there had been a fog, and the siren had blown—devastatingly—at three-minute intervals. Icebergs cause fog—he knew that.

"These things always come," said the parson, "from a sense of guilt. You feel guilty about something. I won't be so rude as to inquire what it is. But if you could rid yourself of the sense of guilt—"

And later still, when the sky was pink:

"But is it anything to worry about?" said Miss Dean. "Really?"

"No, I suppose not."

"Then don't worry. We aren't children any longer!"

"Aren't we? I wonder!"

They leaned, shoulders touching, on the deck-rail, and looked at the sea, which was multitudinously incarnadined. Mr. Arcularis scanned the horizon in vain for an iceberg.

"Anyway," he said, "the colder we are the less we feel!"

"I hope that's no reflection on *you*," said Miss Dean.

"Here . . . feel my hand," said Mr. Arcularis.

"Heaven knows, it's cold!"

"It's been to Polaris and back! No wonder."

"Poor thing, poor thing!"

"Warm it."

"May I?"

"You can."

"I'll try."

Laughing, she took his hand between both of hers, one palm under and one palm over, and began rubbing it briskly. The decks were deserted, no one was near them, everyone was dressing for dinner. The sea grew darker, the wind blew colder.

"I wish I could remember who you are," he said.

"And you—who are you?"

"Myself."

"Then perhaps *I* am yourself."

"Don't be metaphysical!"

"But I *am* metaphysical!"

She laughed, withdrew, pulled the light coat about her shoulders.

The bugle blew the summons for dinner—"The Roast Beef of Old England"—and they walked together along the darkening deck toward the door, from which a shaft of soft light fell across the deck-rail. As they stepped over the brass door-sill Mr. Arcularis felt the throb of the engines again; he put his hand quickly to his side.

"Auf wiedersehen," he said. *"Tomorrow and tomorrow and tomorrow."*

Mr. Arcularis was finding it impossible, absolutely impossible, to keep warm. A cold fog surrounded the ship, had done so, it seemed, for days. The sun had all but disappeared, the transition from day to night was almost unnoticeable. The ship, too, seemed scarcely to be moving—it was as if anchored among walls of ice and rime. Monstrous that, merely because it was June, and supposed, therefore, to be warm, the ship's authorities should consider it unnecessary to turn on the heat! By day, he wore his heavy coat and sat shivering in the corner of the smoking room. His teeth chattered, his hands were blue. By night, he heaped blankets on his bed, closed the porthole's black eye against the sea, and drew the yellow curtains across it, but in vain. Somehow, despite everything, the fog crept in, and the icy fingers touched his throat. The steward, questioned about it, merely said, "Icebergs." Of course—any fool knew that. But how long, in God's name, was it going to last? They surely ought to be past the Grand Banks by this time! And surely it wasn't necessary to sail to England by way of Greenland and Iceland!

Miss Dean—Clarice—was sympathetic.

"It's simply because," she said, "your vitality has been lowered by your illness. You can't expect to be your normal self so soon after an operation! When *was* your operation, by the way?"

Mr. Arcularis considered. Strange—he couldn't be quite sure. It was all a little vague—his sense of time had disappeared.

"Heavens knows!" he said. "Centuries ago. When I was a tadpole and you were a fish. I should think it must have been at about the time of the Battle of Teutoburg Forest. Or perhaps when I was a Neanderthal man with a club!"

"Are you sure it wasn't farther back still?"

What did she mean by that?

"Not at all. Obviously, we've been on this damned ship for ages—for eras—for æons. And even on this ship, you must remember, I've had plenty of time, in my nocturnal wanderings, to go several times to Orion and back. I'm thinking, by the way, of going farther still. There's a nice little star off to the left, as you round Betelgeuse, which looks as if it might be right at the edge. The last outpost of the finite. I think I'll have a look at it and bring you back a frozen rime-feather."

"It would melt when you got it back."

"Oh, no, it wouldn't—not on *this* ship!"

Clarice laughed.

"I wish I could go with you," she said.

"If only you would! If only—"

He broke off his sentence and looked hard at her—how lovely she was, and how desirable! No such woman had ever before come into his life; there had been no one with whom he had at once felt so profound a sympathy and understanding. It was a miracle, simply—a miracle. No need to put his arm around her or to kiss her—delightful as such small vulgarities would be. He had only to look at her, and to feel, gazing into those extraordinary eyes, that she knew him, had always known him. It was as if, indeed, she might be his own soul.

But as he looked thus at her, reflecting, he noticed that she was frowning.

"What is it?" he said.

She shook her head, slowly.

"I don't know."

"Tell me."

"Nothing. It just occurred to me that perhaps you weren't looking quite so well."

Mr. Arcularis was startled. He straightened himself up.

"What nonsense! Of course, this pain bothers me—and I feel astonishingly weak—"

"It's more than that—much more than that. Something is worrying you horribly." She paused, and then with an air of challenging him, added, "Tell me, did you—"

Her eyes were suddenly asking him blazingly the question he had been afraid of. He flinched, caught his breath, looked away. But it was no use, as he knew; he would have to tell her. He had known all along that he would have to tell her.

"Clarice," he said—and his voice broke in spite of his effort to control it—"it's killing me, it's ghastly! Yes, I did."

His eyes filled with tears, he saw that her own had done so also. She put her hand on his arm.

"I knew," she said. "I knew. But tell me."

"It's happened twice again—*twice*— and each time I was farther away. The same dream of going round a star, the same terrible coldness and helplessness. That awful whistling curve. . . ." He shuddered.

"And when you woke up"—she spoke quietly—"where were you when you woke up? Don't be afraid!"

"The first time I was at the farther end of the dining saloon. I had my hand on the door that leads into the pantry."

"I see. Yes. And the next time?"

Mr. Arcularis wanted to close his eyes in terror—he felt as if he were going mad. His lips moved before he could speak, and when at last he did speak it was in a voice so low as to be almost a whisper.

"I was at the bottom of the stairway that leads down from the pantry to the hold, past the refrigerating plant. It was dark, and I was crawling on my hands and knees . . . *crawling on my hands and knees!* . . ."

"Oh!" she said, and again, "Oh!"

He began to tremble violently; he felt the hand on his arm trembling also. And then he watched a look of unmistakable horror come slowly into Clarice's eyes, and a look of understanding, as if she saw. . . . She tightened her hold on his arm.

"Do you think. . . ." she whispered.

They stared at each other.

"I know," he said. "And so do you. . . . Twice more—three times—and I'll be looking down into an empty. . . ."

It was then that they first embraced— then, at the edge of the infinite, at the last signpost of the finite. They clung together desperately, forlornly, weeping as they kissed each other, staring hard one moment and closing their eyes the next. Passionately, passionately, she kissed him, as if she were indeed trying to give him her warmth, her life.

"But what nonsense!" she cried, leaning back, and holding his face between her hands, her hands which were wet with his tears. "What nonsense! It can't be!"

"It is," said Mr. Arcularis slowly.

"But how do you know? . . . How do you know where the—"

For the first time Mr. Arcularis smiled. "Don't be afraid, darling—you mean the coffin?"

"How could you know where it is?"

"I don't need to," said Mr. Arcularis. . . . "I'm already almost there."

Before they separated for the night, in the smoking room, they had several whisky cocktails.

"We must make it gay!" Mr. Arcularis said. "Above all, we must make it gay. Perhaps even now it will turn out to be nothing but a nightmare from which both of us will wake! And even at the worst, at my present rate of travel, I ought to need two more nights! It's a long way, still, to that little star."

The parson passed them at the door.

"What! turning in so soon?" he said. "I was hoping for a game of chess."

"Yes, both turning in. But tomorrow?"

"Tomorrow, then, Miss Dean! And good night!"

"Good night."

They walked once round the deck, then leaned on the railing and stared into the fog. It was thicker and whiter than ever. The ship was moving barely perceptibly, the rhythm of the engines was slower, more subdued and remote, and at regular intervals, mournfully, came the long reverberating cry of the foghorn. The sea was calm, and lapped only very tenderly against the side of the ship, the sound coming up to them clearly, however, because of the profound stillness.

" 'On such a night as this—' " quoted Mr. Arcularis grimly.

" 'On such a night as this—' "

Their voices hung suspended in the night, time ceased for them, for an eternal instant they were happy. When at last they parted it was by tacit agreement on a note of the ridiculous.

"Be a good boy and take your bromide!" she said.

"Yes, mother, I'll take my medicine!"

In his stateroom, he mixed himself a strong potion of bromide, a very strong one, and got into bed. He would have no trouble in falling asleep; he felt more tired, more supremely exhausted, than he had ever been in his life; nor had bed ever seemed so delicious. And that long, magnificent, delirious swoop of dizziness . . . the Great Circle . . . the swift pathway to Arcturus. . . .

It was all as before, but infinitely more rapid. Never had Mr. Arcularis achieved such phenomenal, such supernatural, speed. In no time at all he was beyond the moon, shot past the North Star as if it were standing still (which perhaps it was?), swooped in a long, bright curve round the Pleiades, shouted his frosty greetings to Betelgeuse, and was off to the little blue star which pointed the way to the Unknown. Forward into the untrodden! Courage, old man, and hold on to your umbrella! Have you got your garters on? Mind your hat! In no time at all we'll be back to Clarice with the frozen rime-feather, the time-feather, the snowflake of the Absolute, the Obsolete. If only we don't wake . . . if only we needn't wake . . . if only we don't wake in that—in that—time and space . . . somewhere or nowhere . . . cold and dark . . . "Cavalleria Rusticana" sobbing among the palms; if a lonely . . . if only . . . the coffers of the poor—not coffers, not coffers, not coffers, Oh, God, not coffers, but light, delight, supreme white and brightness, whirling lightness above all —and freezing—freezing—freezing. . . .

At this point in the void the surgeon's last effort to save Mr. Arcularis's life had failed. He stood back from the operating table and made a tired gesture with a rubber-gloved hand.

"It's all over," he said. "As I expected."

He looked at Miss Hoyle, whose gaze was downward, at the basin she held. There was a moment's stillness, a pause, a brief flight of unexchanged comment, and then the ordered life of the hospital was resumed.

IN DREAMS BEGIN RESPONSIBILITIES

Delmore Schwartz
(1913–1966)

I

I think it is the year 1909. I feel as if I were in a moving-picture theater, the long arm of light crossing the darkness and spinning, my eyes fixed upon the screen. It is a silent picture, as if an old Biograph one, in which the actors are dressed in ridiculously old-fashioned clothes, and one flash succeeds another with sudden jumps, and the actors, too, seem to jump about, walking too fast. The shots are full of rays and dots, as if it had been raining when the picture was photographed. The light is bad.

It is Sunday afternoon, June 12th, 1909, and my father is walking down the quiet streets of Brooklyn on his way to visit my mother. His clothes are newly pressed, and his tie is too tight in his high collar. He jingles the coins in his pocket, thinking of the witty things he will say. I feel as if I had by now relaxed entirely in the soft darkness of the theater; the organist peals out the obvious approximate emotions on which the audience rocks unknowingly. I am anonymous. I have forgotten myself: it is always so when one goes to a movie, it is, as they say, a drug.

My father walks from street to street of trees, lawns and houses, once in a while coming to an avenue on which a streetcar skates and yaws, progressing slowly. The motorman, who has a handle-bar mustache, helps a young lady wearing a hat like a feathered bowl onto the car. He leisurely makes change and rings his bell as the passengers mount the car. It is obviously Sunday, for everyone is wearing Sunday clothes and the streetcar's noises emphasize the quiet of the holiday. (Brooklyn is said to be the city of churches). The shops are closed and their shades drawn but for an occasional stationery store or drugstore with great green balls in the window.

My father has chosen to take this long walk because he likes to walk and think. He thinks about himself in the future and so arrives at the place he is to visit in a mild state of exaltation. He pays no attention to the houses he is passing, in which the Sunday dinner is being eaten, nor to the many trees which line each street, now coming to their full green and the time when they will enclose the whole street in leafy shadow. An occasional carriage passes, the horses' hooves falling like stones in the quiet afternoon, and once in a while an automobile, looking like an enormous upholstered sofa, puffs and passes.

My father thinks of my mother, of how lady-like she is, and of the pride which will be his when he introduces her to his family. They are not yet engaged and he is not yet sure that he loves my mother, so that, once in a while, he becomes panicky about the bond already established. But then he reassures himself by thinking of the big men he admires who are married: William Randolph Hearst and William Howard Taft, who has just become the President of the United States.

My father arrives at my mother's house. He has come too early and so is suddenly embarrassed. My aunt, my mother's younger sister, answers the loud bell with her napkin in her hand, for the family is still at dinner. As my father enters, my grandfather rises from the table and shakes hands with him. My mother has run upstairs to tidy herself. My grandmother asks my father if he has had dinner and tells him that my mother will be down soon. My grandfather opens the conversation by remarking about the mild June weather. My father sits uncomfortably near the table, holding his hat in his hand. My grandmother tells my aunt to take my father's hat. My uncle, twelve years old, runs into the house, his hair tousled. He shouts a greeting to my father, who has often given him nickels, and then runs upstairs, as my grandmother shouts after him. It is evident that the respect in which my father is held in this house is tempered by a good deal of mirth. He is impressive, but also very awkward.

II

Finally my mother comes downstairs and my father, being at the moment engaged in conversation with my grandfather, is made uneasy by her entrance, for he does not know whether to greet my mother or to continue the conversation. He gets up from his chair clumsily and says "Hello" gruffly. My grandfather watches this, examining their congruence, such as it is, with a critical eye, and meanwhile rubbing his bearded cheek roughly, as he always does when he reasons. He is worried; he is afraid that my father will not make a good husband for his oldest daughter. At this point something happens to the film, just as my father says something funny to my mother: I am awakened to myself and my unhappiness just as my interest has become most intense. The audience begins to clap impatiently. Then the trouble is attended to, but the film has been returned to a portion just shown, and once more I see my grandfather rubbing his bearded cheek, pondering my father's character. It is difficult to get back into the picture once more and forget myself, but as my mother giggles at my father's words, the darkness drowns me.

My father and mother depart from the house, my father shaking hands with my grandfather once more, out of some unknown uneasiness. I stir uneasily also, slouched in the hard chair of the theater. Where is the older uncle, my mother's older brother? He is studying in his bedroom upstairs, studying for his final examinations at the College of the City of New York, having been dead of double pneumonia for the last twenty-one years. My mother and father walk down the same quiet streets once more. My mother is holding my father's arm and telling him of the novel she has been reading and my father utters judgments of the characters as the plot is made clear to him. This is a habit which he very much enjoys, for he feels the utmost superiority and confidence when he is approving or condemning the behavior of other people. At times he feels moved to utter a brief "Ugh," whenever the story becomes what he would call sugary. This tribute is the assertion of his manliness. My mother feels satisfied by the interest she has awakened; and she is showing my father how intelligent she is and how interesting.

They reach the avenue, and the streetcar leisurely arrives. They are going to Coney Island this afternoon, although my mother really considers such pleasures inferior. She has made up her mind to indulge only in a walk on the boardwalk and a pleasant dinner, avoiding the riotous amusements as being beneath the dignity of so dignified a couple.

My father tells my mother how much money he has made in the week just past, exaggerating an amount which need not have been exaggerated. But my father has always felt that actualities somehow fall short, no matter how fine they are. Suddenly I begin to weep. The determined old lady who sits next to me in the theater is annoyed and looks at me with an angry face, and being intimidated, I stop. I drag out my handkerchief and dry my face, licking the drop which has fallen near my lips. Meanwhile I have missed something, for here are my father and mother alighting from the streetcar at the last stop, Coney Island.

III

They walk toward the boardwalk and my mother commands my father to inhale the pungent air from the sea. They both breathe in deeply, both of them laughing as they do. They have in common a great interest in health, although my father is strong and husky, and my mother is frail. They are both full of theories about what is good to eat and not good to eat, and sometimes have heated discussions about it, the whole matter ending in my father's announcement, made with a scornful bluster, that you have to die sooner or later anyway. On the boardwalk's flagpole, the American flag is pulsing in an intermittent wind from the sea.

My father and mother go to the rail of the boardwalk and look down on the beach where a good many bathers are casually walking about. A few are in the surf. A peanut whistle pierces the air with its pleasant and active whine, and my father goes to buy peanuts. My mother remains at the rail and stares at the ocean. The ocean seems merry to her; it pointedly sparkles and again and again the pony waves are released. She notices the children digging in the wet sand, and the bathing costumes of the girls who are her own age. My father returns with the peanuts. Overhead the sun's lightning strikes and strikes, but neither of them are at all aware of it. The boardwalk is full of people dressed in their Sunday clothes and casually strolling. The tide does not reach as far as the boardwalk, and the strollers would feel no danger if it did. My father and mother lean on the rail of the boardwalk and absently stare at the ocean. The ocean is becoming rough; the waves come in slowly, tugging strength from far back. The moment before they somersault, the moment when they arch their backs so beautifully, showing white veins in the green and black, that moment is intolerable. They finally crack, dashing fiercely upon the sand, actually driving, full force downward, against it, bouncing upward and forward, and at last petering out into a small stream of bubbles which slides up the beach and then is recalled. The sun overhead does not disturb my father and my mother. They gaze idly at the ocean scarcely interested in its harshness. But I stare at the terrible sun which breaks up sight, and the fatal merciless passionate ocean. I forget my parents. I stare fasci-

nated, and finally, shocked by their indifference, I burst out weeping once more. The old lady next to me pats my shoulder and says: "There, there, young man, all of this is only a movie, only a movie," but I look up once more at the terrifying sun and the terrifying ocean, and being unable to control my tears I get up and go to the men's room, stumbling over the feet of the other people seated in my row.

IV

When I return, feeling as if I had just awakened in the morning sick for lack of sleep, several hours have apparently passed and my parents are riding on the merry-go-round. My father is on a black horse, my mother on a white one, and they seem to be making an eternal circuit for the single purpose of snatching the nickel rings which are attached to an arm of one of the posts. A hand-organ is playing; it is inseparable from the ceaseless circling of the merry-go-round.

For a moment it seems that they will never get off the carousel, for it will never stop, and I feel as if I were looking down from the fiftieth story of a building. But at length they do get off; even the hand-organ has ceased for a moment. There is a sudden and sweet stillness, as if the achievement of so much motion. My mother has acquired only two rings, my father, however, ten of them, although it was my mother who really wanted them.

They walk on along the boardwalk as the afternoon descends by imperceptible degrees into the incredible violet of dusk. Everything fades into a relaxed glow, even the ceaseless murmuring from the beach. They look for a place to have dinner. My father suggests the best restaurant on the boardwalk and my mother demurs, according to her principles of economy and housewifeliness.

However they do go to the best place, asking for a table near the window so that they can look out upon the board-walk and the mobile ocean. My father feels omnipotent as he places a quarter in the waiter's hand in asking for a table. The place is crowded and here too there is music, this time from a kind of string trio. My father orders with a fine confidence.

As their dinner goes on, my father tells of his plans for the future and my mother shows with expressive face how interested she is, and how impressed. My father becomes exultant, lifted up by the waltz that is being played and his own future begins to intoxicate him. My father tells my mother that he is going to expand his business, for there is a great deal of money to be made. He wants to settle down. After all, he is twenty-nine, he has lived by himself since his thirteenth year, he is making more and more money, and he is envious of his friends when he visits them in the security of their homes, surrounded, it seems, by the calm domestic pleasures, and by delightful children, and then as the waltz reaches the moment when the dancers all swing madly, then, then with awful daring, then he asks my mother to marry him, although awkwardly enough and puzzled as to how he had arrived at the question, and she, to make the whole business worse, begins to cry, and my father looks nervously about, not knowing at all what to do now, and my mother says: "It's all I've wanted from the first moment I saw you," sobbing, and he finds all of this very difficult, scarcely to his taste, scarcely as he thought it would be, on his long walks over Brooklyn Bridge in the revery of a fine cigar, and it was then, at that point, that I stood up in the theater and shouted: "Don't do it! It's not too late to change your minds, both of you. Nothing good will come of it, only remorse, hatred, scandal, and two children whose characters are monstrous." The whole audience turned to look at me, annoyed, the usher came hurrying down the aisle flashing his searchlight, and the old lady next to me tugged me down into my seat, saying: "Be quiet. You'll be put out, and you paid thirty-five cents to come in." And so I shut my eyes because I could not bear to see what was happening. I sat there quietly.

V

But after a while I begin to take brief glimpses and at length I watch again with thirsty interest, like a child who tries to maintain his sulk when he is offered a bribe of candy. My parents are now having their picture taken in a photographer's booth along the boardwalk. The place is shadowed in the mauve light which is apparently necessary. The camera is set to the side on its tripod and looks like a Martian man. The photographer is instructing my parents in how to pose. My father has his arm over my mother's shoulder, and both of them smile emphatically. The photographer brings my mother a bouquet of flowers to hold in her hand, but she holds it at the wrong angle. Then the photographer covers himself with the black cloth which drapes the camera and all that one sees of him is one protruding arm and his hand with which he holds tightly to the rubber ball which he squeezes when the picture is taken. But he is not satisfied with their appearance. He feels that somehow there is something wrong in their pose. Again and again he comes out from his hiding place with new directions. Each suggestion merely makes matters worse. My father is becoming impatient. They try a seated pose. The photographer explains that he has his pride, he wants to make beautiful pictures, he is not merely interested in all of this for the money. My father says: "Hurry up, will you? We haven't got all night." But the photographer only scurries about apologetically, issuing new directions. The photographer charms me, and I approve of him with all my heart, for I know exactly how he feels, and as he criticizes each revised pose according to some obscure idea of rightness, I become quite hopeful. But then my father says angrily: "Come on, you've had enough time, we're not going to wait any longer." And the photographer, sighing unhappily, goes back into the black covering, and holds out his hand, saying: "One, two, three, Now!" and the picture is taken, with my father's smile turned to a grimace and my mother's bright and false. It takes a few minutes for the picture to be developed and as my parents sit in the curious light they become depressed.

VI

They have passed a fortune-teller's booth and my mother wishes to go in, but my father does not. They begin to argue about it. My mother becomes stubborn, my father once more impatient. What my father would like to do now is walk off and leave my mother there, but he knows that that would never do. My mother refuses to budge. She is near tears, but she feels an uncontrollable desire to hear what the palm-reader will say. My father consents angrily and they both go into the booth which is, in a way, like the photographer's, since it is draped in black cloth and its light is colored and shadowed. The place is too warm, and my father keeps saying that this is all nonsense, pointing to the crystal ball on the table. The fortune-teller, a short, fat woman garbed in robes supposedly exotic, comes into the room and greets them, speaking with an accent,

but suddenly my father feels that the whole thing is intolerable; he tugs at my mother's arm but my mother refuses to budge. And then, in terrible anger, my father lets go of my mother's arm and strides out, leaving my mother stunned. She makes a movement as if to go after him, but the fortune-teller holds her and begs her not to do so, and I in my seat in the darkness am shocked and horrified. I feel as if I were walking a tight-rope one hundred feet over a circus audience and suddenly the rope is showing signs of breaking, and I get up from my seat and begin to shout once more the first words I can think of to communicate my terrible fear, and once more the usher comes hurrying down the aisle flashing his searchlight, and the old lady pleads with me, and the shocked audience has turned to stare at me, and I keep shouting: "What are they doing? Don't they know what they are doing? Why doesn't my mother go after my father and beg him not to be angry? If she does not do that, what will she do? Doesn't my father know what he is doing?" But the usher has seized my arm, and is dragging me away, and as he does so, he says: "What are *you* doing? Don't you know you can't do things like this, you can't do whatever you want to do, even if other people aren't about? You will be sorry if you do not do what you should do. You can't carry on like this, it is not right, you will find that out soon enough, everything you do matters too much," and as he said that, dragging me through the lobby of the theater, into the cold light, I woke up into the bleak winter morning of my twenty-first birthday, the window-sill shining with its lip of snow, and the morning already begun.

POEMS

"CLARENCE'S DREAM" *

William Shakespeare
(1564–1616)

(From *Richard III, Act 1, Scene* 4)

[*The Tower*]

Enter Clarence and Keeper.†

Keep. Why looks your Grace so
heavily to-day?
Clar. O, I have pass'd a miserable
night,
So full of fearful dreams, of ugly sights,
That, as I am a Christian faithful man,
I would not spend another such a night, 5
Though 'twere to buy a world of happy
days,
So full of dismal terror was the time.
Keep. What was your dream, my
lord? I pray you, tell me.
Clar. Methoughts that I had broken
from the Tower,
And was embark'd to cross to Bur-
gundy; 10
And in my company my brother Glouces-
ter,
Who from my cabin tempted me to walk

Upon the hatches: there we look'd toward
England,
And cited up a thousand heavy times,
During the wars of York and Lan-
caster, 15
That had befall'n us. As we pac'd along
Upon the giddy footing of the hatches,
Methought that Gloucester stumbled; and,
in falling,
Struck me, that thought to stay him, over-
board,
Into the tumbling billows of the main. 20
O Lord, methought what pain it was to
drown:
What dreadful noise of water in mine
ears!
What sights of ugly death within mine
eyes!
Methoughts I saw a thousand fearful
wracks;
A thousand men that fishes gnaw'd
upon; 25
Wedges of gold, great anchors, heaps of
pearl,
Inestimable stones, unvalu'd jewels,
All scatter'd in the bottom of the sea.
Some lay in dead men's skulls; and in
those holes
Where eyes did once inhabit, there were
crept, 30
As 'twere in scorn of eyes, reflecting gems,
That woo'd the slimy bottom of the deep,
And mock'd the dead bones that lay scat-
ter'd by.
Keep. Had you such leisure in the
time of death

* In this scene, Clarence, the brother of
Richard III, has a foreboding dream just before
being murdered by order of his brother.
† Keeper of the Tower of London where
Clarence is held prisoner.
10. *Burgundy:* the Netherlands, which Clarence thinks of as a haven.

To gaze upon these secrets of the
deep?   35
 Clar. Methought I had; and often did
I strive
To yield the ghost; but still the envious
flood
Stopt in my soul, and would not let it
forth
To find the empty, vast, and wandering
air;
But smother'd it within my panting
bulk,   40
Who almost burst to belch it in the
sea.
 Keep. Awak'd you not in this sore
agony?
 Clar. No, no, my dream was length-
en'd after life;
O! then began the tempest to my soul.
I pass'd, methought, the melancholy
flood,   45
With that sour ferryman which poets write
of,
Unto the kingdom of perpetual night.
The first that there did greet my stranger
soul
Was my great father-in-law, renowned
Warwick;
Who spake aloud, 'What scourge for per-
jury   50
Can this dark monarchy afford false Clar-
ence?'
And so he vanish'd: then came wand'ring
by
A shadow like an angel, with bright
hair
Dabbled in blood; and he shriek'd out
aloud,
'Clarence is come,—false, fleeting, per-
jur'd Clarence,   55
That stabb'd me in the field by Tewkes-
bury;—

Seize on him, Furies; take him unto tor-
ment!'
With that, methought, a legion of foul
fiends
Environ'd me, and howled in mine ears
Such hideous cries, that with the very
noise   60
I trembling wak'd, and for a season after
Could not believe but that I was in hell,
Such terrible impression made my dream.
 Keep. No marvel, lord, though it
affrighted you;
I am afraid, methinks, to hear you tell
it.   65
 Clar. Ah Keeper, Keeper! I have done
these things,
That now give evidence against my soul,
For Edward's sake; and see how he re-
quites me.
O God! if my deep prayers cannot ap-
pease thee,
But thou wilt be aveng'd on my mis-
deeds,   70
Yet execute thy wrath on me alone:
O, spare my guiltless wife and my poor
children!
Keeper, I prithee sit by me a while;
My soul is heavy, and I fain would sleep.
 Keep. I will, my lord. God give your
Grace good rest!
      [*Clarence sleeps.*] 75

KUBLA KHAN; OR, A VISION IN A DREAM *

Samuel Taylor Coleridge
(1770–1834)

 In Xanadu did Kubla Khan
 A stately pleasure-dome decree:
 Where Alph, the sacred river, ran

---

45. *melancholy flood:* the river Styx, across
which Charon ferried souls to Hades.
55–56. *'Clarence is come . . . by Tewkes-
bury . . .':* This is the ghost of Edward, Prince
of Wales, son of Henry VI. Cf. *3 Henry VI*,
V, v.
55. *fleeting:* deceitful.

* In an introduction to this poem Coleridge
maintained that it was a "fragment" drawn from
a vision induced by an "anodyne" (probably
opium).
1. *Kubla Khan:* the grandson of Genghis
Khan, who founded the Mongol dynasty in
China.

Through caverns measureless to man
Down to a sunless sea   5
So twice five miles of fertile ground
With walls and towers were girdled round:
And here were gardens bright with sinuous rills,
Where blossomed many an incense-bearing tree;
And here were forests ancient as the hills,   10
Enfolding sunny spots of greenery.
But oh! that deep romantic chasm which slanted
Down the green hill athwart a cedarn cover!
A savage place! as holy and enchanted
As e'er beneath a waning moon was haunted   15
By woman wailing for her demon-lover!
And from this chasm, with ceaseless turmoil seething,
As if this earth in fast thick pants were breathing
A mighty fountain momently was forced;
Amid whose swift half-intermitted burst   20
Huge fragments vaulted like rebounding hail,
Or chaffy grain beneath the thresher's flail:
And 'mid these dancing rocks at once and ever
It flung up momently the sacred river.
Five miles meandering with a mazy motion   25
Through wood and dale the sacred river ran,
Then reached the caverns measureless to man,
And sank in tumult to a lifeless ocean:
And 'mid this tumult Kubla heard from far
Ancestral voices prophesying war!   30

The shadow of the dome of pleasure
Floated midway on the waves;
Where was heard the mingled measure
From the fountain and the caves.

It was a miracle of rare device,   35
A sunny pleasure-dome with caves of ice!
  A damsel with a dulcimer
  In a vision once I saw:
  It was an Abyssinian maid,
  And on her dulcimer she played,   40
  Singing of Mount Abora.
  Could I revive within me,
  Her symphony and song,
  To such a deep delight 'twould win me,
That with music loud and long,   45
I would build that dome in air,
That sunny dome! those caves of ice!
And all who heard should see them there,
And all should cry, Beware! Beware!
His flashing eyes, his floating hair!   50
Weave a circle round him thrice,
And close your eyes with holy dread,
For he on honey-dew hath fed,
And drunk the milk of Paradise.

DARKNESS

George Gordon, Lord Byron
(1788–1824)

I had a dream, which was not all a dream.
The bright sun was extinguished, and the stars
Did wander darkling in the eternal space,
Rayless, and pathless, and the icy Earth
Swung blind and blackening in the moonless air;   5
Morn came and went—and came, and brought no day,
And men forgot their passions in the dread
Of this their desolation; and all hearts
Were chilled into a selfish prayer for light:
And they did live by watchfires—and the thrones,   10
The palaces of crownèd kings—the huts,
The habitations of all things which dwell,
Were burnt for beacons; cities were consumed,

And men were gathered round their blaz-
ing homes
To look once more into each other's
face;   15
Happy were those who dwelt within the
eye
Of the volcanoes, and their mountain-
torch:
A fearful hope was all the World con-
tained;
Forests were set on fire—but hour by
hour
They fell and faded—and the crackling
trunks   20
Extinguished with a crash—and all was
black.
The brows of men by the despairing
light
Wore an unearthly aspect, as by fits
The flashes fell upon them; some lay
down
And hid their eyes and wept; and some
did rest   25
Their chins upon their clenchèd hands,
and smiled;
And others hurried to and fro, and fed
Their funeral piles with fuel, and looked
up
With mad disquietude on the dull sky,
The pall of a past World; and then
again   30
With curses cast them down upon the
dust,
And gnashed their teeth and howled: the
wild birds shrieked,
And, terrified, did flutter on the ground
And flap their useless wings; the wildest
brutes
Came tame and tremulous; and vipers
crawled   35
And twined themselves among the multi-
tude,
Hissing, but stingless—they were slain for
food:
And War, which for a moment was no
more,
Did glut himself again:—a meal was
bought

With blood, and each sate sullenly apart 40
Gorging himself in gloom: no Love was
left;
All earth was but one thought—and that
was Death,
Immediate and inglorious; and the pang
Of famine fed upon all entrails—men
Died, and their bones were tombless as
their flesh;   45
The meagre by the meagre were devoured,
Even dogs assailed their masters, all save
one,
And he was faithful to a corse, and kept
The birds and beasts and famished men
at bay,
Till hunger clung them, or the dropping
dead   50
Lured their lank jaws; himself sought out
no food,
But with a piteous and perpetual moan,
And a quick desolate cry, licking the
hand
Which answered not with a caress—he
died.
The crowd was famished by degrees, but
two   55
Of an enormous city did survive,
And they were enemies: they met beside
The dying embers of an altar-place
Where had been heaped a mass of holy
things
For an unholy usage; they raked up,   60
And shivering scraped with their cold
skeleton hands
The feeble ashes, and their feeble breath
Blew for a little life, and made a flame
Which was a mockery; then they lifted up
Their eyes as it grew lighter, and be-
held   65
Each other's aspects—saw, and shrieked,
and died—
Even of their mutual hideousness they
died,
Unknowing who he was upon whose brow
Famine had written Fiend. The World
was void,
The populous and the powerful was a
lump,   70

Seasonless, herbless, treeless, manless, life-
less—
A lump of death—a chaos of hard clay.
The rivers, lakes, and ocean all stood still,
And nothing stirred within their silent
depths;
Ships sailorless lay rotting on the sea, 75
And their masts fell down piecemeal: as
they dropped
They slept on the abyss without a surge—
The waves were dead; the tides were in
their grave,
The Moon, their mistress, had expired
before;
The winds were withered in the stagnant
air, 80
And the clouds perished; Darkness had
no need
Of aid from them—She was the Universe.

LA BELLE DAME SANS MERCI *

John Keats
(1795–1821)

O what can ail thee, knight-at-arms!
Alone and palely loitering!
The sedge has withered from the lake,
And no birds sing.

O what can ail thee, knight-at-arms! 5
So haggard and so woe-begone?
The squirrel's granary is full,
And the harvest's done.

I see a lily on thy brow
With anguish moist and fever dew, 10
And on thy cheeks a fading rose
Fast withereth too.

"I met a lady in the meads,
Full beautiful—a faery's child,

Her hair was long, her foot was light, 15
And her eyes were wild.

"I made a garland for her head,
And bracelets too, and fragrant zone;
She looked at me as she did love,
And made sweet moan. 20

"I set her on my pacing steed,
And nothing else saw all day long.
For sidelong would she bend, and sing
A faery's song.

"She found me roots of relish sweet, 25
And honey wild and manna-dew;
And sure in language strange she said,
'I love thee true.'

"She took me to her elfin grot,
And there she wept and sighed full
sore; 30
And there I shut her wild, wild eyes
With kisses four.

"And there she lullèd me asleep,
And there I dreamed—ah! woe be-
tide!—
The latest dream I ever dreamed 35
On the cold hillside.

"I saw pale kings, and princes too,
Pale warriors, death-pale were they all:
They cried—'La Belle Dame sans Merci
Hath thee in thrall!' 40

"I saw their starved lips in the gloam
With horrid warning gapèd wide,
And I woke, and found me here
On the cold hillside.

"And this is why I sojourn here 45
Alone and palely loitering,
Though the sedge is withered from the
lake,
And no birds sing."

---

* "The Beautiful Lady Without Mercy"

18. *zone:* girdle.

"CHILDE ROLAND TO THE DARK TOWER CAME" *

Child Rowland to the dark tower came,
His word was still—Fie, foh, and fum,
I smell the blood of a British man.

Robert Browning
(1812–1889)

My first thought was, he lied in every
  word,
    That hoary cripple, with malicious eye
  Askance to watch the working of his lie
On mine, and mouth scarce able to afford
Suppression of the glee, that pursed and
    scored   5
    Its edge, at one more victim gained
    thereby.

What else should he be set for, with his
  staff?
    What, save to waylay with his lies, en-
    snare
    All travelers who might find him posted
    there,
And ask the road? I guessed what skull-
  like laugh   10
Would break, what crutch 'gin write my
  epitaph
    For pastime in the dusty thoroughfare,

If at his counsel I should turn aside
    Into that ominous tract which, all agree,
    Hides the Dark Tower. Yet acquiesc-
    ingly   15
I did turn as he pointed—neither pride
Nor hope rekindling at the end descried,
    So much as gladness that some end
    might be.

For, what with my whole world-wide wandering,
    What with my search drawn out
      through years, my hope   20
    Dwindled into a ghost not fit to cope

With that obstreperous joy success would
  bring—
I hardly tried now to rebuke the spring
    My heart made, finding failure in its
    scope.

As when a sick man very near to death 25
    Seems dead indeed, and feels begin and
    end
    The tears, and takes the farewell of
    each friend,
And hears one bid the other go, draw
  breath
Freelier outside ("since all is o'er," he
  saith,
    "And the blow fallen no grieving can
    amend"),   30

While some discuss if near the other
  graves
    Be room enough for this, and when a
    day
    Suits best for carrying the corpse away,
With care about the banners, scarves, and
  staves;
And still the man hears all, and only
  craves   35
    He may not shame such tender love
    and stay.

Thus, I had so long suffered in this quest,
    Heard failure prophesied so oft, been
    writ
    So many times among "The Band"—
    to wit,
The knights who to the Dark Tower's
  search addressed   40
Their steps—that just to fail as they,
  seemed best,
    And all the doubt was now—should I
    be fit?

So, quiet as despair, I turned from him,
    That hateful cripple, out of his high-
    way
    Into the path he pointed. All the day 45
Had been a dreary one at best, and dim

* See Edgar's mad song in *King Lear* (III,
iv, 187–189):

Was settling to its close, yet shot one grim
  Red leer to see the plain catch its estray.

For mark! no sooner was I fairly found
  Pledged to the plain, after a pace or
    two,   50
  Than, pausing to throw backward a
    last view
O'er the safe road, 'twas gone; gray plain
  all round—
Nothing but plain to the horizon's bound.
I might go on; naught else remained to
  do.

So, on I went. I think I never saw   55
  Such starved ignoble nature; nothing
    throve;
  For flowers—as well expect a cedar
    grove!
But cockle, spurge, according to their law
Might propagate their kind, with none to
  awe,
  You'd think; a burr had been a treasure
    trove.   60

No! penury, inertness, and grimace,
  In some strange sort, were the land's
    portion. "See
  Or shut your eyes," said Nature peev-
    ishly,
"It nothing skills—I cannot help my case;
'Tis the Last Judgment's fire must cure
  this place,   65
  Calcine its clods, and set my prisoners
    free."

If there pushed any ragged thistle-stalk
  Above its mates, the head was chopped;
    the bents
  Were jealous else. What made those
    holes and rents
In the dock's harsh swarth leaves, bruised
  as to balk   70
All hope of greenness? 'Tis a brute must
  walk

Pashing their life out, with a brute's
  intents.

As for the grass, it grew as scant as hair
  In leprosy; thin dry blades pricked the
    mud,
  Which underneath looked kneaded up
    with blood.   75
One stiff blind horse, his every bone
  a-stare,
Stood stupefied, however he came there—
  Thrust out past service from the devil's
    stud!

Alive? He might be dead for aught I
  know,
  With that red gaunt and colloped neck
    a-strain,   80
  And shut eyes underneath the rusty
    mane;
Seldom went such grotesqueness with
  such woe;
I never saw a brute I hated so;
  He must be wicked to deserve such
    pain.

I shut my eyes and turned them on my
  heart.   85
  As a man calls for wine before he
    fights,
  I asked one draft of earlier, happier
    sights,
Ere fitly I could hope to play my part.
Think first, fight afterwards—the soldier's
  art;
  One taste of the old time sets all to
    rights.   90

Not it! I fancied Cuthbert's reddening face
  Beneath its garniture of curly gold,
  Dear fellow, till I almost felt him fold
An arm in mine to fix me to the place,
That way he used. Alas, one night's dis-
  grace!   95
  Out went my heart's new fire and left
    it cold.

48. *estray:* one who has strayed.
66. *Calcine:* reduce to powder by heat.
68. *bents:* coarse grasses.

80. *colloped:* in folds.

Giles then, the soul of honor—there he
stands
    Frank as ten years ago when knighted
first.
    What honest man should dare (he said)
he durst.
Good—but the scene shifts—faugh! what
hangman hands   100
Pin to his breast a parchment? His own
bands
    Read it. Poor traitor, spit upon and
cursed!

Better this present than a past like that;
    Back therefore to my darkening path
again!
    No sound, no sight as far as eye could
strain.   105
Will the night send a howlet or a bat?
I asked—when something on the dismal
flat
    Came to arrest my thoughts and change
their train.

A sudden little river crossed my path
    As unexpected as a serpent comes. 110
    No sluggish tide congenial to the
glooms;
This, as it frothed by, might have been a
bath
For the fiend's glowing hoof—to see the
wrath
    Of its black eddy bespate with flakes
and spumes.

So petty yet so spiteful! All along,   115
    Low scrubby alders kneeled down over
it;
    Drenched willows flung them headlong
in a fit
Of mute despair, a suicidal throng;
The river which had done them all the
wrong,
    Whate'er that was, rolled by, deterred
no whit.   120

Which, while I forded—good saints, how
I feared
    To set my foot upon a dead man's
cheek,
    Each step, or feel the spear I thrust to
seek
For hollows, tangled in his hair or beard!
—It may have been a water rat I
speared,   125
    But, ugh! it sounded like a baby's shriek.

Glad was I when I reached the other
bank.
    Now for a better country. Vain presage!
    Who were the strugglers, what war did
they wage,
Whose savage trample thus could pad the
dank   130
Soil to a plash? Toads in a poisoned tank,
    Or wild cats in a red-hot iron cage—

The fight must so have seemed in that fell
cirque.
    What penned them there, with all the
plain to choose?
    No footprint leading to that horrid
mews,   135
None out of it. Mad brewage set to work
Their brains, no doubt, like galley-slaves
the Turk
    Pits for his pastime, Christians against
Jews.

And more than that—a furlong on—why,
there!
    What bad use was that engine for, that
wheel,   140
    Or brake, not wheel—that harrow fit to
reel
Men's bodies out like silk? with all the air
Of Tophet's tool, on earth left unaware,
    Or brought to sharpen its rusty teeth of
steel.

Then came a bit of stubbed ground, once
a wood,   145

106. *howlet:* an owl.
114. *bespate:* spattered.

133. *cirque:* circular arena.
135. *mews:* enclosure.
143. *Tophet:* a valley. in hell.

Next a marsh, it would seem, and now
    mere earth
Desperate and done with—so a fool
    finds mirth,
Makes a thing and then mars it, till his
    mood
Changes and off he goes!—within a rood,
    Bog, clay, and rubble, sand, and stark
    black dearth.   150

Now blotches rankling, colored gay and
    grim,
    Now patches where some leanness of
    the soil's
    Broke into moss or substances like
    boils;
Then came some palsied oak, a cleft in
    him
Like a distorted mouth that splits its
    rim   155
    Gaping at death, and dies while it re-
    coils.

And just as far as ever from the end!
    Naught in the distance but the evening,
    naught
    To point my footstep further! At the
    thought
A great black bird, Apollyon's bosom
    friend,   160
Sailed past, nor beat his wide wing
    dragon-penned
    That brushed my cap—perchance the
    guide I sought.

For, looking up, aware I somehow grew,
    'Spite of the dusk, the plain had given
    place
    All round to mountains—with such
    name to grace   165
Mere ugly heights and heaps now stolen
    in view.
How thus they had surprised me—solve
    it, you!

How to get from them was no clearer
    case.

Yet half I seemed to recognize some trick
    Of mischief happened to me, God
    knows when—   170
    In a bad dream, perhaps. Here ended,
    then,
Progress this way. When, in the very nick
Of giving up, one time more, came a click
    As when a trap shuts—you're inside
    the den!

Burningly it came on me all at once,   175
    This was the place! those two hills on
    the right,
    Crouched like two bulls locked horn in
    horn in fight;
While to the left, a tall scalped mountain
    . . . Dunce,
Dotard, a-dozing at the very nonce,
    After a life spent training for the
    sight!   180

What in the midst lay but the Tower itself?
    The round squat turret, blind as the
    fool's heart,
    Built of brown stone, without a coun-
    terpart
In the whole world. The tempest's mock-
    ing elf
Points to the shipman thus the unseen
    shelf   185
    He strikes on, only when the timbers
    start.

Not see? because of night, perhaps?—
    why, day
    Came back again for that! before it left,
    The dying sunset kindled through a
    cleft;
The hills, like giants at a hunting, lay 190
Chin upon hand, to see the game at bay—
    "Now stab and end the creature—to
    the heft!"

160. *Apollyon's:* the devil's.
161. *dragon-penned:* with feathers like a
dragon.

179. *nonce:* moment.
192. *heft:* handle of a dagger.

Not hear? when noise was everywhere! it
  tolled
  Increasing like a bell. Names in my
    ears,
  Of all the lost adventurers my
    peers—   195
How such a one was strong, and such was
  bold,
And such was fortunate, yet each of old
  Lost, lost! one moment knelled the woe
  of years.

There they stood, ranged along the hill-
  sides, met
  To view the last of me, a living
    frame   200
  For one more picture! in a sheet of
    flame
I saw them and I knew them all. And yet
Dauntless the slug-horn to my lips I set,
  And blew. *"Childe Roland to the Dark
    Tower came."*

203. *slug-horn:* a trumpet.

THE DARK CHÂTEAU

Walter de la Mare
(1873–1956)

In dreams a dark château
  Stands ever open to me,
In far ravines dream-waters flow,
  Descending soundlessly;
Above its peaks the eagle floats,   5
  Lone in a sunless sky;
Mute are the golden woodland throats
  Of the birds flitting by.

No voice is audible. The wind
  Sleeps in its peace.   10
No flower of the light can find
  Refuge beneath its trees;
Only the darkening ivy climbs
  Mingled with wilding rose,

And cypress, morn and evening, time's 15
  Black shadow throws.

All vacant, and unknown;
  Only the dreamer steps
From stone to hollow stone,
  Where the green moss sleeps,   20
Peers at the river in its deeps,
  The eagle lone in the sky,
While the dew of evening drips,
  Coldly and silently.

Would that I could steal in!—   25
  Into each secret room;
Would that my sleep-bright eyes could win
  To the inner gloom;
Gaze from its high windows,
  Far down its mouldering walls,   30
Where amber-clear still Lethe flows,
  And foaming falls.

But ever as I gaze,
  From slumber soft doth come
Some touch my stagnant sense to raise 35
  To its old earthly home;
Fades then that sky serene;
  And peak of ageless snow;
Fades to a paling dawn-lit green,
  My dark château.   40

31. *Lethe:* a river in Hades whose waters
caused forgetfulness.

AFTER APPLE-PICKING

Robert Frost
(1875–1963)

My long two-pointed ladder's sticking
  through a tree
Toward heaven still,
And there's a barrel that I didn't fill
Beside it, and there may be two or
  three
Apples I didn't pick upon some bough. 5

But I am done with apple-picking now.
Essence of winter sleep is on the night,
The scent of apples: I am drowsing off.
I cannot rub the strangeness from my
    sight
I got from looking through a pane of
    glass   10
I skimmed this morning from the drink-
    ing trough
And held against the world of hoary grass.
It melted, and I let it fall and break.
But I was well
Upon my way to sleep before it fell,   15
And I could tell
What form my dreaming was about to
    take.
Magnified apples appear and disappear,
Stem end and blossom end,
And every fleck of russet showing
    clear.   20
My instep arch not only keeps the
    ache,
It keeps the pressure of a ladder-round.
I feel the ladder sway as the boughs bend.
And I keep hearing from the cellar bin
The rumbling sound   25
Of load on load of apples coming in.

For I have had too much
Of apple-picking: I am overtired
Of the great harvest I myself desired.
There were ten thousand thousand fruit
    to touch,   30
Cherish in hand, lift down, and not let
    fall.
For all
That struck the earth,
No matter if not bruised or spiked with
    stubble,
Went surely to the cider-apple heap   35
As of no worth.
One can see what will trouble
This sleep of mine, whatever sleep it is.
Were he not gone,
The woodchuck could say whether it's
    like his   40
Long sleep, as I describe its coming on,
Or just some human sleep.

MARGINALIA

Richard Wilbur
(1921–   )

Things concentrate at the edges; the
    pond-surface
Is bourne to fish and man and it is spread
In textile scum and damask light, on
    which
The lily pads are set; and there are also
    Inlaid ruddy twigs, becalmed pine-
        leaves,   5
    Air-baubles, and the chain mail of
        froth.

Descending into sleep (as when the night-
    lift
Falls past a brilliant floor), we glimpse a
    sublime
Décor and hear, perhaps, a complete
    music,
But this evades us, as in the night
    meadows   10
    The crickets' million roundsong dies
        away
    From all advances, rising in every
        distance.

Our riches are centrifugal; men compose
Daily, unwittingly, their final dreams,
And those are our own voices whose
    remote   15
Consummate chorus rides on the whirl-
    pool's rim,
    Past which we flog our sails, toward
        which we drift,
    Plying our trades, in hopes of a good
        drowning.

THE VENETIAN BLIND

Randall Jarrell
(1914–1965)

It is the first day of the world
Man wakes into: the bars of the blind

And their key-signature, a leaf,
Stream darkly to two warmths;
One trembles, becomes his face.   5
He floats from the sunlight
Into a shadowed place:
There is a chatter, a blur of wings—
But where is the edge of things?
Where does the world begin?   10
                              His dreams
Have changed into this day, this dream;
He thinks, "But where am I?"
A voice calls patiently:
"Remember."   15
He thinks, "But where am I?"
His great limbs are curled
Through sunlight, about space.
What is that, *remember?*
He thinks that he is younger   20
˒Than anything has ever been.
He thinks that he is the world.

But his soul and his body
Call, as the bird calls, their one word—
And he remembers.   25

He is lost in himself forever.

And the Angel he makes from the sun-
    light
Says in mocking tenderness:
"Poor stateless one, wert thou the
    world?"
His soul and his body   30
Say, "What hast thou made of us, thy
    servants?
We are sick. We are dull. We are old."
"Who is this man? We know him not,"
    says the world.

They have spoken as he would have made
    them speak;
And who else is there to speak?   35

The bars of the sunlight fall to his face.

And yet something calls, as it has called:
"But where am *I?* But where am *I?*"

THE SNOWFALL

Donald Justice
(1925–   )

The classic landscapes of dreams are not
More pathless, though footprints leading
    nowhere
Would seem to prove that a people once
Survived for a little even here.

Fragments of a pathetic culture   5
Remain, the lost mittens of children,
And a single, bright, detasseled snow-cap,
Evidence of some frantic migration.

The landmarks are gone. Nevertheless
There is something familiar about this
    country.   10
Slowly now we begin to recall

The terrible whispers of our elders
Falling softly about our ears
In childhood, never believed till now.

▪ ▪ ▪

THE SECOND COMING

W. B. Yeats
(1865–1939)

Turning and turning in the widening gyre
The falcon cannot hear the falconer;
Things fall apart: the center cannot hold;
Mere anarchy is loosed upon the world,
The blood-dimmned tide is loosed, and
    everywhere   5
The ceremony of innocence is drowned;
The best lack all conviction, while the
    worst
Are full of passionate intensity.

Surely some revelation is a hand;
Surely the Second Coming is at hand. 10

1. *gyre:* whirl in a spiral motion.

The Second Coming! Hardly are those
words out
When a vast image out of *Spiritus
Mundi*
Troubles my sight: somewhere in sands of
the desert
A shape with lion body and the head of a
man,
A gaze blank and pitiless as the sun,   15

Is moving its slow thighs, while all
about it
Reel shadows of the indignant desert
birds.
The darkness drops again; but now I
know
That twenty centuries of stony sleep
Were vexed to nightmare by a rocking
cradle,   20
And what rough beast, its hour come
round at last,
Slouches towards Bethlehem to be born?

12. *Spiritus Mundi:* Spirit or Soul of the Universe, which Yeats held to be the source of images and symbols.

VI

THE INDIVIDUAL
AND SOCIETY

FOREWORD

The advantages of a highly technological and centralized society include order, comfort, and longevity. But what must be paid for such gains? Are restrictions on individual freedom and integrity worth social stability? Can man place machines and the steel and concrete of cities between himself and personal contact with the rhythms of nature, yet preserve his humanity and sanity?

Such questions are particularly pertinent to our age of technological and social "progress." No one writer in this section offers a dogmatic and comprehensive answer, but each in his own way confronts some of the conflicts of the individual and society in our time.

Thoreau and Herbert Gold, though separated by almost a century, agree that the road American society has taken will lead to the repression of individual freedom, creativity, and humanity. Glenn T. Seaborg and Harvey Cox are more optimistic. The former views the machine and the latter the city as the means whereby, if they are properly controlled, man can enhance rather than diminish his human potentials.

It is perhaps significant that we could find no modern short story of high quality that cast our bureaucratic, cybernetic age in a positive light. E. B. White's tale evokes the horror of a city where the language, the materials, and even the human brain seem to be disintegrating. In the stories by Chekhov and E. M. Forster, individuals are forced to choose between personal integrity and social conformity.

The majority of the poets in this section, including W. B. Yeats, are in accord in condemning any pressures that narrow individual choice and blind us to "dappled things." Shakespeare, in contrast, is able to extol the merits of the social order, and Wordsworth, in one of his poems, can acknowledge the triumphs of the Industrial Revolution over time and space.

ESSAYS

CIVIL DISOBEDIENCE

Henry David Thoreau
(1817–1862)

I heartily accept the motto,—"That government is best which governs least;" and I should like to see it acted up to more rapidly and systematically. Carried out, it finally amounts to this, which also I believe,—"That government is best which governs not at all;" and when men are prepared for it, that will be the kind of government which they will have. Government is at best but an expedient; but most governments are usually, and all governments are sometimes, inexpedient. The objections which have been brought against a standing army, and they are many and weighty, and deserve to prevail, may also at last be brought against a standing government. The standing army is only an arm of the standing government. The government itself, which is only the mode which the people have chosen to execute their will, is equally liable to be abused and perverted before the people can act through it. Witness the present Mexican war, the work of comparatively a few individuals using the standing government as their tool; for, in the outset, the people would not have consented to this measure.

This American government,—what is it but a tradition, though a recent one, endeavoring to transmit itself unimpaired to posterity, but each instant losing some of its integrity? It has not the vitality and force of a single living man; for a single man can bend it to his will. It is a sort of wooden gun to the people themselves. But it is not the less necessary for this; for the people must have some complicated machinery or other, and hear its din, to satisfy that idea of government which they have. Governments show thus how successfully men can be imposed on, even impose on themselves, for their own advantage. It is excellent, we must all allow. Yet this government never of itself furthered any enterprise, but by the alacrity with which it got out of its way. *It* does not keep the country free. *It* does not settle the West. *It* does not educate. The character inherent in the American people has done all that has been accomplished; and it would have done somewhat more, if the government had not sometimes got in its way. For government is an expedient by which men would fain succeed in letting one another alone; and, as has been said, when it is most expedient, the governed are most let alone by it. Trade and commerce, if they were not made of india-rubber, would never manage to bounce over the obstacles which legislators are continually putting in their way; and, if one were to judge these men wholly by the effects of their actions and not partly by their intentions, they would deserve to be classed and punished with those mischievous persons who put obstructions on the railroads.

But, to speak practically and as a citizen, unlike those who call themselves no-government men, I ask for, not at once no government, but *at once* a better government. Let every man make known what kind of government would command his respect, and that will be one step toward obtaining it.

After all, the practical reason why, when the power is once in the hands of the people, a majority are permitted, and for a long period continue, to rule is not because they are most likely to be in the right, nor because this seems fairest to the minority, but because they are physically the strongest. But a government in which the majority rule in all cases cannot be based on justice, even as far as men understand it. Can there be a government in which majorities do not virtually decide right and wrong, but conscience?—in which majorities decide only those questions to which the rule of expediency is applicable? Must the citizen ever for a moment, or in the least degree, resign his conscience to the legislator? Why has every man a conscience, then? I think that we should be men first, and subjects afterward. It is not desirable to cultivate a respect for the law, so much as for the right. The only obligation which I have a right to assume is to do at any time what I think right. It is truly enough said that a corporation has no conscience; but a corporation of conscientious men is a corporation *with* a conscience. Law never made men a whit more just; and, by means of their respect for it, even the well-disposed are daily made the agents of injustice. A common and natural result of an undue respect for law is, that you may

see a file of soldiers, colonel, captain, corporal, privates, powder-monkeys, and all, marching in admirable order over hill and dale to the wars, against their wills, ay, against their common sense and consciences, which makes it very steep marching indeed, and produces a palpitation of the heart. They have no doubt that it is a damnable business in which they are concerned; they are all peaceably inclined. Now, what are they? Men at all? or small movable forts and magazines, at the service of some unscrupulous man in power? Visit the Navy-Yard, and behold a marine, such a man as an American government can make, or such as it can make a man with its black arts,—a mere shadow and reminiscence of humanity, a man laid out alive and standing, and already, as one may say, buried under arms with funeral accompaniments, though it may be.—

"Not a drum was heard, not a funeral
    note,
    As his corse to the rampart we hurried;
Not a soldier discharged his farewell shot
    O'er the grave where our hero we
        buried."

The mass of men serve the state thus, not as men mainly, but as machines, with their bodies. They are the standing army, and the militia, jailers, constables, *posse comitatus,* etc. In most cases there is no free exercise whatever of the judgment or of the moral sense; but they put themselves on a level with wood and earth and stones; and wooden men can perhaps be manufactured that will serve the purpose as well. Such command no more respect than men of straw or a lump of dirt. They have the same sort of worth only as horses and dogs. Yet such as these even are commonly esteemed good citizens. Others—as most legislators, politicians, lawyers, ministers, and office-holders—serve the state chiefly with their heads; and, as they rarely make any moral distinctions, they are as likely to serve the devil, without *intending* it, as God. A very few,—as heroes, patriots, martyrs, reformers in the great sense, and *men*—serve the state with their consciences also, and so necessarily resist it for the most part; and they are commonly treated as enemies by it. A wise man will only be useful as a man, and will not submit to be "clay," and "stop a hole to keep the wind away," but leave that office to his dust at least:—

"I am too high-born to be propertied,
To be a secondary at control,
Or useful serving-man and instrument
To any sovereign state throughout the
    world."

He who gives himself entirely to his fellow-men appears to them useless and selfish; but he who gives himself partially to them is pronounced a benefactor and philanthropist.

How does it become a man to behave toward this American government to-day? I answer, that he cannot without disgrace be associated with it. I cannot for an instant recognize that political organization as *my* government which is the *slave's* government also.

All men recognize the right of revolution; that is, the right to refuse allegiance to, and to resist, the government, when its tyranny or its inefficiency are great and unendurable. But almost all say that such is not the case now. But such was the case, they think, in the Revolution of '75. If one were to tell me that this was a bad government because it taxed certain foreign commodities brought to its ports, it is most probable that I should not make an ado about it, for I can do without them. All machines have their friction; and possibly this does enough good to counterbalance the evil. At any rate, it is a great evil to make a stir about it. But

when the friction comes to have its machine, and oppression and robbery are organized, I say, let us not have such a machine any longer. In other words, when a sixth of the population of a nation which has undertaken to be the refuge of liberty are slaves, and a whole country is unjustly overrun and conquered by a foreign army, and subjected to military law, I think that it is not too soon for honest men to rebel and revolutionize. What makes this duty the more urgent is the fact that the country so overrun is not our own, but ours is the invading army.

Paley, a common authority with many on moral questions, in his chapter on the "Duty of Submission to Civil Government," resolves all civil obligation into expediency; and he proceeds to say "that so long as the interest of the whole society requires it, that is, so long as the established government cannot be resisted or changed without public inconveniency, it is the will of God . . . that the established government be obeyed,—and no longer. This principle being admitted, the justice of every particular case of resistance is reduced to a computation of the quantity of the danger and grievance on the one side, and of the probability and expense of redressing it on the other." Of this, he says, every man shall judge for himself. But Paley appears never to have contemplated those cases to which the rule of expediency does not apply, in which a people, as well as an individual, must do justice, cost what it may. If I have unjustly wrested a plank from a drowning man, I must restore it to him though I drown myself. This, according to Paley, would be inconvenient. But he that would save his life, in such a case, shall lose it. This people must cease to hold slaves, and to make war on Mexico, though it cost them their existence as a people.

In their practice, nations agree with

Paley; but does any one think that Massachusetts does exactly what is right at the present crisis?

"A drab of state, a cloth-o'-silver slut,
To have her train borne up, and her soul trail in the dirt."

Practically speaking, the opponents to a reform in Massachusetts are not a hundred thousand politicians at the South, but a hundred thousand merchants and farmers here, who are more interested in commerce and agriculture than they are in humanity, and are not prepared to do justice to the slave and to Mexico, *cost what it may*. I quarrel not with far-off foes, but with those who, near at home, coöperate with, and do the bidding of, those far away, and without whom the latter would be harmless. We are accustomed to say, that the mass of men are unprepared; but improvement is slow, because the few are not materially wiser or better than the many. It is not so important that many should be as good as you, as that there be some absolute goodness somewhere; for that will leaven the whole lump. There are thousands who are *in opinion* opposed to slavery and to the war, who yet in effect do nothing to put an end to them; who, esteeming themselves children of Washington and Franklin, sit down with their hands in their pockets, and say that they know not what to do, and do nothing; who even postpone the question of freedom to the question of free trade, and quietly read the prices-current along with the latest advices from Mexico, after dinner, and, it may be, fall asleep over them both. What is the price-current of an honest man and patriot to-day? They hesitate, and they regret, and sometimes they petition; but they do nothing in earnest and with effect. They will wait, well disposed, for others to remedy the evil, that they may no longer have it to regret. At most, they give only a cheap vote, and a feeble countenance and God-speed, to the right, as it goes by them. There are nine hundred and ninety-nine patrons of virtue to one virtuous man. But it is easier to deal with the real possessor of a thing than with the temporary guardian of it.

All voting is a sort of gaming, like checkers or backgammon, with a slight moral tinge to it, a playing with right and wrong, with moral questions; and betting naturally accompanies it. The character of the voters is not staked. I cast my vote, perchance, as I think right; but I am not vitally concerned that that right should prevail. I am willing to leave it to the majority. Its obligation, therefore, never exceeds that of expediency. Even voting *for the right* is *doing* nothing for it. It is only expressing to men feebly your desire that it should prevail. A wise man will not leave the right to the mercy of chance, nor wish it to prevail through the power of the majority. There is but little virtue in the action of masses of men. When the majority shall at length vote for the abolition of slavery, it will be because they are indifferent to slavery, or because there is but little slavery left to be abolished by their vote. *They* will then be the only slaves. Only *his* vote can hasten the abolition of slavery who asserts his own freedom by his vote.

I hear of a convention to be held at Baltimore or elsewhere, for the selection of a candidate for the Presidency, made up chiefly of editors, and men who are politicians by profession; but I think, what is it to any independent, intelligent, and respectable man what decision they may come to? Shall we not have the advantage of his wisdom and honesty, nevertheless? Can we not count upon some independent votes? Are there not many individuals in the country who do not attend conventions? But no: I find that the respectable man, so called, has immediately drifted from his position, and despairs of his country, when his country has more reason to despair of him. He forthwith adopts one of the candidates thus selected as the only *available* one, thus proving that he is himself *available* for any purposes of the demagogue. His vote is of no more worth than that of any unprincipled foreigner or hireling native, who may have been bought. O for a man who is a *man,* and, as my neighbor says, has a bone in his back which you cannot pass your hand through! Our statistics are at fault: the population has been returned too large. How many *men* are there to a square thousand miles in this country? Hardly one. Does not America offer any inducement for men to settle here? The American has dwindled into an Odd Fellow,—one who may be known by the development of his organ of gregariousness, and a manifest lack of intellect and cheerful self-reliance; whose first and chief concern, on coming into the world, is to see that the alms-houses are in good repair; and, before yet he has lawfully donned the virile garb, to collect a fund for the support of the widows and orphans that may be; who, in short, ventures to live only by the aid of the Mutual Insurance company, which has promised to bury him decently.

It is not a man's duty, as a matter of course, to devote himself to the eradication of any, even the most enormous, wrong; he may still properly have other concerns to engage him; but it is his duty, at least, to wash his hands of it, and, if he gives it no thought longer, not to give it practically his support. If I devote myself to other pursuits and contemplations, I must first see, at least, that I do not pursue them sitting upon another man's shoulders. I must get off him first, that he may pursue his contemplations too. See what gross inconsistency is tolerated. I have heard some of my townsmen say, "I should like to have them order me out to help put down an insurrection of the slaves, or to march to Mexico;—see if I would go;" and yet these very men have each, directly by their allegiance, and so indirectly, at least, by their money, furnished a substitute. The soldier is applauded who refuses to serve in an unjust war by those who do not refuse to sustain the unjust government which makes the war; is applauded by those whose own act and authority he disregards and sets at naught; as if the state were penitent to that degree that it hired one to scourge it while it sinned, but not to that degree that it left off sinning for a moment. Thus, under the name of Order and Civil Government, we are all made at last to pay homage to and support our own meanness. After the first blush of sin comes its indifference; and from immoral it becomes, as it were, *un*moral, and not quite unnecessary to that life which we have made.

The broadest and most prevalent error requires the most disinterested virtue to sustain it. The slight reproach to which the virtue of patriotism is commonly liable, the noble are most likely to incur. Those who, while they disapprove of the character and measures of a government, yield to it their allegiance and support are undoubtedly its most conscientious supporters, and so frequently the most serious obstacles to reform. Some are petitioning the State to dissolve the Union, to disregard the requisitions of the President. Why do they not dissolve it themselves,—the union between themselves and the State,—and refuse to pay their quota into its treasury? Do not they stand in the same relation to the State that the States does to the Union? And have not the same reasons prevented the State from resisting the Union which have prevented them from resisting the State?

How can a man be satisfied to entertain an opinion merely, and enjoy *it?* Is there any enjoyment in it, if his opinion is that he is aggrieved? If you are cheated out of a single dollar by your neighbor, you do not rest satisfied with knowing that you are cheated, or with saying that you are cheated, or even with petitioning him to pay you your due; but you take effectual steps at once to obtain the full amount, and see that you are never cheated again. Action from principle, the perception and the performance of right, changes things and relations; it is essentially revolutionary, and does not consist wholly with anything which was. It not only divides States and churches, it divides families; ay, it divides the *individual,* separating the diabolical in him from the divine.

Unjust laws exist: shall we be content to obey them, or shall we endeavor to amend them, and obey them until we have succeeded, or shall we transgress them at once? Men generally, under such a government as this, think that they ought to wait until they have persuaded the majority to alter them. They think that, if they should resist, the remedy would be worse than the evil. But it is the fault of the government itself that the remedy *is* worse than the evil. *It* makes it worse. Why is it not more apt to anticipate and provide for reform? Why does it not cherish its wise minority? Why does it cry and resist before it is hurt? Why does it not encourage its citizens to be on the alert to point out its faults, and *do* better than it would have them? Why does it always crucify Christ, and excommunicate Copernicus and Luther, and pronounce Washington and Franklin rebels?

One would think, that a deliberate and practical denial of its authority was the only offense never contemplated by government; else why has it not assigned its definite, its suitable and proportionate penalty? If a man who has no property refuses but once to earn nine shillings for the State, he is put in prison for a period unlimited by any law that I know, and determined only by the discretion of those who placed him there; but if he should steal ninety times nine shillings from the State, he is soon permitted to go at large again.

If the injustice is part of the necessary friction of the machine of government, let it go, let it go: perchance it will wear smooth,—certainly the machine will wear out. If the injustice has a spring, or a pulley, or a rope, or a crank, exclusively for itself, then perhaps you may consider whether the remedy will not be worse than the evil; but if it is of such a nature that it requires you to be the agent of injustice to another, then, I say, break the law. Let your life be a counter friction to stop the machine. What I have to do is to see, at any rate, that I do not lend myself to the wrong which I condemn.

As for adopting the ways which the State has provided for remedying the evil, I know not of such ways. They take too much time, and a man's life will be gone. I have other affairs to attend to. I came into this world, not chiefly to make this a good place to live in, but to live in it, be it good or bad. A man has not everything to do, but something; and because he cannot do *everything,* it is not necessary that he should do *something* wrong. It is not my business to be petitioning the Governor or the Legislature any more than it is theirs to petition me; and if they should not hear my petition, what should I do then? But in this case the State has provided no way: its very Constitution is the evil. This may seem to be harsh and stubborn and unconciliatory; but it is to treat with the utmost kindness and consideration the only spirit that can appreciate or deserves it. So is all change for the better, like birth and death, which convulse the body.

I do not hesitate to say, that those who call themselves Abolitionists should at once effectually withdraw their support, both in person and property, from the government of Massachusetts, and not wait till they constitute a majority of one, before they suffer the right to prevail through them. I think that it is enough if they have God on their side, without waiting for that other one. Moreover, any man more right than his neighbors constitutes a majority of one already.

I meet this American government, or its representative, the State government, directly, and face to face, once a year—no more—in the person of its tax-gatherer; this is the only mode in which a man situated as I am necessarily meets it; and it then says distinctly, Recognize me; and the simplest, the most effectual, and, in the present posture of affairs, the indispensablest mode of treating with it on this head, of expressing your little satisfaction with and love for it, is to deny it then. My civil neighbor, the tax-gatherer, is the very man I have to deal with,—for it is, after all, with men and not with parchment that I quarrel,—and he has voluntarily chosen to be an agent of the government. How shall he ever know well what he is and does as an officer of the government, or as a man, until he is obliged to consider whether he shall treat me, his neighbor, for whom he has respect, as a neighbor and well-disposed man, or as a maniac and disturber of the peace, and see if he can get over this obstruction to his neighborliness without a ruder and more impetuous thought or speech corresponding with his action. I know this well, that if one thousand, if one hundred, if ten men whom I could name,—if ten *honest* men only,—ay, if *one* HONEST man, in this State of Massachusetts, *ceasing to hold slaves,* were actually to withdraw from this copartnership, and be locked up in the county jail therefore, it would be the abolition of slavery in America. For it matters not how small the beginning may seem to be: what is once well done is done forever. But we love better to talk about it: that we say is our mission. Reform keeps many scores of newspapers in its service, but not one man. If my esteemed neighbor, the State's ambassador, who will devote his days to the settlement of the question of human rights in the Council Chamber, instead of being threatened with the prisons of Carolina, were to sit down the prisoner of Massachusetts, that State which is so anxious to foist the sin of slavery upon her sister,—though at present she can discover only an act of inhospitality to be the ground of a quarrel with her,—the legislature would not wholly waive the subject the following winter.

Under a government which imprisons any unjustly, the true place for a just man is also a prison. The proper place today, the only place which Massachusetts has provided for her freer and less desponding spirits, is in her prisons, to be put out and locked out of the State by her own act, as they have already put themselves out by their principles. It is there that the fugitive slave, and the Mexican prisoner on parole, and the Indian come to plead the wrong of his race should find them; on that separate, but more free and honorable ground, where the State places those who are not *with* her, but *against* her,—the only house in a slave State in which a free man can abide with honor. If any think that their influence would be lost there, and their voices no longer afflict the ear of the State, that they would not be as an enemy within its walls, they do not know by how much truth is stronger than error, nor how much more eloquently and effectively he can combat injustice who has experienced a little in his own person. Cast your whole vote, not a strip of paper merely, but your whole influence. A minority is powerless while it conforms to the majority; it is not even a minority then; but it is irresistible when it clogs by its whole weight. If the alternative is to keep all just men in prison, or give up war and slavery, the State will not hesitate which to choose. If a thousand men were not to pay their tax-bills this year, that would not be a violent and bloody measure, as it would be to pay them, and enable the State to commit violence and shed innocent blood. This is, in fact, the definition of a peaceable revolution, if any such is possible. If the tax-gatherer, or any other public officer, asks me, as one has done, "But what shall I do?" my answer is, "If you really wish to do anything, resign your office." When the subject has refused allegiance, and the officer has resigned his office, then the revolution is accomplished. But even suppose blood should flow. Is there not a sort of blood shed when the conscience is wounded? Through this wound a man's real manhood and immortality flow out, and he bleeds to an everlasting death. I see this blood flowing now.

I have contemplated the imprisonment of the offender, rather than the seizure of his goods,—though both will serve the same purpose,—because they who assert the purest right, and consequently are most dangerous to a corrupt State, commonly have not spent much time in accumulating property. To such the State renders comparatively small service, and a slight tax is wont to appear exorbitant, particularly if they are obliged to earn it by special labor with their hands. If there were one who lived wholly without the use of money, the State itself would hesitate to demand it of him. But the rich man—not to make any invidious comparison—is always sold to the institution which makes him rich. Absolutely speaking, the more money, the less virtue; for

money comes between a man and his objects, and obtains them for him; and it was certainly no great virtue to obtain it. It puts to rest many questions which he would otherwise be taxed to answer; while the only new question which it puts is the hard but superfluous one, how to spend it. Thus his moral ground is taken from under his feet. The opportunities of living are diminished in proportion as what are called the "means" are increased. The best thing a man can do for his culture when he is rich is to endeavor to carry out those schemes which he entertained when he was poor. Christ answered the Herodians according to their condition. "Show me the tribute-money," said he;—and took one penny out of his pocket;—if you use money which has the image of Caesar on it and which he has made current and valuable, that is, *if you are men of the State,* and gladly enjoy the advantages of Caesar's government, then pay him back some of his own when he demands it. "Render therefore to Caesar that which is Caesar's, and to God those things which are God's,"—leaving them no wiser than before as to which was which; for they did not wish to know.

When I converse with the freest of my neighbors, I perceive that whatever they may say about the magnitude and seriousness of the question, and their regard for the public tranquillity, the long and the short of the matter is, that they cannot spare the protection of the existing government, and they dread the consequences to their property and families of disobedience to it. For my own part, I should not like to think that I ever rely on the protection of the State. But, if I deny the authority of the State when it presents its tax-bill, it will soon take and waste all my property, and so harass me and my children without end. This is hard. This makes it impossible for a man to live honestly, and at the same time comfortably, in outward respects. It will not be worth the while to accumulate property; that would be sure to go again. You must hire or squat somewhere, and raise but a small crop, and eat that soon. You must live within yourself, and depend upon yourself always tucked up and ready for a start, and not have many affairs. A man may grow rich in Turkey even, if he will be in all respects a good subject of the Turkish government. Confucius said: "If a state is governed by the principles of reason, poverty and misery are subjects of shame; if a state is not governed by the principles of reason, riches and honors are the subjects of shame." No: until I want the protection of Massachusetts to be extended to me in some distant Southern port, where my liberty is endangered, or until I am bent solely on building up an estate at home by peaceful enterprise, I can afford to refuse allegiance to Massachusetts, and her right to my property and life. It costs me less in every sense to incur the penalty of disobedience to the State than it would to obey. I should feel as if I were worth less in that case.

Some years ago, the State met me in behalf of the Church, and commanded me to pay a certain sum toward the support of a clergyman whose preaching my father attended, but never I myself. "Pay," it said, "or be locked up in the jail." I declined to pay. But, unfortunately, another man saw fit to pay it. I did not see why the schoolmaster should be taxed to support the priest, and not the priest the schoolmaster; for I was not the State's schoolmaster, but I supported myself by voluntary subscription. I did not see why the lyceum should not present its tax-bill, and have the State to back its demand, as well as the Church. However, at the request of the selectmen, I condescended to make some such statement as this in writing:—
"Know all men by these presents, that I, Henry Thoreau, do not wish to be re-

garded as a member of any incorporated society which I have not joined." This I gave to the town clerk; and he has it. The State, having thus learned that I did not wish to be regarded as a member of that church, has never made a like demand on me since; though it said that it must adhere to its original presumption that time. If I had known how to name them, I should then have signed off in detail from all the societies which I never signed on to; but I did not know where to find a complete list.

I have paid no poll-tax for six years. I was put into a jail once on this account, for one night; and, as I stood considering the walls of solid stone, two or three feet thick, the door of wood and iron, a foot thick, and the iron grating which strained the light, I could not help being struck with the foolishness of that institution which treated me as if I were mere flesh and blood and bones, to be locked up. I wondered that it should have concluded at length that this was the best use it could put me to, and had never thought to avail itself of my services in some way. I saw that, if there was a wall of stone between me and my townsmen, there was a still more difficult one to climb or break through before they could get to be as free as I was. I did not for a moment feel confined, and the walls seemed a great waste of stone and mortar. I felt as if I alone of all my townsmen had paid my tax. They plainly did not know how to treat me, but behaved like persons who are underbred. In every threat and in every compliment there was a blunder; for they thought that my chief desire was to stand the other side of that stone wall. I could not but smile to see how industriously they locked the door on my meditations, which followed them out again without let or hindrance, and *they* were really all that was dangerous. As they could not reach me, they had resolved to punish my body; just as boys, if they cannot come at some person against whom they have a spite, will abuse his dog. I saw that the State was half-witted, that it was timid as a lone woman with her silver spoons, and that it did not know its friends from its foes, and I lost all my remaining respect for it, and pitied it.

Thus the State never intentionally confronts a man's sense, intellectual or moral, but only his body, his senses. It is not armed with superior wit or honesty, but with superior physical strength. I was not born to be forced. I will breathe after my own fashion. Let us see who is the strongest. What force has a multitude? They only can force me who obey a higher law than I. They force me to become like themselves. I do not hear of *men* being *forced* to live this way or that by masses of men. What sort of life were that to live? When I meet a government which says to me, "Your money or your life," why should I be in haste to give it my money? It may be in a great strait, and not know what to do: I cannot help that. It must help itself; do as I do. It is not worth the while to snivel about it. I am not responsible for the successful working of the machinery of society. I am not the son of the engineer. I perceive that, when an acorn and a chestnut fall side by side, the one does not remain inert to make way for the other, but both obey their own laws, and spring and grow and flourish as best they can, till one, perchance, overshadows and destroys the other. If a plant cannot live according to its nature, it dies; and so a man.

The night in prison was novel and intertesting enough. The prisoners in their shirt-sleeves were enjoying a chat and the evening air in the doorway, when I entered. But the jailer said, "Come, boys, it is time to lock up;" and so they dispersed, and I heard the sound of their steps returning into the hollow apartments. My room-mate was introduced to me by the jailer as "a first-rate fellow and a clever man." When the door was locked, he showed me where to hang my hat, and how he managed matters there. The rooms were whitewashed once a month; and this one, at least, was the whitest, most simply furnished, and probably the neatest apartment in the town. He naturally wanted to know where I came from, and what brought me there; and, when I had told him, I asked him in my turn how he came there, presuming him to be an honest man, of course; and, as the world goes, I believe he was. "Why," said he, "they accuse me of burning a barn; but I never did it." As near as I could discover, he had probably gone to bed in a barn when drunk, and smoked his pipe there; and so a barn was burnt. He had the reputation of being a clever man, had been there some three months waiting for his trial to come on, and would have to wait as much longer; but he was quite domesticated and contented, since he got his board for nothing, and thought that he was well treated.

He occupied one window, and I the other; and I saw that if one stayed there long, his principal business would be to look out the window. I had soon read all the tracts that were left there, and examined where former prisoners had broken out, and where a gate had been sawed off, and heard the history of the various occupants of that room, for I found that even here there was a history and a gossip which never circulated beyond the walls of the jail. Probably this is the only house in the town where verses are composed, which are afterward printed in circular form, but not published. I was shown quite a long list of verses which were composed by some young men who had been detected in an attempt to escape, who avenged themselves by singing them.

I pumped my fellow-prisoner as dry as I could, for fear I should never see him again; but at length he showed me which was my bed, and left me to blow out the lamp.

It was like traveling into a far country, such as I had never expected to behold, to lie there for one night. It seemed to me that I never had heard the town clock strike before, nor the evening sounds of the village; for we slept with the windows open, which were inside the grating. It was to see my native village in the light of the Middle Ages, and our Concord was turned into a Rhine stream, and visions of knights and castles passed before me. They were the voices of old burghers that I heard in the streets. I was an involuntary spectator and auditor of whatever was done and said in the kitchen of the adjacent village-inn,—a wholly new and rare experience to me. It was a closer view of my native town. I was fairly inside of it. I never had seen its institutions before. This is one of the peculiar institutions; for it is a shire town. I began to comprehend what its inhabitants were about.

In the morning, our breakfasts were put through the hole in the door, in small oblong-square tin pans, made to fit, and holding a pint of chocolate, with brown bread, and an iron spoon. When they called for the vessels again, I was green enough to return what bread I had left; but my comrade seized it, and said that I should lay that up for lunch or dinner. Soon after he was let out to work at haying in a neighboring field, whither he went every day, and would not be back till noon; so he bade me good-day, saying that he doubted if he should see me again.

When I came out of prison,—for some one interfered, and paid that tax,—I did not perceive that great changes had taken place on the common, such as he observed who went in a youth and emerged a tottering and gray-headed man; and yet a change had to my eyes come over the scene,—the town, and State, and country, —greater than any that mere time could

effect. I saw yet more distinctly the State in which I lived. I saw to what extent the people among whom I lived could be trusted as good neighbors and friends; that their friendship was for summer weather only; that they did not greatly propose to do right; that they were a distinct race from me by their prejudices and superstitions, as the Chinamen and Malays are; that in their sacrifices to humanity they ran no risks, not even to their property; that after all they were not so noble but they treated the thief as he had treated them, and hoped, by a certain outward observance and a few prayers, and by walking in a particular straight though useless path from time to time, to save their souls. This may be to judge my neighbors harshly; for I believe that many of them are not aware that they have such an institution as the jail in their village.

It was formerly the custom in our village, when a poor debtor came out of jail, for his acquaintances to salute him, looking through their fingers, which were crossed to represent the grating of a jail window, "How do ye do?" My neighbors did not thus salute me, but first looked at me, and then at one another, as if I had returned from a long journey. I was put into jail as I was going to the shoemaker's to get a shoe which was mended. When I was let out the next morning, I proceeded to finish my errand, and, having put on my mended shoe, joined a huckleberry party, who were impatient to put themselves under my conduct; and in half an hour,—for the horse was soon tackled, —was in the midst of a huckleberry field, on one of our highest hills, two miles off, and then the State was nowhere to be seen.

This is the whole history of "My Prisons."

I have never declined paying the highway tax, because I am as desirous of being a good neighbor as I am of being a bad subject; and as for supporting schools, I am doing my part to educate my fellow-countrymen now. It is for no particular item in the tax-bill that I refuse to pay it. I simply wish to refuse allegiance to the State, to withdraw and stand aloof from it effectually. I do not care to trace the course of my dollar, if I could, till it buys a man or a musket to shoot one with,—the dollar is innocent,—but I am concerned to trace the effects of my allegiance. In fact, I quickly declare war with the State, after my fashion, though I will still make what use and get what advantage of her I can, as is usual in such cases.

If others pay the tax which is demanded of me, from a sympathy with the State, they do but what they have already done in their own case, or rather they abet injustice to a greater extent than the State requires. If they pay the tax from a mistaken interest in the individual taxed, to save his property, or prevent his going to jail, it is because they have not considered wisely how far they let their private feelings interfere with the public good.

This, then, is my position at present. But one cannot be too much on his guard in such a case, lest his action be biased by obstinacy or an undue regard for the opinions of men. Let him see that he does only what belongs to himself and to the hour.

I think sometimes, Why, this people mean well, they are only ignorant; they would do better if they know how: why give your neighbors this pain to treat you as they are not inclined to? But I think again, This is no reason why I should do as they do, or permit others to suffer much greater pain of a different kind. Again, I sometimes say to myself, When many millions of men, without heat, without ill will, without personal feeling of any kind, demand of you a few shillings only, without the possibility, such is their constitution, of retracting or altering their present demand, and without the possibility, on your side, of appeal to any other millions, why expose yourself to this overwhelming brute force? You do not resist cold and hunger, the winds and the waves, thus obstinately; you quietly submit to a thousand similar necessities. You do not put your head into the fire. But just in proportion as I regard this as not wholly a brute force, but partly a human force, and consider that I have relations to those millions as to so many millions of men, and not of mere brute or inanimate things, I see that appeal is possible, first and instantaneously, from them to the Maker of them, and, secondly, from them to themselves. But if I put my head deliberately into the fire, there is no appeal to fire or to the Maker of fire, and I have only myself to blame. If I could convince myself that I have any right to be satisfied with men as they are, and to treat them accordingly, and not according, in some respects, to my requisitions and expectations of what they and I ought to be, then, like a good Mussulman and fatalist, I should endeavor to be satisfied with things as they are, and say it is the will of God. And, above all, there is this difference between resisting this and a purely brute or natural force, that I can resist this with some effect; but I cannot expect, like Orpheus, to change the nature of the rocks and trees and beasts.

I do not wish to quarrel with any man or nation. I do not wish to split hairs, to make fine distinctions, or set myself up as better than my neighbors. I seek rather, I may say, even an excuse for conforming to the laws of the land. I am but too ready to conform to them. Indeed, I have reason to suspect myself on this head; and each year, as the tax-gatherer comes round, I find myself disposed to review the acts and position of the general and State governments, and the spirit of the people, to discover a pretext for conformity.

"We must affect our country as our
    parents,
And if at any time we alienate
Our love or industry from doing it
    honor,
We must respect effects and teach
    the soul
Matter of conscience and religion,
And not desire of rule or benefit."

I believe that the State will soon be able to take all my work of this sort out of my hands, and then I shall be no better a patriot than my fellow-countrymen. Seen from a lower point of view, the Constitution, with all its faults, is very good; the law and the courts are very respectable; even this State and this American government are, in many respects, very admirable, and rare things, to be thankful for, such as a great many have described them; but seen from a point of view a little higher, they are what I have described them; seen from a higher still, and the highest, who shall say what they are, or that they are worth looking at or thinking of at all?

However, the government does not concern me much, and I shall bestow the fewest possible thoughts on it. It is not many moments that I live under a government, even in this world. If a man is thought-free, fancy-free, imagination-free, that which *is not* never for a long time appearing *to be* to him, unwise rulers or reformers cannot fatally interrupt him.

I know that most men think differently from myself; but those whose lives are by profession devoted to the study of these or kindred subjects content me as little as any. Statesmen and legislators, standing so completely within the institution, never distinctly and nakedly behold it. They speak of moving society, but have no resting-place without it. They may be men of a certain experience and discrimination, and no doubt invented ingenious and even useful systems, for which we sincerely thank them; but all their wit and usefulness lie within certain not very wide limits. They are wont to forget that the world is not governed by policy and expediency. Webster never goes behind government, and so cannot speak with authority about it. His words are wisdom to those legislators who contemplate no essential reform in the existing government; but for thinkers, and those who legislate for all time, he never once glances at the subject. I know of those whose serene and wise speculations on this theme would soon reveal the limits of his mind's range and hospitality. Yet, compared with the cheap professions of most reformers, and the still cheaper wisdom and eloquence of politicians in general, his are almost the only sensible and valuable words, and we thank Heaven for him. Comparatively, he is always strong, original, and, above all, practical. Still, his quality is not wisdom, but prudence. The lawyer's truth is not Truth, but consistency or a consistent expediency. Truth is always in harmony with herself, and is not concerned chiefly to reveal the justice that may consist with wrong-doing. He well deserves to be called, as he has been called, the Defender of the Constitution. There are really no blows to be given by him but defensive ones. He is not a leader, but a follower. His leaders are the men of '87. "I have never made an effort," he says, "and never propose to make an effort; I have never countenanced an effort, and never mean to countenance an effort, to disturb the arrangement as originally made, by which the various States came into the Union." Still thinking of the sanction which the Constitution gives to slavery, he says, "Because it was a part of the original compact,—let it stand." Notwithstanding his special acuteness and ability, he is unable to take a fact out of its merely political relations, and behold it as it lies absolutely to be disposed of by the intellect,—what, for instance, it behooves a man to do here in America to-day with regard to slavery,—but ventures, or is driven, to make some such desperate answer as the following, while professing to speak absolutely, and as a private man,—from which what new and singular code of social duties might be inferred? "The manner," says he, "in which the governments of those States where slavery exists are to regulate it is for their own consideration, under their responsibility to their constituents, to the general laws of propriety, humanity, and justice, and to God. Associations formed elsewhere, springing from a feeling of humanity, or any other cause, have nothing whatever to do with it. They have never received any encouragement from me, and they never will."

They who know of no purer sources of truth, who have traced up its stream no higher, stand, and wisely stand, by the Bible and the Constitution, and drink at it there with reverence and humility; but they who behold where it comes trickling into this lake or that pool, gird up their loins once more, and continue their pilgrimage toward its fountain-head.

No man with a genius for legislation has appeared in America. They are rare in the history of the world. There are orators, politicians, and eloquent men, by the thousand, but the speaker has not yet opened his mouth to speak who is capable of settling the much-vexed questions of the day. We love eloquence for its own sake, and not for any truth which it may utter, or any heroism it may inspire. Our legislators have not yet learned the comparative value of free trade and of freedom, of union, and of rectitude, to a nation. They have no genius or talent for comparatively humble questions of taxation and finance, commerce and manufactures and agriculture. If we were left solely to the wordy wit of legislators in Congress for our guidance, uncorrected by the seasonable experience and the effectual complaints of the people, America would not long retain her rank among the nations. For eighteen hundred years, though perchance I have no right to say it, the New Testament has been written; yet where is the legislator who has wisdom and practical talent enough to avail himself of the light which it sheds on the science of legislation?

The authority of government, even such as I am willing to submit to,—for I will cheerfully obey those who know and can do better than I, and in many things even those who neither know nor can do so well,—is still an impure one: to be strictly just, it must have the sanction and consent of the governed. It can have no pure right over my person and property but what I concede to it. The progress from an absolute to a limited monarchy, from a limited monarchy to a democracy, is a progress toward a true respect for the individual. Even the Chinese philosopher was wise enough to regard the individual as the basis of the empire. Is a democracy, such as we know it, the last improvement possible in government? Is it not possible to take a step further towards reorganizing and organizing the rights of man? There will never be a really free and enlightened State until the State comes to recognize the individual as a higher and independent power, from which all its own power and authority are derived, and treats him accordingly. I please myself with imagining a State at last which can afford to be just to all men, and to treat the individual with respect as a neighbor; which even would not think it inconsistent with its own repose if a few were to live aloof from it, not meddling with it, nor embraced by it, who fulfilled all the duties of neighbors and fellow-men. A State which bore this kind of fruit, and suffered it to drop off as fast as it ripened, would prepare the way for a still more perfect and glorious State, which also I have imagined, but not yet anywhere seen.

THE AGE OF HAPPY PROBLEMS

Herbert Gold
(1924–   )

Recently I have had occasion to live again near my old college campus. I went into a hole-in-the-wall bakery where the proprietor recognized me after ten years. "You haven't changed a bit, son," he said, "but can you still digest my pumpernickel? The stomach gets older, no? Maybe you want something softer now—a nice little loaf I got here."

He had worn slightly. But for me the change was from twenty-two to thirty-two, and it is this ten-year time that I want to think about—the generation which came back from the war to finish college on the GI Bill and is now deep into its career. We are the generation which knew the Depression only through the exhilaration of the burgeoning New Deal and the stunned passion of war. I remember the bank crash because my mother wept and I said, "If we're poor now, can I wear corduroy pants?" For the most part, we were taken care of and never hopelessly hunted jobs. Now some of us say we are cool, say we are beat; but most of us are allrightniks—doing okay. We are successful. In the late forties and the fifties, it was hard to know economic struggle and want—and for the most part we didn't experience these traditional elements of youth—and it was hard for the

skilled and the trained not to know success. We did not doubt overmuch. We have done well. How well?

"Money money money," as Theodore Roethke says.

> I have married my hands to perpetual agitation,
> I run, I run to the whistle of money.

> Money money money
> Water water water

I should like to take a look at some of the college idealists. The lawyer, fascinated by "the philosophy of law," now uses his study to put a smooth surface on his cleverness. Cardozo and Holmes? Very interesting, but let's find that loophole. The doctor who sent flowers to the first mother whose baby he delivered now specializes in "real-estate medicine"—his practice gives him capital for buying apartment houses. The architect who sat up all night haranguing his friends about Lewis Mumford and Frank Lloyd Wright now works for a mass builder who uses bulldozers to level trees and slopes, then puts up tri-level, semi-detached, twenty-year mortgaged, fundamentally identical dormitories for commuters. He admits that his designs make no decent sense, but they do have that trivial, all-important meaning: "It's what the market wants, man. You'd rather I taught city planning for six thousand a year?"

The actor becomes a disk jockey, the composer an arranger, the painter a designer; the writer does TV scripts in that new classic formula, "happy stories about happy people with happy problems." How hard it is to be used at our best! One of the moral issues of every age has been that of finding a way for men and women to test, reach, and overreach their best energies. Society has always worked to level us. Socrates has always made it hot for the citizens in the market place. But there was usually room for the heroic—hemlock not a serious deterrent—and perhaps rarely so much room on all levels as in the frontier turbulence of the nineteenth and early twentieth century in America. Hands reached out like the squirming, grasping, struggling railroad networks; the open society existed; freedom had a desperate allure for the strongly ambitious, and men stepped up to take their chances—Abraham Lincoln and William James, Mark Twain and Melville, Edison and Rockefeller and Bet-a-Million Gates.

Allowing for a glitter of nostalgia on what we imagine about the past, still something has happened to change the old, movemented, free, open American society to something persuasive, plausible, comfortable, and much less open. We are prosperous, we get what we think we want, we have a relatively stable economy without totalitarian rule. "I'm not selling out," my friend the architect say, "I'm buying in." Without attempting a simple explanation of the causes of this age of happy problems, let us look at its consequences for the new post-war young people who should be in full action toward their ambitions and the surest, sturdiest signs of a civilization's health.

What are these personal symptoms? How is the vital individual human creature doing in his staff meetings, at his family's table, over the baby's bassinet, and with that distant secret self that he may sometimes meet at the water cooler? Well, for this man it is very hard to be exceptional. Talent apart, he has too much to do, too much on his mind, to give himself over to his best energies. Think, for example, of the writers in the advertising agencies, on TV, or in the colleges. They all wanted to write great books; they tend now to prefer "competence" as an ideal to greatness. Some of them are trying, but they risk the situation of the girl in the short-story writing class: "I can't be a creative writer, I can't, because I'm still a stupid virgin." She will take up going steady, she will take up marriage; she will be mildly disappointed; she will remain as she was, but aging—"adjusted," "integrated," virgin to danger, struggle, and the main chance of love and work.

In composite, in our thirties, we of this prosperous and successful generation are still in good health and rather fast at tennis (but practicing place shots which will eliminate the need to rush the net); hair receding but still attractive to college girls, or at least recent graduates; a slight heaviness at the middle which makes us fit our jackets with especial care (sullen jowls beginning, too) or, if not that, a skinniness of anxiety (etching around the mouth, dryness of lips). We go to an athletic club. We play handball in heavy shirts "to sweat it off."

The girls we marry are beautiful in wondrous ways. Savant make-up is no longer sufficient. Blemishes are scraped until the skin is pink and new; scars are grown away by cortisone injections—what reason to be marked in this world?; noses are remade, the same for mother and daughter, just like heredity. Money is spent much more gracefully than in those fantastic times when silver coins were put in ears and jewels in navels.

The old truth—"we must all come from someplace"—is amended in 1956. We can create ourselves in our own image. And what is our own image? The buttery face in the Pond's advertisement, the epicene face in the Marlboro publicity.

The matters that we are told to worry about—and perhaps we think we worry about them—do not really trouble us. The prospect of war is like a vague headache, no worse. The memory of war is even dimmer. A depression is something which will reduce the value of our shares in the mutual fund, make us keep the old car another year. Radioactive fall-out and the slow destruction of the human species through cancerous mutation—well, what is so much bother to imagine cannot really come to pass. Who lets the newspaper interfere with a good meal?

II

Still, we are not blithe spirits; birds we are not. This generation is particularly distinguished by its worry about making its wives happy, about doing right by its kids (title of a hugely popular paperbound book: *How to Play with Your Child*), about acquiring enough leisure and symbols of leisure, which it hopes to cash in for moral comfort. *Fortune* reports a method used by salesmen to get the second room air conditioner to the couple which already has one in its bedroom. "The machine operates as expected? Fine? You sleep better with it? So do I, that's just dandy. But, friends, let me tell you how I sleep so much better now that I know my kiddies are cool and comfy, too."

This capitalizes on the child-oriented anxiety which the class known commercially as Young Marrieds has been taught to feel by modern psychiatry. Advertisements for *McCall's,* "The Magazine of Togetherness," demonstrate Togetherness in a brilliant summer scene. The man, wearing a white shirtlike apron and a proud simper, is bending to serve a steak to his wife (summer frock, spike heels), who will season it for them and for their happy gamboling children. The little boy and girl are peeking and smiling. The wife is lying in a garden chair. Togetherness consists in the husband's delighting his wife and kids by doing the cooking.

Actually, of course, most American women don't want to go this far. They are already equal with men. Women are usually too wise to define "equal" as "better than." It is not momism or any such simple psychological gimmick that tells this sad tale. The consumer culture—in which leisure is a menace to be met by anxious continual consuming—devours both the masculinity of men and the femininity of women. The life of consuming requires a neuter anxiety, and the pressure to conform, to watch for our cues, to consume, makes us all the same—we are customers—only with slightly different gadgets. Women have long bought men's shirts; men are buying colognes with "that exciting musky masculine tang."

Togetherness represents a curious effort by a woman's magazine to bring men back into the American family. Togetherness does not restore to the man a part of his old-time independence. It does not even indicate that he may be the provider with an independent role defined partly by ambitions outside his family. Instead, it suggests the joys of being a helpmate, a part of the woman's full life, and battens greedily on the contemporary male's anxiety about pleasing his wife. The Togetherness theme has been a great commercial success. A full-page advertisement by that canny old American institution, the New York Stock Exchange, shows a photograph of a harried young man pleading with a young woman on a parlor couch. She remains unconvinced, pouting, hands gloved and folded together, as brutal as the shocked beauties in the classical halitosis or B.O. tragedies. The caption reads: "Is the girl you want to marry reluctant to say Yes? Do you need to build character with your wife? Then just use the magic words: *I'll start a monthly investmen plan.*"

It used to be thought that answering economic needs was the main purpose of man's economic efforts. Now, however, an appeal to emotional insecurity about money—without crass financial trouble—can do good work for an advertiser. "Do you need to build character with your wife?" This is whimsey with a whammy in it. Money works symbolically to stimulate, then assuage male doubts.

> SHE: What can the stock do for our marriage?
>
> HE: It can help keep it sweet and jolly because when we own stock we are part-owners of the company.

In the image projected by this advertisement, the wife is prosecutor, judge, and jury. She may fall into a less exalted role, however, while her husband is downtown making the money which will go for food, clothing, shelter, and sound common stocks. That she too frets about keeping her marriage sweet and jolly is obvious. The popular media again point to trouble while pitching a new solution to her problems. One of the former radio soap operas is now sponsored by Sleepeze. Apparently almost everyone uses soap these days, but not everyone has caught on to the virtues of non-habit-forming sedatives. Want your husband to love you? This pill will help or your money back. "Ladies! Fall asleep without that unsightly twisting and turning."

It's time to mention Barbara. A tough wise creature of a girl, Barbara comes to this observation out of her marriage and love life: "Men worry too much about making the girl happy. We seem to scare them out of themselves. Let them really be pleased—that's what we want most of all—and then we'll be happy. Delighted. But really."

In other words, long live primary narcissism! And secondary. And tertiary. But let us call it by an older, better name—respect for the possibilities of the self. This includes the possibility of meaningful relationships with meaningful others.

III

Our wounds as a people in this time and place are not unique in kind, but the quality of difference makes this a marvelously disturbing period. The economic problem, no longer rooted in hunger for essential goods, food, housing, clothing, is an illustration of the difference. Sure, we are still busy over food—but packaged foods, luxury foods, goodies in small cans; housing—but the right house in the right neighborhood with the right furnishings and the right mortgage; clothing—but the cap with the strap in the back, Ivy League pants, charcoal gray last year and narrow lapels this year, and male fashions changing as fast as female.

It used to be thought that, given money, relative job security, and the short work week, culture would then bloom like the gardens in the suburbs and the individual spirit would roar with the driving power of a Thunderbird getting away after a red light.

Who could have predicted that we would have to keep pace with a cultural assembly line in the leisure-time sweatshop? At least in the older sweatshop, you sighed, packed, and left the plant at last. Now we are forever harassed to give more, more, more. We no longer have to keep up with the Joneses; we must keep up with Clifton Fadiman. He is watching *you*. The steady pressure to consume, absorb, participate, receive, by eye, ear, mouth, and mail, involves a cruelty to intestines, blood pressure, and psyche unparalleled in history. The frontiersmen could build a stockade against the Indians, but what home is safe from Gilbert Highet? We are being killed with kindness. We are being stifled with cultural and material joys. Our wardrobes are full. What we really need is a new fabric that we don't have to wrinkle, spot, wash, iron, or wear. At a beautiful moment in

Walden, Thoreau tells how he saw a beggar walking along with all his belongings in a single sack on his back. He wanted to weep for the poor man—because he still had that sack to carry.

The old-style sweatshop crippled mainly the working people. Now there are no workers left in America; we are almost all middle class as to income and expectations. Even the cultural elite labors among the latest in hi-fi equipment, trips to Acapulco and Paris, the right books in the sewn paper editions (Elizabeth Bowen, Arnold Toynbee, Jacques Barzun—these are the cultivated ones, remember), *Fortune* and the *Reporter,* art movies and the barbecue pit and the Salzburg music festival. It is too easy to keep up with the Joneses about cars and houses, but the Robert Shaw Chorale is a *challenge.* In the meantime, the man in the sweatshop is divorced or psychoanalyzed (these are perhaps remedies in a few cases); he raises adjusted children, or kills them trying; he practices Togetherness in a home with a wife who is frantic to be a woman and a nonwoman at the same time; he broods about a job which does not ask the best that he can give. But it does give security; it is a good job. (In college this same man learned about the extreme, tragic instances of desire. Great men, great books. Now he reads Evelyn Waugh.)

In his later, philosophical transmogrification, David Riesman consoles the radar-flaunting other-directeds by holding out the reward of someday being "autonomous" if they are very, very good. Same thing, brother, same thing. When he describes the autonomous personality's "intelligent" distinctions among consumer products, exercising his creative imagination by figuring out why "High Noon" is a better western than Gene Autry, well, then, in the words of Elvis Presley:

Ah feel so lonely,
Ah feel so lo-oh-oh-lonely.

We're in Heartbreak Hotel where, as another singer, Yeats, put it:

The ceremony of innocence is drowned;
The best lack all conviction, while the worst
Are filled with a passionate intensity.

Refusal to share to the fullest degree in the close amity of the leisure-time sweatshop is—for Mr. Riesman—a kind of ethical bohemianism. His autonomous consumer, social, trained, and in the know, is a critic of the distinctions between the Book-of-the-Month Club and the Reader's Subscription, Inc., marks the really good shows in his TV guide, buys educational comic books for his children, tastes the difference in fine after-dinner coffee, knows that the novel is a dead form and why. Bumper to bumper in the traffic home from work, or jammed into the commuter train, he has plenty of time to think. And he does think (thinking means worrying) while the radio blares "The House with the Stained Glass Window" or "The Magic of Believing," a little rock-and-roll philosophical number.

Does he have a moral problem, let's say, about leaving a changing neighborhood "for the sake of the children"? He is a liberal, of course, but after all, the Negroes who are moving in come from a different world and he should not inflict his principles on his children. Still, there is a certain discomfort. He discusses it with his analyst. *Why* does he suffer from this moral qualm? Does it have some link with the ever ambiguous relationship with parents? *What* moral problem? They are all psychological. Anxiety can be consumed like any product. And from his new, split-level, sapling-planted housing development he speeds into the city now ten miles further out.

We are a disappointed generation. We are a discontented people. Our manner of life says it aloud even if discreetly our public faces smile. The age of happy problems has brought us confusion and anxiety amid the greatest material comfort the world has ever seen. Culture has become a consolation for the sense of individual powerlessness in politics, work, and love. With gigantic organizations determining our movements, manipulating the dominion over self which alone makes meaningful communion with others possible, we ask leisure, culture, and recreation to return to us a sense of ease and authority. But work, love, and culture need to be connected. Otherwise we carry our powerlessness with us onto the aluminum garden furniture in the back yard. Power lawn mowers we can buy, of course.

The solution in our age of happy problems is not to install (on time) a central air-conditioning system and a color TV this year because the room air conditioner and the black-and-white TV last year did not change our lives in any important respect. The solution is not in stylish religious conversions or a new political party. The answer is not even that Panglossian fantasy about "the autonomous personality" which will naturally emerge out of the fatal meeting of the other-directed consumer with a subscription to the *Saturday Review*.

The ache of unfulfilled experience throbs within us. Our eyes hurt. Vicarious pleasures buzz in our heads. Isn't there something more, something more?

There is still awareness; there is still effort. "It should be every man's ambition to be his own doctor." This doesn't mean that he should not see a dentist when his tooth hurts, perhaps a psychoanalyst when

his psyche hurts; but he must hold in mind the ideal maximum of humanity —the exercise of intelligence and desire within a context of active health. The Stoic philosophers had a great although impossible idea for these crowding times: cultivate your garden. We cannot retreat from the world any more—we never really could—but we can look for our best gardens within the world's trouble. There we must give ourselves silence and space; we can see what the will wants; we can make decisions. Only then—having come to terms with our own particularities—can we give the world more than a graceless prefabricated commodity.

Hope? Some sweet Barbara is hope. And a work we love. And the strength, O Lord, not to accept the easy pleasures (easy anxieties) which have pleased us (made us anxious) so far. And the strength, O Lord, you who reign undefined above the psychoanalysts and the sociologists, the market researchers and the advertising agencies, the vice presidents and the book clubs, to refuse the easy solutions which have becalmed us so far.

Then with good belly luck we will be able to digest strong, irregular, yeasty, black bread.

THE CYBERNETIC AGE: AN OPTIMIST'S VIEW

Glenn T. Seaborg
(1912–   )

What we need is a computer that will tell us where all other computers are leading us. We have computers that make up corporation payrolls, review a nation's tax returns, diagnose diseases, help design, produce, and market new products, control air and auto traffic, operate bakeries, hire and fire, read and write, learn and teach, and even play Cupid—though fortunately not yet to other computers, just among people. But the ultimate computer that can assess the significance of all this has yet to be built and programed. This task is still left to humans.

And it is an incredibly difficult task. Why? Because the ultimate potential of the computer puts us to the test as human beings. It brings up questions we have lived with for centuries, but never have been asked to answer fully or act upon if we believed we knew the answers. It gives us new freedom and yet tremendous responsibilities which, if not acted upon, could result in a loss of almost all freedom. It presents us with choices and decisions of enormous consequences. It offers man a remarkable new chance to shape his own destiny, but asks him to be God-like enough to select that destiny without much margin for error.

Let me project a few thoughts on how the computer may forge our future—and, more important, on some of the ideas and alternatives with which we must come to grips if we are going to control the direction of that future.

To begin with, I believe that cybernation—the complete adaptation of computer-like equipment to industrial, economic, and social activity—will represent a quantum jump in the extension of man. The Industrial Revolution amplified (and to a large extent replaced) man's muscle as a productive force. Still, a large percentage of our production resulted from the energies of man and beast. Today in the United States, only a fraction of 1 per cent of our productive power results from the physical energy of human beings or animals.

Springing from our Scientific Revolu-

tion of recent decades is what is being called a "Cybernetic Revolution." This revolution, which, comparatively speaking, is only in its infancy, amplifies (and will to a large extent replace) man's nervous system. Actually, this is an understatement because computers amplify the collective intelligence of men—the intelligence of society—and, while the effect of the sum of men's physical energies may be calculated, a totally different and compounded effect results from combining facts and ideas—the knowledge generated within a society or civilization. Add this effect to the productive capacity of the machine driven by an almost limitless energy source like the nucleus of the atom, and the resulting system can perform feats almost staggering to our imagination. With the fullest development of cybernation we could be faced with prospects that challenge our very relationships to such basic concepts as freedom and the nature of work and leisure.

Let me suggest a few random scenes from the coming Cybernetic Age which contain some significant implications. I will not vouch for the accuracy of these forecasts or try to predict the year they might occur, but perhaps you can imagine yourself in one of these three situations:

Situation No. 1: You have flown out of town on a business trip and upon arrival at your destination have a few spare hours in which to visit an old friend. At the airport you rent a car, or some other type of ground vehicle. The procedure for putting you in the driver's seat is simple and efficient. You place an identifying card containing your bank account number and a microfiche of your fingerprints in a slot, and the fingers of your free hand over a flat, innocent-looking plate. Within seconds you have been identified as the owner of the card and your credit rating has been checked.

The keys to your rented car are released to you and you are on your way.

Driving through town you encounter a minimum of delay at the busiest hour because the traffic lights are controlled by computers. But, anxious to see your old friend, you step up your speed once you are on the outskirts of town and, without realizing it, you exceed the speed limit by a few miles an hour. You remain unaware of this violation until you return home, at which time you receive a notice of it and learn that the violation calls for a fine, which, you also learn, has already been charged to your bank account.

How did this happen? It was almost as simple as renting the car. An inconspicuous device clocked your speed and recorded your auto tags. It reported the violation to the owner of the vehicle whose own computer had your records at hand and instantly "turned you in." The computer operated by the long arm of the law had no difficulty in tracking down both you and your bank account, so justice was swift and complete.

You are fairly well conditioned to this sort of situation by now, but sometimes you have moments of doubt and anxiety about what happened. If someone, or something, was watching you that closely on the road, where else might they be watching you? What if the system was in error—if someone, somewhere, was "adjusting" it so as to create more violators and bring in a little more revenue? But paying the fine was far easier than trying to investigate that possibility, so you give up what you once considered a legitimate right. Furthermore, you've heard that next year they're installing systems which will automatically regulate your speed on those roads, so you won't have to worry about exceeding the limit. You won't have that worry—or choice.

I will not belabor the implications of this situation. I believe they speak for themselves. Let me move on to situation No. 2:

For several days you have not been feeling well, and you call your local health center for an appointment. You can remember when you used to call your doctor, but it's been many years since he's bothered with initial diagnoses, and he would be the first to admit he could not be as thorough or accurate as the health center.

At the center you give all the necessary information to a medical secretary, whose typewriter feeds it into a computer system. First comes your identification number, which automatically supplies the system with your previous medical history, then all your new complaints and symptoms. On the basis of the information given so far and a comparison with your previous history, the computer may venture an immediate diagnosis, but if it has any doubts—and it is a highly conservative computer—it recommends one or several diagnostic tests. The tests are conducted simply and efficiently with the aid of one or two capable medical technicians and a battery of equipment.

The battery of diagnostic equipment programs its findings into the central computer which already has your previous medical history and your current complaints. Within seconds, after the tests are completed, the system presents its full diagnosis. At the same time it also makes recommendation for treatment, perhaps printing out a prescription which can be filled before you leave the center.

Does your doctor ever see patients? The computer refers a few cases to him because of their unusual interest. The high level of medicine he practices now enables him to help these patients. Their cases also help him in his work with engineers to improve the design of diagnostic and treatment systems and to train the many medical technicians who are needed to handle the increased population.

As in the first situation, there are a multitude of implications in this project. But let me proceed to situation No. 3:

You are a key man in a company that produces certain products for the home. You feel quite fortunate because you have a creative job in a highly automated plant. Market surveys analyzed by computers tell the company of the need for a new product. You sit at a desk containing a large fluorescent screen and with an electronic "lightpen" draw your conception of the new product. As you design the product you "tell" the computerized screen what materials you want the product to be made of. The system coordinates the information from the lightpen with your other instructions. As you work, it guides you in your design by making recommendations, by showing you on command the stress and strain in various points of your design, by correcting your errors, by recommending alternatives and improvements.

When both you and the system are satisfied with your handiwork, you release the design for manufacture. The system has theoretically tested the product so that no initial sample or test model is necessary. It turns the design over to another department—probably other computers—which calculates and orders the materials necessary to produce it, sets up the required manufacturing equipment, and prepares the production schedule. You never see the product, but you know it has been turned out just the way you envisioned it. And how long will it be before the computer will make it without you?

To some people these three examples sound like science fiction. Others will refer to them as "windy futurism." But they are far from being either. Some of the devices and methods mentioned are already in existence and in practical use. Others are in the development stages. And many more are not only technically feasible but may someday become economically and socially acceptable.

What are some of the implications in these examples, and what bearing will they have on our future? Running through all three examples were many common features: depersonalization, a separation of man and product, a collapse of time, a further reduction of human work, and a shift of needs and skills. All of these offer both threats and promises. I believe that the promises will eventually override the threats, but not before they have made us face and solve a great many problems we have not had to face before. This in itself is going to account for a great deal of human growth.

There is no doubt that the Cybernetic Revolution is going to make us re-examine the relationship between our freedoms and our responsibilities within the framework of society and find ways to guarantee a maximum of freedom for the individual within a highly organized society.

Another way in which the Cybernetic Revolution is going to force considerable human growth is in making us take a more rational, long-range approach in handling our affairs—our relationships with our fellow man and with nature. We are beginning to learn that the crisis-to-crisis approach that we have been using to carry on will no longer work. Science and technology have shrunk time by increasing the rate of change and have forged the world into a global civilization capable of exerting tremendous forces in a highly interrelated sphere of activity. We must make the fullest use of tools like the computer to help us prevent chaos and self-annihilation in such a complex world.

Looking at the most positive aspects of the computer, and projecting how its growing applications might control and multiply the forces of science and technology, one can foresee some remarkable "alternative futures." The most promising among these would be an era of abundance for all mankind—one in which most goods and services are provided by cybernated systems. And this brings us to the most striking aspect of human growth that could take place as a result of the Cybernetic Revolution—the change in our relationship to labor and leisure.

For a good part of our history we have been shaping through the manipulation of wealth what Peter Drucker calls "economic man." Perhaps the Cybernetic Revolution will carry us to a new level of man—a higher level—at which we will enjoy different values. On this subject it is interesting to recall what the great economist John Maynard Keynes wrote in 1932 in his *Essays in Persuasion:*

> When the accumulation of wealth is no longer of high social importance there will be great changes in the code of morals. We shall be able to rid ourselves of many of the pseudo-moral principles which have hag-ridden us for 200 years, by which we have exalted some of the most distasteful of human qualities into the position of highest values.

If the Cybernetic Revolution produces such a social millennium, a radical change in man's relationship to work would take place and the growth of leisure time would pose new problems to be solved.

As a result, our ideas on leisure would change drastically. Most people today do not recognize the true value of leisure. A little leisure has always been treasured, and there have been societies in which certain men and women lived in almost complete leisure, though at the expense of others' labor. But the idea of almost an entire civilization living in even relative leisure is beyond the comprehension of many of us and still frowned upon by most others.

A civilization equipped and educated to live in an era of relative leisure can bring about a new Golden Age—one without a slave base, other than those mechanical and cybernetic slaves produced by the ingenuity of a higher level of man. Such an age does not have to be, as a few predict, a civilization of drugged, purposeless people controlled by a small elite. But it could tragically become that, if we did nothing but let ourselves be swept along by some of the forces in motion today.

There are indications that some of these forces are just that overwhelming. There are also indications, however, that society is reacting to the "feedback" of certain personal and social effects of technology. This feedback is coming from more and more people in all levels of society and all walks of life. It is expressing an increasing uneasiness about the state of our personal and community lives in a highly materialistic society, a concern over the individual's role in the growing complexity and impersonalization of that society, a groping for "national purpose," and a feeling that the unity of man, referred to by poets and philosophers throughout the ages, is becoming a reality with immense psychological and physical implications.

To me, these feelings forecast the need for a huge re-evaluation of our goals and values, and it will be in our universities where such a re-evaluation will take place. Perhaps its seeds have already been sown in the current unrest on the campuses of many of our universities. From this re-evaluation, from the debates and soul-searching that take place, will evolve both a new understanding and reinforcement of those old ideals which are still valid, and new ideals and goals. Together they may provide us with something like a comprehensive philosophy of life to match the physical unity of mankind rapidly being fostered by today's science and technology.

If we can use this new philosophy to guide the great scientific and technological forces we have created, we could witness, possibly within a few decades, the equivalent of a new "human breakthrough"—an advance to a new stage of social development—one that was initiated by our reactions to today's trends.

In such a development the university, the greatest depository and dispenser of man's knowledge, should play a major role. In fact, I can see no other institution more logically equipped to be the central force in this evolutionary process, to develop, refine, and pass on to the new generations a new heritage of a higher level of mankind.

But if we are to carry out such a monumental task, many changes will probably have to take place in the universities and our educational system in general. One such change will involve reconciling the continuing importance of specialization with a growing need for interdisciplinary thinking—not only in science and technology, but in all areas of our economic, social, and human development. Specialization has been giving us increasing amounts of knowledge, but the world cries out today for more of something beyond knowledge —for *wisdom*.

All of this demands a new role of leadership from our educational system.

Most of today's schools are involved to a great degree in serving the requirements of an industrial age, in fulfilling the needs of a society which has been only partly and indirectly of their making. In the future, this role will shift to one in which the nature of society is determined more by the thinking of the university, and in which the industrial community will tend to serve goals created by that thinking.

What we must look for from the universities is the development of an education that turns out individuals of the highest intellect and broadest outlook, able to understand man and machine, and live creatively with both. Such an education could not be expected in a four-year curriculum or even a six- or eight-year one. It would start as early as the beginning of school or sooner and involve continuing education of one type or another throughout a person's lifetime. And, as Robert Theobald indicates, education in the age of the Cybernetic Revolution would not be directed toward "earning a living" but toward "total living."

This is a big order involving imagination, energy, and bold leadership from the academic world. But the time is certainly ripe for this kind of leadership.

The coming Cybernetic Revolution which calls forth these new goals for education will also give education valuable new tools and technologies for pursuing them. The computer will make knowledge more accessible. It will perform miracles in compiling, organizing, and analyzing information. It should link the knowledge of the world's libraries and depositories of information into networks responding like a giant brain. And it should put at the fingertips of anyone who wishes to be a modern-day Faust all the knowledge he desires without selling his soul to the Devil.

Some believe that, in a cybernated utopia, human incentives will diminish and we will completely stagnate. I don't believe this will happen at all. New incentives will arise as man moves up to higher levels of needs. The quest for new knowledge will always grow. The domain of science is practically boundless. We are only beginning our adventures in space, and we still have a long way to go in understanding many things about this planet and the life on it.

Much has been said about the impersonalization caused by the growth of machines, but as a result of this growth I can see a new and better relationship arising among men. If in the past we have spent most of our time working with machines, serving and being served by them, naturally we feel a sense of isloation and alienation among them. But when machines have truly freed us from the necessity of physical work, perhaps we can better accept them for what they are and have the time to see and relate to other people in a different light. When we have more time to be with other people—not accidentally, on crowded buses, in elevators, in markets and offices, but in places of our own choosing at our own leisure—we may feel differently toward one another.

When we are less likely to be in competition with one another, much of the hypocrisy of society will vanish and more honest relationships will be formed. And, finally, when we can walk down the street—anywhere in the world—in a community free from want, where every human being has a sense of dignity not gained at the expense of others, we might not only walk free from fear but with a great feeling of exaltation.

If we can make the transition of living with and using the complex machines of the future in a *human-oriented* society, the rewards will be worth any effort we can make. As everyone knows, such a transition will not be easy, because it involves so much of what Eric Hoffer has called "The Ordeal of Change." But I think we will have to make such a transition eventually. We may have already begun to do so.

THE MAN AT THE GIANT SWITCHBOARD *

Harvey Cox
(1929–   )

Technopolitan man sits at a vast and immensely complicated switchboard. He is *homo symbolicus,* man the communicator, and the metropolis is a massive network of communications. A whole world of possibilities for communication lies within his reach. The contemporary urban region represents an ingenious device for vastly enlarging the range of human communication and widening the scope of individual choice. Urbanization thus contributes to the freedom of man. This is perfectly evident when we think for example of cinema theaters and restaurants. Residents of a city of 10,000 may be limited to one or two theaters, while people who live in a city of a million can choose among perhaps fifty films on a given night. The same principle holds for restaurants, schools, and even in some measure for job opportunities or prospective marriage partners. Urban man is free to choose from a wider range of alternatives. Thus his manhood as *homo symbolicus* is enhanced.

But freedom always demands discipline. The mere availability of such a

* This is part of a chapter that appeared in *The Secular City* (New York: The Macmillan Company, 1965).

wide spectrum of possibilities requires an adjustment of urban man's behavior. He must exercise choice more frequently, and choice always means exclusion. He doesn't just "go to the movies" on a free evening, as his more rural counterpart might; he must choose one from among the fifty films now showing. This means a conscious decision *not* to see the other forty-nine.

In the area of personal relationships this selectivity becomes more demanding. Urban man has a wider variety of "contacts" than his rural counterpart; he can choose only a limited number for friends. He must have more or less impersonal relationships with most of the people with whom he comes in contact precisely in order to choose certain friendships to nourish and cultivate. This selectivity can best be symbolized perhaps by the unplugged telephone or the unlisted number. A person does not request an unlisted number to cut down on the depth of his relationships. Quite the opposite; he does so to guard and deepen the worthwhile relationship he has against being dissolved in the deluge of messages that would come if one were open on principle and on an equal basis to anyone who tried to get through, including the increasing army of telephone salesmen who violate one's privacy so arrogantly. Those we want to know have our number; others do not: We are free to use the switchboard without being victimized by its infinite possibilities.

Urban man must distinguish carefully between his private life and his public relationships. Since he depends on such a complex net of services to maintain himself in existence in a modern city, the majority of his transactions will have to be public and will be what sociologists call functional or secondary. In most of his relationships he will be dealing with people he cannot afford to be interested

in as individuals but must deal with in terms of the services they render to him and he to them. This is essential in urban life. Supermarket checkers or gas-meter readers who became enmeshed in the lives of the people they were serving would be a menace. They would soon cause a total breakdown in the essential systems of which they are integral parts. Urban life demands that we treat most of the people we meet as persons—not as things, but not as intimates either. This in turn produces the kind of "immunization" against personal encounters which Louis Wirth explains this way:

> Characteristically, urbanites meet one another in highly segmental roles. They are, to be sure, dependent upon more people for the satisfactions of their life-needs than are rural people and thus are associated with a greater number of organized groups, but they are less dependent upon particular persons, and their dependence upon others is confined to a highly fractionalized aspect of the other's round of activity. This is essentially what is meant by saying that the city is characterized by secondary rather than primary contacts. The contacts of the city may indeed be face to face, but they are nevertheless impersonal, superficial, transitory, and segmental. The reserve, the indifference, and the blasé outlook which urbanites manifest in their relationships may thus be regarded as devices for immunizing themselves against the personal claims and expectations of others.[1]

This immunization results in a way of life which often appears cold and even heartless to those unfamiliar with the dynamics of urban living. Here both

[1] Louis Wirth, "Urbanism as a Way of Life" in Paul Hatt and Albert J. Reiss, Jr. (eds.), *Cities and Society* (Glencoe, Ill.: The Free Press, 1958), p. 54.

writers and sociologists have missed the point. Cultural romantics such as Rilke and Ortega recoiled in distaste at what they took to be the cruelty of the city. In sociology a similar criticism was also voiced. Relationships in the city, it was complained, tended to be divested of their really human substance and made mechanical and lifeless.

One of the most influential sociological critics of the shape of urban life was a German scholar named Ferdinand Tönnies (1855–1936), whose work has continued to exert a considerable influence on modern sociology and cultural analysis. In 1887 Tönnies published a book in which he contrasted the coherent, organic togetherness of *Gemeinschaft* (community) with the more rational, planned, and partial nexus of the *Gesellschaft* (society). Kaspar Naegele summarizes Tönnies' distinction:

> Relations of the *Gemeinschaft* type are more inclusive; persons confront each other as ends, they cohere more durably. . . . In *Gesellschaft* their mutual regard is circumscribed by a sense of specific, if not formal obligation. . . . A transaction can occur without any other encounters, leaving both parties virtually anonymous.[2]

Tönnies is talking about what some sociologists describe as "primary" versus "secondary" relationships, or "organic" versus "functional" relationships. Having lived both as a villager and as an urbanite I know just what these terms mean. During my boyhood, my parents never referred to "the milkman," "the insurance agent," "the junk collector." These people were, respectively, Paul Weaver, Joe Villanova, and Roxy Barazano. All of our

family's market transactions took place within a web of wider and more inclusive friendship and kinship ties with the same people. They were never anonymous. In fact, the occasional salesman or repairman whom we did not know was always viewed with dark suspicion until we could make sure where he came from, who his parents were, and whether his family was "any good." Trips to the grocery store, gasoline station, or post office were inevitably social visits, never merely functional contacts.

Now, as an urbanite, my transactions are of a very different sort. If I need to have the transmission on my car repaired, buy a television antenna, or cash a check, I find myself in functional relationships with mechanics, salesmen, and bank clerks whom I never see in any other capacity. These "contacts" are in no sense "mean, nasty or brutish," though they do tend to be short, at least not any longer than the time required to make the transaction and to exchange a brief pleasantry. Some of these human contacts occur with considerable frequency, so that I come to know the mannerisms and maybe even the names of some of the people. But the relationships are unifaceted and "segmental." I meet these people in no other context. To me they remain essentially just as anonymous as I do to them. Indeed, in the case of the transmission repairman, I hope I never see him again— not because he is in any way unpleasant, but because my only possible reason for seeing him again would be a new and costly breakdown in my car's gear box. The important point here is that my relationships with bank clerks and garagemen are no less human or authentic merely because we both prefer to keep them anonymous. Here is where much theological analysis of urbanization has gone hopelessly astray.

Theologians have spent themselves in

well-intentioned forays against the "de-personalization of urban life," often fed by a misunderstanding of Martin Buber's philosophy of "I and Thou" relationships. In contrast to those who utilize his categories in a different manner, Buber himself never claimed that *all* our relationships should be of the deep, interpersonal I–Thou variety. He knew this experience was a rich and rare one. But Buber did open the door for misunderstanding by neglecting to study with sufficient thoroughness the place of types of relationships which actually constitute most of our lives, a point to which we shall return shortly.

A recent survey by some Protestant ministers in a new urban high-rise apartment area where they intended to establish house church groups illustrates the misplaced emphasis on I–Thou relationships that has marked modern Christian theology. In conducting their study, the pastors were shocked to discover that the recently arrived apartment dwellers, whom they expected to be lonely and desperate for relationships, did not want to meet their neighbors socially and had no interest whatever in church or community groups. At first the ministers deplored what they called a "social pathology" and a "hedgehog" psychology. Later, however, they found that what they had encountered was a sheer survival technique. Resistance against efforts to subject them to neighborliness and socialization is a skill apartment dwellers must develop if they are to maintain any human relationships at all. It is an essential element in the shape of the secular city.

In condemning urban anonymity, the ministers had made the mistake of confusing a preurban ethos with the Christian concept of *koinonia*. The two are not the same. The ministers had wanted to develop a kind of village togetherness among people, one of whose main reasons for moving to high-rise apartments is to escape the relationships enforced on them by the lack of anonymity of the village. Apartment dwellers, like most urbanites, live a life in which relationships are founded on free selection and common interest, usually devoid of spatial proximity. Studies have shown that even friendship patterns within a large apartment complex follow age, family-size, and personal-interest lines. They do not ordinarily spring from the mere adjacence of apartments. Thus, to complain that apartment people often live for years just down the hall from another family but do not "really get to know them" overlooks the fact that many specifically choose *not* to "know" their spatial neighbors in any intimate sense. This allows them more time and energy to cultivate the friends they themselves select. This does not mean the apartment dweller cannot love his next-door neighbor. He can and often does so, certainly no less frequently than the small-town resident. But he does so by being a dependable fellow tenant, by bearing his share of the common responsibility they both have in that segment of their lives shaped by residence. This does not require their becoming cronies.

All this means that the urban secular man is summoned to a different *kind* of neighborliness than his town-dwelling predecessor practiced. Much like the Samaritan described by Jesus in the story he told in response to the question "Who is my neighbor?," his main responsibility is to do competently what needs to be done to assure his neighbor's health and well-being. The man who fell among thieves was not the next-door neighbor of the Samaritan, but he helped him in an efficient, unsentimental way. He did not form an I–Thou relationship with him but bandaged his wounds and made sure the innkeeper had enough cash to cover his expenses.

Urban anonymity need not be heartless. Village sociability can mask a murderous hostility. Loneliness is undoubtedly a serious problem in the city, but it cannot be met by dragooning urban people into relationships which decimate their privacy and reduce their capacity to live responsibly with increasing numbers of neighbors. The church investigators who shook their heads over the evasiveness of the apartment dwellers had forgotten this. They had come to the city with a village theology and had stumbled upon an essential protective device, the polite refusal to be chummy, without which urban existence could not be human. They had overlooked the fact that technopolitan man *must* cultivate and guard his privacy. He must restrict the number of people who have his number or know his name.

The small-town dweller, on the other hand, lives within a restricted web of relationships and senses a larger world he may be missing. Since the people he knows also know one another, he gossips more and yearns to hear gossip. His private life is public and vice versa. While urban man is unplugging his telephone, town man (or his wife) may be listening in on the party line or its modern equivalent, gossiping at the kaffee-klatsch.

Urban man, in contrast, wants to maintain a clear distinction between private and public. Otherwise public life would overwhelm and dehumanize him. His life represents a point touched by dozens of systems and hundreds of people. His capacity to know some of them better necessitates his minimizing the depth of his relationships to many others. Listening to the postman gossip becomes for urban man an act of sheer graciousness, since he probably has no interest in the people the postman wants to talk about. Unlike my parents, who suspected all strangers, he tends to be wary not of the functionaries he doesn't know but of those he does.

SHORT STORIES

THE BET

Anton P. Chekhov
(1860–1904)

I

It was a dark autumn night. The old banker was pacing from corner to corner of his study, recalling to his mind the party he gave in the autumn fifteen years before. There were many clever people at the party and much interesting conversation. They talked among other things of capital punishment. The guests, among them not a few scholars and journalists, for the most part disapproved of capital punishment. They found it obsolete as a means of punishment, unfitted to a Christian State and immoral. Some of them thought that capital punishment should be replaced universally by life-imprisonment.

"I don't agree with you," said the host. "I myself have experienced neither capital punishment nor life-imprisonment, but if one may judge *a priori,* then in my opinion capital punishment is more moral and more humane than imprisonment. Execution kills instantly, life-imprisonment kills by degrees. Who is the more humane executioner, one who kills you in a few seconds or one who draws the life out of you incessantly, for years?"

"They're both equally immoral," remarked one of the guests, "because their purpose is the same, to take away life. The State is not God. It has no right to take away that which it cannot give back, if it should so desire."

Among the company was a lawyer, a young man of about twenty-five. On being asked his opinion, he said:

"Capital punishment and life-imprisonment are equally immoral; but if I were offered the choice between them, I would certainly choose the second. It's better to live somehow than not to live at all."

There ensued a lively discussion. The banker who was then younger and more nervous suddenly lost his temper, banged his fist on the table, and turning to the young lawyer, cried out:

"It's a lie. I bet you two millions you wouldn't stick in a cell even for five years."

"If you mean it seriously," replied the lawyer, "then I bet I'll stay not five but fifteen."

"Fifteen! Done!" cried the banker "Gentlemen, I stake two millions."

"Agreed. You stake two millions, I my freedom," said the lawyer.

So this wild, ridiculous bet came to pass. The banker, who at that time had too many millions to count, spoiled and capricious, was beside himself with rapture. During supper he said to the lawyer jokingly:

"Come to your senses, young man, before it's too late. Two millions are nothing to me, but you stand to lose three or four of the best years of your life. I say three or four, because you'll never stick it out any longer. Don't forget either, you unhappy man, that voluntary is much heavier than enforced imprisonment. The idea that you have the right to free yourself at any moment will poison the whole of your life in the cell. I pity you."

And now the banker, pacing from corner to corner, recalled all this and asked himself:

"Why did I make this bet? What's the good? The lawyer loses fifteen years of his life and I throw away two millions. Will it convince people that capital punishment is worse or better than imprisonment for life? No, no! all stuff and rubbish. On my part, it was the caprice of a well-fed man; on the lawyer's pure greed of gold."

He recollected further what happened after the evening party. It was decided that the lawyer must undergo his imprisonment under the strictest observation, in a garden wing of the banker's house. It was agreed that during the period he would be deprived of the right to cross the threshold, to see living people, to hear human voices, and to receive letters and newspapers. He was permitted to have a musical instrument, to read books, to write letters, to drink wine and smoke tobacco. By the agreement he could communicate, but only in silence, with the outside world through a little window specially constructed for this purpose. Everything necessary, books, music, wine, he could receive in any quantity by sending a note through the window. The agreement provided for all the minutest

details, which made the confinement strictly solitary, and it obliged the lawyer to remain exactly fifteen years from twelve o'clock of November 14th, 1870 to twelve o'clock of November 14th, 1885. The least attempt on his part to violate the conditions, to escape if only for two minutes before the time freed the banker from the obligation to pay him the two millions.

During the first year of imprisonment, the lawyer, as far as it was possible to judge from his short notes, suffered terribly from loneliness and boredom. From his wing day and night came the sound of the piano. He rejected wine and tobacco. "Wine," he wrote, "excites desires, and desires are the chief foes of a prisoner; besides, nothing is more boring than to drink good wine alone, and tobacco spoils the air in his room." During the first year the lawyer was sent books of a light character; novels with a complicated love interest, stories of crime and fantasy, comedies, and so on.

In the second year the piano was heard no longer and the lawyer asked only for classics. In the fifth year, music was heard again, and the prisoner asked for wine. Those who watched him said that during the whole of that year he was only eating, drinking, and lying on his bed. He yawned often and talked angrily to himself. Books he did not read. Sometimes at nights he would sit down to write. He would write for a long time and tear it all up in the morning. More than once he was heard to weep.

In the second half of the sixth year, the prisoner began zealously to study languages, philosophy, and history. He fell on these subjects so hungrily that the banker hardly had time to get books enough for him. In the space of four years about six hundred volumes were bought at his request. It was while that passion lasted that the banker received the following letter from the prisoner: "My dear gaoler, I am writing these lines in six languages. Show them to experts. Let them read them. If they do not find one single mistake, I beg you to give orders to have a gun fired off in the garden. By the noise I shall know that my efforts have not been in vain. The geniuses of all ages and countries speak in different languages; but in them all burns the same flame. Oh, if you knew my heavenly happiness now that I can understand them!" The prisoner's desire was fulfilled. Two shots were fired in the garden by the banker's order.

Later on, after the tenth year, the lawyer sat immovable before his table and read only the New Testament. The banker found it strange that a man who in four years had mastered six hundred erudite volumes, should have spent nearly a year in reading one book, easy to understand and by no means thick. The New Testament was then replaced by the history of religions and theology.

During the last two years of his confinement the prisoner read an extraordinary amount, quite haphazard. Now he would apply himself to the natural sciences, then he would read Byron or Shakespeare. Notes used to come from him in which he asked to be sent at the same time a book on chemistry, a text-book of medicine, a novel, and some treatise on philosophy or theology. He read as though he were swimming in the sea among broken pieces of wreckage, and in his desire to save his life was eagerly grasping one piece after another.

II

The banker recalled all this, and thought:

"To-morrow at twelve o'clock he receives his freedom. Under the agreement, I shall have to pay him two millions. If I pay, it's all over with me. I am ruined for ever . . .''

Fifteen years before he had too many millions to count, but now he was afraid to ask himself which he had more of, money or debts. Gambling on the Stock-Exchange, risky speculation, and the recklessness of which he could not rid himself even in old age, had gradually brought his business to decay; and the fearless, self-confident, proud man of business had become an ordinary banker, trembling at every rise and fall in the market.

"That cursed bet," murmured the old man clutching his head in despair. . . . "Why didn't the man die? He's only forty years old. He will take away my last farthing, marry, enjoy life, gamble on the Exchange, and I will look on like an envious beggar and hear the same words from him every day: 'I'm obliged to you for the happiness of my life. Let me help you.' No, it's too much! The only escape from bankruptcy and disgrace—is that the man should die."

The clock had just struck three. The banker was listening. In the house every one was asleep, and one could hear only the frozen trees whining outside the windows. Trying to make no sound, he took out of his safe the key of the door which had not been opened for fifteen years, put on his overcoat, and went out of the house. The garden was dark and cold. It was raining. A damp, penetrating wind howled in the garden and gave the trees no rest. Though he strained his eyes, the banker could see neither the ground, nor the white statues, nor the garden-wing, nor the trees. Approaching the garden-wing, he called the watchman twice. There was no answer. Evidently the watchman had taken shelter from the bad weather and was now asleep somewhere in the kitchen or the greenhouse.

"If I have the courage to fulfil my intention," thought the old man, "the suspicion will fall on the watchman first of all."

In the darkness he groped for the steps and the door and entered the hall of the garden-wing, then poked his way into a narrow passage and struck a match. Not a soul was there. Some one's bed, with no bedclothes on it, stood there, and an iron stove loomed dark in the corner. The seals on the door that led into the prisoner's room were unbroken.

When the match went out, the old man, trembling from agitation, peeped into the little window.

In the prisoner's room a candle was burning dimly. The prisoner himself sat by the table. Only his back, the hair on his head and his hands were visible. Open books were strewn about on the table, the two chairs, and on the carpet near the table.

Five minutes passed and the prisoner never once stirred. Fifteen years' confinement had taught him to sit motionless. The banker tapped on the window with his finger, but the prisoner made no movement in reply. Then the banker cautiously tore the seals from the door and put the key into the lock. The rusty lock gave a hoarse groan and the door creaked. The banker expected instantly to hear a cry of surprise and the sound of steps. Three minutes passed and it was as quiet inside as it had been before. He made up his mind to enter.

Before the table sat a man, unlike an ordinary human being. It was a skeleton, with tight-drawn skin, with long curly hair like a woman's, and a shaggy beard. The colour of his face was yellow, of an earthy shade; the cheeks were sunken, the back long and narrow, and the hand upon which he leaned his hairy head was so lean and skinny that it was painful to look upon. His hair was already silvering with grey, and no one who glanced at the senile emaciation of the face would have believed that he was only forty years old. On the table, before his bended head, lay a sheet of paper on which something was written in a tiny hand.

"Poor devil," thought the banker, "he's asleep and probably seeing millions in his dreams. I have only to take and throw this half-dead thing on the bed, smother him a moment with the pillow, and the most careful examination will find no trace of unnatural death. But, first, let us read what he has written here."

The banker took the sheet from the table and read:

"To-morrow at twelve o'clock midnight, I shall obtain my freedom and the right to mix with people. But before I leave this room and see the sun I think it necessary to say a few words to you. On my own clear conscience and before God who sees me I declare to you that I despise freedom, life, health, and all that your books call the blessings of the world.

"For fifteen years I have diligently studied earthly life. True, I saw neither the earth nor the people, but in your books I drank fragrant wine, sang songs, hunted deer and wild boar in the forests, loved women. . . . And beautiful women, like clouds ethereal, created by the magic of your poets' genius, visited me by night, and whispered to me wonderful tales, which made my head drunken. In your books I climbed the summits of Elbruz and Mont Blanc and saw from there how the sun rose in the morning, and in the evening suffused the sky, the ocean and the mountain ridges with a purple gold. I saw from there how above me lightnings glimmered cleaving the clouds; I saw green forests, fields, rivers, lakes, cities; I heard sirens singing, and the playing of the pipes of Pan; I touched the wings of beautiful devils who came flying to me to speak of God. . . . In your books I cast myself into bottomless abysses, worked miracles, burned cities to the ground, preached new religions, conquered whole countries. . . .

"Your books gave me wisdom. All that unwearying human thought created in the centuries is compressed to a little lump in my skull. I know that I am cleverer than you all.

"And I despise your books, despise all worldly blessings and wisdom. Everything is void, frail, visionary and delusive as a mirage. Though you be proud and wise and beautiful, yet will death wipe you from the face of the earth like the mice underground; and your posterity, your history, and the immortality of your men of genius will be as frozen slag, burnt down together with the terrestrial globe.

"You are mad, and gone the wrong way. You take falsehood for truth and ugliness for beauty. You would marvel if suddenly apple and orange trees should bear frogs and lizards instead of fruit, and if roses should begin to breathe the odour of a sweating horse. So do I marvel at you, who have bartered heaven for earth. I do not want to understand you.

"That I may show you in deed my contempt for that by which you live, I waive the two millions of which I once dreamed as of paradise, and which I now despise. That I may deprive myself of my right to them, I shall come out from here five minutes before the stipulated term, and thus shall violate the agreement."

When he had read, the banker put the sheet on the table, kissed the head of the strange man, and began to weep. He went out of the wing. Never at any other time, not even after his terrible losses on the Exchange, had he felt such contempt for himself as now. Coming home, he lay down on his bed, but agitation and tears kept him a long time from sleeping. . . .

The next morning the poor watchman came running to him and told him that they had seen the man who lived in the wing climb through the window into the garden. He had gone to the gate and disappeared. The banker instantly went with his servants to the wing and established the escape of his prisoner. To avoid unnecessary rumours he took the paper with the renunciation from the table and, on his return, locked it in his safe.

Translated by *Constance Garnett.*

THE OTHER SIDE OF THE HEDGE

E. M. Forster
(1879–   )

My pedometer told me that I was twenty-five; and, though it is a shocking thing to stop walking, I was so tired that I sat down on a milestone to rest. People outstripped me, jeering as they did so, but I was too apathetic to feel resentful, and even when Miss Eliza Dimbleby, the great educationist, swept past, exhorting me to persevere, I only smiled and raised my hat.

At first I thought I was going to be like my brother, whom I had had to leave by the roadside a year or two round the corner. He had wasted his breath on singing, and his strength on helping others. But I had travelled more wisely, and now it was only the monotony of the highway that oppressed me—dust under foot and brown crackling hedges on either side, ever since I could remember.

And I had already dropped several things—indeed, the road behind was strewn with the things we all had dropped; and the white dust was settling down on them, so that already they looked no better than stones. My muscles were so weary that I could not even bear the weight of those things I still carried. I slid off the milestone into the road, and lay there prostrate, with my face to the great parched hedge, praying that I might give up.

A little puff of air revived me. It seemed to come from the hedge; and, when I opened my eyes, there was a glint of light through the tangle of boughs and dead leaves. The hedge could not be as thick as usual. In my weak, morbid state, I longed to force my way in, and see what was on the other side. No one was in sight, or I should not have dared to try. For we of the road do not admit in conversation that there is another side at all.

I yielded to the temptation, saying to myself that I would come back in a minute. The thorns scratched my face, and I had to use my arms as a shield, depending on my feet alone to push me forward. Halfway through I would have gone back, for in the passage all the things I was carrying were scraped off me, and my clothes were torn. But I was so wedged that return was impossible, and I had to wriggle blindly forward, expecting every moment that my strength would fail me, and that I should perish in the undergrowth.

Suddenly cold water closed round my head, and I seemed sinking down for ever. I had fallen out of the hedge into a deep pool. I rose to the surface at last, crying for help, and I heard someone on the opposite bank laugh and say: "Another!" And then I was twitched out and laid panting on the dry ground.

Even when the water was out of my eyes, I was still dazed, for I had never been in so large a space, nor seen such grass and sunshine. The blue sky was no longer a strip, and beneath it the earth had risen grandly into hills—clean, bare buttresses, with beech trees in their folds, and meadows and clear pools at their feet. But the hills were not high, and there was in the landscape a sense of human oc-cupation—so that one might have called it a park or garden, if the words did not imply a certain triviality and constraint.

As soon as I got my breath, I turned to my rescuer and said:

"Where does this place lead to?"

"Nowhere, thank the Lord!" said he, and laughed. He was a man of fifty or sixty—just the kind of age we mistrust on the road—but there was no anxiety in his manner, and his voice was that of a boy of eighteen.

"But it must lead somewhere!" I cried, too much surprised at his answer to thank him for saving my life.

"He wants to know where it leads!" he shouted to some men on the hillside, and they laughed back, and waved their caps.

I noticed then that the pool into which I had fallen was really a moat which bent round to the left and to the right, and that the hedge followed it continually. The hedge was green on this side—its roots showed through the clear water, and fish swam about in them—and it was wreathed over with dog-roses and Traveller's Joy. But it was a barrier, and in a moment I lost all pleasure in the grass, the sky, the trees, the happy men and women, and realized that the place was but a prison, for all its beauty and extent.

We moved away from the boundary, and then followed a path almost parallel to it, across the meadows. I found it difficult walking, for I was always trying to out-distance my companion, and there was no advantage in doing this if the place led nowhere. I had never kept step with anyone since I left my brother.

I amused him by stopping suddenly and saying disconsolately, "This is perfectly terrible. One cannot advance: one cannot progress. Now we of the road—"

"Yes. I know."

"I was going to say, we advance continually."

"I know."

"We are always learning, expanding, developing. Why, even in my short life I have seen a great deal of advance—the Transvaal War, the Fiscal Question, Christian Science, Radium. Here for example—"

I took out my pedometer, but it still marked twenty-five, not a degree more.

"Oh, it's stopped! I meant to show you. It should have registered all the time I was walking with you. But it makes me only twenty-five."

"Many things don't work in here," he said. "One day a man brought in a Lee-Metford, and that wouldn't work."

"The laws of science are universal in their application. It must be the water in the moat that has injured the machinery. In normal conditions everything works. Science and the spirit of emulation—those are the forces that have made us what we are."

I had to break off and acknowledge the pleasant greetings of people whom we passed. Some of them were singing, some talking, some engaged in gardening, hay-making, or other rudimentary industries. They all seemed happy; and I might have been happy too, if I could have forgotten that the place led nowhere.

I was startled by a young man who came sprinting across our path, took a little fence in fine style, and went tearing over a ploughed field till he plunged into a lake, across which he began to swim. Here was true energy, and I exclaimed: "A cross-country race! Where are the others?"

"There are no others," my companion replied; and, later on, when we passed some long grass from which came the voice of a girl singing exquisitely to herself, he said again: "There are no others." I was bewildered at the waste in production, and murmured to myself, "What does it all mean?"

He said: "It means nothing but itself"

—and he repeated the words slowly, as if I were a child.

"I understand," I said quietly, "but I do not agree. Every achievement is worthless unless it is a link in the chain of development. And I must not trespass on your kindness any longer. I must get back somehow to the road, and have my pedometer mended."

"First, you must see the gates," he replied, "for we have gates, though we never use them."

I yielded politely, and before long we reached the moat again, at a point where it was spanned by a bridge. Over the bridge was a big gate, as white as ivory, which was fitted into a gap in the boundary hedge. The gate opened outwards, and I exclaimed in amazement, for from it ran a road—just such a road as I had left—dusty under foot, with brown crackling hedges on either side as far as the eye could reach.

"That's my road!" I cried.

He shut the gate and said: "But not your part of the road. It is through this gate that humanity went out countless ages ago, when it was first seized with the desire to walk."

I denied this, observing that the part of the road I myself had left was not more than two miles off. But with the obstinacy of his years he repeated: "It is the same road. This is the beginning, and though it seems to run straight away from us, it doubles so often, that it is never far from our boundary and sometimes touches it." He stooped down by the moat, and traced on its moist margin an absurd figure like a maze. As we walked back through the meadows, I tried to convince him of his mistake.

"The road sometimes doubles, to be sure, but that is part of our discipline. Who can doubt that its general tendency is onward? To what goal we know not—it may be to some mountain where we shall touch the sky, it may be over precipices into the sea. But that it goes forward —who can doubt that? It is the thought of that that makes us strive to excel, each in his own way, and gives us an impetus which is lacking with you. Now that man who passed us—it's true that he ran well, and jumped well, and swam well; but we have men who can run better, and men who can jump better, and who can swim better. Specialization has produced results which would surprise you. Similarly, that girl—"

Here I interrupted myself to exclaim: "Good gracious me! I could have sworn it was Miss Eliza Dimbleby over there, with her feet in the fountain!"

He believed that it was.

"Impossible! I left her on the road, and she is due to lecture this evening at Tunbridge Wells. Why, her train leaves Cannon Street in—of course my watch has stopped like everything else. She is the last person to be here."

"People always are astonished at meeting each other. All kinds come through the hedge, and come at all times—when they are drawing ahead in the race, when they are lagging behind, when they are left for dead. I often stand near the boundary listening to the sounds of the road—you know what they are—and wonder if anyone will turn aside. It is my great happiness to help someone out of the moat, as I helped you. For our country fills up slowly, though it was meant for all mankind."

"Mankind have other aims," I said gently, for I thought him well-meaning; "and I must join them." I bade him good evening, for the sun was declining, and I wished to be on the road by nightfall. To my alarm, he caught hold of me, crying: "You are not to go yet!" I tried to shake him off, for we had no interests in common, and his civility was becoming irksome to me. But for all my struggles the tiresome old man would not let go; and, as wrestling is not my specialty, I was obliged to follow him.

It was true that I could have never found alone the place where I came in, and I hoped that, when I had seen the other sights about which he was worrying, he would take me back to it. But I was determined not to sleep in the country, for I mistrusted it, and the people too, for all their friendliness. Hungry though I was, I would not join them in their evening meals of milk and fruit, and, when they gave me flowers, I flung them away as soon as I could do so unobserved. Already they were lying down for the night like cattle—some out on the bare hillside, others in groups under the beeches. In the light of an orange sunset I hurried on with my unwelcome guide, dead tired, faint for want of food, but murmuring indomitably: "Give me life, with its struggles and victories, with its failures and hatreds, with its deep moral meaning and its unknown goal!"

At last we came to a place where the encircling moat was spanned by another bridge, and where another gate interrupted the line of the boundary hedge. It was different from the first gate; for it was half transparent like horn, and opened inwards. But through it, in the waning light, I saw again just such a road as I had left—monotonous, dusty, with brown crackling hedges on either side, as far as the eye could reach.

I was strangely disquieted at the sight, which seemed to deprive me of all self-control. A man was passing us, returning for the night to the hills, with a scythe over his shoulder and a can of some liquid in his hand. I forgot the destiny of our race. I forgot the road that lay before my eyes, and I sprang at him, wrenched the can out of his hand, and began to drink.

It was nothing stronger than beer, but in my exhausted state it overcame me in a moment. As in a dream, I saw the old man shut the gate, and heard him say: "This is where your road ends, and through this gate humanity—all that is left of it—will come in to us."

Though my senses were sinking into oblivion, they seemed to expand ere they reached it. They perceived the magic song of nightingales, and the odour of invisible hay, and stars piercing the fading sky. The man whose beer I had stolen lowered me down gently to sleep off its effects, and, as he did so, I saw that he was my brother.

THE DOOR

E. B. White
(1899–   )

Everything (he kept saying) is something it isn't. And everybody is always somewhere else. Maybe it was the city, being in the city, that made him feel how queer everything was and that it was something else. Maybe (he kept thinking) it was the names of the things. The names were tex and frequently koid. Or they were flex and oid or they were duroid (sani) or flexsan (duro), but everything was glass (but not quite glass) and the thing that you touched (the surface, washable, crease-resistant) was rubber, only it wasn't quite rubber and you didn't quite touch it but almost. The wall, which was glass but thrutex, turned out on being approached not to be a wall, it was something else, it was an opening or doorway —and the doorway (through which he saw himself approaching) turned out to be something else, it was a wall. And what he had eaten not having agreed with him.

He was in a washable house, but he wasn't sure. Now about those rats, he kept saying to himself. He meant the rats that the Professor had driven crazy by forcing them to deal with problems which were beyond the scope of rats, the insoluble problems. He meant the rats that had been trained to jump at the square card with the circle in the middle, and the card (because it was something it wasn't) would give way and let the rat into a place where the food was, but then one day it would be a trick played on the rat, and the card would be changed, and the rat would jump but the card wouldn't give way, and it was an impossible situation (for a rat) and the rat would go insane and into its eyes would come the unspeakably bright imploring look of the frustrated, and after the convulsions were over and the frantic racing around, then the passive stage would set in and the willingness to let anything be done to it, even if it was something else.

He didn't know which door (or wall) or opening in the house to jump at, to get through, because one was an opening that wasn't a door (it was a void, or koid) and the other was a wall that wasn't an opening, it was a sanitary cupboard of the same color. He caught a glimpse of his eyes staring into his eyes, in the thrutex, and in them was the expression he had seen in the picture of the rats—weary after convulsions and the frantic racing around, when they were willing and did not mind having anything done to them. More and more (he kept saying) I am confronted by a problem which is incapable of solution (for this time even if he chose the right door, there would be no food behind it) and that is what madness is, and things seeming different from what they are. He heard, in the house where he was, in the city to which he had gone (as toward a door which might, or might not, give way), a noise—not a loud noise but more of a low prefabricated humming. It came from a place in the base of the wall (or stat) where the flue carrying the filterable air was, and not far from the Minipiano, which was made of the same material nailbrushes are made of, and which was under the stairs. "This, too, has has been tested," she said, pointing, but not at it, "and found viable." It wasn't a loud noise, he kept thinking, sorry that he had seen his eyes, even though it was through his own eyes that he had seen them.

First will come the convulsions (he said), then the exhaustion, then the willingness to let anything be done. "And you believe it *will* be."

All his life he had been confronted by situations which were incapable of being solved, and there was a deliberateness behind all this, behind this changing of the card (or door), because they would always wait till you had learned to jump at the certain card (or door)—the one with the circle—and then they would change it on you. There have been so many doors changed on me, he said, in the last twenty years, but it is now becoming clear that it is an impossible situation, and the question is whether to jump again, even though they ruffle you in the rump with a blast of air—to make you jump. He wished he wasn't standing by the Minipiano. First they would teach you the prayers and the Psalms, and that would be the right door (the one with the circle), and the long sweet words with the holy sound, and that would be the one to jump at to get where the food was. Then one day you jumped and it didn't give way, so that all you got was the bump on the nose, and the first bewilderment, the first young bewilderment.

I don't know whether to tell her about the door they substituted or not, he said, the one with the equation on it and the picture of the amoeba reproducing itself by division. Or the one with the photostatic copy of the check for thirty-two

dollars and fifty cents. But the jumping was so long ago, although the bump is . . . how those old wounds hurt! Being crazy this way wouldn't be so bad if only, if only. If only when you put your foot forward to take a step, the ground wouldn't come up to meet your foot the way it does. And the same way in the street (only I may never get back to the street unless I jump at the right door), the curb coming up to meet your foot, anticipating ever so delicately the weight of the body, which is somewhere else. "We could take your name," she said, "and send it to you." And it wouldn't be so bad if only you could read a sentence all the way through without jumping (your eye) to something else on the same page; and then (he kept thinking) there was that man out in Jersey, the one who started to chop his trees down, one by one, the man who began talking about how he would take his house to pieces, brick by brick, because he faced a problem incapable of solution, probably, so he began to hack at the trees in the yard, began to pluck with trembling fingers at the bricks in the house. Even if a house is not washable, it is worth taking down. It is not till later that the exhaustion sets in.

But it is inevitable that they will keep changing the doors on you, he said, because that is what they are for; and the thing is to get used to it and not let it unsettle the mind. But that would mean not jumping, and you can't. Nobody can not jump. There will be no not-jumping. Among rats, perhaps, but among people never. Everybody has to keep jumping at a door (the one with the circle on it) because that is the way everybody is, especially some people. You wouldn't want me, standing here, to tell you, would you, about my friend the poet (deceased) who said, "My heart has followed all my days something I cannot name"? (It had the circle on it.) And like many poets, although few so beloved, he is gone. It killed him, the jumping. First, of course, there were the preliminary bouts, the convulsions, and the calm and the willingness.

I remember the door with the picture of the girl on it (only it was spring), her arms outstretched in loveliness, her dress (it was the one with the circle on it) uncaught, beginning the slow, clear, blinding cascade—and I guess we would all like to try that door again, for it seemed like the way and for a while it was the way, the door would open and you would go through winged and exalted (like any rat) and the food would be there, the way the Professor had it arranged, everything O.K., and you had chosen the right door, for the world was young. The time they changed that door on me, my nose bled for a hundred hours—how do you like that, Madam? Or would you prefer to show me further through this so strange house, or you could take my name and send it to me, for although my heart has followed all my days something I cannot name, I am tired of the jumping and I do not know which way to go, Madam, and I am not even sure that I am not tried beyond the endurance of man (rat, if you will) and have taken leave of sanity. What are you following these days, old friend, after your recovery from the last bump? What is the name, or is it something you cannot name? The rats have a name for it by this time, perhaps, but I don't know what they call it. I call it plexikoid and it comes in sheets, something like insulating board, unattainable and ugli-proof.

And there was the man out in Jersey, because I keep thinking about his terrible necessity and the passion and trouble he had gone to all those years in the indescribable abundance of a householder's detail, building the estate and the planting of the trees and in spring the lawn-dressing and in fall the bulbs for the spring burgeoning, and the watering of the grass on the long light evenings in summer and the gravel for the driveway (all had to be thought out, planned) and the decorative borders, probably, the perennials and the bug spray, and the building of the house from plans of the architect, first the sills, then the studs, then the full corn in the ear, the floors laid on the floor timbers, smoothed, and then the carpets upon the smooth floors and the curtains and the rods therefor. And then, almost without warning, he would be jumping at the same old door and it wouldn't give: they had changed it on him, making life no longer supportable under the elms in the elm shade, under the maples in the maple shade.

"Here you have the maximum of openness in a small room."

It was impossible to say (maybe it was the city) what made him feel the way he did, and I am not the only one either, he kept thinking—ask any doctor if I am. The doctors, they know how many there are, they even know where the trouble is only they don't like to tell you about the prefrontal lobe because that means making a hole in your skull and removing the work of centuries. It took so long coming, this lobe, so many, many years. (Is it something you read in the paper, perhaps?) And now, the strain being so great, the door having been changed by the Professor once too often . . . but it only means a whiff of ether, a few deft strokes, and the higher animal becomes a little easier in his mind and more like the lower one. From now on, you see, that's the way it will be, the ones with the small prefrontal lobes will win because the other ones are hurt too much by this incessant bumping. They can stand just so much, eh, Doctor? (And what is that, pray, that you have in your hand?) Still, you never can tell, eh, Madam?

He crossed (carefully) the room, the thick carpet under him softly, and went toward the door carefully, which was glass and he could see himself in it, and which, at his approach, opened to allow him to pass through; and beyond he half expected to find one of the old doors that he had known, perhaps the one with the circle, the one with the girl, her arms outstretched in loveliness and beauty before him. But he saw instead a moving stairway, and descended in light (he kept thinking) to the street below and to the other people. As he stepped off, the ground came up slightly, to meet his foot.

POEMS

"DEGREE BEING VIZARDED" *

William Shakespeare
(1564–1616)

(From *Troilus and Cressida,* I, iii, 83–124)

Degree being vizarded,
Th' unworthiest shews as fairly in the
    mask.
The heavens themselves, the planets, and
    this center   85
Observe degree, priority, and place,
Insisture, course, proportion, season, form,
Office, and custom, in all line of order;
And therefore is the glorious planet Sol
In noble eminence enthron'd and
    spher'd   90
Amidst the other, whose med'cinable eye
Corrects the ill aspects of planets evil,
And posts, like the commandment of a
    king,
Sans check, to good and bad. But when
    the planets

In evil mixture to disorder wander,   95
What plagues and what portents, what
    mutiny,
What raging of the sea, shaking of earth,
Commotion in the winds! Frights,
    changes, horrors
Divert and crack, rend and deracinate
The unity and married calm of states   100
Quite from their fixture. O, when degree
    is shak'd,
Which is the ladder to all high designs,
The enterprise is sick. How could com-
    munities,
Degrees in schools, and brotherhoods in
    cities,
Peaceful commerce from dividable
    shores,   105
The primogenitive and due of birth,
Prerogative of age, crowns, scepters,
    laurels,
But by degree, stand in authentic place?
Take but degree away, untune that
    string,
And hark, what discord follows! Each
    thing meets   110
In mere oppugnancy. The bounded waters
Should lift their bosoms higher than the
    shores
And make a sop of all this solid globe.
Strength should be lord of imbecility,
And the rude son should strike his father
    dead.   115

* In this scene the wily Ulysses advises the commander of the Greek forces that the Greeks must maintain order and a sense of authority if they hope to be victorious in their war with the Trojans.
  83. *Degree:* levels of authority.
     vizarded: masked.
  85. *center:* the earth.
  87. *Insisture:* constancy.
  92. *aspects:* astrological term referring to relative position and influences of the planets.

  99. *deracinate:* uproot.
  101. *fixure:* stability.
  114. *imbecility:* physical weakness.

Force should be right; or rather, right
  and wrong,
Between whose endless jar justice resides,
Should lose her names, and so should
  justice too.
Then everything includes itself in power,
Power into will, will into appetite,   120
And appetite, an universal wolf,
So doubly seconded with will and power,
Must make perforce an universal prey
And last eat up himself.

119. *includes:* incloses.

THE WORLD IS TOO MUCH WITH US

William Wordsworth
(1770–1850)

The world is too much with us; late and
  soon,
Getting and spending, we lay waste our
  powers:
Little we see in Nature that is ours;
We have given our hearts away, a sordid
  boon!
The sea that bares her bosom to the
  moon;   5
The winds that will be howling at all
  hours,
And are up-gathered now like sleeping
  flowers;
For this, for everything, we are out of
  tune;
It moves us not.—Great God! I'd rather
  be
A Pagan suckled in a creed outworn;   10
So might I, standing on this pleasant lea,
Have glimpses that would make me less
  forlorn;
Have sight of Proteus rising from the sea;
Or hear old Triton blow his wreathéd
  horn.

13. *Proteus:* a sea-god who had the power of
changing his shape.
14. *Triton:* a sea-deity who used a conch shell
for a trumpet.

STEAMBOATS, VIADUCTS, AND RAILWAYS

William Wordsworth
(1770–1850)

Motions and Means, on land and sea at
  war
With old poetic feeling, not for this,
Shall ye, by Poets even, be judged amiss!
Nor shall your presence, howsoe'er it mar
The loveliness of Nature, prove a bar   5
To the Mind's gaining that prophetic
  sense
Of future change, that point of vision,
  whence
May be discovered what in soul ye are.
In spite of all that beauty may disown
In your harsh features, Nature doth em-
  brace   10
Her lawful offspring in Man's art; and
  Time,
Pleased with your triumphs o'er his
  brother Space,
Accepts from your bold hands the prof-
  fered crown
Of hope, and smiles on you with cheer
  sublime.

ULYSSES

Alfred, Lord Tennyson
(1809–1892)

It little profits that an idle king,
By this still hearth, among these barren
  crags,
Matched with an aged wife, I mete and
  dole
Unequal laws unto a savage race,
That hoard, and sleep, and feed, and
  know not me.   5
I cannot rest from travel; I will drink
Life to the lees. All times I have enjoyed

Greatly, have suffered greatly, both with
  those
That loved me, and alone; on shore, and
  when
Through scudding drifts the rainy
  Hyades   10
Vexed the dim sea. I am become a
  name;
For always roaming with a hungry heart
Much have I seen and known—cities of
  men
And manners, climates, councils, govern-
  ments,
Myself not least, but honored of them
  all—   15
And drunk delight of battle with my
  peers,
Far on the ringing plains of windy Troy.
I am a part of all that I have met;
Yet all experience is an arch where-
  through
Gleams that untraveled world whose
  margin fades   20
Forever and forever when I move.
How dull it is to pause, to make an end,
To rust unburnished, not to shine in use!
As though to breathe were life! Life piled
  on life
Were all too little, and of one to me   25
Little remains; but every hour is saved
From that eternal silence, something
  more,
A bringer of new things; and vile it were
For some three suns to store and hoard
  myself,
And this gray spirit yearning in desire   30
To follow knowledge like a sinking star,
Beyond the utmost bound of human
  thought.
    This is my son, mine own Telemachus,
To whom I leave the scepter and the
  isle—
Well-loved of me, discerning to ful-
  fill   35
This labor, by slow prudence to make
  mild

A rugged people, and through soft de-
  grees
Subdue them to the useful and the good.
Most blameless is he, centered in the
  sphere
If common duties, decent not to fail   40
In offices of tenderness, and pay
Meet adoration to my household gods,
When I am gone. He works his work, I
  mine.
    There lies the port; the vessel puffs her
  sail;
There gloom the dark, broad seas. My
  mariners,   45
Souls that have toiled, and wrought, and
  thought with me—
That ever with a frolic welcome took
The thunder and the sunshine, and op-
  posed
Free hearts, free foreheads—you and
  I are old;
Old age hath yet his honor and his
  toil.   50
Death closes all; but something ere the
  end,
Some work of noble note, may yet be
  done,
Not unbecoming men that strove with
  gods.
The lights begin to twinkle from the
  rocks;
The long day wanes; the slow moon
  climbs; the deep   55
Moans round with many voices. Come,
  my friends.
'Tis not too late to seek a newer world.
Push off, and sitting well in order
  smite
The sounding furrows; for my purpose
  holds
To sail beyond the sunset, and the
  baths   60
Of all the western stars, until I die.
It may be that the gulfs will wash us
  down;
It may be we shall touch the Happy Isles,

10. *Hyades:* a constellation associated with
spring rain.

63. *the Happy Isles:* Elysium, the abode of
heroes after death.

And see the great Achilles, whom we
    knew.
Though much is taken, much abides; and
    though   65
We are not now that strength which in
    old days
Moved earth and heaven, that which we
    are, we are—
One equal temper of heroic hearts,
Made weak by time and fate, but strong
    in will
To strive, to seek, to find, and not to
    yield.   70

PIED BEAUTY *

Gerard Manley Hopkins
(1844–1889)

Glory be to God for dappled things—
    For skies of couple-color as a brinded
        cow;
        For rose-moles all in stipple upon
        trout that swim;
Fresh-firecoal chestnut-falls; finches'
    wings;
    Landscape plotted and pieced—fold,
        fallow, and plow;   5
        And all trades, their gear and tackle
        and trim.

All things counter, original, spare,
    strange;
    Whatever is fickle, freckled (who
        knows how?)
        With swift, slow; sweet, sour;
        adazzle, dim;
He fathers-forth whose beauty is past
    change:
        Praise him.   10

* multicolored beauty.
2. *brinded:* spotted.
3. *stipple:* pattern of dots.
4. *chestnut-falls:* husked chestnuts.
7. *counter:* contrasting.
    spare: rare.

THE SOUL SELECTS HER OWN SOCIETY

Emily Dickinson
(1830–1886)

The soul selects her own society
Then shuts the door;
On her divine majority
Obtrude no more.

Unmoved, she notes the chariot's paus-
    ing   5
At her low gate;
Unmoved, an emperor is kneeling
Upon her mat.

I've known her from an ample nation
Choose one;   10
Then close the valves of her attention
Like stone.

THE LOVE SONG OF J. ALFRED PRUFROCK

T. S. Eliot
(1888–1965)

S'io credesse che mia risposta fosse
A persona che mai tornasse al mondo,
Questa fiamma staria senza piu scosse.
Ma perciocche giammai di questo fondo
Non torno vivo alcun, s'i'odo il vero,
*Senza tema d'infamia ti rispondo.**

Let us go then, you and I,
When the evening is spread out against
    the sky
Like a patient etherised upon a table;
Let us go, through certain half-deserted
    streets,
The muttering retreats   5

* "If I thought my answer would be to one
who could return to the world, this flame would
shake no more. But since no one has ever returned alive from this depth, if what I hear is
true, without fear of infamy I answer you."
Dante, *Inferno*, XXVII, 61–66.

Of restless nights in one-night cheap
hotels
And sawdust restaurants with oyster-
shells:
Streets that follow like a tedious argu-
ment
Of insidious intent
To lead you to an overwhelming ques-
tion . . .   10
Oh, do not ask, "What is it?"
Let us go and make our visit.

In the room the women come and go
Talking of Michelangelo.

The yellow fog that rubs its back upon
the window-panes,   15
The yellow smoke that rubs its muzzle
on the window-panes
Licked its tongue into the corners of the
evening,
Lingered upon the pools that stand in
drains,
Let fall upon its back the soot that falls
from chimneys,
Slipped by the terrace, made a sudden
leap,   20
And seeing that it was a soft October
night,
Curled once about the house, and fell
asleep.

And indeed there will be time
For the yellow smoke that slides along
the street,
Rubbing its back upon the window-
panes;   25
There will be time, there will be time
To prepare a face to meet the faces that
you meet;
There will be time to murder and create,
And time for all the works and days of
hands

That lift and drop a question on your
plate;   30
Time for you and time for me,
And time yet for a hundred indecisions,
And for a hundred visions and revisions,
Before the taking of a toast and tea.

In the room the women come and go   35
Talking of Michelangelo.

And indeed there will be time
To wonder, "Do I dare?" and, "Do I
dare?"
Time to turn back and descend the stair,
With a bald spot in the middle of my
hair—   40
(They will say: "How his hair is grow-
ing thin!")
My morning coat, my collar mounting
firmly to the chin,
My necktie rich and modest, but asserted
by a simple pin—
(They will say: "But how his arms and
legs are thin!")
Do I dare   45
Disturb the universe?
In a minute there is time
For decisions and revisions which a
minute will reverse.

For I have known them all already,
known them all:—
Have known the evenings, mornings,
afternoons,   50
I have measured out my life with coffee
spoons;
I know the voices dying with a dying fall
Beneath the music from a farther room.
So how should I presume?

And I have known the eyes already,
known them all—   55
The eyes that fix you in a formulated
phrase,

23. Cf. Andrew Marvell's "To His Coy Mistress": "Had we but world enough and
time . . ."
29. Cf. Hesiod's *Work and Days*. A poem
written in the eighth century B.C. in praise of
farming life.

52. *a dying fall:* Cf. *Twelfth Night* (I,i.4);
"That strain again! It had a dying fall."

And when I am formulated, sprawling on
a pin,
When I am pinned and wriggling on the
wall,
Then how should I begin
To spit out all the butt-ends of my days
and ways?   60
    And how should I presume?

And I have known the arms already,
known them all—
Arms that are braceleted and white and
bare
(But in the lamplight, downed with light
brown hair!)
Is it perfume from a dress   65
That makes me so digress?
Arms that lie along a table, or wrap about
a shawl.
    And should I then presume?
    Ana how should I begin?

Shall I say, I have gone at dusk through
narrow streets   70
And watched the smoke that rises from
the pipes
Of lonely men in shirt-sleeves, leaning
out of windows? . . .

I should have been a pair of ragged claws
Scuttling across the floors of silent seas.

And the afternoon, the evening, sleeps so
peacefully!   75
Smoothed by long fingers,
Asleep . . . tired . . . or it malingers,
Stretched on the floor, here beside you
and me.
Should I, after tea and cakes and ices,
Have the strength to force the moment to
its crisis?   80
But though I have wept and fasted, wept
and prayed,
Though I have seen my head (grown
slightly bald) brought in upon a
platter,

I am no prophet—and here's no great
matter;
I have seen the moment of my greatness
flicker,
And I have seen the eternal Footman
hold my coat, and snicker,   85
And in short, I was afraid.

And would it have been worth it, after
all,
After the cups, the marmalade, the
tea,
Among the porcelain, among some talk
of you and me,
Would it have been worth while,   90
To have bitten off the matter with a
smile,
To have squeezed the universe into a ball
To roll it toward some overwhelming
question,
To say: "I am Lazarus, come from the
dead,
Come back to tell you all, I shall tell
you all"—   95
If one, setting a pillow by her head,
    Should say: "That is not what I meant
at all.
    That is not it, at all."
And would it have been worth it, after all,
Would it have been worth while,   100
After the sunsets and the dooryards and
the sprinkled streets,
After the novels, after the teacups, after
the skirts that trail along the floor—
And this, and so much more?—
It is impossible to say just what I mean!
But as if a magic lantern threw the nerves
in patterns on a screen: 105
Would it have been worth while
If one, settling a pillow or throwing off a
shawl,
And turning toward the window, should
say:
    "That is not it at all,

---

82. See Mark vi, 17–28 and Matthew xiv,
3–11. An allusion to the beheading of John the
Baptist.

92. Cf. Marvell's "To His Coy Mistress":
"Let us roll all our strength and all/Our sweetness up into a ball."
94–95. Cf. John xi, 1–44 and Luke xii, 19–31.

That is not what I mean, at all." 110

No! I am not Prince Hamlet, nor was
    meant to be;
Am an attendant lord, one that will do
To swell a progress, start a scene or two,
Advise the prince; no doubt, an easy tool,
Deferential, glad to be of use, 115
Politic, cautious, and meticulous;
Full of high sentence, but a bit obtuse;
At times, indeed, almost ridiculous—
Almost, at times, the Fool.

I grow old . . . I grow old . . . 120
I shall wear the bottoms of my trousers
    rolled.

Shall I part my hair behind? Do I dare to
    eat a peach?
I shall wear white flannel trousers, and
    walk upon the beach.
I have heard the mermaids singing, each
    to each.

I do not think that they will sing to
    me. 125

I have seen them riding seaward on the
    waves
Combing the white hair of the waves
    blown back
When the wind blows the water white and
    black.

We have lingered in the chambers of the
    sea
By sea-girls wreathed with seaweed red
    and brown 130
Till human voices wake us, and we drown.

THE EXPRESS

Stephen Spender
(1909–   )

After the first powerful plain manifesto
The black statement of pistons, without
    more fuss
But gliding like a queen, she leaves the
    station.
Without bowing and with restrained un-
    concern
She passes the houses which humbly
    crowd outside, 5
The gasworks and at last the heavy
    page
Of death, printed by gravestones in the
    cemetery.
Beyond the town there lies the open
    country
Where, gathering speed, she acquires
    mystery,
The luminous self-possession of ships on
    ocean. 10
It is now she begins to sing—at first quite
    low
Then loud, and at last with a jazzy mad-
    ness—
The song of her whistle screaming at
    curves,
Of deafening tunnels, brakes, innumer-
    able bolts.
And always light, aerial, underneath 15
Goes the elate metre of her wheels.
Steaming through metal landscape on her
    lines
She plunges new eras of wild happi-
    ness
Where speed throws up strange shapes,
    broad curves
And parallels clean like the steel of
    guns. 20
At last, further than Edinburgh or Rome,
Beyond the crest of the world, she reaches
    night
Where only a low streamline brightness
Of phosphorus on the tossing hills is
    white.
Ah, like a comet through flame she moves
    entranced 25
Wrapt in her music no bird song, no,
    nor bough
Breaking with honey buds, shall ever
    equal.

DEPARTMENTAL

Robert Frost
(1875–1963)

An ant on the tablecloth
Ran into a dormant moth
Of many times his size.
He showed not the least surprise.
His business wasn't with such.   5
He gave it scarcely a touch,
And was off on his duty run.
Yet if he encountered one
Of the hive's enquiry squad
Whose work is to find out God   10
And the nature of time and space,
He would put him onto the case.
Ants are a curious race;
One crossing with hurried tread
The body of one of their dead   15
Isn't given a moment's arrest—
Seems not even impressed.
But he no doubt reports to any
With whom he crosses antennae,

And they no doubt report   20
To the higher up at court.
Then word goes forth in Formic:
"Death's come to Jerry McCormic,
Our selfless forager Jerry.
With the special Janizary   25
Whose office it is to bury
The dead of the commissary
Go bring him home to his people.
Lay him in state on a sepal.
Wrap him for shroud in a petal.   30
Embalm him with ichor of nettle.
This is the word of your Queen."
And presently on the scene
Appears a solemn mortician;
And taking formal position   35
With feelers calmly atwiddle,
Seizes the dead by the middle,
And heaving him high in air,
Carries him out of there.
No one stands round to stare.   40
It is nobody else's affair.
It couldn't be called ungentle.
But how thoroughly departmental.

THE UNKNOWN CITIZEN

W. H. Auden
(1907–   )

(To JS/07/M/378
This Marble Monument
Is Erected by the State)

He was found by the Bureau of Statistics to be
One against whom there was no official complaint,
And all the reports on his conduct agree
That, in the modern sense of an old-fashioned word, he was a saint,
For in everything he did he served the Greater Community.   5
Except for the War till the day he retired
He worked in a factory and never got fired,
But satisfied his employers, Fudge Motors Inc.
Yet he wasn't a scab or odd in his views,
For his Union reports that he paid his dues,   10
(Our report on his Union shows it was sound)
And our Social Psychology workers found
That he was popular with his mates and liked a drink.
The Press are convinced that he bought a paper every day

And that his reactions to advertisements were normal in every way.   15
Policies taken out in his name prove that he was fully insured,
And his Health-card shows he was once in hospital but left it cured.
Both Producers Research and High-Grade Living declare
He was full sensible to the advantages of the Instalment Plan
And had everything necessary to the Modern Man,   20
A phonograph, a radio, a car and a frigidaire.
Our researchers into Public Opinion are content
That he held the proper opinions for the time of year;
When there was peace, he was for peace; when there was war, he went.
He was married and added five children to the population,   25
Which our Eugenist says was the right number for a parent of his
     generation,
And our teachers report that he never interfered with their education.
Was he free? Was he happy? The question is absurd:
Had anything been wrong, we should certainly have heard.

DOLOR

Theodore Roethke
(1908–1963)

I have known the inexorable sadness of pencils,
Neat in their boxes, dolor of pad and paper-weight,
All the misery of manilla folders and mucilage,
Desolation in immaculate public places,
Lonely reception room, lavatory, switchboard,   5
The unalterable pathos of basin and pitcher,
Ritual of multigraph, paper-clip, comma,
Endless duplication of lives and objects.
And I have seen dust from the walls of institutions,
Finer than flour, alive, more dangerous than silica,   10
Sift, almost invisible through long afternoons of tedium,
Dropping a fine film on nails and delicate eyebrows,
Glazing the pale hair, the duplicate gray standard faces.

■ ■ ■

SAILING TO BYZANTIUM

W. B. Yeats
(1865–1939)

I

That is no country for old men. The
     young
In one another's arms, birds in the trees,
—Those dying generations—at their
     song,
The salmon-falls, the mackerel-crowded
     seas,
Fish, flesh, or fowl, commend all sum-
     mer long   5
Whatever is begotten, born, and dies.

Caught in that sensual music all neglect
Monuments of unageing intellect.

II

An aged man is but a paltry thing,
A tattered coat upon a stick, unless   10
Soul clap its hands and sing, and louder
   sing
For every tatter in its mortal dress,
Nor is there singing school, but studying
Monuments of its own magnificence;
And therefore I have sailed the seas and
   come   15
To the holy city of Byzantium.

III

O sages standing in God's holy fire
As in the gold mosaic of a wall,

Come from the holy fire, perne in a gyre,
And be the singing-masters of my
   soul.   20
Consume my heart away; sick with de-
   sire
And fastened to a dying animal
It knows not what it is; and gather me
Into the artifice of eternity.

IV

Once out of nature I shall never take 25
My bodily form from any natural thing;
But such a form as Grecian goldsmiths
   make
Of hammered gold and gold enamelling
To keep a drowsy Emperor awake;
Or set upon a golden bough to sing   30
To lords and ladies of Byzantium
Of what is past, or passing, or to come.

17–18. Like figures in mosaic on the walls of the Church of Hagia Sophia ("Holy Wisdom") in Byzantium.

19. *perne:* literally "a spool." Yeats used it as a verb meaning "to spin round."
   gyre: whirl in a spiral motion.

VII

PERSPECTIVES
OF STYLE
AND STRUCTURE

FOREWORD

The essays in this section provide a reasonably wide spectrum of changing artistic perspectives in the twentieth century. T. S. Eliot affirms the continuing influence of literary tradition upon the responsible artist in our age. The changes both in artistic approach and public response are seen by Virginia Woolf in the fiction of the first quarter of the century and by John Ciardi in modern poetry. Earl Rovit is one of many contemporary critics who report or predict the breakdown of traditional artistic modes.

The story by Somerset Maugham demonstrates the conventional but admirably skillful approach typical of the fiction written prior to World War I. Since that time literary perspectives have been radically altered by the artist's increasing reliance on techniques utilizing complexity and indirection. James Joyce in "Clay" speaks to us through complex symbolism and introduces his characters through indirection, details, and fragments. In Julio Cortázar's "Blow-Up," the time sequence is broken, perception and conception merge, characterization is fragmented, symbols no longer have consistent meanings, communication between characters is frustrated. Here, even more obviously, complexity and indirection permeate the literary work. It is perhaps significant that this story was the basis of an avant-garde film directed by Michelangelo Antonioni.

The continuing tradition advocated by T. S. Eliot in his essay is represented by the five poems in our first group. The second group of poems illustrates some of the new directions in modern poetry discussed by John Ciardi. We have gathered at the close a number of contemporary poems, some of which reflect the break with tradition, others of which remain well within traditional modes. The three selections from Yeats exemplify in a single poet the full trajectory of the stylistic shift from a type of traditionalism to a modern complexity and indirection.

ESSAYS

TRADITION AND THE INDIVIDUAL TALENT

T. S. Eliot
(1888–1965)

I

In English writing we seldom speak of tradition, though we occasionally apply its name in deploring its absence. We cannot refer to "the tradition" or to "a tradition"; at most, we employ the adjective in saying that the poetry of So-and-so is "traditional" or even "too traditional." Seldom, perhaps, does the word appear except in a phrase of censure. If otherwise, it is vaguely approbative, with the implication, as to the work approved, of some pleasing archaeological reconstruction. You can hardly make the word agreeable to English ears without this comfortable reference to the reassuring science of archaeology.

Certainly the word is not likely to appear in our appreciations of living or dead writers. Every nation, every race, has not only its own creative, but its own critical turn of mind; and is even more oblivious of the shortcomings and limitations of its critical habits than of those of its creative genius. We know, or think we know, from the enormous mass of critical writing that has appeared in the French language the critical method or habit of the French; we only conclude (we are such unconscious people) that the French are "more critical" than we, and sometimes even plume ourselves a little with the fact, as if the French were the less spontaneous. Perhaps they are; but we might remind ourselves that criticism is as inevitable as breathing, and that we should be none the worse for articulating what passes in our minds when we read a book and feel an emotion about it, for criticizing our own minds in their work of criticism. One of the facts that might come to light in this process is our tendency to insist, when we praise a poet, upon those aspects of his work in which he least resembles anyone else. In these aspects or parts of his work we pretend to find what is the peculiar essence of the man. We dwell with satisfaction upon the poet's difference from his predecessors, especially his immediate predecessors; we endeavor to find something that can be isolated in order to be enjoyed. Whereas if we approach a poet without this prejudice we shall often find that not only the best, but the most individual parts of his work may be those in which the dead poets, his ancestors, assert their immortality most vigorously. And I do not mean the impressionable period of adolescence, but the period of full maturity.

Yet if the only form of tradition, of handing down, consisted in following the ways of the immediate generation before us in a blind or timid adherence to its successes, "tradition" should positively be discouraged. We have seen many such simple currents soon lost in the sand; and novelty is better than repetition. Tradition is a matter of much wider significance. It cannot be inherited, and if you want it you must obtain it by great labor. It involves, in the first place, the historical sense, which we may call nearly indispensable to any one who would continue to be a poet beyond his twenty-fifth year; and the historical sense involves a perception, not only of the pastness of the past, but of its presence; the historical sense compels a man to write not merely with his own generation in his bones, but with a feeling that the whole of the literature of Europe from Homer and within it the whole of the literature of his own country has a simultaneous existence and composes a simultaneous order. This historical sense, which is a sense of the timeless as well as of the temporal and of the timeless and of the temporal together, is what makes a writer traditional. And it is at the same time what makes a writer most acutely conscious of his place in time, of his own contemporaneity.

No poet, no artist of any art, has his complete meaning alone. His significance, his appreciation is the appreciation of his relation to the dead poets and artists. You cannot value him alone; you must set him, for contrast and comparison, among the dead. I mean this as a principle of aesthetic, not merely historical, criticism. The necessity that he shall conform, that he shall cohere, is not one-sided; what happens when a new work of art is created is something that happens simultaneously to all the works of art which preceded it. The existing monuments form an ideal order among themselves, which is modified by the introduction of the new (the really new) work of art among them.

The existing order is complete before the new work arrives; for order to persist after the supervention of novelty, the *whole* existing order must be, if ever so slightly, altered; and so the relations, proportions, values of each work of art toward the whole are readjusted; and this is conformity between the old and the new. Whoever has approved this idea of order, of the form of European, of English literature will not find it preposterous that the past should be altered by the present as much as the present is directed by the past. And the poet who is aware of this will be aware of great difficulties and responsibilities.

In a peculiar sense he will be aware also that he must inevitably be judged by the standards of the past. I say judged, not amputated, by them; not judged to be as good as, or worse or better than, the dead; and certainly not judged by the canons of dead critics. It is a judgment, a comparison, in which two things are measured by each other. To conform merely would be for the new work not really to conform at all; it would not be new, and would therefore not be a work of art. And we do not quite say that the new is more valuable because it fits in; but its fitting in is a test of its value—a test, it is true, which can only be slowly and cautiously applied, for we are none of us infallible judges of conformity. We say: it appears to conform, and is perhaps individual, or it appears individual, and may conform; but we are hardly likely to find that it is one and not the other.

To proceed to a more intelligible exposition of the relation of the poet to the past: he can neither take the past as a lump, an indiscriminate bolus, nor can he form himself wholly on one or two private admirations, nor can he form himself wholly upon one preferred period. The first course is inadmissible, the second is an important experience of youth, and the third is a pleasant and highly desirable supplement. The poet must be very conscious of the main current, which does not at all flow invariably through the most distinguished reputations. He must be quite aware of the obvious fact that art never improves, but that the material of art is never quite the same. He must be aware that the mind of Europe—the mind of his own country—a mind which he learns in time to be much more important than his own private mind—is a mind which changes, and that this change is a development which abandons nothing en route, which does not superannuate either Shakespeare, or Homer, or the rock drawing of the Magdalenian draftsmen. That this development, refinement perhaps, complication certainly, is not, from the point of view of the artist, any improvement. Perhaps not even an improvement from the point of view of the psychologist or not to the extent which we imagine; perhaps only in the end based upon a complication in economics and machinery. But the difference between the present and the past is that the conscious present is an awareness of the past in a way and to an extent which the past's awareness of itself cannot show.

Someone said: "The dead writers are remote from us because we *know* so much more than they did." Precisely, and they are that which we know.

I am alive to a usual objection to what is clearly part of my program for the métier of poetry. The objection is that the doctrine requires a ridiculous amount of erudition (pedantry), a claim which can be rejected by appeal to the lives of poets in any pantheon. It will even be affirmed that much learning deadens or perverts poetic sensibility. While, however, we persist in believing that a poet ought to know as much as will not encroach upon his necessary receptivity and necessary laziness, it is not desirable to confine knowledge to whatever can be put into a useful shape for examinations, drawing rooms, or the still more pretentious modes of publicity. Some can absorb knowledge, the more tardy must sweat for it. Shakespeare acquired more essential history from Plutarch than most men could from the whole British Museum. What is to be insisted upon is that the poet must develop or procure the consciousness of the past and that he should continue to develop this consciousness throughout his career.

What happens is a continual surrender of himself as he is at the moment to something which is more valuable. The progress of an artist is a continual self-sacrifice, a continual extinction of personality.

There remains to define this process of depersonalization and its relation to the sense of tradition. It is in this depersonalization that art may be said to approach the condition of science. I, therefore, invite you to consider, as a suggestive analogy, the action which takes place when a bit of finely filiated platinum is introduced into a chamber containing oxygen and sulphur dioxide.

II

Honest criticism and sensitive appreciation are directed not upon the poet but upon the poetry. If we attend to the confused cries of the newspaper critics and the *susurrus* [1] of popular repetition that follows, we shall hear the names of poets in great numbers; if we seek not Bluebook [2] knowledge but the enjoyment of poetry, and ask for a poem, we shall seldom find it. I have tried to point out the importance of the relation of the poem to other poems by other authors, and suggested the conception of poetry as a living whole of all the poetry that has ever been written. The other aspect of this Imper-

[1] Murmuring.
[2] British government publication.

sonal theory of poetry is the relation of the poem to its author. And I hinted, by an analogy, that the mind of the mature poet differs from that of the immature one not precisely in any valuation of "personality," not being necessarily more interesting, or having "more to say," but rather by being a more finely perfected medium in which special, or very varied, feelings are at liberty to enter into new combinations.

The analogy was that of the catalyst. When the two gases previously mentioned are mixed in the presence of a filament of platinum, they form sulphurous acid. This combination takes place only if the platinum is present; nevertheless the newly formed acid contains no trace of platinum, and the platinum itself is apparently unaffected; has remained inert, neutral, and unchanged. The mind of the poet is the shred of platinum. It may partly or exclusively operate upon the experience of the man himself; but, the more perfect the artist, the more completely separate in him will be the man who suffers and the mind which creates; the more perfectly will the mind digest and transmute the passions which are its material.

The experience, you will notice, the elements which enter the presence of the transforming catalyst, are of two kinds: emotions and feelings. The effect of a work of art upon the person who enjoys it is an experience different in kind from any experience not of art. It may be formed out of one emotion, or may be a combination of several; and various feelings, inhering for the writer in particular words or phrases or images, may be added to compose the final result. Or great poetry may be made without the direct use of any emotion whatever: composed out of feelings solely. Canto XV of the *Inferno* (Brunetto Latini) is a working up of the emotion evident in the situation; but the effect, though single as that of any

work of art, is obtained by considerable complexity of detail. The last quatrain gives an image, a feeling attaching to an image, which "came," which did not develop simply out of what precedes, but which was probably in suspension in the poet's mind until the proper combination arrived for it to add itself to. The poet's mind is in fact a receptacle for seizing and storing up numberless feelings, phrases, images, which remain there until all the particles which can unite to form a new compound are present together.

If you compare several representative passages of the greatest poetry you see how great is the variety of types of combination, and also how completely any semi-ethical criterion of "sublimity" misses the mark. For it is not the "greatness," the intensity, of the emotions, the components, but the intensity of the artistic process, the pressure, so to speak, under which the fusion takes place, that counts. The episode of Paolo and Francesca [3] employs a definite emotion, but the intensity of the poetry is something quite different from whatever intensity in the supposed experience it may give the impression of. It is no more intense, furthermore, than Canto XXVI, the voyage of Ulysses, which has not the direct dependence upon an emotion. Great variety is possible in the process of transmutation of emotion: the murder of Agamemnon, or the agony of Othello, gives an artistic effect apparently closer to a possible original than the scenes from Dante. In the *Agamemnon,* the artistic emotion approximates to the emotion of an actual spectator; in *Othello* to the emotion of the protagonist himself. But the difference between art and the event is always absolute; the combination which is the murder of Agamemnon is probably as complex as that which is the voyage of Ulysses. In

[3] Two illicit lovers, whose punishment in hell is described by Dante in *Inferno,* V.

either case there has been a fusion of elements. The ode of Keats contains a number of feelings which have nothing particular to do with the nightingale, but which the nightingale, partly, perhaps, because of its attractive name, and partly because of its reputation, served to bring together.

The point of view which I am struggling to attack is perhaps related to the metaphysical theory of the substantial unity of the soul: for my meaning is, that the poet has, not a "personality" to express, but a particular medium, which is only a medium and not a personality, in which impressions and experiences combine in peculiar and unexpected ways. Impressions and experiences which are important for the man may take no place in the poetry, and those which become important in the poetry may play quite a negligible part in the man, the personality.

I will quote a passage which is unfamiliar enough to be regarded with fresh attention in the light—or darkness—of these observations:

And now methinks I could e'en chide
    myself
For doting on her beauty, though her
    death
Shall be revenged after no common
    action.   °
Does the silkworm expend her yellow
    labors
For thee? For thee does she undo herself?
Are lordships sold to maintain ladyships
For the poor benefit of a bewildering
    minute?
Why does yon fellow falsify highways,
And put his life between the judge's
    lips,
To refine such a thing—keeps horse
    and men

To beat their valors for her? . . .[4]

In this passage (as is evident if it is taken in its context) there is a combination of positive and negative emotion: an intensely strong attraction toward beauty and an equally intense fascination by the ugliness which is contrasted with it and which destroys it. This balance of contrasted emotion is in the dramatic situation to which the speech is pertinent, but that situation alone is inadequate to it. This is, so to speak, the structural emotion, provided by the drama. But the whole effect, the dominant tone, is due to the fact that a number of floating feelings, having an affinity to this emotion by no means superficially evident, have combined with it to give us a new art emotion.

It is not in his personal emotions, the emotions provoked by particular events in his life, that the poet is in any way remarkable or interesting. His particular emotions may be simple, or crude, or flat. The emotion in his poetry will be a very complex thing, but not with the complexity of the emotions of people who have very complex or unusual emotions in life. One error, in fact, of eccentricity in poetry is to seek for new human emotions to express; and in this search for novelty in the wrong place it discovers the perverse. The business of the poet is not to find new emotions, but to use the ordinary ones and, in working them up into poetry, to express feelings which are not in actual emotions at all. And emotions which he has never experienced will serve his turn as well as those familiar to him. Consequently, we must believe that "emotion recollected in tranquility"[5] is an inexact formula. For it is neither emotion, nor recollection, nor, without distortion of

[4] From Cyril Tourneur's *The Revenger's Tragedy,* III, iv.
[5] From William Wordsworth's Preface to *Lyrical Ballads.*

meaning, tranquility. It is a concentration, and a new thing resulting from the concentration, of a very great number of experiences which to the practical and active person would not seem to be experiences at all; it is a concentration which does not happen consciously or of deliberation. These experiences are not "recollected," and they finally unite in an atmosphere which is "tranquil" only in that it is a passive attending upon the event. Of course this is not quite the whole story. There is a great deal, in the writing of poetry, which must be conscious and deliberate. In fact, the bad poet is usually unconscious where he ought to be conscious, and conscious where he ought to be unconscious. Both errors tend to make him "personal." Poetry is not a turning loose of emotion, but an escape from emotion; it is not the expression of personality, but an escape from personality. But, of course, only those who have personality and emotions know what it means to want to escape from these things.

III

ὁ δὲ νοῦς ἴσως Θειότερόν τι χαὶ ἀπαθές ἐστίν.[6]

This essay proposes to halt at the frontier of metaphysics or mysticism, and confine itself to such practical conclusions as can be applied by the responsible person interested in poetry. To divert interest from the poet to the poetry is a laudable aim: for it would conduce to a juster estimation of actual poetry, good and bad. There are many people who appreciate the expression of sincere emotion in verse, and there is a smaller number of people who can appreciate technical excellence. But very few know when there is an expression of *significant* emotion, emotion

---

[6] "The mind is doubtless something more divine and unimpressionable." Aristotle, *De Anima*, I, 4.

which has its life in the poem and not in the history of the poet. The emotion of art is impersonal. And the poet cannot reach this impersonality without surrendering himself wholly to the work to be done. And he is not likely to know what is to be done unless he lives in what is not merely the present, but the present moment of the past, unless he is conscious, not of what is dead, but of what is already living.

DIALOGUE WITH THE AUDIENCE

John Ciardi
(1916–   )

"I'm not exactly illiterate," says the Citizen. "I'm a pretty fair historian. I can read Freud—at least some of him—without being entirely in the dark. But I get nowhere with this modern poetry. I've given up trying."

The Poet has heard it all before, but the Citizen obviously wants to talk about it. The Poet, as a matter of fact, rather likes the Citizen. Maybe, the Poet thinks, if I can peg the talk to something specific it won't just ramble on aimlessly and forever. Aloud he says: "Just for the fun of it—who is the last particular poet you gave up on?"

"It was Wallace Stevens," says the Citizen. "I read your review of the *Collected Poems* and I shelled out $7.50 for it on your say-so." He reaches up to a shelf and hauls down the book. "Here it is," he says, tossing it on the table, "a big fat collection of unintelligibility."

"Sorry," says the Poet, "no refunds, if that's what you're getting at. But do me a favor: show me a specific poem that you take to be unintelligible."

The Citizen stares. "Do you mean to

say you understand every poem in this book?"

The Poet shakes his head. "Far from it. I don't even understand White House news releases. But I like Stevens better."

"Without knowing what it is you like?"

"Let's keep the talk as specific as we can. I've asked you to cite a poem: turn around is fair play—find a poem called 'Asides on the Oboe.' Here, take this passage:

The obsolete fiction of the wide river in
An empty land; the Gods that Boucher killed;
And the metal heroes that time granulates—
The philosophers' man alone still walks in dew,
Still by the sea-side mutters milky lines
Concerning an immaculate imagery.
If you say on the hautboy man is not enough,
Can never stand as god, is ever wrong
In the end, however naked, tall, there is still
The impossible possible philosophers' man,
The man who has had the time to think enough,
The central man, the human globe, responsive
As a mirror with a voice, the man of glass,
Who in a million diamonds sums us up.

"Let us get it straight," says the Citizen. "Is this an example of a passage you do understand, or of one you don't?"

"As a matter of fact, it's an example of both," says the Poet. "Suppose I were to say I found it elusive, yet clear—would that make any sense? I can't unravel it detail by detail. I encounter areas of obscurity in it. Yet the total force of the passage is both unmistakable and moving, and just beyond every momentary ob-

scurity I keep emerging into areas of immediate clarity."

"No, in a word. It makes no sense to me."

"Well, what do you mean by sense? Stevens does not write for factual-information sense. Why should he? He picks up a theme and orchestrates it. His 'sense' is a structure. The reader must keep that total structure in mind in order to grasp Stevens's kind of sense. He does not, moreover, 'mean' any one thing, but rather all the possibilities of all the relationships he is orchestrating."

"Clear as Navy coffee," says the Citizen. "Am I supposed to swallow it?"

"You do in music," says the Poet, glancing at the Citizen's collection of recordings, "why not in poetry?"

"Because, among other things, words have meanings."

"They have," says the Poet, "but far more meanings that anyone thinks about in reading factual prose. A word is not a meaning but a complex of meanings consisting of all its possibilities: its ability to identify something, the image it releases in making that identification, its sound, its history, its association-in-context with the other words of the passage. Good poets use *more* of the word than most readers are used too."

"Yes," says the Citizen, who is proud of being a fair-minded person, "I suppose that *is* true."

"But not only is the individual word a complex. It is used in a phrase that is itself a complex of complexes. And the phrase is in turn used in the complex of the total poem's structure."

"So a poem is a complex of complexes of complexes," says the Citizen, half-indignant now. "I'm beginning to get a complex myself."

"No," says the Poet, "that's a complex you've always had. You are used to words basically as denotations in statements intended or purporting to intend to convey facts. You have the 'practicality complex' and your basic symptoms is 'why doesn't he say it straight?' "

"Well, why doesn't he?"

"As a matter of fact he does at times— even in your terms. Take the line, 'The man who has had the time to think enough.' How much 'straighter' could he make the phrase of that line?"

"I can agree there," says the Citizen. "But what about 'milky lines'? Why does he have to say it on 'the hautboy'? And what's all that about a mirror with a voice?"

"One at a time," says the Poet. "The 'milky lines' is one of those details I remain unsure of. I suspect that Stevens was thinking of the sea as a kind of mother-of-life and that he used 'milky' in that connection. If my guess is right that makes 'milky lines' mean something like 'lines fed by the essential life fluid of all-mothering nature.' But that is only a guess and I have no way of verifying it. In fact, some of what follows in the poem—not in this passage—troubles my guess. That is one of the obscurities I feel in the passage. One I feel and *welcome,* may I say.

"The hautboy, on the other hand, is a straightforward Stevens signature, a part of his personal idiom, like his blue-guitar. The hautboy is the kind of detail that reveals itself immediately as you get to know more about the way the poet writes. For the time being I can only suggest that you take the hautboy to be one of the instruments of art. On that instrument of artifice, Stevens must make the 'fiction' (always a special term in his writing) that can replace the 'obsolete fiction' of the gods. In Stevens, the rituals of art constantly take the place of the rituals of religion—themselves richly obscure.

"As for the 'mirror with a voice,'— there I have to charge you with petulant misreading. Stevens has established the contrast of his statement clearly enough for any willing reader, and it is no reading at all to ignore the context. What he is saying is roughly 'that it is *as if* the responsive man were a mirror with a voice reflecting all of us in a heightened way, *as if* summing us up in the million-diamond-reflection of his artifice.' I am satisfied that the gist of it is about that, though I confess I am uncertain about it later when the poem becomes unmistakably Leibnizian. At that later point, I conclude I don't know Leibniz well enough to guess out Stevens's sense of him. I am left puzzled. But I am also left considerably richer. Certainly, I should be willing to read a much longer and much more obscure poem than this if only to meet that man 'who has had the time to think enough.' I want him in my mind."

"Yes," says the Citizen, "I can go along with some of that. Even with most of it. But why must he be so elusive about it?"

The Poet smiles. "We're back to the business of 'saying it straight' again. I suggest, first, that the thought itself is elusive. And, second, that it's a kind of thinking you're not used to, partly because you have not read enough Stevens to catch the flavor of his thinking, and partly because you're not really a reader of poetry and never have been."

The Citizen draws himself up. "Now I don't know about that," he says. "I took quite a lot of English courses in school and . . ."

"And you haven't read as many as three books of new poems a year since then."

"Well," says the Citizen slowly. "I guess you have me there. Maybe if I were a more practised reader I'd see more. But isn't some of it the poet's fault? Why do they make it so hard for a man to read them? I'm no genius, but I'm reasonably intelligent."

"And rational," suggests the Poet.

"Certainly. What's wrong with rationality?"

"Ask yourself that question as you read through an issue of the *Reader's Digest* sometimes," says the Poet. "Or let me ask you how rationally you got married? Or by what sequence of syllogisms you begot your children? Or what Certified Public Accountant writes the scripts of your dreamlife?"

The Poet is talking fast now, warming to his most fundamental sermon. "We all contain elements of rationality, but we're all much more than those elements. A poet thinks with his senses, his nerve endings, his whole body. He hooks at his thought physically, and he hooks from many directions at once. He *feels* what he thinks, and he feels it most in the act of making a poetic structure of it. Just as a composer feels himself into his musical structure. There is no auditing of rationalities in that process; there is, rather, the accomplishment into form of some part of a whole life."

The Citizen is being fair-minded again. "I can't grasp entirely your way of putting things," he says after a while, "but I can get a glimpse of what I think you're saying—especially when I try to feel it in terms of what a composer does inside his music." He rubs his jaw. "I don't know. There are too many ideas in it that are new to me. I suppose if you say so . . ."

"The last time you started supposing on my say-so it cost you $7.50," says the Poet. "Suppose me nothing on my say-so: I refuse to be trusted by any man who can trust himself, and I doubly refuse to be trusted by a man who can't trust himself. Make up your own mind on the basis of what makes sense in itself."

"That's just the trouble," says the Citizen. "You make it sound sensible enough, but then I turn to a poem and I just can't get my hooks into it."

"That's just what I started to ask you in the beginning. There's the book: give me a for-instance."

"I remember one queer thing called 'Bantam in Pine Woods,' " says the Citizen, thumbing the pages. "I swear I spent a day trying to make sense of the first two lines. Here they are."

Chieftain Iffucan of Azcan in caftan
Of tan with henna hackles, halt!

"What's the problem?" says the Poet.

"No problem," says the Citizen. "Just gibberish. What the devil is all this henna-hackled Iffucan of Azcan trashcan stuff?"

"Ah!" says the Poet, "I see. To tell you the truth I hadn't ever thought of those lines as a difficulty: they're having such fun with themselves—all those lovely exaggerated sound-sequences and that big spoofing tone."

"Is all that—whatever it is—enough excuse for writing nonsense-syllables?"

"Ask Lewis Carroll," says the Poet. "But the fact is they're not nonsense syllables. Note the title. A bantam may certainly be taken as a pretentious and pompous bird strutting around in his half-pint ego as if he owned the world, and refusing to be dwarfed even by pine woods . . ."

"I'm still lost in the Azcan ashcan. And at this point I've had enough of your symbol-threading."

"But the Azcan business is a fact from the world," says the Poet. "Have you ever looked into a pedigree book? I assume this to be a pure-bred bantam and that he is registered as Chieftain Iffucan of Azcan. Stevens begins by reporting the fact, obviously relishing its pretentiousness. 'Caftan' is his first 'poetic' addition. But note this: a caftan is a garment that hangs down just about the way the leg-feathers of a bantam do. The detail is physically right. And the sound of the word itself is exactly right for the sound-sequence.

Stevens builds. That's always a sign of the poet—the ability to do more than one thing at once and to have his choices come out equally right on all levels."

The Citizen sits thoughtfully, turning it over in his mind. The Poet, watching the Citizen, once more has the impression of a painful fair-mindedness at work. Somehow that sense depresses him. He has a vision of the Citizen forever laboring to be open-minded and forever lost to the real life of the poem.

"I have to conclude that you're right," says the Citizen. "But I also know I could never have seen it that way. And I still don't understand the poem."

"Nor do I, completely," confesses the Poet. "But what of it? I don't understand 'Kubla Khan,' nor 'Tiger, Tiger.' Not in detail. But I can certainly experience them as poems. I can, to put it metaphorically, identify their emotional frequencies and the areas into which they transmit."

The Citizen is not satisfied. "I'm still thinking of this Iffucan of Azcan business. There I bogged down on a detail I did not recognize. And perhaps I'll never be any better at identifying odd details. But what about the poem that comes right after it? This one—'Anecdote of a Jar.' Now there is a poem I spent a lot of time on and although I understand every word and every sentence, I'm blessed if I know what Stevens is talking about." He reads it over:

I placed a jar in Tennessee,
And round it was upon a hill.
It made the slovenly wilderness
Surround that hill.

The wilderness rose up to it,
And sprawled around, no longer wild.
The jar was round upon the ground
And tall and of a port in air.

It took dominion everywhere.
The jar was gray and bare.

It did not give of bird or bush,
Like nothing else in Tennessee.

The Citizen finishes reading and looks up. "I was bothered at first by 'port,' " he says, "but I checked the word in the dictionary and I think I see what he's doing with it. But how am I supposed to understand 'It made the slovenly wilderness surround that hill'? How can a jar make a wilderness surround a hill? The wilderness was already surrounding the hill, and long before Stevens and his jar came along."

"In a sense, yes," says the Poet, "but only in the most usual prose-sense. Poetry constantly makes over that usual sense of things. The jar is a made-form; as such it stands for all artifice. The wilderness is nature as-it-happens, the opposite of made-form. But to 'surround' is 'to take position around a center.' And what is formless has no center. It is human artifice, the assertion of human artifice, that puts a center to the wilderness. Because the wilderness is formless it still 'sprawls' but now it sprawls 'up to' the jar. It approaches form, that is, and therefore it is 'no longer wild.' "

"Wait a minute," says the Citizen, "aren't you the one who is doing the paraphrasing now?"

"Yes, surely. I have no quarrel with paraphrase: only with paraphrase as a substitute for the poem. I am not trying to say 'this is what the poem comes to.' Far from it. I am trying to point out the symbolic areas in which the poem moves. The two poles of Stevens's thought seem clearly enough to be 'artifice' and 'formless nature.' Why shouldn't those poles be identified? But the poles are not the poem. The poem is much better seen as those poles plus the force-field they create."

"That does it!" says the Citizen and slams the book shut. "Symbolic areas, force-fields, artifice versus formless-nature—what is all this jargon? Didn't you write once that a poem is an emotion or nothing?"

"I certainly did."

"Then tell how on earth I am supposed to get an emotion from this sort of haywire theorizing?"

The Poet smiles sadly. "I'm about ready to grant you that all criticism is in fact haywire, but would you grant me that criticism is not the poem? At that, one can still rig a weathervane out of haywire, and that vane can point to the weather. The poem is not the vane, nor is it the haywire from which the vane is improvised: the poem is the weather that is pointed-to.

"Stevens, as it happens, had very strong feelings about form versus the formless. Those feelings crowd all his poems. They are fundamental to his very sense of reality. His emotions, to be sure, are intellectual things. If you refuse to think a sense of esthetic-reality as opposed to some other more common ideas of reality is worth an emotion, you are breaking no law, but Stevens is obviously not for you. And that, I find myself thinking, is your loss rather than his."

"Maybe so," says the Citizen, but now he is sitting up as if squared for battle. "I'll even say he is obviously not for me. Who *is* he for? I'm the one who brought up Stevens, and I'll grant he may be a special case. But Stevens is not the only one who is obviously not for me. Who *are* you modern poets for? Is there no such thing as an audience?"

This charge, too, is a familiar one to the Poet. "You've fired a lot of questions," he says, "and a full answer would call for a long sermon. Let me try the short form.

"What is the idea of 'the audience'? Is it enough to argue 'I have bought this book of poems and therefore I have certain audience-rights'? I think, first, one must distinguish between two ideas of 'the audience.'

"One idea may be called the horizontal audience and the other the vertical audience. The horizontal audience consists of everybody who is alive at this moment. The vertical audience consists of everyone, vertically through time, who will ever read a given poem.

"Isn't it immediately obvious that Stevens can only 'be for' a tiny percentage of the horizontal audience? Even Frost, who is the most seemingly-clear and the most widely loved of our good poets, certainly does not reach more than a small percentage of the total population, or even of that part of the population that thinks of itself as literate—as at least literate enough to buy a best-seller. The fact is that no horizontal audience since the age of folk-poetry has been much interested in good poetry. And you may be sure that a few spokesmen sounding off in the name of that horizontal audience are not going to persuade the poets.

"All good poets write for the vertical audience. The vertical audience for Dante, for example, is now six centuries old. And it is growing. If the human race has any luck at all, part of Dante's audience is still thousands of years short of being born.

"Now try a flight of fancy. Imagine that you held an election tomorrow and asked the horizontal audience to vote for Dante as opposed to Eddie Guest. Guest would certainly swamp Dante in such an election. More people in the horizontal audience have read Guest and even, God save the mark, been moved by him—if only to their own inanition. But moved, nevertheless. And we're a democracy, aren't we? The majority rules: bless the majority?

"Not in art. Not horizontally at least. The verdict in art is vertical. Take the idea of majority vote a step further. Imagine that you held the same election on Judgment Day, calling for a total vote of the human race down through time. Can you fail to believe that Dante would then swamp Eddie Guest plus all the horizontalists from Robert Service to Carl Sandburg?

"The point is that the horizontal audience always outnumbers the vertical at any one moment, but that the vertical audience for good poetry always outnumbers the horizontal in time-enough. And not only for the greatest poets. Andrew Marvell is certainly a minor poet, but given time enough, more people certainly will have read 'To His Coy Mistress' than will ever have subscribed to *Time, Life,* and *Fortune.* Compared to what a good poem can do, Luce is a piker at getting circulation."

"Impressive, if true," says the Citizen, "but how does any given poet get his divine sense of this vertical audience?"

"By his own ideal projection of his own best sense of himself. It's as simple as that," says the Poet. "He may be wrong, but he has nothing else to go by. And there is one thing more—all good poets are difficult when their work is new. And their work always becomes less difficult as their total shape becomes more and more visible. As that shape impresses itself upon time, one begins to know how to relate the parts to their total. Even Keats and Shelley confounded their contemporary critics as 'too difficult' and 'not for me.'"

The Citizen throws his hands up. "All right, all right: I've been out-talked. But who *does* write for me?"

The Poet spreads his hands palms out. "Keats and Shelley—now that they have lost their first difficulty."

"And are dead enough?" says the Citizen. "Well, may be. But why is it so impossible for *you* to think about writing for me? I'm willing to give it a try."

The Poet shrugs. "The sort of try you gave Stevens? But no matter. The point is why *should* I write for you?—you're going to be dead the next time anyone looks. We all are for that matter. But not the poem. Not if it's made right. If I make it for you I have to take the chance that it will die with you. I'm not sure you're that good an investment. Besides which, I have to invest in myself. If we happen to share some of the same sense of poetry, it may work out that I do happen to write for you. But that would be a happy bonus at best. I still cannot think of you as a main investment—not till you show a better 'vertical-sense.'"

"We who are about to die," says the Citizen, "salute the poems we cannot grasp. Is that it?"

"Like nothing else in Tennessee," says the Poet bowing.

MR. BENNETT AND MRS. BROWN

Virginia Woolf (1882–1941)

It seems to me possible, perhaps desirable, that I may be the only person in this room who has committed the folly of writing, trying to write, or failing to write, a novel. And when I asked myself, as your invitation to speak to you about modern fiction made me ask myself, what demon whispered in my ear and urged me to my doom, a little figure rose before me—the figure of a man, or of a woman, who said, "My name is Brown. Catch me if you can."

Most novelists have the same experience. Some Brown, Smith, or Jones comes before them and says in the most seductive and charming way in the world, "Come and catch me if you can." And so, led on by this will-o'-the-wisp, they flounder through volume after volume, spending the best years of their lives in the pursuit, and receiving for the most part very little cash in exchange. Few catch the phantom; most have to be content with a scrap of her dress or a wisp of her hair.

My belief that men and women write novels because they are lured on to create some character which has thus imposed itself upon them has the sanction of Mr. Arnold Bennett. In an article from which I will quote he says, "The foundation of good fiction is character-creating and nothing else. . . . Style counts; plot counts; originality of outlook counts. But none of these counts anything like so much as the convincingness of the characters. If the characters are real the novel will have a chance; if they are not, oblivion will be its portion. . . ." And he goes on to draw the conclusion that we have no young novelists of first-rate importance at the present moment, because they are unable to create characters that are real, true, and convincing.

These are the questions that I want with greater boldness than discretion to discuss tonight. I want to make out what we mean when we talk about "character" in fiction; to say something about the question of reality which Mr. Bennett raises; and to suggest some reasons why the younger novelists fail to create characters, if, as Mr. Bennett asserts, it is true that fail they do. This will lead me, I am well aware, to make some very sweeping and some very vague assertions. For the question is an extremely difficult one. Think how little we know about character—think how little we know about art. But, to make a clearance before I begin, I will suggest that we range Edwardians and Georgians into two camps; Mr. Wells, Mr. Bennett, and Mr. Galsworthy I will call the Edwardians; Mr. Forster, Mr. Lawrence, Mr. Strachey, Mr. Joyce, and Mr. Eliot I will call the Georgians. And

if I speak in the first person, with intolerable egotism, I will ask you to excuse me. I do not want to attribute to the world at large the opinions of one solitary, ill-informed, and misguided individual.

My first assertion is one that I think you will grant—that every one in this room is a judge of character. Indeed it would be impossible to live for a year without disaster unless one practised character-reading and had some skill in the art. Our marriages, our friendships depend on it; our business largely depends on it; every day questions arise which can only be solved by its help. And now I will hazard a second assertion, which is more disputable perhaps, to the effect that on or about December, 1910, human character changed.

I am not saying that one went out, as one might into a garden, and there saw that a rose had flowered, or that a hen had laid an egg. The change was not sudden and definite like that. But a change there was, nevertheless; and, since one must be arbitrary, let us date it about the year 1910. The first signs of it are recorded in the books of Samuel Butler, in *The Way of All Flesh* in particular; the plays of Bernard Shaw continue to record it. In life one can see the change, if I may use a homely illustration, in the character of one's cook. The Victorian cook lived like a leviathan in the lower depths, formidable, silent, obscure, inscrutable; the Georgian cook is a creature of sunshine and fresh air; in and out of the drawing-room, now to borrow the *Daily Herald,* now to ask advice about a hat. Do you ask for more solemn instances of the power of the human race to change? Read the *Agamemnon,* and see whether, in process of time, your sympathies are not almost entirely with Clytemnestra. Or consider the married life of the Carlyles and bewail the waste, the futility, for him and for her, of the horrible domestic tradition which made it seemly for a woman of genius to spend her time chasing beetles, scouring saucepans, instead of writing books. All human relations have shifted—those between masters and servants, husbands and wives, parents and children. And when human relations change there is at the same time a change in religion, conduct, politics, and literature. Let us agree to place one of these changes about the year 1910.

I have said that people have to acquire a good deal of skill in character-reading if they are to live a single year of life without disaster. But it is the art of the young. In middle age and in old age the art is practised mostly for its uses, and friendships and other adventures and experiments in the art of reading character are seldom made. But novelists differ from the rest of the world because they do not cease to be interested in character when they have learnt enough about it for practical purposes. They go a step further, they feel that there is something permanently interesting in character in itself. When all the practical business of life has been discharged, there is something about people which continues to seem to them of overwhelming importance, in spite of the fact that it has no bearing whatever upon their happiness, comfort, or income. The study of character becomes to them an absorbing pursuit; to impart character an obsession. And this I find it very difficult to explain: what novelists mean when they talk about character, what the impulse is that urges them so powerfully every now and then to embody their view in writing.

So, if you will allow me, instead of analysing and abstracting, I will tell you a simple story which, however pointless, has the merit of being true, of a journey from Richmond to Waterloo, in the hope that I may show you what I mean by character in itself; that you may realize the different aspects it can wear; and the hideous perils that beset you directly you try to describe it in words.

One night some weeks ago, then, I was late for the train and jumped into the first carriage I came to. As I sat down I had the strange and uncomfortable feeling that I was interrupting a conversation between two people who were already sitting there. Not that they were young or happy. Far from it. They were both elderly, the woman over sixty, the man well over forty. They were sitting opposite each other, and the man, who had been leaning over and talking emphatically to judge by his attitude and the flush on his face, sat back and became silent. I had disturbed him, and he was annoyed. The elderly lady, however, whom I will call Mrs. Brown, seemed rather relieved. She was one of those clean, threadbare old ladies whose extreme tidiness—everything buttoned, fastened, tied together, mended and brushed up—suggests more extreme poverty than rags and dirt. There was something pinched about her—a look of suffering, of apprehension, and, in addition, she was extremely small. Her feet, in their clean little boots, scarcely touched the floor. I felt that she had nobody to support her; that she had to make up her mind for herself; that, having been deserted, or left a widow, years ago, she had led an anxious, harried life, bringing up an only son, perhaps, who, as like as not, was by this time beginning to go to the bad. All this shot through my mind as I sat down, being uncomfortable, like most people, at travelling with fellow passengers unless I have somehow or other accounted for them. Then I looked at the man. He was no relation to Mrs. Brown's I felt sure; he was of a bigger, burlier, less refined type. He was a man of business I imagined, very likely a respectable corn-chandler from the North, dressed in good blue serge with a pocket-knife and a silk handkerchief, and a stout leather bag. Obviously, however, he had an unpleasant business to settle with Mrs. Brown; a secret, perhaps sinister business, which they did not intend to discuss in my presence.

"Yes, the Crofts have had very bad luck with their servants," Mr. Smith (as I will call him) said in a considering way, going back to some earlier topic, with a view to keeping up appearances.

"Ah, poor people," said Mrs. Brown, a trifle condescendingly. "My grandmother had a maid who came when she was fifteen and stayed till she was eighty" (this was said with a kind of hurt and aggressive pride to impress us both perhaps).

"One doesn't often come across that sort of thing nowadays," said Mr. Smith in conciliatory tones.

Then they were silent.

"It's odd they don't start a golf club there—I should have thought one of the young fellows would," said Mr. Smith, for the silence obviously made him uneasy.

Mrs. Brown hardly took the trouble to answer.

"What changes they're making in this part of the world," said Mr. Smith, looking out of the window, and looking furtively at me as he did so.

It was plain, from Mrs. Brown's silence, from the uneasy affability with which Mr. Smith spoke, that he had some power over her which he was exerting disagreeably. It might have been her son's downfall, or some painful episode in her past life, or her daughter's. Perhaps she was going to London to sign some document to make over some property. Obviously against her will she was in Mr. Smith's hands. I was beginning to feel a great deal of pity for her, when she said, suddenly and inconsequently:

"Can you tell me if an oak-tree dies when the leaves have been eaten for two years in succession by caterpillars?"

She spoke quite brightly, and rather precisely, in a cultivated, inquisitive voice.

Mr. Smith was startled, but relieved to have a safe topic of conversation given him. He told her a great deal very quickly about plagues of insects. He told her that he had a brother who kept a fruit farm in Kent. He told her what fruit farmers do every year in Kent, and so on, and so on. While he talked a very odd thing happened. Mrs. Brown took out her little white handkerchief and began to dab her eyes. She was crying. But she went on listening quite composedly to what he was saying, and he went on talking, a little louder, a little angrily, as if he had seen her cry often before; as if it were a painful habit. At last it got on his nerves. He stopped abruptly, looked out of the window, then leant towards her as he had been doing when I got in, and said in a bullying, menacing way, as if he would not stand any more nonsense:

"So about that matter we were discussing. It'll be all right? George will be there on Tuesday?"

"We shan't be late," said Mrs. Brown, gathering herself together with superb dignity.

Mr. Smith said nothing. He got up, buttoned his coat, reached his bag down, and jumped out of the train before it had stopped at Clapham Junction. He had got what he wanted, but he was ashamed of himself; he was glad to get out of the old lady's sight.

Mrs. Brown and I were left alone together. She sat in her corner opposite, very clean, very small, rather queer, and suffering intensely. The impression she made was overwhelming. It came pouring out like a draught, like a smell of burning. What was it composed of—that overwhelming and peculiar impression? Myriads of irrelevant and incongruous ideas crowd into one's head on such occasions; one sees the person, one sees Mrs. Brown, in the centre of all sorts of different scenes. I thought of her in a seaside house, among queer ornaments: sea-urchins, models of ships in glass cases. Her husband's medals were on the mantelpiece. She popped in and out of the room, perching on the edges of chairs, picking meals out of saucers, indulging in long, silent stares. The caterpillars and the oak-trees seemed to imply all that. And then, into this fantastic and secluded life, in broke Mr. Smith. I saw him blowing in, so to speak, on a windy day. He banged, he slammed. His dripping umbrella made a pool in the hall. They sat closeted together.

And then Mrs. Brown faced the dreadful revelation. She took her heroic decision. Early, before dawn, she packed her bag and carried it herself to the station. She would not let Smith touch it. She was wounded in her pride, unmoored from her anchorage; she came of gentlefolks who kept servants—but details could wait. The important thing was to realize her character, to steep oneself in her atmosphere. I had no time to explain why I felt it somewhat tragic, heroic, yet with a dash of the flighty and fantastic, before the train stopped, and I watched her disappear, carrying her bag, into the vast blazing station. She looked very small, very tenacious; at once very frail and very heroic. And I have never seen her again, and I shall never know what became of her.

The story ends without any point to it. But I have not told you this anecdote to illustrate either my own ingenuity or the pleasure of travelling from Richmond to Waterloo. What I want you to see in it is this. Here is a character imposing itself upon another person. Here is Mrs. Brown making someone begin almost automatically to write a novel about her.

I believe that all novels begin with an old lady in the corner opposite. I believe that all novels, that is to say, deal with character, and that it is to express character—not to preach doctrines, sing songs, or celebrate the glories of the British Empire, that the form of the novels, so clumsy, verbose, and undramatic, so rich, elastic, and alive, has been evolved. To express character, I have said; but you will at once reflect that the very widest interpretation can be put upon those words. For example, old Mrs. Brown's character will strike you very differently according to the age and country in which you happen to be born. It would be easy enough to write three different versions of that incident in the train, an English, a French, and a Russian. The English writer would make the old lady into a "character"; he would bring out her oddities and mannerisms; her buttons and wrinkles; her ribbons and warts. Her personality would dominate the book. A French writer would rub out all that; he would sacrifice the individual Mrs. Brown to give a more general view of human nature; to make a more abstract, proportioned, and harmonious whole. The Russian would pierce through the flesh; would reveal the soul—the soul alone, wandering out into the Waterloo Road, asking of life some tremendous question which would sound on and on in our ears after the book was finished. And then besides age and country there is the writer's temperament to be considered. You see one thing in character, and I another. You say it means this, and I that. And when it comes to writing each makes a further selection on principles of his own. Thus Mrs. Brown can be treated in an infinite variety of ways, according to the age, country, and temperament of the writer.

But now I must recall what Mr. Arnold Bennett says. He says that it is only if the characters are real that the novel has any chance of surviving. Otherwise, die it must. But, I ask myself, what is reality? And who are the judges of reality? A character may be real to Mr. Bennett and quite unreal to me. For instance, in this article he says that Dr. Watson in *Sherlock Holmes* is real to him: to me Dr. Watson is a sack stuffed with straw, a dummy, a figure of fun. And so it is with character after character—in book after book. There is nothing that people differ about more than the reality of characters, especially in contemporary books. But if you take a large view I think that Mr. Bennett is perfectly right. If, that is, you think of the novels which seem to you great novels—*War and Peace, Vanity Fair, Tristram Shandy, Madame Bovary, Pride and Prejudice, The Mayor of Casterbridge, Villette*— if you think of these books, you do at once think of some character who has seemed to you so real (I do not by that mean so lifelike) that it has the power to make you think not merely of it itself, but of all sorts of things through its eyes —of religion, of love, of war, of peace, of family life, of balls in country towns, of sunsets, moonrises, the immortality of the soul. There is hardly any subject of human experience that is left out of *War and Peace* it seems to me. And in all these novels all these great novelists have brought us to see whatever they wish us to see through some character. Otherwise, they would not be novelists; but poets, historians, or pamphleteers.

But now let us examine what Mr. Bennett went on to say—he said that there was no great novelist among the Georgian writers because they cannot create characters who are real, true, and convincing. And there I cannot agree. There are reasons, excuses, possibilities which I think put a different colour upon the case. It seems so to me at least, but I am well aware that this is a matter about which I am likely to be prejudiced, sanguine, and near-sighted. I will put my view before you in the hope that you will make it impartial, judicial, and broad-minded. Why, then, is it so hard for novelists at present to create characters which seem real, not only to Mr. Bennett, but to the world at large? Why, when October comes round, do the publishers always fail to supply us with a masterpiece?

Surely one reason is that the men and women who began writing novels in 1910 or thereabouts had this great difficulty to face—that there was no English novelist living from whom they could learn their business. Mr. Conrad is a Pole; which sets him apart, and makes him, however admirable, not very helpful. Mr. Hardy has written no novel since 1895. The most prominent and successful novelists in the year 1910 were, I suppose, Mr. Wells, Mr. Bennett, and Mr. Galsworthy. Now it seems to me that to go to these men and ask them to teach you how to write a novel—how to create characters that are real—is precisely like going to a boot maker and asking him to teach you how to make a watch. Do not let me give you the impression that I do not admire and enjoy their books. They seem to me of great value, and indeed of great necessity. There are seasons when it is more important to have boots than to have watches. To drop metaphor, I think that after the creative activity of the Victorian age it was quite necessary, not only for literature but for life, that some-one should write the books that Mr. Wells, Mr. Bennett, and Mr. Galsworthy have written. Yet what odd books they are! Sometimes I wonder if we are right to call them books at all. For they leave one with so strange a feeling of incom-pleteness and dissatisfaction. In order to complete them it seems necessary to do something—to join a society, or, more desperately, to write a cheque. That done, the restlessness is laid, the book finished; it can be put upon the shelf, and need never be read again. But with the work of other novelists it is different. *Tristram Shandy* or *Pride and Prejudice* is complete in itself; it is self-contained; it leaves one with no desire to do anything, except indeed to read the book again, and to understand it better. The difference perhaps is that both Sterne and Jane Austen were interested in things in themselves; in character, in itself; in the book in itself. Therefore everything was inside the book, nothing outside. But the Edwardians were never interested in character in itself; or in the book in itself. They were interested in something outside. Their books, then, were incomplete as books, and required that the reader should finish them, actively and practically, for himself.

Perhaps we can make this clear if we take the liberty of imagining a little party in the railway carriage—Mr. Wells, Mr. Galsworthy, Mr. Bennett are travelling to Waterloo with Mrs. Brown. Mrs. Brown, I have said, was poorly dressed and very small. She had an anxious, harassed look. I doubt whether she was what you call an educated woman. Seizing upon all these symptoms of the unsatisfactory condition of our primary schools with a rapidity to which I can do no justice, Mr. Wells would instantly project upon the window-pane a vision of a better, breezier, jollier, happier, more adventurous and gallant world, where these musty railway carriages and fusty old women do not exist; where miraculous barges bring tropical fruit to Camberwell by eight o'clock in the morning; where there are public nurseries, fountains, and libraries, dining-rooms, drawing-rooms, and marriages; where every citizen is generous and candid, manly and magnificent, and rather like Mr.

Wells himself. But nobody is in the least like Mrs. Brown. There are no Mrs. Browns in Utopia. Indeed I do not think that Mr. Wells, in his passion to make her what she ought to be, would waste a thought upon her as she is. And what would Mr. Galsworthy see? Can we doubt that the walls of Doulton's factory would take his fancy? There are women in that factory who make twenty-five dozen earthenware pots every day. There are mothers in the Mile End Road who depend upon the farthings which those women earn. But there are employers in Surrey who are even now smoking rich cigars while the nightingale sings. Burning with indignation, stuffed with information, arraigning civilization, Mr. Galsworthy would only see in Mrs. Brown a pot broken on the wheel and thrown into the corner.

Mr. Bennett, alone of the Edwardians, would keep his eyes in the carriage. He, indeed, would observe every detail with immense care. He would notice the advertisements; the pictures of Swanage and Portsmouth; the way in which the cushion bulged between the buttons; how Mrs. Brown wore a brooch which had cost three-and-ten-three at Whitworth's bazaar; and had mended both gloves—indeed the thumb of the left-hand glove had been replaced. And he would observe, at length, how this was the non-stop train from Windsor which calls at Richmond for the convenience of middle-class residents, who can afford to go to the theatre but have not reached the social rank which can afford motor-cars, though it is true, there are occasions (he would tell us what), when they hire them from a company (he would tell us which). And so he would gradually sidle sedately towards Mrs. Brown, and would remark how she had been left a little copyhold, not freehold, property at Datchet, which, however, was mortgaged to Mr. Bungay the solicitor—but why should I presume to invent Mr. Bennett? Does not Mr. Bennett write novels himself? I will open the first book that chance puts in my way—*Hilda Lessways*. Let us see how he makes us feel that Hilda is real, true, and convincing, as a novelist should. She shut the door in a soft, controlled way, which showed the constraint of her relations with her mother. She was fond of reading *Maud;* she was endowed with the power to feel intensely. So far, so good; in his leisurely, surefooted way Mr. Bennett is trying in these first pages, where every touch is important, to show us the kind of girl she was.

But then he begins to describe, not Hilda Lessways, but the view from her bedroom window, the excuse being that Mr. Skellorn, the man who collects rents, is coming along that way. Mr. Bennett proceeds:

"The bailiwick of Turnhill lay behind her; and all the murky district of the Five Towns, of which Turnhill is the northern outpost, lay to the south. At the foot of Chatterley Wood the canal wound in large curves on its way towards the undefiled plains of Cheshire and the sea. On the canal-side, exactly opposite to Hilda's window, was a flour-mill, that sometimes made nearly as much smoke as the kilns and the chimneys closing the prospect on either hand. From the flour-mill a bricked path, which separated a considerable row of new cottages from their appurtenant gardens, led straight into Lessways Street, in front of Mrs. Lessway's house. By this path Mr. Skellorn should have arrived, for he inhabited the farthest of the cottages."

One line of insight would have done more than all those lines of description; but let them pass as the necessary drudgery of the novelist. And now—where is Hilda? Alas. Hilda is still looking out of the window. Passionate and dissatisfied as she was, she was a girl with an eye for houses. She often compared this old Mr. Skellorn with the villas she saw from her bedroom window. Therefore the villas must be described. Mr. Bennett proceeds:

"The row was called Freehold Villas: a consciously proud name in a district where much of the land was copyhold and could only change owners subject to the payment of 'fines,' and to the feudal consent of a 'court' presided over by the agent of a lord of the manor. Most of the dwellings were owned by their occupiers, who, each an absolute monarch of the soil, niggled in his sooty garden of an evening amid the flutter of drying shirts and towels. Freehold Villas symbolized the final triumph of Victorian economics, the apotheosis of the prudent and industrious artisan. It corresponded with a Building Society Secretary's dream of paradise. And indeed it was a very real achievement. Nevertheless, Hilda's irrational contempt would not admit this."

Heaven be praised, we cry! At last we are coming to Hilda herself. But not so fast. Hilda may have been this, that, and the other; but Hilda not only looked at houses, and thought of houses; Hilda lived in a house. And what sort of a house did Hilda live in? Mr. Bennett proceeds:

"It was one of the two middle houses of a detached terrace of four houses built by her grandfather Lessways, the teapot manufacturer; it was the chief of the four, obviously the habitation of the proprietor of the terrance. One of the corner houses comprised a grocer's shop, and this house had been robbed of its just proportion of garden so that the seigneurial garden-plot might be triflingly larger than the other. The terrace was not a terrace of cottages, but of houses rated at from twenty-six to thirty-six pounds a year; beyond the means of artisans and petty insurance agents and rent-collectors. And further, it was well-built, generously built; and its architecture, though debased, showed some faint traces of Georgian amenity. It was admittedly the best row of houses in that newly-settled quarter of the town. In coming to it out of Freehold Villas Mr. Skellorn obviously came to something superior, wider, more liberal. Suddenly Hilda heard her mother's voice. . . ."

But we cannot hear her mother's voice, or Hilda's voice; we can only hear Mr. Bennett's voice telling us facts about rents and freeholds and copyholds and fines. What can Mr. Bennett be about? I have formed my own opinion of what Mr. Bennett is about —he is trying to make us imagine for him; he is trying to hypnotize us into the belief that, because he has made a house, there must be a person living there. With all his powers of observation, which are marvellous, with all his sympathy and humanity, which are great, Mr. Bennett has never once looked at Mrs. Brown in her corner. There she sits in the corner of the carriage—that carriage which is travelling, not from Richmond to Waterloo, but from one age of English literature to the next, for Mrs. Brown is eternal, Mrs. Brown is human nature, Mrs. Brown changes only on the surface, it is the novelists who get in and out—there she sits and not one of the Edwardian writers has so much as looked at her. They have looked very powerfully, searchingly, and sympathetically out of the window; at factories, at Utopias, even at the decoration and upholstery of the carriage; but never at her, never at life, never at human nature. And so they have developed a technique of novel-writing which suits their purpose; they have made tools and established conventions which do their business. But those tools are not our tools, and that business is not our

business. For us those conventions are ruin, those tools are death.

You may well complain of the vagueness of my language. What is a convention, a tool, you may ask, and what do you mean by saying that Mr. Bennett's and Mr. Wells's and Mr. Galsworthy's conventions are the wrong conventions for the Georgians'? The question is difficult: I will attempt a short cut. A convention in writing is not much different from a convention in manners. Both in life and in literature it is necessary to have some means of bridging the gulf between the hostess and her unknown guest on the one hand, the writer and his unknown reader on the other. The hostess bethinks her of the weather, for generations of hostesses have established the fact that this is a subject of universal interest in which we all believe. She begins by saying that we are having a wretched May, and, having thus got into touch with her unknown guest, proceeds to matters of greater interest. So it is in literature. The writer must get into touch with his reader by putting before him something which he recognizes, which therefore stimulates his imagination, and makes him willing to co-operate in the far more difficult business of intimacy. And it is of the highest importance that this common meeting-place should be reached easily, almost instinctively, in the dark, with one's eyes shut. Here is Mr. Bennett making use of this common ground in the passage which I have quoted. The problem before him was to make us believe in the reality of Hilda Lessways. So he began, being an Edwardian, by describing accurately and minutely the sort of house Hilda lived in, and the sort of house she saw from the window. House property was the common ground from which the Edwardians found it easy to proceed to intimacy. Indirect as it seems to us, the convention worked admirably, and thousands of Hilda Lessways were launched upon the world by this means. For that age and generation, the convention was a good one.

But now, if you will allow me to pull my own anecdote to pieces, you will see how keenly I felt the lack of a convention, and how serious a matter it is when the tools of one generation are useless for the next. The incident had made a great impression on me. But how was I to transmit it to you? All I could do was to report as accurately as I could what was said, to describe in detail what was worn, to say, despairingly, that all sorts of scenes rushed into my mind, to proceed to tumble them out pell-mell, and to describe this vivid, this overmastering impression by likening it to a draught or a smell of burning. To tell you the truth, I was also strongly tempted to manufacture a three-volume novel about the old lady's son, and his adventures crossing the Atlantic, and her daughter, and how she kept a milliner's shop in Westminister, the past life of Smith himself, and his house at Sheffield, though such stories seem to me the most dreary, irrelevant, and humbugging affairs in the world.

But if I had done that I should have escaped the appalling effort of saying what I meant. And to have got at what I meant I should have had to go back and back and back; to experiment with one thing and another; to try this sentence and that, referring each word to my vision, matching it as exactly as possible, and knowing that somehow I had to find a common ground between us, a convention which would not seem to you too odd, unreal, and far-fetched to believe in. I admit that I shirked that arduous undertaking. I let my Mrs. Brown slip through my fingers. I have told you nothing whatever about her. But that is partly the great Edwardians' fault. I asked them—they are my elders and betters—How shall I begin to describe this woman's character? And they said: "Begin by saying that her father kept a shop in Harrogate. Ascertain the rent. Ascertain the wages of shop assistants in the year 1878. Discover what her mother died of. Describe cancer. Describe calico. Describe—" But I cried: "Stop! Stop!" And I regret to say that I threw that ugly, that clumsy, that incongruous tool out of the window, for I knew that if I began describing the cancer and the calico, my Mrs. Brown, that vision to which I cling though I know no way of imparting it to you, would have been dulled and tarnished and vanished for ever.

That is what I mean by saying that the Edwardian tools are the wrong ones for us to use. They have laid an enormous stress upon the fabric of things. They have given us a house in the hope that we may be able to deduce the human beings who live there. To give them their due, they have made that house much better worth living in. But if you hold that novels are in the first place about people, and only in the second about the houses they live in, that is the wrong way to set about it. Therefore, you see, the Georgian writer had to begin by throwing away the method that was in use at the moment. He was left alone there facing Mrs. Brown without any method of conveying her to the reader. But that is inaccurate. A writer is never alone. There is always the public with him—if not on the same seat, at least in the compartment next door. Now the public is a strange travelling companion. In England it is a very suggestible and docile creature, which, once you get it to attend, will believe implicitly what it is told for a certain number of years. If you say to the public with sufficient conviction: "All women have tails, and all men humps," it will actually learn to see women with tails and men with humps, and will think it very revolutionary and probably improper if you say: "Nonsense. Monkeys have tails and camels humps. But men and women have brains, and they have hearts; they think and they feel,"—that will seem to it a bad joke, and an improper one into the bargain.

But to return. Here is the British public sitting by the writer's side and saying in its vast and unanimous way: "Old women have houses. They have fathers. They have incomes. They have servants. They have hot-water bottles. That is how we know that they are old women. Mr. Wells and Mr. Bennett and Mr. Galsworthy have always taught us that this is the way to recognize them. But now with your Mrs. Brown—how are we to believe in her? We do not even know whether her villa was called Albert or Balmoral; what she paid for her gloves; or whether her mother died of cancer or of consumption. How can she be alive? No; she is a mere figment of your imagination."

And old women of course ought to be made of freehold villas and copyhold estates, not of imagination.

The Georgian novelist, therefore, was in an awkward predicament. There was Mrs. Brown protesting that she was different, quite different, from what people made out, and luring the novelist to her rescue by the most fascinating if fleeting glimpse of her charms; there were the Edwardians handing out tools appropriate to house building and house breaking; and there was the British public asseverating that they must see the hot-water bottle first. Meanwhile the train was rushing to that station where we must all get out.

Such, I think, was the predicament in which the young Georgians found themselves about the year 1910. Many of them—I am thinking of Mr. Forster and Mr. Lawrence in particular—spoilt their early work because, instead of throwing away those tools, they tried to use them. They tried to compromise. They tried to combine their own direct sense of the oddity and significance of some character with Mr. Galsworthy's knowledge of the Factory Acts, and Mr. Bennett's knowledge of the Five Towns. They tried it, but they had too keen, too overpowering a sense of Mrs. Brown and her peculiarities to go on trying it much longer. Something had to be done. At whatever cost of life, limb, and damage to valuable property Mrs. Brown must be rescued, expressed, and set in her high relations to the world before the train stopped and she disappeared for ever. And so the smashing and the crashing began. Thus it is that we hear all round us, in poems and novels and biographies, even in newspaper articles and essays, the sound of breaking and falling, crashing and destruction. It is the prevailing sound of the Georgian age—rather a melancholy one if you think what melodious days there have been in the past, if you think of Shakespeare and Milton and Keats or even of Jane Austen and Thackeray and Dickens; if you think of the language, and the heights to which it can soar when free, and see the same eagle captive, bald, and croaking.

In view of these facts—with these sounds in my ears and these fancies in my brain—I am not going to deny that Mr. Bennett has some reason when he complains that our Georgian writers are unable to make us believe that our characters are real. I am forced to agree that they do not pour out three immortal masterpieces with Victorian regularity every autumn. But, instead of being gloomy, I am sanguine. For this state of things is, I think, inevitable whenever from hoar old age or callow youth the convention ceases to be a means of communication between writer and reader, and becomes instead an obstacle and an impediment. At the present moment we are suffering, not from decay, but from having no code of manners which writers and readers accept as a prelude to the more exciting intercourse of friendship. The literary convention of the time is so artificial— you have to talk about the weather and nothing but the weather throughout the entire visit—that, naturally, the feeble are tempted to outrage, and the strong are led to destroy the very foundations and rules of literary society. Signs of this are everywhere apparent. Grammar is violated; syntax disintegrated; as a boy staying with an aunt for the week-end rolls in the geranium bed out of sheer desperation as the solemnities of the sabbath wear on. The more adult writers do not, of course, indulge in such wanton exhibitions of spleen. Their sincerity is desperate, and their courage tremendous; it is only that they do not know which to use, a fork or their fingers. Thus, if you read Mr. Joyce and Mr. Eliot you will be struck by the indecency of the one, and the obscurity of the other. Mr. Joyce's indecency in *Ulysses* seems to me the conscious and calculated indecency of a desperate man who feels that in order to breathe he must break the windows. At moments, when the window is broken, he is magnificent. But what a waste of energy! And, after all, how dull indecency is, when it is not the overflowing of a superabundant energy or savagery, but the determined and public-spirited act of a man who needs fresh air! Again, with the obscurity of Mr. Eliot. I think that Mr. Eliot has written some of the loveliest single lines in modern poetry. But how intolerant he is of the old usages and politeness of society— respect for the weak, consideration for the dull! As I sun myself upon the intense and ravishing beauty of one of his lines, and reflect that I must make a dizzy and dangerous leap to the next, and so on

from line to line, like an acrobat flying precariously from bar to bar, I cry out, I confess, for the old decorums, and envy the indolence of my ancestors who, instead of spinning madly through mid-air, dreamt quietly in the shade with a book. Again, in Mr. Strachey's books, *Eminent Victorians* and *Queen Victoria,* the effort and strain of writing against the grain and current of the times is visible too. It is much less visible, of course, for not only is he dealing with facts, which are stubborn things, but he has fabricated, chiefly from eighteenth-century material, a very discreet code of manners of his own, which allows him to sit at table with the highest in the land and to say a great many things under cover of that exquisite apparel which, had they gone naked, would have been chased by the men-servants from the room. Still, if you compare *Eminent Victorians* with some of Lord Macaulay's essays, though you will feel that Lord Macaulay is always wrong, and Mr. Strachey always right, you will also feel a body, a sweep, a richness in Lord Macaulay's essays which show that his age was behind him; all his strength went straight into his work; none was used for purposes of concealment or of conversion. But Mr. Strachey has had to open our eyes before he made us see; he has had to search out and sew together a very artful manner of speech; and the effort, beautifully though it is concealed, has robbed his work of some of the force that should have gone into it, and limited his scope.

For these reasons, then, we must reconcile ourselves to a season of failures and fragments. We must reflect that where so much strength is spent on finding a way of telling the truth, the truth itself is bound to reach us in rather an exhausted and chaotic condition. Ulysses, Queen Victoria, Mr. Prufrock—to give Mrs. Brown some of the names she has made famous lately—is a little pale and dishevelled by the time her rescuers reach her. And it is the sound of their axes that we hear—a vigorous and stimulating sound in my ears—unless of course you wish to sleep, when, in the bounty of his concern, Providence has provided a host of writers anxious and able to satisfy your needs.

Thus I have tried, at tedious length, I fear, to answer some of the questions which I began by asking. I have given an account of some of the difficulties which in my view beset the Georgian writer in all his forms. I have sought to excuse him. May I end by venturing to remind you of the duties and responsibilities that are yours as partners in this business of writing books, as companions in the railway carriage, as fellow travellers with Mrs. Brown? For she is just as visible to you who remain silent as to us who tell stories about her. In the course of your daily life this past week you have had far stranger and more interesting experiences than the one I have tried to describe. You have overheard scraps of talk that filled you with amazement. You have gone to bed at night bewildered by the complexity of your feelings. In one day thousands of ideas have coursed through your brains; thousands of emotions have met, collided, and disappeared in astonishing disorder. Nevertheless, you allow the writers to palm off upon you a version of all this, an image of Mrs. Brown, which has no likeness to that surprising apparition whatsoever. In your modesty you seem to consider that writers are different blood and bone from yourselves; that they know more of Mrs. Brown that you do. Never was there a more fatal mistake. It is this division between reader and writer, this humility on your part, these professional airs and graces on ours, that corrupt and emasculate the books which should be the healthy offspring of a close and equal alliance between us. Hence spring those sleek, smooth novels, those portentous and ridiculous biographies, that milk and watery criticism, those poems melodiously celebrating the innocence of roses and sheep which pass so plausibly for literature at the present time.

Your part is to insist that writers shall come down off their plinths and pedestals, and describe beautifully if possible, truthfully at any rate, our Mrs. Brown. You should insist that she is an old lady of unlimited capacity and infinite variety; capable of appearing in any place; wearing any dress; saying anything and doing heaven knows what. But the things she says and the things she does and her eyes and her nose and her speech and her silence have an overwhelming fascination, for she is, of course, the spirit we live by, life itself.

But do not expect just at present a complete and satisfactory presentment of her. Tolerate the spasmodic, the obscure, the fragmentary, the failure. Your help is invoked in a good cause. For I will make one final and surpassingly rash prediction—we are trembling on the verge of one of the great ages of English literature. But it can only be reached if we are determined never, never to desert Mrs. Brown.

ON THE CONTEMPORARY APOCALYPTIC IMAGINATION

Earl Rovit
(1927–   )

I suppose that every period possesses its own fashions in terminology and metaphor; that there have always been "in" concepts and "out" concepts; and that it has been ever incumbent upon students of the time to come to terms with the prevailing weathers of thought, no matter how vulgarized they may be by ignorance and enthusiasm or how adulterated by cynical exploitation. The questions that people ask are generally more significant than the answers they give. When a single question seems to be repeated everywhere, when it recurs with only slight variation in the most heterogeneous situations and provenances, and when, in its most extreme form, it can be responded to only by violent repression or permissive silence, we would do well to attend to the question very carefully. Recently I have been struck by the frequency, variety and intensity of such a question on our contemporary scene. A deceptively simple, thoroughly loaded question: *Why not?* Once my mind became attuned to its resonances, I seemed to be able to discern it at or near the root of every radical dissension of which I was aware. In art, in science, in politics. In the chatter of private and public disputation. Over and over again in the classroom, in dissident social discussions, in my own introspective dialogues, in any situation where the utility or justification of an action was under deliberation. But *why not?* is not so much a question as it is an answer, or, better still, a declaration of polymorphous intent. It seems to be the instinctive response of a large segment of our collective mind to any expression of restriction, prohibition, formal limitation. Thou shalt not commit a disrespect to thine elders, thy conventional pieties, thy tradition. Why not? Thou shalt not murder with napalm or enslave with sanctimonious fetters. Why not? Thou shalt not venture into inner or outer space with impunity. Why not? Here is a boundary line; this limitation cannot be broken. Why not?

Those of us with any pretensions to some formal intellectual training may be particularly disturbed in the face of this adamant *why not.* Part of our uneasiness is doubtless caused by the threat that is posed to our tenuous security; but, more important I think, we are made uncomfortable in an almost philosophical way because we have been brought up within the circumscriptions of a very different question, the traditional *why?* Our intelligences, such as they are, have been geared to analyze "givens," to search out the complexity of causes that may lead to an isolated effect. The overwhelming course of the Enlightenment and the empirical tradition has tended to enclose our words into comprehensible capsules of why-and-because. And the shock of the twentieth century on our tender rational sensibilities is caused—as much as by anything else—by the increasing irrelevance and unreliability of the answers we are able to produce. Why the death camps? Why the dread of nuclear annihilation? Why our loss of rational control over our private and public lives? Why the quality of dissociated terror and loneliness that seems pervasive beneath the mannered surfaces of our behavior? Oh, we have no trouble in garnering bumper harvests of measured answers. With the devices of our computer age, we can dissect and analyze by the wholesale gross. But it is as though we have perfected a high-speed autopsy technique while the plague accelerates and the corpses of new questions roll up to the door faster than our electronic analyses can be trucked away for filing. *Why* begets its multitudinous spawn of *becauses,* and these in turn beget an urgent host of new *why's,* and the shiny machines work beautifully, but the fever level mounts. For *why* is predicated on the unassailable ontological certainty that what is—simply *is.* The counterquestion, *why not?,* is the apocalyptic gesture of dismissal. It casually rejects all *becauses* since it denies even the minimal certainty of a bounded problem. *Why not* is the shrug that, at best, cares enough not to care—and, at worst, doesn't care at all. It is the response that invites us to believe that "anything goes." And when anything goes, it means that everything flies apart. *Why not* is the apocalyptic shiver of the stoop-shouldered earth just a moment before the avalanche, just a moment before the mountains skip like lambs and the great rock-faces crumble and crush everything in their fall.

How can you think about an apocalypse with only one mind—with a rational intelligence that is designed to make precise exclusions of anything that is chaos? You can't even talk about an apocalypse univocally—with one voice—with one discreet why-and-because voice. It eludes the single-chorded voice; it will not even cast a shadow on the gleaming logicalities of the intelligence. But we have more than one level of mind and more than one voice and our feelings are porous to many different depths. It is possible to make the world move without touching it and men have always known that cacophony and disharmony are not inherently meaningless. Nor was irony invented merely to discriminate between categories; irony is promiscuously copulative, and *why not?* enunciates as readily to the accompaniment of a snicker as it does to a gesture of stubborn ferocity.

The truth of the matter is, I personally find the very notion of an apocalypse unsettling. It makes a mash of my ordered world. It destroys my past and throws my thoughts of a future into an ash heap. Its fashion of assault is omnivorous, uncompromising, and treacherously sophisticated in its capacities for instant adaptation. It has fathered the movement for silence and outrage in the arts; for anarchy and violence in social and political affairs; for polymorphous perversity in psychology, religion and metaphysics. Ultimately— and it is never less than ultimate—it will accept nothing save spontaneity, imme-

diacy of response, and the obliteration of all stabilities. And while it offers the lip-service promise of a restored innocence and purity—a miraculous rebirth of life —as a reward for its services, these blandishments are the least beguiling facets of its appeal. I don't want to break windows in order to let the fresh air in; the fact is, I'm hopelessly in love with the sound of smashing glass. So how can I trust myself when I can hardly skim the surfaces of my own dreads and desires? And how can I be trusted when I pretend to tread dispassionately and complacently in the fathomless waters of the apocalyptic imagination? And yet that is the element in which we must learn to swim, and unless we attempt some honest account of it, we will not only drown—our fate anyway—but we will touch nothing firmly in our descent.

So I take the safe scholarly resort in etymology. *Apocalypse*—from the Greek verb meaning "to uncover, to disclose." Set in its early Messianic-Christian context, this is historically understandable enough. It points to a prophetic revelation of the day of wrath, an hysterical prophecy of a total un-covering, a complete dis-closure, when all boundaries will be shattered, when all the concealed and buried forces will be released from their quotidian restraints. The visitation of fire and ice, the pestilence in the whirlwind. This is the final tolling of time, the Day of the Last Judgment, because afterwards, with everything open and unconcealed, all bonds dissolved, both time and the act of judgment will be obsolescent. The ambiguities of seeming and appearance will exist no more; everything will simply and immediately and completely *be*. On any level of literary meaning, the Apocalypse was surely a magnificent metaphor, sired by frustration and mothered by a mighty hope that turned rapidly into sour vengeful desire. Nor was it a metaphor restricted to a particularly oppressive historical circumstance. Every infant's psyche nurtures its own apocalyptic dream: the blood sacrifice at the very pit of the sweet disposition; the maiming of all the fathers, the delicious abuse of all the mothers. Nemesis, that most satisfying wish-fantasy of retributive justice, is one of the metamorphic shapes of the Apocalypse. Thus has it ever been, but why so suddenly fashionable in our time? Is it only that the world possesses more embittered children today than ever before? Or that our children are louder and more eagerly catered to as our economies have shifted from production to consumption? Or, perhaps, that our children remain childish long past the physiological frontiers of adulthood? "Don't trust anyone over thirty." Would you believe forty? Forty-five? Suffer little children to come unto me. Trailing clouds of marijuana and clutching switchblade knives in their pudgy little fists. No, weasel-scholar, that's clearly insufficient. A good enough *because* for the sociologist to worry about: the relationship between maturation, a machine technology and social responsibility. But clearly inadequate for our needs. A metaphor is volatile. A mighty metaphor is mightily volatile. It breeds meanings in multiple litters, but it is itself protean and without essential meaning. The one undeniable illustration of an existential shape, or shapelessness. Ah, see how quickly the scholar weasels from etymology to penology. If the value judgment is built into the process, how can I be trusted?

A different tack, then. Follow the metaphor, not its motivations. Since the Apocalypse is only and always a metaphor—for what else can it be—it is more than likely a product of other metaphors that it has subsumed and digested. A task, then, for literary criticism—the isolation and description of metaphors. A textual analysis of blood and orgy. The anatomy of revolutions. Heal thyself, metaphysician, but post your diagnostic theses on the life side of the grave you dig. The modern version of the Apocalypse is an artist's metaphor, a special rendition of man's creative vision of himself and the world. It may profess to rise out of history into mystery (as all metaphors necessarily do), but it owns at least as much history as it does mystery. At the optimistic peak of the Romantic Revolution, man chanted himself into a flower, a tree, any spontaneous and natural organism connected by deeply buried roots to everything and all. That wonderful, old-fashioned, brave new world. Dionysus with curly tendrils flying, the green exfoliating phallus sprouting at the omphalic center of the new Eden. The belated arrival of the second Adam—as though the first hadn't caused enough trouble. The world as flower, the world in flower. An apocalyptic metaphor of the explosion that is growth, a grand and politic metaphor for the wholesale rape of the natural universe. As the machines began to crush out organic life beneath their massive iron treads, man mirrored himself in the image of a blossom, nodding beautiful and serene in the smoky cab of the accelerating steam engine. A fitting heraldic sign to conquer under. The real flower power. Doomed to a short life and a long, long shadow. On the first day that the flower spirit choked on the soot of its own creation, the metaphor became a cliché and a pious deception. And the modern artist came to birth.

Like all births, his came about through a death. He died to the flower and he struggled to become reborn in a marvelous frantic strangle of shapes and sizes. What role could he not tentatively play? What mask would fail to fit his eager physiognomy? After all, the artist had become the representative surrogate of mankind's fertility, and fertility is the driving principle behind all shape making. When the legislators surrendered their nation-building potency to the subtle engines they had fashioned (divine Robespierre, sublime Jefferson), and the priests turned into ideological eunuchs under the Darwinian dispensation, the seed was obliged to seek a new repository. It was then that the poets announced their inauguration as the new legislators of the world; a wee poetic spirit, a delicately sensitive homunculus took root in everyone's nook and cranny, disseminating a rare effluvium over everything and all. Until the soot blackened their tender pistils. Until their stamens stiffened and withered under electric shock. Until the flower power was mown under without even a chlorophyll shriek. But the seed scattered, diffuse and wondrously fertile. The pandemonic democratization of the arts; a new Lourdes and everyone seeing visions. The lame and the blind and the halt quickening into spurious rebirths which were actually re-coverings. The artist as rebel; as lover; as scientist; as jaded neurasthenic; as shamanistic prophet of the past and the hereafter. Fancy dress costumes to hide their state of orphanage. Bereft castoffs of Nature, muttering their dreadful unmothering. And most of them struggled to create portraits of ladies: Nana's, Anna's, Emma's, hysterical Viennese Jewesses, nostalgic dreams of Motherlands forever impervious to the erosion of time. The artist as orphan; as mother-maker and mother-breaker. The Underground Man and the *Übermensch,* Christ and Faust interchanging roles, dividing the universe between them and their burgeoning offspring. A hero with a thousand alienated faces. Art excruciatingly self-conscious, onanistic, perverse, brazenly whorish in its advances, an eager cripple begging for abuse, a sadist bent upon shock, outrage, emotional and intellectual

submission. Dostoevski, Wagner, Nietzsche, Cézanne. The seed scattered and clustered, and the artist so fully occupied his adopted necessity that he almost ceases to be a human thing at all. Magnificent monstrosities, grotesques bulging at every joint and protuberance from the dreadful pressures of mankind's creativity. Why did Tolstoi abjure his art? Why Rimbaud? The one in a pathetic effort to salvage the last shreds of his humanity, and the other because he was unillusioned enough to perceive that his was irreparably lost. The artist had convinced himself that he was the sole repository of the world's seed, the self-appointed and self-anointed celestial stud. But, *mirabile dictu,* the world withheld itself from his impregnating thrust. He coaxed, cozened and raped, and the world was unaware of his amorous fertilizations. What more comic anguish than a ravishment in which the victim remains inert, unstirred, ignorant of its own humiliation! This is the cause of the fatal alienation—the castration of symbolic functions; fecundity harbored in gall, dissevered from any natural flow or release, storing up its own uranium pile for future detonation.

By definition, creativity is an ex post facto condition; it has already found some object or medium to work upon. The matter doesn't matter; it's the spirit of the thing. Anything is malleable to its pressures, its sly impregnations. Air becomes wine; light crystallizes; dust is silver, and excrement gold. All is poetry. Transubstantiation needs only spirit-space and spirit-time. The world ignorantly withheld itself from the onslaught of symbolic conception. Not that it was a virtuous virgin; it simply had no choice. How could it be aware of its identity? It didn't even know its name! The artist found himself entirely alone with his own many names and himself became the materials of his creation. The orphan must grow a womb for his own gestation, or how can he find rest? Self-portraiture replaces the abortive portraits of the lady-mothers. Self-portraiture makes up the motion-picture frames of our modern artistic history. Freud's self-portrait is the spitted image of my soul. Joyce's. Proust's. Kafka's. The ponderous route of intro-spection—staggering, involuted, obses-sively circling ever inward—inevitably falls into the shape of a gyre, a spiral staircase where I meet myself on every turning, where I am inside and outside, at the bottom and the top, where the begin-ning and the end are alike unbegun and unending. If I am my total milieu, only I can complete myself. But my knowledge of me must necessarily partake of the desperate descent toward an infinite re-gression. God is He who is inevitably complete. When man apes God, he mocks his own inadequacy to be whole. And therefore the doomed yearning for the infantile, the point of ultimate return, the vacated womb, which has been bull-dozed in a Mom-clearance project. I would be as a little child again in order to make a proper assumption of my adult-hood. I exhort mankind to regain some primitive infancy of its own—not in order to start some new beginning—but that it may arrive at last at a conclusion. Eros trapped in its own coiled and unreleaseable ardor. The eyes and the ears send useless sensory messages because they face out-ward. Down with the eyes! Off with the ears! The cramp in the kidney is a more viable message, the ache in the groin, the constriction of the carotid artery. Marco Polo has trekked to Walden Pond and learned that he can make a trip without traveling at all. You who would be sea-worthy, cut off your nose to spite your facing outward! Root out your tongue and be silent! The *tactile* alone is the con-nective. All the other senses are suspi-cious. They would cause me to suspect that perhaps I am not an entire world after all. Art, psychology, sociology—what modes of thought cannot become the obsessive compositions of my dream life—garish, violent designs projected out of the fantastic churning images that I watch behind my closed eyelids. The Apocalypse is the un-covering, the strik-ing of the seals, the pompous disclosures that I ascribe to the world.

And still the world withholds itself, shivering only a little under the assaults of poisoned air and poisoned waters and sudden craters of powdered lime where once a mountain stood. *It doesn't know its name!* And the artist remains alone in his globular tumescence. Alas, the most carefully wrought solipsism develops leaks and drains; the most firmly barred gates acquire the fenestration of a sieve. Sus-picions must be allayed; the line of clos-ure must be held. A new myth comes into existence—a cunning defense mechanism guaranteed to make early and late warn-ings from the outside unnecessary and unheedable. If I, the miser-artist, have withdrawn the principle of creativity from the common order of human life, what can there be left for humanity? Dry leaves on the fetid riverbank. Cigarette butts. Hollow men buffeted in a wind of auto-matic responses. Shadow gestures without substance. I have reenacted the Prome-thean posture, cosmological hero, I. I have stolen the fire from my enemy, the world; the hearth is burnt out. I have given the world its name: a wasteland, a barren lunar pothole. And so we shake our ar-tistic fists at the unheeding world, we who monopolize the world's sensitivity, we self-stuffed seed carriers. We leave the mute paralyzed world to its dull, un-regenerative death. God is proclaimed to be dead in the world because we are not there. We ourselves are God in the proc-esses of partial creation, dividing the firmament and bringing forth the waters and the dry lands from within ourselves, laboring to give birth to the new man who shall be first and last. Is it any wonder that modern thought is a consecration of the absurd? Is it any wonder that modern art is helplessly—as well as hopelessly—comic? For there is no seventh day on which he can rest, the modern artist with a godhead on his shoulders. Self-defined as entirely infolded within himself, he can never use himself up. How can the maker be itself wholly made? The artist withdraws from the withholding indifferent world, poor alienated shard, and focuses his narcissistic delight on the nuances of his own self-portrait. But the same brushstrokes that caress his tortured sensitivity etch wild distorted fantasies of death and passionless corruption on what he pretends to be the world that has denied him. No, it is not the world that is a heap of broken images; it is the artist. And this is the secret connection between the artistic myth of a wasteland world and the zealously cherished fraudulence of the alienated consciousness. It is the fascist's *apologia pro morte sua*. It is the movement from the historical to the hysterical. And it produces the metaphor of the Apocalypse in its jazzed-up modern megaton version.

But there has been yet one other channel that the seed has followed; another role that the artist has arrogated to his presumptuous repertoire. The politician-as-artist, the demagogue-manipulator, the executive-genius of real apocalypses. We too easily forget those early models of dictating machines that had a one-thousand-year guarantee to record and translate the inchoate will of the masses into effective historical design. The artist as total creator—author, producer, executor and principal actor. A mixed-media production with a cast of millions—and all of them "extras"—and a turntable stage that rotated on its own axis once every twenty-four hours. From history to mystery moves the Apocalypse, from history to the sacred mysteries of crematorium smoke, of broken bodies as the discarded phrases of a romantic poem that failed, of an abortive drama of destiny where the narrative focus was the impersonality of fear, intimidation, and the horrendous release of unimaginable energy sources. The "happenings" were programmed into the script and the happening was always the same. The transformation of energy into inert matter, the fever of being reduced to point zero, grave technology solving the pesky problem of stage exits through the abolition of cemeteries. The politician of the Apocalypse nurtured his sweet alienation from the world and discovered within himself a fuel with which to explode the world. Concentration camps, high-concentration bombs, concentrated circles and cycles of force in relentless implosion. Always concentration; never easeful relaxation. Alienation requires a constant energy of restraint, a holding back of human empathies, a denial of flow. It is not because gullible men believed in the power of symbols that our century's most dreadful events occurred; it is because we failed to believe enough to be properly terrified. The Apocalypse unveils the awesome power of symbols. The symbols themselves, naked and unconcealed, too fearful to be looked at directly. And the metaphor takes on new daily shapes. Protean, it ingests whatever is vital in any shape—love, beauty, wisdom, justice—and it swells in its own gargantuan splendor. Cancer is one of its more successful shapes. Explosion, another. The Principle of Indeterminacy is at the base of all its reckonings. The naked form of the Apocalypse, the Word in metamorphosis, flesh becoming the Word and the Word spewing itself back into the world as macerated flesh.

The Apocalypse is the cancerous dream that the alienated libido requires for its autoerotic consumption. It is the *Endlosung,* the extravagant solution of dissolution, whereby man shall be consumed with that which he was nourished by. The end of his exile, all the words torn syllable by syllable into flying fragments; the dismemberment of all remembrance; Orpheus, boy-bomb. The fire next time is a suicide that will settle for no conflagration less than total holocaust. And this in the name of thwarted love. Victims and victimizers merge into one fatal ashen identity because no Other exists beyond myself. No more barriers between man and man, between men and their universe. No internal divisions within the psyche of man itself. The kinetic alone makes a sure and trustworthy contact; all else is illusion, rationalization, the deceptive fakery of power politics on a physiological level. Hail to the orgasm, the ultimate breakthrough! Hail to all breaking words. The final breakdown; the irrevocable glacial breakup. Otherness conquered, given a last name, legitimized like a prodigal bastard son in the midst of my death throes. And this too in the name of unrequited love. Love, the low-comedy version of the modern Apocalypse.

No! No, we must strain to be clear on these matters, for they are perilous to us. Like the carnival clown, satire will ultimately protect its own tents. We thought we had a raucous friend, but his truths can only be half-truths because his soul is not his own.

Mimic it, expose it, caricature its most egregious extravagances, the metaphor of the Apocalypse *is* our best model for viewing our contemporary human condition. It alone gives us a large and flexible mythic form that is grand enough to allow a full expression of our agonies and aspirations. What other myth do we possess that is as responsive to the major cataclysms of twentieth-century life and death? Nuclear explosion of global magnitude, genocide, the repressive strangle of gigantic and abstracted power complexes, technological capacities that can be measured only in mathematical terms. The human validity of the apocalyptic metaphor seems to me undeniable as an attempt to express man's sense of himself in his awesome new world. For not only does it have the cosmic grandeur that is sufficiently vast to absorb a world of overkill, space probes, the development of synthetic life-forms, and the violent surge of masses of resentment and denied energies; it also contains a built-in thrust of passionate urgency. That is, it not only describes our situation with some accuracy, but it also provides a just emotional setting for that description. It is, if you like, a blueprint that bleeds; a cosmological case history transcribed under the brooding auspices of pity and terror. And it is, preeminently, an artist's metaphor, fortuitously keyed to the emotional needs and aesthetic capacities of our own time. Modern music—dodecaphonic and aleatoric—is composed in terms of its notations of structural determinism and random chance. The complete freedom of the sculptor and painter to employ the vast resources of our plastic-electronic age is profoundly connected to the apocalyptic drive to go "beyond art." And the resurgent promise of a truly "epic" theater would be unthinkable without that sense of world-audience and the technical means to engage that audience which is at the root of apocalyptic symbolism. It is easy to overlook the religious origins of the apocalyptic imagination, especially when the uses of that imagination become associated with the profane, the violent and the obscene; yet it has never lost its Messianic beginnings, and the desire to push "beyond art" has inevitably terminated in some variety of religious experience.

But, perhaps most important of all, the *structure* of the apocalyptic metaphor is a source of incredible significance in the kinds of meaningful images that modern man is empowered to cast for himself. The apocalyptic myth is most revolutionary in that it provides a fully "open-ended" form, circumferential without being what we normally think of as circular and spherical. Here I think we are barely on the verge of understanding or exploiting the implications of such a notion of structure. Traditionally our major forms have tended to be "closed" forms—bounded by a cyclical control of architectonic design or plot (sometimes called Destiny) or a harmonic pattern of interest. To be sure, there have been innumerable deviations or wanderings outside the rigidities of control—errant excursions into peripheral possibilities of imbalance, irrelevance or discord—but these have usually been tangential gropings or experiments that have petered out and returned finally, in one way or another, to the ordering force of an unmoved mover implacably fixed at the center of the cyclical design. The intersection of two planes gives us the culturally encapsulating figure of the cross; this has had the effect of nailing down for us a quasi-permanent center point for an infinite number of expanding, self-enclosing circles. The most exciting challenge of the new apocalyptic structure is its radical propensity to burst the circumference of a spherical form without making a return —actual or symbolic—to some primal matrix, some given and unalterable crucifixional center. Precisely how this will happen—or has even already happened— I cannot adequately describe, but it seems obvious that such a revolution in forms cannot come about either amorphously or autonomously. The current task of criticism would seem to me to be exactly that kind of detailed and analytical description that will render the new apocalyptic form comprehensible; and all the maudlin rhetoric about "antiform" and "formlessness" that surrounds these efforts can serve only as a detriment to our understanding. For the abandonment of the fixed center point means that not only man, but God as well, has been released from configurational thralldom, and the energies that are open to us are literally unimaginable.

For some cursory illustrations of what the new apocalyptic structures may be like, we might think of such recent books as Lowell's *Life Studies,* Nabokov's *Pale Fire,* Norman O. Brown's *Love's Body,* or Leonard Cohen's *Beautiful Losers.* Surely these are very different imaginative works in scope, focus, and success of achievement, but they are all, in their different ways, absorbed in the technical and thematic problems of reconciling order and creativity. And what they share, it seems to me, is a sense of circumferential form —an unfamiliar and even shocking concept of unity which is terribly difficult for the traditionally oriented mind to comprehend. There is no center in these four books; no thematic "given" or immutable seed out of which they can be said to have grown and within which their meanings are latently infolded. They bypass the organic metaphor that still more or less locks the structures of the great experimenters of our century—of Proust and Joyce and Rilke. In these four books, the surfaces, not the centers, are in explosion and they are built, as it were, from the outside-in, rather than in the normal reverse relationship. To put it bleakly, they deny centers—which is to say, they deny the basic concept of Self as it has been passed down to us from the Greeks through the Judaic-Christian tradition, even with the modifications of Marx and

Freud. The comforting notion of the static self (self-reliance, self-realization, self-expression, identity-quest) is supplanted by a counternotion of the self as a dynamic structure of interrelationships —ephemeral, metamorphic and utterly volatile. Each of these books is fashioned in terms of their individual aims and it would be silly to generalize too broadly from them; but what seems to be true of them all is a stunning reversal of the old axiom to make it read now that the parts are always greater than the sum. Hence we find their emphasis to be on their parts, on their discrete fragments; each piece exists for its own sake, and not in terms of a functional subservience to some greater whole. The wholes themselves—the completed works—are curiously incomplete; they aspire to be fragmentary, to be fragments-in-motion, to be fragments-as-wholes.

In other areas I think we can discern similar examples of this same notion of circumferential form manifesting itself in opposition to the established center-oriented forms. Hannah Arendt's theoretical formulation of spontaneous revolutionary "cells" as the unconnected nuclei of social upheaval is analogous to what I have in mind. The seeming anarchism of the New Left may be a more radical and lasting political alignment than is usually thought. A painting like Picasso's *Guernica,* Buckminster Fuller's geodesic dome, the wild certainties with which city planners contemplate exploding metropolises, the accelerating shift from psychoanalysis to group therapy, some—at least—of McLuhan's insights and strategies in the making of the global village, our current confusions on radical and lasting political alignment —all of these may very well be symptomatic of the enormous and violent changes that life takes when the human imagination seizes upon a new metaphor

through which to view and reshape its world. It is as though the old tried-and-true centers cannot hold the magnitude of energy release that our age has mustered, and the apocalyptic mode is emerging spontaneously in all fields of action and thought. We may very well be on the brink of a brand-new epistemology—a new technique and concept of rationality, which may build on the advances of binary computation, field theory and games theory, and include the irrationalities of extrasensory perception, mental telepathy, hallucinogenic drugs, and other open-ended, nonteleological modes of understanding. This, of course, does not mean that man and his world have changed in any cardinal, unnatural way. Men will continue to be born, to suffer, and to die. The constants of human experience will remain inevitable and constant. But the dominant metaphor from which man draws his meanings and values may be in the throes of an explosive transformation. I would suggest that the importance of the New Apocalypse is its signaling that a different balance of the complementary forces of order and creativity is in the process of taking place in our time; that the older metaphors have become inadequate for the channeling of our creative energies, and are no longer accurate—or even approximate—in their definition of the present limitations and possibilities of the human spirit.

But I must add a note of my own confusion—a note, perhaps, of my own cowardice. Metaphors are always and only metaphors. They may be life-conducive or life-denying; they possess no life of their own. The Apocalypse is an unspeakably powerful metaphor; it invites all men to become saints or prophets. It will be as inevitably abused as the metaphor of a resurrected soul or a crucified body. It enjoins us to lay violent hands upon all our false barriers. But we fail, however, at the moment that our arrogance or zeal or pusillanimity claims dominion over that which is *other* than ourselves. It is not given everyone to be wholly pure in action—to be a saint; nor is it given everyone to see clearly in obscurity—to be a prophet. Few men have unerring judgment over what is properly within their own hearts' keeping. It is rare indeed that love seeks out and finds its own level without becoming defiled. Nor can I believe that it's a particularly good thing for men to pursue saintliness or prophecy if they are to fail in their quests. We have seen too often what a staggering amount of human wreckage surrounds the charlatan-saint and the corrupt prophet. The apocalyptic ethic utters a challenging command: "Distrust thyself!" it says. "Trust rather in thy congeries of selves. Look to the peripheries of thy being, for that is where life exists, not in some hollow center." This commandment scares me even as it excites me. I

feel unjustly judged and evasive before it. I find myself casting about for some secure resting-place for my spirit. I am ready to enunciate a homily on the sanctity of compromise, of humility, of that acceptance of limitation that is the strategy of humor. The magic of man may, after all, lie in his capacity to enter into and exit from the metaphors that seek to capture him in rigid definitions. The ideal of polymorphous perversity—an ideal of complete fluidity—can be as inflexible and inhuman as any other absolute. The parts may very possibly be greater than the sum. It is the parts, of course, that touch our lives most directly and cogently. But it takes only the slightest shift of the vision to restore the sum to its supremacy. And I wonder reluctantly whether it is not, finally, in the constant shifting of the vision—from part to sum, from I to other, from desire to restraint—that moral space is created in the universe.

SHORT STORIES

THE LOTUS EATER

W. Somerset Maugham
(1874–1965)

Most people, the vast majority in fact, lead the lives that circumstances have thrust upon them, and though some repine, looking upon themselves as round pegs in square holes, and think that if things had been different they might have made a much better showing, the greater part accept their lot, if not with serenity, at all events with resignation. They are like tramcars travelling for ever on the selfsame rails. They go backwards and forwards, backwards and forwards, inevitably, till they can go no longer and then are sold as scrap-iron. It is not often that you find a man who has boldly taken the course of his life into his own hands. When you do, it is worth while having a good look at him.

That was why I was curious to meet Thomas Wilson. It was an interesting and a bold thing he had done. Of course the end was not yet and until the experiment was concluded it was impossible to call it successful. But from what I had heard it seemed he must be an odd sort of fellow and I thought I should like to know him. I had been told he was reserved, but I had a notion that with patience and tact I could persuade him to confide in me. I wanted to hear the facts from his own

lips. People exaggerate, they love to romanticise, and I was quite prepared to discover that his story was not nearly so singular as I had been led to believe.

And this impression was confirmed when at last I made his acquaintance. It was on the Piazza in Capri, where I was spending the month of August at a friend's villa, and a little before sunset, when most of the inhabitants, native and foreign, gather together to chat with their friends in the cool of the evening. There is a terrace that overlooks the Bay of Naples, and when the sun sinks slowly into the sea the island of Ischia is silhouetted against a blaze of splendour. It is one of the most lovely sights in the world. I was standing there with my friend and host watching it, when suddenly he said:

"Look, there's Wilson."

"Where?"

"The man sitting on the parapet, with his back to us. He's got a blue shirt on."

I saw an undistinguished back and a small head of grey hair short and rather thin.

"I wish he'd turn round," I said.

"He will presently."

"Ask him to come and have a drink with us at Morgano's."

"All right."

The instant of overwhelming beauty had passed and the sun, like the top of an orange, was dipping into a wine-red sea. We turned round and leaning our backs against the parapet looked at the people who were sauntering to and fro. They were all talking their heads off and the cheerful noise was exhilarating. Then the church bell, rather cracked, but with a fine resonant note, began to ring. The Piazza at Capri, with its clock tower over the footpath that leads up from the harbour, with the church up a flight of steps, is a perfect setting for an opera by Donizetti, and you felt that the voluble crowd might at any moment break out into a rattling chorus. It was charming and unreal.

I was so intent on the scene that I had not noticed Wilson get off the parapet and come towards us. As he passed us my friend stopped him.

"Hulloa, Wilson, I haven't seen you bathing the last few days."

"I've been bathing on the other side for a change."

My friend then introduced me. Wilson shook hands with me politely, but with indifference; a great many strangers come to Capri for a few days, or a few weeks, and I had no doubt he was constantly meeting people who came and went; and then my friend asked him to come along and have a drink with us.

"I was just going back to supper," he said.

"Can't it wait?" I asked.

"I suppose it can," he smiled.

Though his teeth were not very good his smile was attractive. It was gentle and kindly. He was dressed in a blue cotton shirt and a pair of grey trousers, much creased and none too clean, of a thin canvas, and on his feet he wore a pair of very old espadrilles. The get-up was picturesque, and very suitable to the place and the weather, but it did not at all go with his face. It was a lined, long face, deeply sunburned, thin-lipped, with small grey eyes rather close together and tight, neat features. The grey hair was carefully brushed. It was not a plain face, indeed in his youth Wilson might have been good-looking, but a prim one. He wore the blue shirt, open at the neck, and the grey canvas trousers, not as though they belonged to him, but as though, shipwrecked in his pyjamas, he had been fitted out with odd garments by compassionate strangers. Notwithstanding this careless attire he looked like the manager of a branch office in an insurance company, who should by rights be wearing a black coat with pepper-and-salt trousers, a white collar and an unobjectionable tie. I could very well see myself going to him to claim the insurance money when I had lost a watch, and being rather disconcerted while I answered the questions he put to me by his obvious impression, for all his politeness, that people who made such claims were either fools or knaves.

Moving off, we strolled across the Piazza and down the street till we came to Morgano's. We sat in the garden. Around us people were talking in Russian, German, Italian, and English. We ordered drinks. Donna Lucia, the host's wife, waddled up and in her low, sweet voice passed the time of day with us. Though middle-aged now and portly, she had still traces of the wonderful beauty that thirty years before had driven artists to paint so many bad portraits of her. Her eyes, large and liquid, were the eyes of Hera and her smile was affectionate and gracious. We three gossiped for a while, for there is always a scandal of one sort or another in Capri to make a topic of conversation, but nothing was said of particular interest and in a little while Wilson got up and left us. Soon afterwards we strolled up to my friend's villa to dine. On the way he asked me what I had thought of Wilson.

"Nothing," I said. "I don't believe there's a word of truth in your story."

"Why not?"

"He isn't the sort of man to do that sort of thing."

"How does anyone know what anyone is capable of?"

"I should put him down as an absolutely normal man of business who's retired on a comfortable income from gilt-edged securities. I think your story's just the ordinary Capri tittle-tattle."

"Have it your own way," said my friend.

We were in the habit of bathing at a beach called the Baths of Tiberius. We took a fly down the road to a certain point and then wandered through lemon groves and vineyards, noisy with cicadas and heavy with the hot smell of the sun, till we came to the top of the cliff down which a steep winding path led to the sea. A day or two later, just before we got down my friend said:

"Oh, there's Wilson back again."

We scrunched over the beach, the only drawback to the bathing-place being that it was shingle and not sand, and as we came along Wilson saw us and waved. He was standing up, a pipe in his mouth, and he wore nothing but a pair of trunks. His body was dark brown, thin but not emaciated, and, considering his wrinkled face and grey hair, youthful. Hot from our walk, we undressed quickly and plunged at once into the water. Six feet from the shore it was thirty feet deep, but so clear that you could see the bottom. It was warm, yet invigorating.

When I got out Wilson was lying on his belly, with a towel under him reading a book. I lit a cigarette and went and sat down beside him.

"Had a nice swim?" he asked.

He put his pipe inside his book to mark the place and closing it put it down on the pebbles beside him. He was evidently willing to talk.

"Lovely," I said. "It's the best bathing in the world."

"Of course people think those were the Baths of Tiberius." He waved his hand towards a shapeless mass of masonry that stood half in the water and half out. "But that's all rot. It was just one of his villas, you know."

I did. But it is just as well to let people tell you things when they want to. It disposes them kindly towards you if you suffer them to impart information. Wilson gave a chuckle.

"Funny old fellow, Tiberius. Pity they're saying now there's not a word of truth in all those stories about him."

He began to tell me all about Tiberius. Well, I had read my Suetonius too and I had read histories of the Early Roman Empire, so there was nothing very new to me in what he said. But I observed that he was not ill-read. I remarked on it.

"Oh, well, when I settled down here I was naturally interested, and I have plenty of time for reading. When you live in a place like this, with all its associations, it seems to make history so actual. You might almost be living in historical times yourself."

I should remark here that this was in 1913. The world was an easy, comfortable place and no one could have imagined that anything might happen seriously to disturb the serenity of existence.

"How long have you been here?" I asked.

"Fifteen years." He gave the blue and placid sea a glance, and a strangely tender smile hovered on his thin lips. "I fell in love with the place at first sight. You've heard, I daresay, of the mythical German who came here on the Naples boat just for lunch and a look at the Blue Grotto and stayed forty years; well, I can't say I exactly did that, but it's come to the same thing in the end. Only it won't be forty years in my case. Twenty-five. Still, that's better than a poke in the eye with a sharp stick."

I waited for him to go on. For what he had just said looked indeed as though there might be something after all in the singular story I had heard. But at that moment my friend came dripping out of the water very proud of himself because he had swum a mile, and the conversation turned to other things.

After that I met Wilson several times, either in the Piazza or on the beach. He was amiable and polite. He was always pleased to have a talk and I found out that he not only knew every inch of the island but also the adjacent mainland. He had read a great deal on all sorts of subjects, but his speciality was the history of Rome and on this he was very well informed. He seemed to have little imagination and to be of no more than average intelligence. He laughed a good deal, but with restraint, and his sense of humour was tickled by simple jokes. A commonplace man. I did not forget the odd remark he had made during the first short chat we had had by ourselves, but he never so much as approached the topic again. One day on our return from the beach, dismissing the cab at the Piazza, my friend and I told the driver to be ready to take us up to Anacapri at five. We were going to climb Monte Solaro, dine at a tavern we favoured, and walk down in the moonlight. For it was full moon and the views by night were lovely. Wilson was standing by while we gave the cabman instructions, for we had given him a lift to save him the hot dusty walk, and more from politeness than for any other reason I asked him if he would care to join us.

"It's my party," I said.

"I'll come with pleasure," he answered.

But when the time came to set out my friend was not feeling well, he thought he had stayed too long in the water, and would not face the long and tiring walk. So I went alone with Wilson. We climbed the mountain, admired the spacious view, and got back to the inn as night was falling, hot, hungry and thirsty. We had ordered our dinner beforehand. The food was good, for Antonio was an excellent cook, and the wine came from his own vineyard. It was so light that you felt you could drink it like water and we finished the first bottle with our macaroni. By the time we had finished the second we felt that there was nothing much wrong with life. We sat in a little garden under a great vine laden with grapes. The air was exquisitely soft. The night was still and we were alone. The maid brought us *bel paese* cheese and a plate of figs. I ordered coffee and strega, which is the best liqueur they make in Italy. Wilson would not have a cigar, but lit his pipe.

"We've got plenty of time before we need start," he said, "the moon won't be over the hill for another hour."

"Moon or no moon," I said briskly, "of course we've got plenty of time. That's one of the delights of Capri, that there's never any hurry."

"Leisure," he said. "If people only knew! It's the most priceless thing a man can have and they're such fools they don't even know it's something to aim at. Work? They work for work's sake. They haven't got the brains to realise that the only object of work is to obtain leisure."

Wine has the effect on some people of making them indulge in general reflections. These remarks were true, but no one could have claimed that they were original. I did not say anything, but struck a match to light my cigar.

"It was full moon the first time I came to Capri," he went on reflectively. "It might be the same moon as to-night."

"It was, you know," I smiled.

He grinned. The only light in the garden was what came from an oil lamp that hung over our heads. It had been scanty to eat by, but it was good now for confidences.

"I didn't mean that. I mean, it might be yesterday. Fifteen years it is, and when I look back it seems like a month. I'd never been to Italy before. I came for my summer holiday. I went to Naples by boat from Marseilles and I had a look round, Pompeii, you know, and Paestum and one or two places like that; then I came here for a week. I liked the look of the place right away, from the sea, I mean, as I watched it come closer and closer; and then when we got into the little boats from the steamer and landed at the quay, with all that crowd of jabbering people who wanted to take your luggage, and the hotel touts, and the tumbledown houses on the Marina and the walk up to the hotel, and dining on the terrace—well, it just got me. That's the truth. I didn't know if I was standing on my head or my heels. I'd never drunk Capri wine before, but I'd heard of it; I think I must have got a bit tight. I sat on that terrace after they'd all gone to bed and watched the moon over the sea, and there was Vesuvius with a great red plume of smoke rising up from it. Of course I know now that wine I drank was ink, Capri wine my eye, but I thought it all right then. But it wasn't the wine that made me drunk, it was the shape of the island and those jabbering people, the moon and the sea and the oleander in the hotel garden. I'd never seen an oleander before."

It was a long speech and it had made him thirsty. He took up his glass, but it was empty. I asked him if he would have another strega.

"It's sickly stuff. Let's have a bottle of wine. That's sound, that is, pure juice of the grape and can't hurt anyone."

I ordered more wine, and when it came filled the glasses. He took a long drink and after a sigh of pleasure went on.

"Next day I found my way to the bathing-place we go to. Not bad bathing, I thought. Then I wandered about the island. As luck would have it, there was a *festa* up at Punta di Timberio and I ran straight into the middle of it. An image of the Virgin and priests, acolytes

swinging censers, and a whole crowd of jolly, laughing, excited people, a lot of them all dressed up. I ran across an Englishman there and asked him what it was all about. 'Oh, it's the feast of the Assumption,' he said, 'at least that's what the Catholic Church says it is, but that's just their hanky-panky. It's the festival of Venus. Pagan, you know. Aphrodite rising from the sea and all that.' It gave me quite a funny feeling to hear him. It seemed to take one a long way back, if you know what I mean. After that I went down one night to have a look at the Faraglioni by moonlight. If the fates had wanted me to go on being a bank manager they oughtn't to have let me take that walk."

"You were a bank manager, were you?" I asked.

I had been wrong about him, but not far wrong.

"Yes. I was manager of the Crawford Street branch of the York and City. It was convenient for me because I lived up Hendon way. I could get from door to door in thirty-seven minutes."

He puffed at his pipe and relit it.

"That was my last night, that was. I'd got to be back at the bank on Monday morning. When I looked at those two great rocks sticking out of the water, with the moon above them, and all the little lights of the fishermen in their boats catching cuttle-fish, all so peaceful and beautiful, I said to myself, well, after all, why should I go back? It wasn't as if I had anyone dependent on me. My wife had died of bronchial pneumonia four years before and the kid went to live with her grandmother, my wife's mother. She was an old fool, she didn't look after the kid properly and she got blood-poisoning, they amputated her leg, but they couldn't save her and she died, poor little thing."

"How terrible," I said.

"Yes, I was cut up at the time, though of course not so much as if the kid had been living with me, but I dare say it was a mercy. Not much chance for a girl with only one leg. I was sorry about my wife too. We got on very well together. Though I don't know if it would have continued. She was the sort of woman who was always bothering about what other people'd think. She didn't like travelling. Eastbourne was her idea of a holiday. D'you know, I'd never crossed the Channel till after her death."

"But I suppose you've got other relations, haven't you?"

"None. I was an only child. My father had a brother, but he went to Australia before I was born. I don't think anyone could easily be more alone in the world than I am. There wasn't any reason I could see why I shouldn't do exactly what I wanted. I was thirty-four at that time."

He had told me he had been on the island for fifteen years. That would make him forty-nine. Just about the age I should have given him.

"I'd been working since I was seventeen. All I had to look forward to was doing the same old thing day after day till I retired on my pension. I said to myself, is it worth it? What's wrong with chucking it all up and spending the rest of my life down here? It was the most beautiful place I'd even seen. But I'd had a business training. I was cautious by nature. 'No,' I said, 'I won't be carried away like this, I'll go to-morrow like I said I would and think it over. Perhaps when I get back to London I'll think quite differently.' Damned fool, wasn't I? I lost a whole year that way."

"You didn't change your mind, then?"

"You bet I didn't. All the time I was working I kept thinking of the bathing here and the vineyards and the walks over the hills and the moon and the sea, and the Piazza in the evening when everyone walks about for a bit of a chat after the day's work is over. There was only one thing that bothered me: I wasn't sure if I was justified in not working like everybody else did. Then I read a sort of history book, by a man called Marion Crawford it was, and there was a story about Sybaris and Crotona. There were two cities; and in Sybaris they just enjoyed life and had a good time, and in Crotona they were hardy and industrious and all that. And one day the men of Crotona came over and wiped Sybaris out, and then after a while a lot of other fellows came over from somewhere else and wiped Crotona out. Nothing remains of Sybaris, not a stone, and all that's left of Crotona is just one column. That settled the matter for me."

"Oh?"

"It came to the same in the end, didn't it? And when you look back now, who were the mugs?"

I did not reply and he went on.

"The money was rather a bother. The bank didn't pension one off till after thirty years' service, but if you retired before that they gave you a gratuity. With that and what I'd got for the sale of my house and the little I'd managed to save, I just hadn't enough to buy an annuity to last the rest of my life. It would have been silly to sacrifice everything so as to lead a pleasant life and not have a sufficient income to make it pleasant. I wanted to have a little place of my own, a servant to look after me, enough to buy tobacco, decent food, books now and then, and something over for emergencies. I knew pretty well how much I needed. I found I had just enough to buy an annuity for twenty-five years."

"You were thirty-five at the time?"

"Yes. It would carry me on till I was sixty. After all, no one can be certain of living longer than that, a lot of men die in their fifties, and by the time a man's sixty he's had the best of life."

"On the other hand no one can be sure of dying at sixty," I said.

"Well, I don't know. It depends on himself, doesn't it?"

"In your place I should have stayed on at the bank till I was entitled to my pension."

"I should have been forty-seven then. I shouldn't have been too old to enjoy my life here, I'm older than that now and I enjoy it as much as I ever did, but I should have been too old to experience the particular pleasure of a young man. You know, you can have just as good a time at fifty as you can at thirty, but it's not the same sort of good time. I wanted to live the perfect life while I still had the energy and the spirit to make the most of it. Twenty-five years seemed a long time to me, and twenty-five years of happiness seemed worth paying something pretty substantial for. I'd made up my mind to wait a year and I waited a year. Then I sent in my resignation and as soon as they paid me my gratuity I bought the annuity and came on here."

"An annuity for twenty-five years?"

"That's right."

"Have you never regretted?"

"Never. I've had my money's worth already. And I've got ten years more. Don't you think after twenty-five years of perfect happiness one ought to be satisfied to call it a day?"

"Perhaps."

He did not say in so many words what he would do then, but his intention was clear. It was pretty much the story my friend had told me, but it sounded different when I heard it from his own lips. I stole a glance at him. There was nothing about him that was not ordinary. No one, looking at that neat, prim face, could have thought him capable of an unconventional action. I did not blame him. It was his own life that he had arranged in this strange manner, and I did not see why he should not do what he liked with it. Still, I could not prevent the little shiver that ran down my spine.

"Getting chilly?" he smiled. "We might as well start walking down. The moon'll be up by now."

Before we parted Wilson asked me if I would like to go and see his house one day; and two or three days later, finding out where he lived, I strolled up to see him. It was a peasant's cottage, well away from the town, in a vineyard, with a view of the sea. By the side of the door grew a great oleander in full flower. There were only two small rooms, a tiny kitchen and a lean-to in which firewood could be kept. The bedroom was furnished like a monk's cell, but the sitting-room, smelling agreeably of tobacco, was comfortable enough, with two large arm-chairs that he had brought from England, a large roll-top desk, a cottage piano and crowded bookshelves. On the walls were framed engravings of pictures by G. F. Watts and Lord Leighton. Wilson told me that the house belonged to the owner of the vineyard who lived in another cottage higher up the hill, and his wife came in every day to do the rooms and the cooking. He had found the place on his first visit to Capri, and taking it on his return for good had been there ever since. Seeing the piano and music open on it, I asked him if he would play.

"I'm no good, you know, but I've always been fond of music and I get a lot of fun out of strumming."

He sat down at the piano and played one of the movements from a Beethoven sonata. He did not play very well. I looked at his music, Schumann and Schubert, Beethoven, Bach and Chopin. On the table on which he had his meals was a greasy pack of cards. I asked him if he played patience.

"A lot."

From what I saw of him then and from what I heard from other people I made for myself what I think must have been a fairly accurate picture of the life he had led for the last fifteen years. It was certainly a very harmless one. He bathed; he walked a great deal, and he seemed never to lose his sense of the beauty of the island which he knew so intimately; he played the piano and he played patience; he read. When he was asked to a party he went and, though a trifle dull, was agreeable. He was not affronted if he was neglected. He liked people, but with an aloofness that prevented intimacy. He lived thriftily, but with sufficient comfort. He never owed a penny. I imagine he had never been a man whom sex had greatly troubled, and if in his younger days he had had now and then a passing affair with a visitor to the island whose head was turned by the atmosphere, his emotion, while it lasted, remained, I am pretty sure, well under his control. I think he was determined that nothing should interfere with his independence of spirit. His only passion was for the beauty of nature, and he sought felicity in the simple and natural things that life offers to everyone. You may say that it was a grossly selfish existence. It was. He was of no use to anybody, but on the other hand he did nobody any harm. His only object was his own happiness, and it looked as though he had attained it. Very few people know where to look for happiness; fewer still find it. I don't know whether he was a fool or a wise man. He was certainly a man who knew his own mind. The odd thing about him to me was that he was so immensely commonplace. I should never have given him a second thought but for what I knew, that on a certain day, ten years from then, unless a chance illness cut the thread before, he must deliberately take leave of the world he loved so well. I wondered whether it was the thought of this, never quite absent from his mind, that gave him the peculiar zest with which he enjoyed every moment of the day.

I should do him an injustice if I omitted to state that he was not at all in the habit of talking about himself. I think the friend I was staying with was the only person in whom he had confided. I believe he only told me the story because he suspected I already knew it, and on the evening on which he told it me he had drunk a good deal of wine.

My visit drew to a close and I left the island. The year after, war broke out. A number of things happened to me, so that the course of my life was greatly altered, and it was thirteen years before I went to Capri again. My friend had been back some time, but he was no longer so well off, and had moved into a house that had no room for me; so I was putting up at the hotel. He came to meet me at the boat and we dined together. During dinner I asked him where exactly his house was.

"You know it," he answered. "It's the little place Wilson had. I've built on a room and made it quite nice."

With so many other things to occupy my mind I had not given Wilson a thought for years; but now, with a little shock, I remembered. The ten years he had before him when I made his acquaintance must have elapsed long ago.

"Did he commit suicide as he said he would?"

"It's rather a grim story."

Wilson's plan was all right. There was only one flaw in it and this, I suppose, he could not have foreseen. It had never occurred to him that after twenty-five years of complete happiness, in this quiet backwater, with nothing in the world to disturb his serenity, his character would gradually lose its strength. The will needs obstacles in order to exercise its power; when it is never thwarted, when no effort is needed to achieve one's desires, because one has placed one's desires only in the things that can be obtained by stretching out one's hand, the will grows impotent. If you walk on a level all the time the muscles you need to climb a mountain will atrophy. These observations are trite, but there they are. When Wilson's annuity expired he had no longer the resolution to make the end which was the price he had agreed to pay for that long period of happy tranquillity. I do not think, as far as I could gather, both from what my friend told me and afterwards from others, that he wanted courage. It was just that he couldn't make up his mind. He put it off from day to day.

He had lived on the island for so long and had always settled his accounts so punctually that it was easy for him to get credit; never having borrowed money before, he found a number of people who were willing to lend him small sums when now he asked for them. He had paid his rent regularly for so many years that his landlord, whose wife Assunta still acted as his servant, was content to let things slide for several months. Everyone believed him when he said that a relative had died and that he was temporarily embarrassed because owing to legal formalities he could not for some time get the money that was due to him. He managed to hang on after this fashion for something over a year. Then he could get no more credit from the local tradesmen, and there was no one to lend him any more money. His landlord gave him notice to leave the house unless he paid up the arrears of rent before a certain date.

The day before this he went into his tiny bedroom, closed the door and the window, drew the curtain and lit a brazier of charcoal. Next morning when Assunta came to make his breakfast she found him insensible but still alive. The roof was draughty, and though he had done this and that to keep out the fresh air he had not done it very thoroughly. It almost looked as though at the last moment, and desperate though his situation was, he had suffered from a certain infirmity

of purpose. Wilson was taken to the hospital, and though very ill for some time he at last recovered. But as a result either of the charcoal poisoning or of the shock he was no longer in complete possession of his faculties. He was not insane, at all events not insane enough to be put in an asylum, but he was quite obviously no longer in his right mind.

"I went to see him," said my friend. "I tried to get him to talk, but he kept looking at me in a funny sort of way, as though he couldn't quite make out where he'd seen me before. He looked rather awful lying there in bed, with a week's growth of grey beard on his chin; but except for that funny look in his eyes he seemed quite normal."

"What funny look in his eyes?"

"I don't know exactly how to describe it. Puzzled. It's an absurd comparison, but suppose you threw a stone up into the air and it didn't come down but just stayed there . . ."

"It would be rather bewildering," I smiled.

"Well, that's the sort of look he had."

It was difficult to know what to do with him. He had no money and no means of getting any. His effects were sold, but for too little to pay what he owed. He was English, and the Italian authorities did not wish to make themselves responsible for him. The British Consul in Naples had no funds to deal with the case. He could of course be sent back to England, but no one seemed to know what could be done with him when he got there. Then Assunta, the servant, said that he had been a good master and a good tenant, and as long as he had the money had paid his way; he could sleep in the woodshed in the cottage in which she and her husband lived, and he could share their meals. This was suggested to him. It was difficult to know whether he understood or not. When Assunta came to take him from the hospital he went with her without remark. He seemed to have no longer a will of his own. She had been keeping him now for two years.

"It's not very comfortable, you know," said my friend. "They've rigged him up a ramshackle bed and given him a couple of blankets, but there's no window, and it's icy cold in winter and like an oven in summer. And the food's pretty rough. You know how these peasants eat: macaroni on Sundays and meat once in a blue moon."

"What does he do with himself all the time?"

"He wanders about the hills. I've tried to see him two or three times, but it's no good; when he sees you coming he runs like a hare. Assunta comes down to have a chat with me now and then and I give her a bit of money so that she can buy him tobacco, but God knows if he ever gets it."

"Do they treat him all right?" I asked.

"I'm sure Assunta's kind enough. She treats him like a child. I'm afraid her husband's not very nice to him. He grudges the cost of his keep. I don't believe he's cruel or anything like that, but I think he's a bit sharp with him. He makes him fetch water and clean the cowshed and that sort of thing."

"It sounds pretty rotten," I said.

"He brought it on himself. After all, he's only got what he deserved."

"I think on the whole we all get what we deserve," I said. "But that doesn't prevent its being rather horrible."

Two or three days later my friend and I were taking a walk. We were strolling along a narrow path through an olive grove.

"There's Wilson," said my friend suddenly. "Don't look, you'll only frighten him. Go straight on."

I walked with my eyes on the path, but out of the corners of them I saw a man hiding behind an olive tree. He did not move as we approached, but I felt that

he was watching us. As soon as we had passed I heard a scamper. Wilson, like a hunted animal, had made for safety. That was the last I ever saw of him.

He died last year. He had endured that life for six years. He was found one morning on the mountainside lying quite peacefully as though he had died in his sleep. From where he lay he had been able to see those two great rocks called the Faraglioni which stand out of the sea. It was full moon and he must have gone to see them by moonlight. Perhaps he died of the beauty of that sight.

CLAY

James Joyce
(1882–1941)

The matron had given her leave to go out as soon as the women's tea was over and Maria looked forward to her evening out. The kitchen was spick and span: the cook said you could see yourself in the big copper boilers. The fire was nice and bright and on one of the side-tables were four very big barmbracks. These barmbracks seemed uncut; but if you went closer you would see that they had been cut into long thick even slices and were ready to be handed round at tea. Maria had cut them herself.

Maria was a very, very small person indeed but she had a very long nose and a very long chin. She talked a little through her nose, always soothingly: *"Yes, my dear,"* and *"No, my dear."* She was always sent for when the women quarrelled over their tubs and always succeeded in making peace. One day the matron had said to her:

"Maria, you are a veritable peacemaker!"

And the sub-matron and two of the Board ladies had heard the compliment.

And Ginger Mooney was always saying what she wouldn't do to the dummy who had charge of the irons if it wasn't for Maria. Everyone was so fond of Maria.

The women would have their tea at six o'clock and she would be able to get away before seven. From Ballsbridge to the Pillar, twenty minutes; from the Pillar to Drumcondra, twenty minutes; and twenty minutes to buy the things. She would be there before eight. She took out her purse with the silver clasps and read again the words *A Present from Belfast*. She was very fond of that purse because Joe had brought it to her five years before when he and Alphy had gone to Belfast on a Whit-Monday trip. In the purse were two half-crowns and some coppers. She would have five shillings clear after paying tram fare. What a nice evening they would have, all the children singing! Only she hoped that Joe wouldn't come in drunk. He was so different when he took any drink.

Often he had wanted her to go and live with them; but she would have felt herself in the way (though Joe's wife was ever so nice with her) and she had become accustomed to the life of the laundry. Joe was a good fellow. She had nursed him and Alphy too; and Joe used often say:

"Mamma is mamma but Maria is my proper mother."

After the break-up at home the boys had got her that position in the *Dublin by Lamplight* laundry, and she liked it. She used to have such a bad opinion of Protestants but now she thought they were very nice people, a little quiet and serious, but still very nice people to live with. Then she had her plants in the conservatory and she liked looking after them. She had lovely ferns and wax-plants and, whenever anyone came to visit her, she always gave the visitor one or two slips from her conservatory. There was one thing she didn't like and that was the tracts on the walks; but the matron was such a nice person to deal with, so genteel.

When the cook told her everything was ready she went into the women's room and began to pull the big bell. In a few minutes the women began to come in by twos and threes, wiping their steaming hands in their petticoats and pulling down the sleeves of their blouses over their red steaming arms. They settled down before their huge mugs which the cook and the dummy filled up with hot tea, already mixed with milk and sugar in huge tin cans. Maria superintended the distribution of the barmbrack and saw that every woman got her four slices. There was a great deal of laughing and joking during the meal. Lizzie Fleming said Maria was sure to get the ring and, though Fleming had said that for so many Hallow Eves, Maria had to laugh and say she didn't want any ring or man either; and when she laughed her grey-green eyes sparkled with disappointed shyness and the tip of her nose nearly met the tip of her chin. Then Ginger Mooney lifted up her mug of tea and proposed Maria's health while all the other women clattered with their mugs on the table, and said she was sorry she hadn't a sup of porter to drink it in. And Maria laughed again till the tip of her nose nearly met the tip of her chin and till her minute body nearly shook itself asunder because she knew that Mooney meant well though, of course, she had the notions of a common woman.

But wasn't Maria glad when the women had finished their tea and the cook and the dummy had begun to clear away the tea-things! She went into her little bedroom and, remembering that the next morning was a mass morning, changed the hand of the alarm from seven to six. Then she took off her working skirt and her house-boots and laid her best skirt out on the bed and her tiny dress-boots beside the foot of the bed. She changed her blouse too and, as she stood before the mirror, she thought of how she used to dress for mass on Sunday morning when she was a young girl; and she looked with quaint affection at the diminutive body which she had so often adorned. In spite of its years she found it a nice tidy little body.

When she got outside the streets were shining with rain and she was glad of her old brown waterproof. The tram was full and she had to sit on the little stool at the end of the car, facing all the people, with her toes barely touching the floor. She arranged in her mind all she was going to do and thought how much better it was to be independent and to have your own money in your pocket. She hoped they would have a nice evening. She was sure they would but she could not help thinking what a pity it was Alphy and Joe were not speaking. They were always falling out now but when they were boys together they used to be the best of friends: but such was life.

She got out of her tram at the Pillar and ferreted her way quickly among the crowds. She went into Downes's cakeshop but the shop was so full of people that it was a long time before she could get herself attended to. She bought a dozen of mixed penny cakes, and at last came out of the shop laden with a big bag. Then she thought what else would she buy: she wanted to buy something really nice. They would be sure to have plenty of apples and nuts. It was hard to know what to buy and all she could think of was cake. She decided to buy some plumcake but Downes's plumcake had not enough almond icing on top of it so she went over to a shop in Henry Street. Here she was a long time in suiting herself and the stylish young lady behind the counter, who was evidently a little annoyed by her, asked her was it weddingcake she wanted to buy. That made Maria blush and smile at the young lady; but the young lady took it all very seriously

and finally cut a thick slice of plumcake, parcelled it up and said:

"Two-and-four, please."

She thought she would have to stand in the Drumcondra tram because none of the young men seemed to notice her but an elderly gentleman made room for her. He was a stout gentleman and he wore a brown hard hat; he had a square red face and a greyish moustache. Maria thought he was a colonel-looking gentleman and she reflected how much more polite he was than the young men who simply stared straight before them. The gentleman began to chat with her about Hallow Eve and the rainy weather. He supposed the bag was full of good things for the little ones and said it was only right that the youngsters should enjoy themselves while they were young. Maria agreed with him and favoured him with demure nods and hems. He was very nice with her, and when she was getting out at the Canal Bridge she thanked him and bowed, and he bowed to her and raised his hat and smiled agreeably; and while she was going up along the terrace, bending her tiny head under the rain, she thought how easy it was to know a gentleman even when he has a drop taken.

Everybody said: *"O, here's Maria!"* when she came to Joe's house. Joe was there, having come home from business, and all the children had their Sunday dresses on. There were two big girls in from next door and games were going on. Maria gave the bag of cakes to the eldest boy, Alphy, to divide and Mrs. Donnelly said it was too good of her to bring such a big bag of cakes and made all the children say:

"Thanks, Maria."

But Maria said she had brought something special for papa and mamma, something they would be sure to like, and she began to look for her plumcake. She tried in Downes's bag and then in the pockets of her waterproof and then on the hall-stand but nowhere could she find it. Then she asked all the children had any of them eaten it—by mistake, of course—but the children all said no and looked as if they did not like to eat cakes if they were to be accused of stealing. Everybody had a solution for the mystery and Mrs. Donnelly said it was plain that Maria had left it behind her in the tram. Maria, remembering how confused the gentleman with the greyish moustache had made her, coloured with shame and vexation and disappointment. At the thought of the failure of her little surprise and of the two and four-pence she had thrown away for nothing she nearly cried outright.

But Joe said it didn't matter and made her sit down by the fire. He was very nice with her. He told her all that went on in his office, repeating for her a smart answer which he had made to the manager. Maria did not understand why Joe laughed so much over the answer he had made but she said that the manager must have been a very overbearing person to deal with. Joe said he wasn't so bad when you knew how to take him, that he was a decent sort so long as you didn't rub him the wrong way. Mrs. Donnelly played the piano for the children and they danced and sang. Then the two next-door girls handed round the nuts. Nobody could find the nutcrackers and Joe was nearly getting cross over it and asked how did they expect Maria to crack nuts without a nutcracker. But Maria said she didn't like nuts and that they weren't to bother about her. Then Joe asked would she take a bottle of stout and Mrs. Donnelly said there was port wine too in the house if she would prefer that. Maria said she would rather they didn't ask her to take anything: but Joe insisted.

So Maria let him have his way and they sat by the fire talking over old times and Maria thought she would put in a good word for Alphy. But Joe cried that God might strike him stone dead if ever he

spoke a word to his brother again and Maria said she was sorry she had mentioned the matter. Mrs. Donnelly told her husband it was a great shame for him to speak that way of his own flesh and blood but Joe said that Alphy was no brother of his and there was nearly being a row on the head of it. But Joe said he would not lose his temper on account of the night it was and asked his wife to open some more stout. The two next-door girls had arranged some Hallow Eve games and soon everything was merry again. Maria was delighted to see the children so merry and Joe and his wife in such good spirits. The next-door girls put some saucers on the table and then led the children up to the table, blindfold. One got the prayer-book and the other three got the water; and when one of the next-door girls got the ring Mrs. Donnelly shook her finger at the blushing girl as much as to say: *O, I know all about it!* They insisted then on blindfolding Maria and leading her up to the table to see what she would get; and, while they were putting on the bandage, Maria laughed and laughed again till the tip of her nose nearly met the tip of her chin.

They led her up to the table amid laughing and joking and she put her hand out in the air as she was told to do. She moved her hand about here and there in the air and descended on one of the saucers. She felt a soft wet substance with her fingers and was surprised that nobody spoke or took off her bandage. There was a pause for a few seconds; and then a great deal of scuffling and whispering. Somebody said something about the garden, and at last Mrs. Donnelly said something very cross to one of the next-door girls and told her to throw it out at once: that was no play. Maria understood that it was wrong that time and so she had to do it over again: and this time she got the prayer-book.

After that Mrs. Donnelly played Miss

McCloud's Reel for the children and Joe made Maria take a glass of wine. Soon they were all quite merry again and Mrs. Donnelly said Maria would enter a convent before the year was out because she had got the prayer-book. Maria had never seen Joe so nice to her as he was that night, so full of pleasant talk and reminiscences. She said they were all very good to her.

At last the children grew tired and sleepy and Joe asked Maria would she not sing some little song before she went, one of the old songs. Mrs. Donnelly said *"Do, please, Maria!"* and so Maria had to get up and stand beside the piano. Mrs. Donnelly bade the children be quiet and listen to Maria's song. Then she played the prelude and said *"Now, Maria!"* and Maria, blushing very much, began to sing in a tiny quavering voice. She sang *I Dreamt That I Dwelt,* and when she came to the second verse she sang again:

> *"I dreamt that I dwelt in marble halls*
> *With vassals and serfs at my side*
> *And of all who assembled within*
> *those walls*
> *That I was the hope and the pride.*
>
> *"I had riches too great to count,*
> *could boast*
> *Of a high ancestral name,*
> *But I also dreamt, which pleased me*
> *most,*
> *That you loved me still the same."*

But no one tried to show her her mistake; and when she had ended her song Joe was very much moved. He said that there was no time like the long ago and no music for him like poor old Balfe, whatever other people might say; and his eyes filled up so much with tears that he could not find what he was looking for and in the end he had to ask his wife to tell him where the corkscrew was.

BLOW-UP

Julio Cortázar
(1914–   )

It'll never be known how this has to be told, in the first person or in the second, using the third person plural or continually inventing modes that will serve for nothing. If one might say: I will see the moon rose, or: we hurt me at the back of my eyes, and especially: you the blond woman was the clouds that race before my your his our yours their faces. What the hell.

Seated ready to tell it, if one might go to drink a bock over there, and the typewriter continue by itself (because I use the machine), that would be perfection. And that's not just a manner of speaking. Perfection, yes, because here is the aperture which must be counted also as a machine (of another sort, a Contax 1.1.2) and it is possible that one machine may know more about another machine than I, you, she—the blond—and the clouds. But I have the dumb luck to know that if I go this Remington will sit turned to stone on top of the table with the air of being twice as quiet that mobile things have when they are not moving. So, I have to write. One of us all has to write, if this is going to get told. Better that it be me who am dead, for I'm less compromised than the rest; I who see only the clouds and can think without being distracted, write without being distracted (there goes another, with a grey edge) and remember without being distracted, I who am dead (and I'm alive, I'm not trying to fool anybody, you'll see when we get to the moment, because I have to begin some way and I've begun with this period, the last one back, the one at the beginning, which in the end is the best of the periods when you want to tell something).

All of a sudden I wonder why I have to

tell this, but if one begins to wonder why he does all he does do, if one wonders why he accepts an invitation to lunch (now a pigeon's flying by and it seems to me a sparrow), or why when someone has told us a good joke immediately there starts up something like a tickling in the stomach and we are not at peace until we've gone into the office across the hall and told the joke over again; then it feels good immediately, one is fine, happy, and can get back to work. For I imagine that no one has explained this, that really the best thing is to put aside all decorum and tell it, because, after all's done, nobody is ashamed of breathing or of putting on his shoes; they're things that you do, and when something weird happens, when you find a spider in your shoe or if you take a breath and feel like a broken window, then you have to tell what's happening, tell it to the guys at the office or to the doctor. Oh, doctor, every time I take a breath . . . Always tell it, always get rid of that tickle in the stomach that bothers you.

And now that we're finally going to tell it, let's put things a little bit in order, we'd be walking down the staircase in this house as far as Sunday, November 7, just a month back. One goes down five floors and stands then in the Sunday in the sun one would not have suspected of Paris in November, with a large appetite to walk around, to see things, to take photos (because we were photographers, I'm a photographer). I know that the most difficult thing is going to be finding a way to tell it, and I'm not afraid of repeating myself. It's going to be difficult because nobody really knows who it is telling it, if I am I or what actually occurred or what I'm seeing (clouds, and once in a while a pigeon) or if, simply, I'm telling a truth which is only my truth, and then is the truth only for my stomach, for this impulse to go running out and to finish up in some manner with, this, whatever it is.

We're going to tell it slowly, what happens in the middle of what I'm writing is coming already. If they replace me, if, so soon, I don't know what to say, if the clouds stop coming and something else starts (because it's impossible that this keep coming, clouds passing continually and occasionally a pigeon), if something out of all this . . . And after the "if" what am I going to put if I'm going to close the sentence structure correctly? But if I begin to ask questions, I'll never tell anything, maybe to tell would be like an answer, at least for someone who's reading it.

Roberto Michel, French-Chilean, translator and in his spare time an amateur photographer, left number 11, rue Monsieur-le-Prince Sunday November 7 of the current year (now there're two small ones passing, with silver linings). He had spent three weeks working on the French version of a treatise on challenges and appeals by José Norberto Allende, professor at the University of Santiago. It's rare that there's wind in Paris, and even less seldom a wind like this that swirled around corners and rose up to whip at old wooden venetian blinds behind which astonished ladies commented variously on how unreliable the weather had been these last few days. But the sun was out also, riding the wind and friend of the cats, so there was nothing that would keep me from taking a walk along the docks of the Seine and taking photos of the Conservatoire and Sainte-Chapelle. It was hardly ten o'clock, and I figured that by eleven the light would be good, the best you can get in the fall; to kill some time I detoured around by the Isle Saint-Louis and started to walk along the quai d'Anjou, I stared for a bit at the hôtel de Lauzun, I recited bits from Apollinaire which always get into my head whenever I pass in front of the hôtel de Lauzun (and at that I ought to be remembering the other poet, but Michel is an obstinate beggar), and when the wind stopped all at once and the sun came out at least twice as hard (I mean warmer, but really it's the same thing), I sat down on the parapet and felt terribly happy in the Sunday morning.

One of the many ways of contesting level-zero, and one of the best, is to take photographs, an activity in which one should start becoming an adept very early in life, teach it to children since it requires discipline, aesthetic education, a good eye and steady fingers. I'm not talking about waylaying the lie like any old reporter, snapping the stupid silhouette of the VIP leaving number 10 Downing Street, but in all ways when one is walking about with a camera, one has almost a duty to be attentive, to not lose that abrupt and happy rebound of sun's rays off an old stone, or the pigtails-flying run of a small girl going home with a loaf of bread or a bottle of milk. Michel knew that the photographer always worked as a permutation of his personal way of seeing the world as other than the camera insidiously imposed upon it (now a large cloud is going by, almost black), but he lacked no confidence in himself, knowing that he had only to go out without the Contax to recover the keynote of distraction, the sight without a frame around it, light without the diaphragm aperture or 1/250 sec. Right now (what a word, *now*, what a dumb lie) I was able to sit quietly on the railing overlooking the river watching the red and black motorboats passing below without it occurring to me to think photographically of the scenes, nothing more than letting myself go in the letting go of objects, running immobile in the stream of time. And then the wind was not blowing.

After, I wandered down the quai de Bourbon until getting to the end of the isle where the intimate square was (intimate because it was small, not that it was hidden, it offered its whole breast to the river

and the sky), I enjoyed it, a lot. Nothing there but a couple and, of course, pigeons; maybe even some of those which are flying past now so that I'm seeing them. A leap up and I settled on the wall, and let myself turn about and be caught and fixed by the sun, giving it my face and ears and hands (I kept my gloves in my pocket). I had no desire to shoot pictures, and lit a cigarette to be doing something; I think it was that moment when the match was about to touch the tobacco that I saw the young boy for the first time.

What I'd thought was a couple seemed much more now a boy with his mother, although at the same time I realized that it was not a kid and his mother, and that it was a couple in the sense that we always allegate to couples when we see them leaning up against the parapets or embracing on the benches in the squares. As I had nothing else to do, I had more than enough time to wonder why the boy was so nervous, like a young colt or a hare, sticking his hands into his pockets, taking them out immediately, one after the other, running his fingers through his hair, changing his stance, and especially why was he afraid, well, you could guess that from every gesture, a fear suffocated by his shyness, an impulse to step backwards which he telegraphed, his body standing as if it were on the edge of flight, holding itself back in a final, pitiful decorum.

All this was so clear, ten feet away— and we were alone against the parapet at the tip of the island—that at the beginning the boy's fright didn't let me see the blond very well. Now, thinking back on it, I see her much better at that first second when I read her face (she'd turned around suddenly, swinging like a metal weathercock, and the eyes, the eyes were there), when I vaguely understood what might have been occurring to the boy and figured it would be worth the trouble to stay and watch (the wind was blowing their words away and they were speaking in a low murmur). I think that I know how to look, if it's something I know, and also that every looking oozes with mendacity, because it's that which expels us furthest outside ourselves, without the least guarantee, whereas to smell, or (but Michel rambles on to himself easily enough, there's no need to let him harangue on this way). In any case, if the likely inaccuracy can be seen beforehand, it becomes possible again to look; perhaps it suffices to choose between looking and the reality looked at, to strip things of all their unnecessary clothing. And surely all that is difficult besides.

As for the boy I remember the image before his actual body (that will clear itself up later), while now I am sure that I remember the woman's body much better than the image. She was thin and willowy, two unfair words to describe what she was, and was wearing an almost-black fur coat, almost long, almost handsome. All the morning's wind (now it was hardly a breeze and it wasn't cold) had blown through her blond hair which pared away her white, bleak face—two unfair words —and put the world at her feet and horribly alone in front of her dark eyes, her eyes fell on things like two eagles, two leaps into nothingness, two puffs of green slime. I'm not describing anything, it's more a matter of trying to understand it. And I said two puffs of green slime.

Let's be fair, the boy was well enough dressed and was sporting yellow gloves which I would have sworn belonged to his older brother, a student of law or sociology; it was pleasant to see the fingers of the gloves sticking out of his jacket pocket. For a long time I didn't see his face, barely a profile, not stupid—a terrified bird, a Fra Filippo angel, rice pudding with milk—and the back of an adolescent who wants to take up judo and has had a scuffle or two in defense of an idea or his sister. Turning fourteen, perhaps fifteen, one would guess that he was dressed and fed by his parents but without a nickel in his pocket, having to debate with his buddies before making up his mind to buy a coffee, a cognac, a pack of cigarettes. He'd walk through the streets thinking of the girls in his class, about how good it would be to go to the movies and see the latest film, or to buy novels or neckties or bottles of liquor with green and white labels on them. At home (it would be a respectable home, lunch at noon and romantic landscapes on the walls, with a dark entryway and a mahogany umbrella stand inside the door) there'd be the slow rain of time, for studying, for being mama's hope, for looking like dad, for writing to his aunt in Avignon. So that there was a lot of walking the streets, the whole of the river for him (but without a nickel) and the mysterious city of fifteen-year-olds with its signs in doorways, its terrifying cats, a paper of fried potatoes for thirty francs, the pornographic magazine folded four ways, a solitude like the emptiness of his pockets, the eagerness for so much that was incomprehensible but illumined by a total love, by the availability analogous to the wind and the streets.

This biography was of the boy and of any boy whatsoever, but this particular one now, you could see he was insular, surrounded solely by the blond's presence as she continued talking with him. (I'm tired of insisting, but two long ragged ones just went by. That morning I don't think I looked at the sky once, because what was happening with the boy and the woman appeared so soon I could do nothing but look at them and wait, look at them and. . . .) To cut it short, the boy was agitated and one could guess without too much trouble what had just occurred a few minutes before, at most half-an-hour. The boy had come onto the tip of the island, seen the woman and thought her marvelous. The woman was waiting for that because she was there waiting for that, or maybe the boy arrived before her and she saw him from one of the balconies or from a car and got out to meet him, starting the conversation with whatever, from the beginning she was sure that he was going to be afraid and want to run off, and that, naturally, he'd stay, stiff and sullen, pretending experience and the pleasure of the adventure. The rest was easy because it was happening ten feet away from me, and anyone could have gauged the stages of the game, the derisive, competitive fencing; its major attraction was not that it was happening but in foreseeing its denouement. The boy would try to end it by pretending a date, an obligation, whatever, and would go stumbling off disconcerted, wishing he were walking with some assurance, but naked under the mocking glance which would follow him until he was out of sight. Or rather, he would stay there, fascinated or simply incapable of taking the initiative, and the woman would begin to touch his face gently, muss his hair, still talking to him voicelessly, and soon would take him by the arm to lead him off, unless he, with an uneasiness beginning to tinge the edge of desire, even his stake in the adventure, would rouse himself to put his arm around her waist and to kiss her. Any of this could have happened, though it did not, and perversely Michel waited, sitting on the railing, making the settings almost without looking at the camera, ready to take a picturesque shot of a corner of the island with an uncommon couple talking and looking at one another.

Strange how the scene (almost nothing: two figures there mismatched in their youth) was taking on a disquieting aura. I thought it was I imposing it, and that my photo, if I shot it, would reconstitute things in their true stupidity. I would have liked to know what he was thinking, a man in a grey hat sitting at the wheel of a car parked on the dock which led up to the footbridge, and whether he was reading the paper or asleep. I had just discovered him because people inside a parked car have a tendency to disappear, they get lost in that wretched, private cage stripped of the beauty that motion and danger give it. And nevertheless, the car had been there the whole time, forming part (or deforming that part) of the isle. A car: like saying a lighted streetlamp, a park bench. Never like saying wind, sunlight, those elements always new to the skin and the eyes, and also the boy and the woman, unique, put there to change the island, to show it to me in another way. Finally, it may have been that the man with the newspaper also became aware of what was happening and would, like me, feel that malicious sensation of waiting for everything to happen. Now the woman had swung around smoothly, putting the young boy between herself and the wall, I saw them almost in profile, and he was taller, though not much taller, and yet she dominated him, it seemed like she was hovering over him (her laugh, all at once, a whip of feathers), crushing him just by being there, smiling, one hand taking a stroll through the air. Why wait any longer? Aperture at sixteen, a sighting which would not include the horrible black car, but yes, that tree, necessary to break up too much grey space . . .

I raised the camera, pretended to study a focus which did not include them, and waited and watched closely, sure that I would finally catch the revealing expression, one that would sum it all up, life that is rhythmed by movement but which a stiff image destroys, taking time in cross section, if we do not choose the essential imperceptible fraction of it. I did not have to wait long. The woman was getting on with the job of handcuffing the boy smoothly, stripping from him what was left of his freedom a hair at a time, in an incredibly slow and delicious torture. I imagined the possible endings (now a small fluffy cloud appears, almost alone in the sky), I saw their arrival at the house (a basement apartment probably, which she would have filled with large cushions and cats) and conjectured the boy's terror and his desperate decision to play it cool and to be led off pretending there was nothing new in it for him. Closing my eyes, if I did in fact close my eyes, I set the scene: the teasing kisses, the woman mildly repelling the hands which were trying to undress her, like in novels, on a bed that would have a lilac-colored comforter, on the other hand she taking off his clothes, plainly mother and son under a milky yellow light, and everything would end up as usual, perhaps, but maybe everything would go otherwise, and the initiation of the adolescent would not happen, she would not let it happen, after a long prologue wherein the awkwardnesses, the exasperating caresses, the running of hands over bodies would be resolved in who knows what, in a separate and solitary pleasure, in a petulant denial mixed with the art of tiring and disconcerting so much poor innocence. It might go like that, it might very well go like that; that woman was not looking for the boy as a lover, and at the same time she was dominating him toward some end impossible to understand if you do not imagine it as a cruel game, the desire to desire without satisfaction, to excite herself for someone else, someone who in no way could be that kid.

Michel is guilty of making literature, of indulging in fabricated unrealities. Nothing pleases him more than to imagine exceptions to the rule, individuals outside the species, not-always-repugnant monsters. But that woman invited speculation, perhaps giving clues enough for the fantasy to hit the bullseye. Before she left, and now that she would fill my imaginings for several days, for I'm given to ruminating, I decided not to lose a moment more. I got it all into the viewfinder (with the tree, the railing, the eleven-o'clock sun) and took the shot. In time to realize that they both had noticed and stood there looking at me, the boy surprised and as though questioning, but she was irritated, her face and body flat-footedly hostile, feeling robbed, ignominiously recorded on a small chemical image.

I might be able to tell it in much greater detail but it's not worth the trouble. The woman said that no one had the right to take a picture without permission, and demanded that I hand her over the film. All this in a dry, clear voice with a good Parisian accent, which rose in color and tone with every phrase. For my part, it hardly mattered whether she got the roll of film or not, but anyone who knows me will tell you, if you want anything from me, ask nicely. With the result that I restricted myself to formulating the opinion that not only was photography in public places not prohibited, but it was looked upon with decided favor, both private and official. And while that was getting said, I noticed on the sly how the boy was falling back, sort of actively backing up though without moving, and all at once (it seemed almost incredible) he turned and broke into a run, the poor kid, thinking that he was walking off and in fact in full flight, running past the side of the car, disappearing like a gossamer filament of angel-spit in the morning air.

But filaments of angel-spittle are also called devil-spit, and Michel had to endure rather particular curses, to hear himself called meddler and imbecile, taking great pains meanwhile to smile and to abate with simple movements of his head such a hard sell. As I was beginning to get tired, I heard the car door slam. The man in the grey hat was there, looking at us. It was only at that point that I realized he was playing a part in the comedy.

He began to walk toward us, carrying in his hand the paper he had been pretending to read. What I remember best is the grimace that twisted his mouth askew, it covered his face with wrinkles, changed somewhat both in location and shape because his lips trembled and the grimace went from one side of his mouth to the other as though it were on wheels, independent and involuntary. But the rest stayed fixed, a flour-powdered clown or bloodless man, dull dry skin, eyes deepset, the nostrils black and prominently visible, blacker than the eyebrows or hair or the black necktie. Walking cautiously as though the pavement hurt his feet; I saw patent-leather shoes with such thin soles that he must have felt every roughness in the pavement. I don't know why I got down off the railing, nor very well why I decided to not give them the photo, to refuse that demand in which I guessed at their fear and cowardice. The clown and the woman consulted one another in silence: we made a perfect and unbearable triangle, something I felt compelled to break with a crack of a whip. I laughed in their faces and begin to walk off, a little more slowly, I imagine, than the boy. At the level of the first houses, beside the iron footbridge, I turned around to look at them. They were not moving, but the man had dropped his newspaper; it seemed to me that the woman, her back to the parapet, ran her hands over the stone with the classical and absurd gesture of someone pursued looking for a way out.

What happened after that happened here, almost just now, in a room on the fifth floor. Several days went by before Michel developed the photos he'd taken on Sunday; his shots of the Conservatoire and of Sainte-Chapelle were all they should be. Then he found two or three proof-shots he'd forgotten, a poor attempt to catch a cat perched astonishingly on the roof of a rambling public urinal, and also the shot of the blond and the kid. The negative was so good that he made an

enlargement; the enlargement was so good that he made one very much larger, almost the size of a poster. It did not occur to him (now one wonders and wonders) that only the shots of the Conservatoire were worth so much work. Of the whole series, the snapshot of the tip of the island was the only one which interested him; he tacked up the enlargement on one wall of the room, and the first day he spent some time looking at it and remembering, that gloomy operation of comparing the memory with the gone reality; a frozen memory, like any photo, where nothing is missing, not even, and especially, nothingness, the true solidifier of the scene. There was the woman, there was the boy, the tree rigid above their heads, the sky as sharp as the stone of the parapet, clouds and stones melded into a single substance and inseparable (now one with sharp edges is going by, like a thunderhead). The first two days I accepted what I had done, from the photo itself to the enlargement on the wall, and didn't even question that every once in a while I would interrupt my translation of José Norberto Allende's treatise to encounter once more the woman's face, the dark splotches on the railing. I'm such a jerk; it had never occurred to me that when we look at a photo from the front, the eyes reproduce exactly the position and the vision of the lens; it's these things that are taken for granted and it never occurs to anyone to think about them. From my chair, with the typewriter directly in front of me, I looked at the photo ten feet away, and then it occurred to me that I had hung it exactly at the point of view of the lens. It looked very good that way; no doubt, it was the best way to appreciate a photo, though the angle from the diagonal doubtless has its pleasures and might even divulge different aspects. Every few minutes, for example when I was unable to find the way to say in good French what José Norberto Allende was saying in very good Spanish, I raised my eyes and looked at the photo; sometimes the woman would catch my eye, sometimes the boy, sometimes the pavement where a dry leaf had fallen admirably situated to heighten a lateral section. Then I rested a bit from my labors, and I enclosed myself again happily in that morning in which the photo was drenched, I recalled ironically the angry picture of the woman demanding I give her the photograph, the boy's pathetic and ridiculous flight, the entrance on the scene of the man with the white face. Basically, I was satisfied with myself; my part had not been too brilliant, and since the French have been given the gift of the sharp response, I did not see very well why I'd chosen to leave without a complete demonstration of the rights, privileges and prerogatives of citizens. The important thing, the really important thing was having helped the kid to escape in time (this in case my theorizing was correct, which was not sufficiently proven, but the running away itself seemed to show it so). Out of plain meddling, I had given him the opportunity finally to take advantage of his fright to do something useful; now he would be regretting it, feeling his honor impaired, his manhood diminished. That was better than the attentions of a woman capable of looking as she had looked at him on that island. Michel is something of a puritan at times, he believes that one should not seduce someone from a position of strength. In the last analysis, taking that photo had been a good act.

Well, it wasn't because of the good act that I looked at it between paragraphs while I was working. At that moment I didn't know the reason, the reason I had tacked the enlargement onto the wall; maybe all fatal acts happen that way, and that is the condition of their fulfillment. I don't think the almost-furtive trembling of the leaves on the tree alarmed me, I was working on a sentence and rounded it out successfully. Habits are like immense herbariums, in the end an enlargement of 32 x 28 looks like a movie screen, where, on the tip of the island, a woman is speaking with a boy and a tree is shaking its dry leaves over their heads.

But her hands were just too much. I had just translated: "In that case, the second key resides in the intrinsic nature of difficulties which societies . . ."— when I saw the woman's hand beginning to stir slowly, finger by finger. There was nothing left of me, a phrase in French which I would never have to finish, a typewriter on the floor, a chair that squeaked and shook, fog. The kid had ducked his head like boxers do when they've done all they can and are waiting for the final blow to fall; he had turned up the collar of his overcoat and seemed more a prisoner than ever, the perfect victim helping promote the catastrophe. Now the woman was talking into his ear, and her hand opened again to lay itself against his cheekbone, to caress and caress it, burning it, taking her time. The kid was less startled than he was suspicious, once or twice he poked his head over the woman's shoulder and she continued talking, saying something that made him look back every few minutes toward that area where Michel knew the car was parked and the man in the grey hat, carefully eliminated from the photo but present in the boy's eyes (how doubt that now) in the words of the woman, in the woman's hands, in the vicarious presence of the woman. When I saw the man come up, stop near them and look at them, his hands in his pockets and a stance somewhere between disgusted and demanding, the master who is about to whistle in his dog after a frolic in the square, I understood, if that was to understand, what had to happen now, what had to have happened then, what would have to happen at that moment, among these people, just where I had poked my nose in to upset an established order, interfering innocently in that which had not happened, but which was now going to happen, now was going to be fulfilled. And what I had imagined earlier was much less horrible than the reality, that woman, who was not there by herself, she was not caressing or propositioning or encouraging for her own pleasure, to lead the angel away with his tousled hair and play the tease with his terror and his eager grace. The real boss was waiting there, smiling petulantly, already certain of the business; he was not the first to send a woman in the vanguard, to bring him the prisoners manacled with flowers. The rest of it would be so simple, the car, some house or another, drinks, stimulating engravings, tardy tears, the awakening in hell. And there was nothing I could do, this time I could do absolutely nothing. My strength had been a photograph, that, there, where they were taking their revenge on me, demonstrating clearly what was going to happen. The photo had been taken, the time had run out, gone; we were so far from one another, the abusive act had certainly already taken place, the tears already shed, and the rest conjecture and sorrow. All at once the order was inverted, they were alive, moving, they were deciding and had decided, they were going to their future; and I on this side, prisoner of another time, in a room on the fifth floor, to not know who they were, that woman, that man, and that boy, to be only the lens of my camera, something fixed, rigid, incapable of intervention. It was horrible, their mocking me, deciding it before my impotent eye, mocking me, for the boy again was looking at the flour-faced clown and I had to accept the fact that he was going to say yes, that the proposition carried money with it or a gimmick, and I couldn't yell for him to run, or even open the road to him again with a new photo, a small and almost meek intervention which would ruin the framework of drool and perfume. Everything was going to resolve itself right there, at that moment; there was like an immense silence which had nothing to do with physical silence. It was stretching it out, setting itself up. I think I screamed, I screamed terribly, and that at that exact second I realized that I was beginning to move toward them, four inches, a step, another step, the tree swung its branches rhythmically in the foreground, a place where the railing was tarnished emerged from the frame, the woman's face turned toward me as though surprised, was enlarging, and then I turned a bit, I mean that the camera turned a little, and without losing sight of the woman, I began to close in on the man who was looking at me with the black holes he had in place of eyes, surprised and angered both, he looked, wanting to nail me onto the air, and at that instant I happened to see something like a large bird outside the focus that was flying in a single swoop in front of the picture, and I leaned up against the wall of my room and was happy because the boy had just managed to escape, I saw him running off, in focus again, sprinting with his hair flying in the wind, learning finally to fly across the island, to arrive at the footbridge, return to the city. For the second time he'd escaped them, for the second time I was helping him to escape, returning him to his precarious paradise. Out of breath, I stood in front of them; no need to step closer, the game was played out. Of the woman you could see just maybe a shoulder and a bit of the hair, brutally cut off by the frame of the picture; but the man was directly center, his mouth half open, you could see a shaking black tongue, and he lifted his hands slowly, bringing them into the foreground, an instant still in perfect focus, and then all of him a lump that blotted out the island, the tree, and I shut my eyes, I didn't want to see any more, and I covered my face and broke into tears like an idiot.

Now there's a big white cloud, as on all these days, all this untellable time. What remains to be said is always a cloud, two clouds, or long hours of a sky perfectly clear, a very clean, clear rectangle tacked up with pins on the wall of my room. That was what I saw when I opened my eyes and dried them with my fingers: the clear sky, and then a cloud that drifted in from the left, passed gracefully and slowly across and disappeared on the right. And then another, and for a change sometimes, everything gets grey, all one enormous cloud, and suddenly the splotches of rain cracking down, for a long spell you can see it raining over the picture, like a spell of weeping reversed, and little by little, the frame becomes clear, perhaps the sun comes out, and again the clouds begin to come, two at a time, three at a time. And the pigeons once in a while, and a sparrow or two.

Translated by *Paul Blackburn.*

POEMS

LONDON SNOW

Robert Bridges
(1844–1930)

When men were all asleep the snow
   came flying,
In large white flakes falling on the city
   brown,
Stealthily and perpetually settling and
   loosely lying,
   Hushing the latest traffic of the drowsy
     town;
Deadening, muffling, stifling its murmurs
   failing;   5
Lazily and incessantly floating down and
   down:
   Silently sifting and veiling road, roof
     and railing;
Hiding difference, making unevenness
   even,
Into angles and crevices softly drifting
   and sailing.
   All night it fell, and when full inches
     seven   10
It lay in the depth of its uncompacted
   lightness,
The clouds blew off from a high and
   frosty heaven;
   And all woke earlier for the unac-
     customed brightness
Of the winter dawning, the strange un-
   heavenly glare:
The eye marveled—marveled at the daz-
   zling whiteness;   15

   The ear hearkened to the stillness of
     the solemn air;
No sound of wheel rumbling nor of foot
   falling,
And the busy morning cries came thin
   and spare.
   Then boys I heard, as they went to
     school, calling;
They gathered up the crystal manna to
   freeze   20
Their tongues with tasting, their hands
   with snowballing;
   Or rioted in a drift, plunging up to
     the knees;
Or peering up from under the white-
   mossed wonder,
"O look at the trees!" they cried, "O look
   at the trees!"
   With lessened load, a few carts creak
     and blunder,   25
Following along the white deserted way,
A country company long dispersed asun-
   der:
   When now already the sun, in pale
     display
Standing by Paul's high dome, spread
   forth below
His sparkling beams, and awoke the stir
   of the day.   30
   For now doors open, and war is waged
     with the snow;
And trains of sombre men, past tale of
   . number,
Tread long brown paths, as toward their
   toil they go:

But even for them awhile no cares encumber
Their mind diverted; the daily word is unspoken,   35
The daily thoughts of labour and sorrow slumber
At the sight of the beauty that greets them, for the charm they have broken.

EVEN IN THE MOMENT OF OUR EARLIEST KISS

Edna St. Vincent Millay
(1892–1950)

Even in the moment of our earliest kiss,
When sighed the straitened bud into the flower,
Sat the dry seed of most unwelcome this;
And that I knew, though not the day and hour.
Too season-wise am I, being country-bred,   5
To tilt at autumn or defy the frost:
Snuffing the chill even as my fathers did,
I say with them, "What's out tonight is lost."
I only hoped, with the mild hope of all
Who watch the leaf take shape upon the tree,   10
A fairer summer and a later fall
Than in these parts a man is apt to see,
And sunny clusters ripened for the wine:
I tell you this across the blackened vine.

THE RETURN

Edwin Muir
(1887–1959)

I see myself sometimes, an old old man
Who has walked so long with time as time's true servant,

That he's grown strange to me—who was once myself—
Almost as strange as time, and yet familiar
With old man's staff and legendary cloak,   5
For see, it is I, it is I. And I return
So altered, so adopted, to the house
Of my own life. There all the doors stand open
Perpetually, and the rooms ring with sweet voices,
And there my long life's seasons sound their changes,   10
Childhood and youth and manhood all together,
And welcome waits, and not a room but is
My own, beloved and longed for. And the voices,
Sweeter than any sound dreamt of or known,
Call me, recall me. I draw near at last,   15
An old old man, and scan the ancient walls
Rounded and softened by the compassionate years,
The old and heavy and long-leaved trees that watch
This my inheritance in friendly darkness.
And yet I cannot enter, for all within   20
Rises before me there, rises against me,
A sweet and terrible labyrinth of longing,
So that I turn aside and take the road
That always, early or late, runs on before.

POET

Karl Shapiro
(1913–   )
*Il arrive que l'esprit demande la poésie.**

Left leg flung out, head cocked to the right,

* "It comes about that the spirit asks for poetry."

Tweed coat or army uniform, with book,
Beautiful eyes, who is this walking down?
Who, glancing at the pane of glass looks
    sharp
And thinks it is not he—as when a poet 5
Comes swiftly on some half-forgotten
    poem
And loosely holds the page, steady of
    mind,
        Thinking it is not his?

And when will *you* exist?—Oh, it is I,
Incredibly skinny, stooped, and neat as
    pie, 10
Ignorant as dirt, erotic as an ape,
Dreamy as puberty—with dirty hair!
Into the room like kangaroo he bounds,
Ears flopping like the most expensive
    hound's;
His chin received all questions as he
    bows 15
        Mouthing a green bon-bon.

Has no more memory than rubber. Stands
Waist-deep in heavy mud of thought and
    broods
At his own wetness. When he would get
    out,
To his surprise he lifts in air a phrase 20
As whole and clean and silvery as a fish.
Which jumps and dangles on his damned
    hooked grin,
But like a name-card on a man's lapel
    Calls him a conscious fool.

And childlike he remembers all his life 25
And cannily constructs it, fact by fact,
As boys paste postage stamps in careful
    books,
Denoting pence and legends and profiles,
Nothing more valuable.—And like a thief,
His eyes glassed over and concealed with
    guilt, 30
Fondles his secrets like a case of tools,
    And waits in empty doors.

By men despised for knowing what he is,

And by himself. But he exists for women.
As dolls to girls, as perfect wives to
    men, 35
So he to women. And to himself a thing,
All ages, epicene, without a trade.
To girls and wives always alive and
    fated;
To men and scholars always dead like
    Greek
        And always mistranslated. 40

Towards exile and towards shame he lures
    himself,
Tongue winding on his arm, and thinks
    like Eve
By biting apple will become most wise.
Sentio ergo sum: he feels his way
And words themselves stand up for him
    like Braille 45
And punch and perforate his parchment
    ear.
All language falls like Chinese on his soul,
        Image of song unsounded.

This is the coward's coward that in his
    dreams
Sees shapes of pain grow tall. Awake at
    night 50
He peers at sounds and stumbles at a
    breeze.
And none holds life less dear. For as a
    youth
Who by some accident observes his love
Naked and in some natural ugly act,
He turns with loathing and with flaming
    hands, 55
        Seared and betrayed by sight.

He is the business man, on beauty trades,
Dealer in arts and thoughts who, like the
    Jew,
Shall rise from slums and hated dialects
A tower of bitterness. Shall be always
    strange, 60
Hunted and then sought after. Shall be sat
Like an ambassador from another race
At tables rich with music. He shall eat
    flowers,

Chew honey and spit out gall. They shall
all smile
  And love and pity him.   65

His death shall be by drowning. In that
hour
When the last bubble of pure heaven's air
Hovers within his throat, safe on his bed,
A small eternal figurehead in terror,
He shall cry out and clutch his days of
straw   70
Before the blackest wave. Lastly, his tomb
Shall list and founder in the troughs of
grass.
  And none shall speak his name.

IN WESTMINSTER ABBEY

John Betjeman
(1906–)

Let me take this other glove off
 As the *vox humana* swells,
And the beauteous fields of Eden
 Bask beneath the Abbey bells.
Here, where England's statesmen lie,   5
Listen to a lady's cry.

Gracious Lord, oh bomb the Germans.
 Spare their women for Thy Sake,
And if that is not too easy
 We will pardon Thy Mistake.   10
But, gracious Lord, whate'er shall be,
Don't let anyone bomb me.

Keep our Empire undismembered
 Guide our Forces by Thy Hand,
Gallant blacks from far Jamaica,   15
 Honduras and Togoland;
Protect them Lord in all their fights,
And, even more, protect the whites.

Think of what our Nation stands for,
 Books from Boots' and country lanes, 20

Free speech, free passes, class distinction,
 Democracy and proper drains.
Lord, put beneath Thy special care
One-eighty-nine Cadogan Square.

Although dear Lord I am a sinner,   25
 I have done no major crime;
Now I'll come to Evening Service
 Whensoever I have the time.
So, Lord, reserve for me a crown,
And do not let my shares go down.   30

I will labour for Thy Kingdom,
 Help our lads to win the war,
Send white feathers to the cowards
 Join the Women's Army Corps,
Then wash the Steps around Thy
 Throne   35
In the Eternal Safety Zone.

Now I feel a little better,
 What a treat to hear Thy Word,
Where the bones of leading statesmen,
 Have so often been interr'd.   40
And now, dear Lord, I cannot wait
Because I have a luncheon date.

■ ■ ■

A SONG AT MORNING

Edith Sitwell
(1887–1964)

The weeping rose in her dark night of
 leaves
Sighed 'Dark is my heart, and dark my
 secret love—
Show not the fire within your heart its
 light—
For to behold a rainbow in the night
Shall be the presage of your overthrow.' 5

But morning came, and the great dews;
 then her philosophies

Of the heart's darkness died. And from
   the chrysalis of my thin sleep
That lay like light or dew upon my form
I rose and wrapped my wings about me,
   went
From the porphyrian darkness. Like the
   rose   10

I too was careless in the morning dews,
Seeing the dead and the dead hour return
To forgive the stain on our hands. I too at
   morning
Am like the rose who shouts of the red
   joys and redder sorrows
Fallen from young veins and heartsprings
   that once held   15
The world's incendiarism and the redness
   of summer,
The hope of the rose. For soon will come
   the morrow
When ancient Prudence and her wintery
   dream
Will be no more than the rose's idle-
   ness. . . .
The light of tears shall only seem the
   rose's light   20
—Nor sorrow darker than her night of
   leaves.

IN DISTRUST OF MERITS

Marianne Moore
(1887–   )

Strengthened to live, strengthened to die
   for
   medals and positioned victories?
They're fighting, fighting, fighting the
   blind
   man who thinks he sees,—
who cannot see that the enslaver is   5
enslaved; the hater, harmed. O shining O
   firm star, O tumultuous
      ocean lashed till small things go
      as they will, the mountainous

wave makes us who look,
      know   10
depth. Lost at sea before they fought! O
   star of David, star of Bethlehem,
O black imperial lion
   of the Lord—-emblem
of a risen world—be joined at last, be   15
joined. There is hate's crown beneath
   which all is
      death; there's love's without which
      none
      is king; the blessed deeds bless
      the halo. As contagion
      of sickness makes sickness,   20
contagion of trust can make trust. They're
   fighting in deserts and caves, one by
one, in battalions and squadrons;
   they're fighting that I
may yet recover from the disease, My   25
Self; some have it lightly; some will die.
   'Man
      wolf to man' and we devour
      ourselves. The enemy could not
      have made a greater breach in our
      defences. One pilot-   30
ing a blind man can escape him, but
   Job disheartened by false comfort knew
that nothing can be so defeating
   as a blind man who
can see. O alive who are dead, who are   35
proud not to see, O small dust of the earth
      that walks so arrogantly,
      trust begets power and faith is
      an affectionate thing. We
      vow, we make this promise   40
to the fighting—it's a promise—'We'll
   never have black, white, red, yellow,
   Jew,
Gentile, Untouchable.' We are
   not competent to
make our vows. With set jaw they are
   fighting,   45
fighting, fighting,—some we love whom
   we know,
      some we love but know not—that

hearts may feel and not be
numb.
It cures me; or am I what
I can't believe in? Some   50

in snow, some on crags, some in quick-
sands,
little by little, much by much, they
are fighting fighting fighting that where
there was death there may
be life. 'When a man is prey to anger,   55
he is moved by outside things; when he
holds
his ground in patience patience
patience, that is action or
beauty,' the soldier's defence
and hardest armour for   60

the fight. The world's an orphans' home.
Shall
we never have peace without sorrow?
without pleas of the dying for
help that won't come? O
quiet form upon the dust, I cannot   65
look and yet I must. If these great patient
dyings—all these agonies
and woundbearings and bloodshed—
can teach us how to live, these
dyings were not wasted.   70

Hate-hardened heat, O heart of iron,
iron is iron till it is rust.
There never was a war that was
not inward; I must
fight till I have conquered in myself
what   75
causes war, but I would not believe it.
I inwardly did nothing.
O Iscariotlike crime!
Beauty is everlasting
and dust is for a time.   80

IF THERE ARE ANY HEAVENS

E. E. Cummings
(1894–1962)

if there are any heavens my mother will
(all by herself) have

one.   It will not be a pansy heaven nor
a fragile heaven of lilies-of-the-valley but
it will be a heaven of blackred roses

my father will be(deep like a rose   5
tall like a rose)

standing near my

swaying over her
silent)
with eyes which are really petals and
see   10

nothing with the face of a poet really
which
is a flower and not a face with
hands
which whisper
This is my beloved my   15

(suddenly in sunlight
he will bow,

& the whole garden will bow)

THIRTEEN WAYS OF LOOKING AT A BLACKBIRD

Wallace Stevens
(1879–1955)

I

Among twenty snowy mountains,
The only moving thing
Was the eye of the blackbird.

II

I was of three minds,
Like a tree   5
In which there are three blackbirds.

III

The blackbird whirled in the autumn winds.
It was a small part of the pantomime.

IV

A man and a woman
Are one.   10
A man and a woman and a blackbird
Are one.

V

I do not know which to prefer,
The beauty of inflections
Or the beauty of innuendoes,   15
The blackbird whistling
Or just after.

VI

Icicles filled the long window
With barbaric glass.
The shadow of the blackbird   20
Crossed it, to and fro.
The mood
Traced in the shadow
An indecipherable cause.

VII

O thin men of Haddam,   25
Why do you imagine golden birds?
Do you not see how the blackbird
Walks around the feet
Of the women about you?

VIII

I know noble accents   30
And lucid, inescapable rhythms;
But I know, too,
That the blackbird is involved
In what I know.

25. *Haddam:* a town in Connecticut.

IX

When the blackbird flew out of sight, 35
It marked the edge
Of one of many circles.

X

At the sight of blackbirds
Flying in a green light,
Even the bawds of euphony   40
Would cry out sharply.

XI

He rode over Connecticut
In a glass coach.
Once, a fear pierced him,
In that he mistook   45
The shadow of his equipage
For blackbirds.

XII

The river is moving.
The blackbird must be flying.

XIII

It was evening all afternoon.   50
It was snowing
And it was going to snow.
The blackbird sat
In the cedar-limbs.

THE WINTER GARDEN

David Gascoyne
(1916–   )

The season's anguish, crashing whirlwind,
   ice,
Have passed, and cleansed the trodden
   paths
The silent gardeners have strewn with ash.

The iron circles of the sky

Are worn away by tempest;   5
Yet in this garden there is no more strife:
The Winter's knife is buried in the earth.
Pure music is the cry that tears
The birdless branches in the wind.
No blossom is reborn. The blue   10
Stare of the pond is blind.

And no-one sees
A restless stranger through the morning
    stray
Across the sodden lawn, whose eyes
Are tired of weeping, in whose breast   15
A savage sun consumes its hidden day.

■   ■   ■

THE STARRY NIGHT

Anne Sexton
(1928–   )

*That does not keep me from having a
terrible need of—shall I say the word—
religion. Then I go out at night to paint
the stars.*

—VINCENT VAN GOGH
in a letter to his brother

The town does not exist
except where one black-haired tree slips
up like a drowned woman into the hot
    sky.
The town is silent. The night boils with
    eleven stars.
Oh starry starry night! This is how   5
I want to die.

It moves. They are all alive.
Even the moon bulges in its orange irons
to push children, like a god, from its eye.
The old unseen serpent swallows up the
    stars.   10
Oh starry starry night! This is how
I want to die:

into that rushing beast of the night,

sucked up by that great dragon, to split
from my life with no flag,   15
no belly,
no cry.

THE WHITSUN WEDDINGS

Philip Larkin
(1922–   )

That Whitsun, I was late getting away:
    Not till about
One-twenty on the sunlit Saturday
Did my three-quarters-empty train pull
    out,
All windows down, all cushions hot, all
    sense   5
Of being in a hurry gone. We ran
Behind the backs of houses, crossed a
    street
Of blinding windscreens, smelt the fish-
    dock; thence
The river's level drifting breadth began,
Where sky and Lincolnshire and water
    meet.   10

All afternoon, through the tall heat that
    slept
    For miles inland,
A slow and stopping curve southwards we
    kept.
Wide farms went by, short-shadowed
    cattle, and
Canals with floatings of industrial froth; 15
A hothouse flashed uniquely: hedges
    dipped
And rose: and now and then a smell of
    grass
Displaced the reek of buttoned carriage-
    cloth
Until the next town, new and nondescript,
Approached with acres of dismantled
    cars.   20

At first, I didn't notice what a noise
    The weddings made

Each station that we stopped at: sun de-
stroys
The interest of what's happening in the
shade,
And down the long cool platforms whoops
and skirls   25
I took for porters larking with the mails,
And went on reading. Once we started,
though,
We passed them, grinning and pomaded,
girls
In parodies of fashion, heels and veils,
All posed irresolutely, watching us go,   30

As if out on the end of an event
  Waving goodbye
To something that survived it. Struck, I
leant
More promptly out next time, more curi-
ously,
And saw it all again in different terms: 35
The fathers with broad belts under their
suits
And seamy foreheads; mothers loud and
fat;
An uncle shouting smut; and then the
perms,
The nylon gloves and jewellery-substi-
tutes,
The lemons, mauves, and olive-ochres
that   40

Marked off the girls unreally from the
rest.
  Yes, from cafés
And banquet-halls up yards, and bunting-
dressed
Coach-party annexes, the wedding-days
Were coming to an end. All down the
line   45
Fresh couples climbed aboard: the rest
stood round;
The last confetti and advice were thrown,
And, as we moved, each face seemed to
define
Just what it saw departing: children
frowned

At something dull; fathers had never
known   50

Success so huge and wholly farcial;
  The women shared
The secret like a happy funeral;
While girls, gripping their handbags
tighter, stared
At a religious wounding. Free at last,   55
And loaded with the sum of all they saw,
We hurried towards London, shuffling
gouts of steam.
Now fields were building-plots, and pop-
lars cast
Long shadows over major roads, and for
Some fifty minutes, that in time would
seem   60

Just long enough to settle hats and say
  I nearly died,
A dozen marriages got under way.
They watched the landscape, sitting side
by side
—An Odeon went past, a cooling tower,   65
And someone running up to bowl—and
none
Thought of the others they would never
meet
Or how their lives would all contain this
hour.
I thought of London spread out in the sun,
Its postal districts packed like squares of
wheat: 70

There we were aimed. And as we raced
across
  Bright knots of rail
Past standing Pullmans, walls of blackened moss
Came close, and it was nearly done, this
frail
Travelling coincidence; and what it
held   75
Stood ready to be loosed with all the
power
That being changed can give. We slowed
again,

And as the tightened brakes took hold,
   there swelled
A sense of falling, like an arrow-shower
Sent out of sight, somewhere becoming
   rain.   80

BENEATH MY HAND AND EYE THE DISTANT HILLS, YOUR BODY

Gary Snyder
(1930–   )

What my hand follows on your body
Is the line. A stream of love
  of heat, of light,   what my
  eye   lascivious
      licks   5
  over, watching
  far snow-dappled Uintah mountains
Is that stream.
Of power.   what my
  hand curves over, following the line. 10
  "hip" and "groin"

7. *Uintah mountains:* a range of the Rocky
Mountains in Utah.

Where "I"
  follow by hand and eye
  the swimming limit of your body.
As when vision idly dallies on the hills 15
Loving what it feeds on.
    soft cinder cones and craters;
    —Drum Hadley in the Pinacate
      took ten minutes more to look
      again—
A leap of power unfurling:
    left,   right—right—
My heart beat faster looking
  at the snowy Uintah mountains.

As my hand feeds on you
  runs down your side and curls beneath
    your hip.   25
  oil pool; stratum; water—

What "is" within   not known
  but feel it
  sinking with a breath
  pusht ruthlessly, surely, down.   30

Beneath this long caress of hand and eye
  "we" learn the flower burning,
    outward, from "below."

THE EXAMINATION

W. D. Snodgrass
(1926–   )

      Under the thick beams of that swirly smoking light,
        The black robes are clustering, huddled in together.
      Hunching their shoulders, they spread short, broad sleeves like night-
        Black grackles' wings and reach out bone-yellow leather-

      Y fingers, each to each. And are prepared. Each turns   5
        His single eye—or since one can't discern their eyes,
      That reflective, single, moon-pale disc which burns
        Over each brow—to watch this uncouth shape that lies

      Strapped to their table. One probes with his ragged nails
        The slate-sharp calf, explores the thigh and the lean thews   10

Of the groin. Others raise, red as piratic sails,
    His wing, stretching, trying the pectoral sinews.

One runs his finger down the whet of that cruel
    Golden beak, lifts back the horny lids from the eyes,
Peers down in one bright eye, malign as a jewel   15
    And steps back suddenly. "He is anaesthetized?"

"He is. He is. Yes. Yes." The tallest of them, bent
    Down by the head, rises. "This drug possesses powers
Sufficient to still all gods in this firmament.
    This is Garuda who was fierce. He's yours for hours."   20

"We shall continue, please." Now, once again, he bends
    To the skull, and its clamped tissues. Into the cra-
Nial cavity, he plunges both of his hands
    Like obstetric forceps and lifts out the great brain.

Holds it aloft, then gives it to the next who stands   25
    Beside him. Each, in turn, accepts it, although loath,
Turns it this way, that way, feels it between his hands
    Like a wasp's nest or some sickening outsized growth.

They must decide what thoughts each part of it must think;
    They tap it, then listen beside, each suspect lobe,   30
Next, with a crow's quill dipped into India ink,
    Mark on its surface, as if on a map or globe,

Those dangerous areas which need to be excised.
    They rinse it, then apply antiseptics to it;
Now, silver saws appear which, inch by inch, slice   35
    Through its ancient folds and ridges, like thick suet.

It's rinsed, dried, and daubed with thick salves. The smoky saws
    Are scrubbed, resterilized, and polished till they gleam.
The brain is repacked in its case. Pinched in their claws,
    Glimmering needles stitch it up, that leave no seam.   40

Meantime, one of them has set blinders to the eyes,
    Inserted light packing beneath each of the ears
And caulked the nostrils in. One, with thin twine, ties
    The genitals off. With long wooden-handled shears,

Another chops pinions out of the scarlet wings.   45
    It's hoped that with disuse he will forget the sky
Or, at least, in time, learn, among other things,
    To fly no higher than his superiors fly.

Well; that's a beginning. The next time, they can split
   His tongue and teach him to talk correctly, can give   50
Him memory of fine books and choose clothing fit
   For the integrated area where he'll live.

Their candidate may live to give them thanks one day.
   He will recover and may hope for such success
He might return to join their ranks. Bowing away,   55
   They nod, whispering, "One of ours; one of ours. Yes. Yes."

THE NIGHT DANCES

Sylvia Plath
(1932–1963)

A smile fell in the grass.
Irretrievable!

And how will your night dances
Lose themselves. In mathematics?

Such pure leaps and spirals—   5
Surely they travel

The world forever, I shall not entirely
Sit emptied of beauties, the gift

Of your small breath, the drenched grass
Smell of your sleeps, lilies, lilies.   10

Their flesh bears no relation.
Cold folds of ego, the calla,

And the tiger, embellishing itself—
Spots, and a spread of hot petals.

The comets   15
Have such a space to cross,

Such coldness, forgetfulness.
So your gestures flake off—

Warm and human, then their pink light
Bleeding and peeling   20

Through the black amnesias of heaven.

Why am I given

These lamps, these planets
Falling like blessings, like flakes

Six-sided, white   25
On my eyes, my lips, my hair

Touching and melting.
Nowhere.

THE CAVERN

Charles Tomlinson
(1927–   )

Obliterate
mythology as you unwind
this mountain-interior
into the negative-dark mind,
as there   5
the gypsum's snow
the limestone stair
and boneyard landscape grow
into the identity of flesh.

Pulses of the water-drop   10
veils and scales, fins
and flakes of the forming
leprous rock,
how should these
inhuman, turn   15
human with such chill affinities.

Hard to the hand,

these mosses not of moss,
but nostrils, pits
of eyes, faces   20
in flight and prints
of feet where no feet ever were,
elude the mind's
hollow that would contain
this canyon within a mountain.   25

Not far
enough from the familiar,
press
in under a deeper dark until
the curtained sex   30
the arch the streaming buttress
have become
the self's unnameable and shaping home.

◼ ◼ ◼

THE LAKE ISLE OF INNISFREE

W. B. Yeats
(1865–1939)

I will arise and go now, and go to Innis-
    free,
And a small cabin build there, of clay and
    wattles made;
Nine bean rows will I have there, a hive
    for the honey bee,
And live alone in the bee-loud glade.

And I shall have some peace there, for
    peace comes dropping slow,   5
Dropping from the veils of the morning
    to where the cricket sings;
There midnight's all a glimmer, and noon
    a purple glow,
And evening full of the linnet's wings.

I will arise and go now, for always night
    and day
I hear lake water lapping with low sounds
    by the shore;   10

2. *wattles:* stakes interwoven with twigs.

While I stand on the roadway, or on the
    pavements gray,
I hear it in the deep heart's core.

AMONG SCHOOL CHILDREN

W. B. Yeats
(1865–1939)

I walk through the long schoolroom ques-
    tioning,
A kind old nun in a white hood replies;
The children learn to cipher and to sing,
To study reading-books and history,
To cut and sew, be neat in everything   5
In the best modern way—the children's
    eyes
In momentary wonder stare upon
A sixty year old smiling public man.

I dream of a Ledaean body, bent
Above a sinking fire, a tale that she   10
Told of a harsh reproof, or trivial event
That changed some childish day to trag-
    edy—
Told, and it seemed that our two natures
    blent
Into a sphere from youthful sympathy,
Or else, to alter Plato's parable,   15
Into the yolk and white of the one shell.

And thinking of that fit of grief or rage
I look upon one child or t'other there
And wonder if she stood so at that age—
For even daughters of the swan can
    share   20
Something of every paddler's heritage—
And had that color upon cheek or hair;

9. *Ledaean:* Cf. "Leda and the Swan." According to legend, the daughters of Leda and
Zeus (Helen of Troy and Clytemnestra) were
hatched from eggs.
    15. *Plato's parable:* According to Aristophanes
in the *Symposium,* man, once spherical and
whole, was divided into two halves. Love is the
attempt of each half to find its complement.
    16. *shell:* see note to line 9 above.

And thereupon my heart is driven wild:
She stands before me as a living child.

Her present image floats into the
    mind—   25
Did quattrocento finger fashion it
Hollow of cheek as though it drank the
    wind
And took a mess of shadows for its meat?
And I though never of Ledaean kind
Had pretty plumage once—enough of
    that,   30
Better to smile on all that smile, and show
There is a comfortable kind of old scare-
    crow.

What youthful mother, a shape upon her
    lap
Honey of generation had betrayed,
And that must sleep, shriek, struggle to
    escape   35
As recollection or the drug decide,
Would think her son, did she but see that
    shape
With sixty or more winters on its head,
A compensation for the pang of his birth,
Or the uncertainty of his setting forth? 40

Plato thought nature but a spume that
    plays
Upon a ghostly paradigm of things;
Solider Aristotle played the taws
Upon the bottom of a king of kings;
World-famous golden-thighed Pythag-
    oras   45

26. *quattrocento:* reference to fifteenth-century
Italian artists, particularly Botticelli.
34. *Honey of generation:* the Neo-Platonic
concept that the child at birth either struggles
and rejects birth or being pacified by the "honey
of generation" forgets his prenatal happiness and
accepts birth.
41–43. *Plato . . . Solider Aristotle:* Plato believed nature to be a mere appearance, whereas
Aristotle held that nature had a solider reality.
43–44. *Aristotle . . . kings:* Aristotle was the
tutor of Alexander the Great.
    Taws: a leather strap divided into strips
used for punishment.
45. *golden-thighed Pythagoras:* a Greek philosopher who was revered as a god with a "thigh
of gold." He advocated the doctrine of "the
harmony of the spheres."

Fingered upon a fiddle stick or strings
What a star sang and careless Muses
    heard:
Old clothes upon old sticks to scare a bird.

Both nuns and mothers worship images,
But those the candles light are not as
    those   50
That animate a mother's reveries,
But keep a marble or a bronze repose.
And yet they too break hearts—O Pres-
    ences
That passion, piety or affection knows,
And that all heavenly glory symbol-
    ize—   55
O self-born mockers of man's enterprise;

Labor is blossoming or dancing where
The body is not bruised to pleasure soul,
Nor beauty born out of its own despair,
Nor blear-eyed wisdom out of midnight
    oil.   60
O chestnut tree, great rooted blossomer,
Are you the leaf, the blossom or the bole?
O body swayed to music, O brightening
    glance,
How can we know the dancer from the
    dance?

53. *Presences:* concepts of the ideal.

CRAZY JANE TALKS WITH THE BISHOP

W. B. Yeats
(1865–1939)

I met the Bishop on the road
And much said he and I.
'Those breasts are flat and fallen now,
Those veins must soon be dry;
Live in a heavenly mansion,   5
Not in some foul sty.'

'Fair and foul are near of kin,
And fair needs foul,' I cried.

'My friends are gone, but that's a truth
Nor grave nor bed denied,   10
Learned in bodily lowliness
And in the heart's pride.

'A woman can be proud and stiff

When on love intent;
But Love has pitched his mansion in   15
The place of excrement;
For nothing can be sole or whole
That has not been rent.'

BIOGRAPHIES

AIKEN, CONRAD
(1889–   )

American poet, novelist, and short story writer. He received a Pulitzer Prize in 1930 for his *Selected Poems*. Among his best known fiction are the novel *The Blue Voyage* (1927) and his stories "Mr. Arcularis" and "Silent Snow, Secret Snow." Characteristic of his prose work are poetic language, the use of evocative settings, and subtle revelations of the influences of unconscious forces on human emotions and actions.

ARNOLD, MATTHEW
(1822–1888)

English poet and critic. His poetry articulated the uneasiness of the Victorian Age that was, in some circles at least, questioning both religious and aesthetic standards. *Poems,* containing some of his finest verse, was published in 1853. Though his own tastes were rather conservative and aristocratic, he looked, in such critical works as *Culture and Anarchy* (1869) and *Essays in Criticism* (1865 and 1888), toward education to abolish all classes through the study of the greatest expressions of the human spirit.

AUDEN, W(YSTAN) H(UGH)
(1907–   )

English poet and critic. He is a satirical and intellectual poet, always experimenting with new verse forms and often using prose rhythms and scientific, abstract language to convey his ideas about the modern world. Since the publication of his *Collected Poetry* in 1945, other volumes of poetry have appeared, such as *The Age of Anxiety* (1947), *Nones* (1951), *The Shield of Achilles* (1955), and *Homage to Clio* (1960). Among his collections of critical essays are *The Enchafèd Flood* (1950) and *The Dyer's Hand and Other Essays* (1962).

BEERBOHM, MAX
(1872–1956)

English essayist, short story writer, and caricaturist. Although best known during the eighteen-nineties, he continued to write until the 1930's. The number of his works is relatively small, but each is graced by wit, culture, and a masterful style. Among his collections of essays are *The Works of Max Beerbohm* (1896), *More* (1899), and *Yet Again* (1909). "William and Mary" appeared in the volume of stories *Seven Men* (1919).

BETJEMAN, JOHN
(1906–   )

English poet. Predominately his poems are light verse satirizing contemporary English life, celebrations of the English landscape, and nostalgic evocations of nineteenth-century England. His *Collected Poems* appeared in 1958. *Summoned by Bells* (1960) is a verse autobiography.

BLAKE, WILLIAM
(1757–1827)

English poet and artist. This pre-Romantic poet's first published volume of poetry was *Poetical Sketches* (1783). The poems in *Songs of Innocence* (1797) and *Songs of Experience* (1794) contrast primarily, as their titles suggest, the perspectives of youth and maturity. These volumes, as with all his later works, he illustrated with his own engravings. His later poetry, which he referred to as Prophetic Books, included *The Book of Thel* (1787), *The Marriage of Heaven and Hell* (1790), and *The Gates of Paradise* (1793).

BRIDGES, ROBERT
(1844–1930)

English poet. He was the author of many beautiful lyrics and a remarkable metrist. His philosophical poem, *The Testament of Beauty* (1929), is a compendium of the wisdom and experience of a rare artistic sensibility. His *Poetical Works* was published in 1913; the same year Bridges was appointed Poet Laureate.

BROWNING, ROBERT
(1812–1889)

English poet. He was particularly skilled in the dramatic monologue, of which "My Last Duchess," which appeared with "Soliloquy of the Spanish Cloister" in *Dramatic Lyrics* (1842), is perhaps the best known. *Men and Women* (1855) includes some of his most memorable poems. This Victorian poet's longest and probably finest work, *The Ring and the Book* (1868–1869), tells in verse from many different points of view the story of a murder in Florence in 1698.

BURNS, ROBERT
(1759–1796)

Scottish poet. His best poetry is essentially an adaptation and transformation of the crude lyrics of forgotten Scottish singers. These songs, which vary from affectionate lightheartedness to full passion, both convey the spirit of a nation and express the brotherhood of man. The collected edition of his poems, entitled *Poems, Chiefly in the Scottish Dialect,* was published in 1793.

BYRON, GEORGE NOEL GORDON, LORD
(1788–1824)

English poet. Popular and famous as Byron became for his narrative and travel poems, his real genius lay in verse satire. His *English Bards and Scotch Reviewers* (1809) was a rash and brilliant satire against those critics who had castigated his earliest book, *Hours of Idleness* (1807). His masterpiece is *Don Juan* (1818–1821), an unfinished verse satire. Among his works are *Childe Harold's Pilgrimage* (1812–1818), *Manfred* (1817), and *The Vision of Judgment* (1821). He also wrote a number of poetic dramas, such as *Sardanapalus* (1821), *Werner* (1822), and *Cain* (1821).

CHEKHOV, ANTON PAVLOVITCH
(1860–1904)

Russian dramatist and short story

writer. He has written satirical and comic stories, but most characteristic are his poignant, lyric, indirect tales of man's inability to understand himself and communicate significantly with others. His full-length plays, written with superb craftsmanship and symbolic overtones that are not always obvious, have basically the same theme as the stories. His stories appear in the series translated by Constance Garnett with the overall title of *The Tales of Chekhov* (1916–1923). His four major plays are *The Sea Gull* (1896), *Uncle Vanya* (1900), *The Three Sisters* (1901), and *The Cherry Orchard* (1904).

CIARDI, JOHN
(1916–   )

American poet, critic, and translator. His volumes of poetry include *Homeward to America* (1940), *As If* (1955), and *In the Stoneworks* (1961). His translation of Dante's *Divine Comedy* is one of the most distinguished to have appeared to date. Liveliness of style and intellectual balance are among the qualities that have made popular his essays on reading and evaluating poetry.

COLERIDGE, SAMUEL TAYLOR
(1772–1834)

English poet and critic. In 1797 Coleridge and William Wordsworth became close friends, an association which greatly stimulated the poetic development of both men. Coleridge contributed "The Rime of the Ancient Mariner" to their joint effort, *Lyrical Ballads* (1798), and during this period also wrote "Cristabel," "Kubla Khan," and "Frost at Midnight." *Biographia Literaria* (1817), made up of autobiography, philosophy, aesthetics, and literary criticism, is his most important single work of prose.

CORTÁZAR, JULIO
(1914–   )

Argentinean novelist and short story writer. In his fiction he uses many experimental and complex devices to present his favorite theme: At any moment in a person's life commonplace reality can be flooded by the mysterious and the monstrous until the real and the fantastic are indistinguishable. A collection of his short stories translated into English in 1967 is *End of the Game and Other Stories*. Two novels recently translated are *The Winners* (U.S.A., 1965) and *Hopscotch* (U.S.A., 1966).

COX, HARVEY GALLAGHER
(1929–   )

American theologian. He attained fame with the publication of *The Secular City* (1965), which underscored the need for organized religions to become more involved in the practical problems of contemporary civilization. He has also written *On Not Leaving It to the Snake* (1967).

CRANE, HART
(1899–1932)

American poet. He attempted to use words and images in unaccustomed ways to break through the veil of familiarity that conceals the central meanings of the realities around us. His major work, *The Bridge* (1930), is an imaginative and complex effort to discover the unifying myth of America itself. *The Collected Poems of Hart Crane* was published in 1933.

CRANE, STEPHEN
(1871–1900).

American novelist, short story writer, and poet. With *Maggie: A Girl of the Streets* (1893) he became one of the first naturalist writers in America. However, he attained fame with the publication of his great Civil War novel, *The Red Badge of Courage* (1895). H. G. Wells called "The Open Boat," which appeared in *The Open Boat and Other Tales of Adventure* (1898), the greatest story ever written. His poems in *The Black Riders* (1895) and *War Is Kind* (1899) are amazingly modern in tone.

CUMMINGS, E(DWARD) E(STLIN) (1894–1962)

American poet. His strikingly original techniques of typography and structure, as well as individuality and intensity of content have made him one of the most famous and controversial of twentieth-century American poets. A comprehensive collection of his work is entitled *Poems 1923–1954*. He is also the author of a novel, *The Enormous Room* (1922), and two plays—*Him* (1928) and *Santa Claus* (1946).

DE LA MARE, WALTER (1873–1956)

English poet, novelist, and essayist. Much of the poetry in *Collected Poems* (1942) reveals his unique combination of technical virtuosity with a childlike sensitivity to the borderland between nature and the supernatural. Among his prose writings are short stories, books for children, the novel *Memoirs of a Midget* (1921), and commentaries in his anthologies *Come Hither* (1923) and *Behold, This Dreamer!* (1939)—the last devoted to dreams.

DICKINSON, EMILY (1830–1886)

American poet. Her style, which is austere, sparse, and intense, is appropriate both to her thoughtful treatment of her favorite subjects—God, death, and immortality—and the Calvinistic New England world in which she was living. Only four of her poems were published during her lifetime. The first volume of her poetry appeared in 1890 and went through a number of editions, but then her work was largely neglected. In 1924 three volumes of letters and further poems were published, and since that time her reputation has grown steadily.

DONNE, JOHN (1573–1631)

English poet and preacher. He was appointed Dean of St. Paul's Cathedral in London (1621) largely because of the fame of his brilliant sermons. His poems, which were not published until after his death, used startling imagery drawn from the new language of science and were the inspiration of the "metaphysical" school of poets. They are distinguished by their metrical originality, dramatic quality, and fusion of thought and feeling. This eloquent style blended with frank self-analysis is found also in such prose as *Devotions upon Emergent Occasions* (1634) and *Fifty Sermons* (1649).

DOSTOEVSKI, FEDOR MIKHAILOVICH (1821–1881)

Russian novelist. He extended the boundaries and enlarged the horizons of the novel by exploring the dark places of the human spirit. The first of his novels was *Poor People* (1846), followed by such works as *Crime and Punishment* (1866), *The Idiot* (1866), *The Possessed* (1871), and the unfinished *The Brothers Karamazov* (1880).

DRAYTON, MICHAEL (1563–1631)

English poet. A friend of Shakespeare

and Ben Jonson, he was among the leading poets of the Elizabethan Age. He wrote sonnets, odes, satires, pastorals, historical verse narratives, and plays (none of which have survived). His best known long poem is *Poly-Olbion* (1612–1622), a historical-geographical poem on Great Britain. For most readers, however, his fame rests on his lively and lovely sonnets in such collections as *Idea* (1594; rev. 1619).

DURANT, WILL(IAM JAMES)
(1885–)

American historian. Between 1935 and 1966, he published the ten volumes of his monumental *Story of Civilization,* spanning human history from its Oriental beginnings to the French Revolution (his wife Ariel Durant was coauthor of the last four volumes). He has also written, among other works, *The Story of Philosophy* (1926), *Adventures in Genius* (1931), and *Program for Americans* (1931).

EBERHART, RICHARD
(1904–)

American poet and dramatist. He is often concerned in his poems with the metaphysical implications of ordinary experiences. *Collected Poems, 1930–1960* appeared in 1960. The author has also written verse dramas. He was a founder of the Poet's Theater at Cambridge, Massachusetts; his own plays are available in *Collected Verse Plays* (1962).

ELIOT, T(HOMAS) S(TEARNS)
(1888–1965)

American poet, dramatist, and critic. He is in his essays an exponent of conservatism and tradition in literature, politics, and religion. One of his most influential collections of essays is entitled *For Lancelot Andrewes* (1928). However, he is anything but traditional in his technical innovations and his experiments with the uses of language and form in his poetry. *Prufrock and Other Observations* appeared in 1917 and was followed by such volumes as *The Waste Land* (1922), *The Hollow Men* (1925), and *Four Quartets* (1943). Among his plays, *Murder in the Cathedral* (1935), *The Cocktail Party* (1949), and *The Confidential Clerk* (1953) have received widespread attention.

FISCHER, JOHN
(1910–)

American journalist and essayist. He was a correspondent for a number of newspapers and editor-in-chief of *Harper's* magazine (1953–1967). He has written articles for such magazines as *Harper's, Life, New Yorker,* and the *Reader's Digest.* His books include *Master Plan: U.S.A.* (1951) and *The Stupidity Problem and Other Harassments* (1964).

FORSTER, E(DWARD) M(ORGAN)
(1879–)

English novelist, short story writer, and essayist. *A Passage to India* (1924), which deals with British and Indian relationships, is probably the most famous of his five novels. He has also written *Collected Tales* (1947), two books of essays, *Abinger Harvest* (1934) and *Two Cheers for Democracy* (1951), and a book of literary criticism, *Aspects of the Novel* (1927).

FROMM, ERICH
(1900–)

American psychologist and writer. His chief interest is exploring how psychoanalytical concepts can help the individual to cope with the problems inherent in a specific culture in a specific age. His writings have won him the respect if not always the agreement of his professional colleagues. An ability to elucidate and popularize his ideas, moreover, has made him known to general readers. Among his most popular books are *Escape from Freedom* (1941), *Man for Himself* (1947), *The Forgotten Language* (1951), and *The Art of Loving* (1956).

FROST, ROBERT
(1875–1963)

American poet. He was for many years the unofficial poet laureate of America. His best poems are notable for their highly skillful rendering of everyday speech into poetic meter. Among many other honors, he won the Pulitzer Prize for Poetry four times: in 1924 for *New Hampshire,* in 1931 for *Collected Poems,* in 1937 for *A Further Range,* and in 1943 for *A Witness Tree.*

GASCOYNE, DAVID
(1916–   )

English poet. He is a visionary poet writing in the surrealist tradition, but he is also aware of the need to find a philosophic basis for his vision. Among his volumes are *Poems: 1937–42* (1942), *A Vagrant and Other Poems* (1950), and *Collected Poems* (1965).

GOLD, HERBERT
(1924–   )

American novelist and essayist. He is a writer distinguished by his mastery of a colloquial style both in dialogue and in narration. He has described his own novels as "studies of men who attempt to discover the nature and purpose of their lives in our competitive, romance-ridden society." Among his novels are *Birth of a Hero* (1951), *The Man Who Was Not With It* (1958), and *Therefore Be Bold* (1960). A collection of short stories bears the title *Love and Like* (1960). His essays have appeared in such magazines as the *New Yorker, Harper's,* and *Atlantic.*

HARDY, THOMAS
(1840–1928)

English novelist and poet. He achieved both popularity and notoriety with such novels as *Far from the Madding Crowd* (1874), *The Return of the Native* (1878), *The Mayor of Casterbridge* (1884–1885), *Tess of the D'Urbervilles* (1891), and *Jude the Obscure* (1859). Angered by moralistic attacks on *Jude,* he then returned to his first love, poetry, and published throughout the rest of his life many volumes of quietly ironic, stoic verse. *Collected Poems* was published in 1925. *The Dynasts,* an epic-drama dealing with the Napoleonic Wars, came out in three parts (1903–1908).

HEMINGWAY, ERNEST
(1898–1961)

American novelist and short story writer. One of the most famous fiction writers of our time. His distinctive style, characterized by dramatic understatement and sparse dialogue, has spawned a slew of imitators. Less influential has been his preoccupation with the challenge of violent death in war, bull-fighting, and wild-game hunting. Among his novels are *The Sun Also Rises* (1926), *A Farewell to Arms* (1929), and *For Whom the Bell Tolls* (1940). Many of his short stories were collected in *The Fifth Column and the First Forty-Nine Stories* (1938). He also wrote the novelette *The Old Man and the Sea* (1952); the following year he was awarded the Nobel Prize for Literature.

HERBERT, GEORGE
(1593–1633)

English poet. Herbert is very much a metaphysical poet in that he uses metaphor as an essential device for conveying and developing ideas. His themes are usually developed with economy and structured clarity and purposefulness, combined with an element of intense personal emotion. His poetry is almost entirely included in *The Temple* (1633), a collection of 160 poems of a religious character.

HOPKINS, GERARD MANLEY
(1844–1889)

English poet. Upon becoming a Jesuit priest in 1868, Hopkins destroyed his poetry, but he later resumed writing. These poems were not published until his friend Robert Bridges brought out a collection in 1918. The contents of his poetry are an account of his intense spiritual experience. His technique with its concentration upon rhythmic effects was so original that even today his poetic structure seems strained and obscure. Hopkins has had much influence on modern poetry.

HOUSMAN, A(LFRED) E(DWARD)
(1859–1936)

English poet. He recorded in his poetry the bleak attitude that the beauty and promise of life had been blighted. This view was presented through the eyes of an English country boy in *A Shropshire Lad* (1896). He also wrote *Last Poems* (1922), *More Poems* (1936), and *Collected Poems* (1939).

HUXLEY, ALDOUS (LEONARD)
(1894–1963)

English novelist and essayist. He was the grandson of Thomas Henry Huxley, the grand-nephew of Matthew Arnold, and the brother of the biologist, Julian Huxley. As a novelist, he gained fame with a series of brilliant, mocking depictions of the emptiness of his society: *Crome Yellow* (1921), *Antic Hay* (1923), *Those Barren Leaves* (1925), *Point Counter Point* (1928). Perhaps his most famous work is a science-fiction fantasy, *Brave New World* (1932). His interest in philosophy and mysticism is reflected in a number of books of essays (such as *Ends and Means*—1937 and *The Perennial Philosophy*—1945) and the novels *Eyeless in Gaza* (1936) and *Time Must Have a Stop* (1945).

HUXLEY, JULIAN
(1887–   )

British biologist and writer. A member of the illustrious Huxley family. As a professional biologist, he has written technical studies, has taught in England and the U.S., and served as secretary of the Zoological Society of London from 1935 to 1942. His humanistic approach to social problems is expressed in a style that is lucid, persuasive, and vigorous. Among his more than forty books are *Essays of a Biologist* (1923), *Man Stands Alone* (1939), *Man in the Modern World* (1947), and *The Humanist Frame* (1961).

JACKSON, SHIRLEY
(1919–1965)

American short story writer and novelist. In much of her fiction she has used an approach that has become associated with her name: She presents neurotic or fantastic characters and situations in realistic settings. Perhaps her best known collection of short stories is *The Lottery* (1949). *The Sundial* (1959), *The Haunting of Hill House* (1960), and *We Have Always Lived in the Castle* (1962) are the titles of three of her novels. In a lighter mood are two autobiographical books on family life: *Life Among the Savages* (1953) and *Raising Demons* (1957).

JARRELL, RANDALL
(1914–1965)

American poet as well as an essayist. Condensed, precise images and symbols influenced by psychoanalytic concepts are characteristic of his poetry. A number of his poems were influenced by his experiences in World War II while serving in the Air Force. *Selected Poems* appeared in 1955. *Poetry and the Age* (1953) and *A Sad Heart at the Supermarket* (1962) are collections of his critical essays. *Pictures from an Institution* (1959) is a novel satirizing university life.

JEFFERS, ROBINSON
(1887–1962)

American poet. Jeffers's poetry usually extols nonhuman nature. Among his collections, which typically begin with a long narrative poem about primitive passions, are *Roan Stallion, Tamar and Other Poems* (1925), *Dear Judas* (1929), *Give Your Heart to the Hawks* (1934), *Be Angry at the Sun* (1941), *The Double Axe* (1948), and *Hungerfield* (1954). He has also adapted Greek drama into English verse. His most successful adaptation was that of Euripides' *Medea* (1946).

JOYCE, JAMES
(AUGUSTINE ALOYSIUS)
(1882–1941)

English novelist, poet, and short story writer. Joyce was probably the most gifted avant-garde writer of modern times. His book of stories, *Dubliners,* was written in 1907 but was not pub-

lished until 1914 because of censorship difficulties. His autobiographical novel, *A Portrait of the Artist as a Young Man* (1916) was followed in 1922 by his very controversial stream-of-consciousness novel *Ulysses.* Joyce apparently carried stream-of-consciousness as far as it can go in his last "novel," *Finnegans Wake* (1939), a work he labored over for fifteen years.

JUSTICE, DONALD
(1925–   )

American poet. His poems have appeared in *The New Yorker, Accent, Paris Review,* and *Poetry.* Two of his collections are *The Summer Anniversaries* (1960) and *A Local Storm* (1963). He has taught at the University of Missouri, Hamline University, and the State University of Iowa.

KAFKA, FRANZ
(1883–1924)

German short story writer and novelist. Kafka is truly a representative writer of "the age of anxiety." He utilizes a form of allegory in which the forces presented are intangible, equivocal, and elusive. His heroes are usually men inflicted with an overwhelming but unexplained sense of guilt. He destroyed more than half of what he wrote during his lifetime, and his major works were published only after his death by his close friend Max Brod. His three novels are *The Castle* (1930, English translation), *The Trial* (1937, English translation), and *Amerika* (1938, English translation).

KEATS, JOHN
(1795–1821)

English poet. As a Romantic, he was passionately concerned with the relationship between emotion and knowledge, between beauty and truth. His first volume, *Poems* (1817), was ignored. His next, *Endymion* (1818), was harshly reviewed by conservative critics. In the next two remarkable years, despite tuberculosis, he produced such great poems as "The Eve of St. Agnes," "La Belle Dame sans Merci," "Ode on a Grecian Urn," and "Ode to a Nightingale." All these poems appeared in the volume *Lamia, Isabella, The Eve of St. Agnes and Other Poems* (1820).

KRUTCH, JOSEPH WOOD
(1893–   )

American essayist and critic. For many years professor of dramatic literature at Columbia University and drama critic for *The Nation*. Until the early thirties his critical studies were primarily Freudian in approach; for example, *Edgar Allan Poe: A Study of Genius* (1926) and *Five Masters* (1929). The essays included in *The Modern Temper* (1929) were also influenced by psychoanalytical doctrines, but those in *The Measure of Man* (1954) and such volumes as *The Desert Years* (1952) are more concerned with the relationship of man and nature.

LAMB, CHARLES
(1775–1834)

English essayist. Lamb's familiar essays have been called prose lyrics. In his essays Lamb revealed his personality in a highly original style, a style entirely personal in its mixture of thoughtfulness and quaintness, deep feeling and extravagance. From 1820 to 1823 Lamb was a contributor to the *London Magazine,* in which appeared the first series of miscellaneous essays, known as the *Essays of Elia* (published in a separate volume in 1823). The second series was published in 1883.

LARKIN, PHILIP
(1922–   )

English poet and novelist. Among his novels, often bleak and angry, are *Jill* (1946) and *A Girl in Winter* (1947). Many of his poems have charm and poignancy, others are satirical and ironic. Among his volumes of poems are *The North Ship* (1945), *The Less Deceived* (1955), and *The Whitsun Weddings* (1964).

LAWRENCE, D(AVID) H(ERBERT)
(1885–1930)

English novelist, short story writer, poet, and essayist. One of the most significant, prolific, and versatile of twentieth-century British writers. Although best known as a novelist and writer of short stories, he also published volumes of poetry, travel sketches, criticism, plays, essays, and philosophical studies. Among his major fiction are the novels *Sons and Lovers* (1913), *The Rainbow* (1915), *Women in Love* (1920), *The Plumed Serpent* (1926), and *Lady Chatterley's Lover* (1928); and the short stories "The Prussian Officer" (1914), "The Fox" (1923), "Sun" (1926), and "The Man Who Died" (1931). Various as these works are, certain subjects continually reappear: man's relationship to nature, primitive religions, sexual relations, and the maladies of modern industrial life.

MACDONALD, DWIGHT
(1906–   )

American political commentator, essayist, and critic. He has been an editor of *Fortune* and *Partisan Review;* he was founder and editor-in-chief of *Politics*. For a number of years, until 1967, he was motion picture critic for *Esquire*. He has written controversial and opinionated but inevitably intelligent and lively essays on many subjects; however, he has been particularly concerned with revealing the foibles of American political attitudes and beliefs. Among his collections of essays are *Memoirs of a Revolutionist* (1957) and *Against the American Grain* (1963).

McKAY, CLAUDE
(1890–1948)

American poet and novelist. He was one of the foremost figures of the "Negro literary renaissance" of the 1920's. Many of his poems, including the one selected for this anthology, are strong protests against discrimination and injustice. The best of his poetic output appears in *Selected Poems* (1953). His four novels are *Home to Harlem* (1927), *Banjo* (1929), *Gingertown* (1931), and *Banana Bottom* (1933).

MACKENZIE, NORMAN
(1921–   )

English economist and writer. Taught at universities in England, Australia, and the United States. He was an editor of the *New Statesman,* and has written articles on British labor, history, and social conditions for the *New Republic* and *Harper's.* Among his books are the following: *A History of Socialism* (1949), *The West Indian in Britain* (1957), *Women in Australia* (1962).

MacLEISH, ARCHIBALD
(1892–   )

American poet and playwright. He has received two Pulitzer Prizes for poetry: the first in 1933—*Conquistador;* the second in 1953—*Collected Poems, 1917–1952.* His poetry is often divided into three periods: 1923–39—subjective and aesthetic; 1930–48—public and political; 1949 to date—personal and philosophical. His verse play *J.B.* was also awarded

a Pulitzer Prize in 1959. Among his other verse plays are *Panic* (1935) and *The Fall of the City* (1937).

MANSFIELD, KATHERINE
(1888–1923)

English short story writer. Her stories are known for their psychological penetration, impressionistic style, experimentation with structure, and ability to invest an ordinary incident with symbolic meaning. Most of her finest stories are to be found in the following volumes: *Bliss and Other Stories* (1920), *The Garden Party and Other Stories* (1922), *The Doves' Nest and Other Stories* (1923).

MARVELL, ANDREW
(1621–1678)

English poet. He is the most eminent of the later metaphysical poets. His nonsatirical poems tend to be reflective and meditative and often have a broad philosophical import. His use of metaphor escapes being grotesque or superficial through his effective use of diction and his subtle and probing thoughtfulness. The bulk of his poems were not published until 1681. His satiric works appeared in 1689 under the title *Poems on Affairs of State.*

MAUGHAM, W(ILLIAM) SOMERSET
(1874–1965)

English novelist, short story writer, and dramatist. His works are characterized by skillful craftsmanship and a dispassionate, clinical view of life. The autobiographical *Of Human Bondage* (1915) is probably his best novel, though *The Moon and Sixpence* (1919), *Cakes and Ale* (1930), and *The Razor's Edge* (1944) are popular. *The Summing Up* (1938) and *A Writer's Notebook* (1949) contain his thoughts on writing. In 1952 his plays were collected in three volumes and his short stories in two.

MEW, CHARLOTTE
(1869–1928)

English poet. A recluse who spent most of her life in poverty and obscurity. Only one volume of her poetry appeared in her lifetime—*The Farmer's Bride* (1916, new ed. in 1921); *The Rambling Sailor* (1929) was published posthumously. She was considered by Thomas Hardy the best woman poet of her day. Her poems are individual, compact, and dramatic.

MILLAY, EDNA ST. VINCENT
(1892–1950)

American poet. A romantic poet particularly associated with the moral iconoclasm of the 1920's. Although her poems were usually conventional in form and possessed the qualities of freshness and fluency, she questioned traditional values with irony and even at times bitterness. In 1923 she won a Pulitzer Prize for *The Harp-Weaver and Other Poems.* Her *Collected Poems* were published posthumously in 1956. She also wrote verse plays (e.g., *Aria da Capo*—1920) and the libretto for the opera *The King's Henchman* (1927)—music by Deems Taylor.

MILTON, JOHN
(1608–1674)

English poet and pamphleteer. The career of this great Puritan writer falls into three divisions. The first period of pure poetic inspiration resulted in poems such as "Lycidas" (1637) and "Comus" (1634). From 1640 to 1660 his major preoccupations were political and social. He devoted himself to the writing of essays such as *Areopagitica* (1644), *Of Education* (1644), and *The Tenure of*

Kings and Magistrates (1649). During the last fourteen years of his life his three greatest works were published: *Paradise Lost* (1667), *Paradise Regained* (1671), and *Samson Agonistes* (1671). In these poems the Puritan spirit and Renaissance learning are nobly wedded in a complex, capacious, and resonant "grand style" that is uniquely Milton's.

MONTAGU, (MONTAGUE FRANCIS) ASHLEY
(1905–   )

American anthropologist and writer. He has stated that his major interest is "the relation of cultural factors to the physical and behavioral evolution of man." Particularly he has been concerned with problems of race; in 1949 he helped draft the UNESCO statement on race. Among his numerous books, notable for their verve and wit, are *Man's Most Dangerous Myth: The Fallacy of Race* (1942), *The Natural Superiority of Women* (1953), *Life Before Birth* (1964), and *The Idea of Race* (1965).

MOORE, MARIANNE
(1882–   )

American poet. Her considerable reputation is based in a large degree on her happy balance between simplicity and complexity, on her precise and detailed observations, which expand into almost metaphysical conceits. *Poems* (1921) and *Observations* (1924) contain her earliest poetry, which is comparatively easy beside the later work in *Selected Poems* (1935), *What Are Years* (1941), and *Collected Poems* (1951). She has also written sensitive translations, such as *The Fables of La Fontaine* (1954).

MUIR, EDWIN
(1887–1959)

English poet, critic, and translator.

His poetry reveals a wide range of interests cast in a style that is usually simple, direct, and traditional. He is particularly fascinated by myths and dream images. *Collected Poems* was published in the United States in 1933. Perhaps the best known of his critical studies is *The Structure of the Novel* (1928). With his wife Willa, he translated a number of modern German writers.

ORWELL, GEORGE
(pseudonym of Eric Blair)
(1903–1950)

English novelist and essayist. For a time he lived, partly by choice, in extreme poverty in Paris and London, and wrote a book about it, *Down and Out in Paris and London* (1933). In 1936 he volunteered for a loyalist brigade fighting Franco in the Spanish Civil War, but became profoundly disillusioned with Communism. His best known book is the futuristic satire on totalitarian regimentation *1984* (1949). Other books are *Burmese Days* (1934), *Homage to Caladonia* (1938), *Animal Farm* (1945), *Dickens, Dali and Others* (1946), and *Shooting an Elephant* (1950) of which the last two are collections of essays.

OWEN, WILFRED
(1893–1918)

English poet. Considered by many the finest of World War I poets, he was killed on the Western Front a week before the Armistice. With few exceptions, his poems describe with savage intensity the horror of war and his feelings of pity for its victims. His experimentations in poetic techniques influenced such poets as Siegfried Sassoon and W. H. Auden. Only four of his poems were published during his lifetime; *Poems* appeared posthumously in 1920.

PAVESE, CESARE
(1908–1950)

Italian novelist and short story writer. A combination of his technical skill (often experimental), poetic style (except when writing in the neorealistic tradition), emotional intensity, and concern with modern political, social, and philosophical problems made him famous in Italy. One of his finest novels, *The Moon and and the Bonfire*, was translated into English in 1952. His other novels and short stories are also being translated. *The Burning Brand: Diaries 1935–1950* attracted considerable attention when it was published in the United States in 1961.

PLATH, SYLVIA
(1932–1962)

American poet. Her poems are imaginative and sure in tone, but their most memorable characteristic is the honest expression of passionate feelings. Her rebelliousness and refusal to accept uncritically traditional Western values also account for the wide appeal of her work. Two of her volumes of poetry are *The Colossus* (1962) and *Ariel* (1965). *The Bell Jar* is a novel published in 1962 under the pseudonym "Victoria Lucas."

PORTER, KATHERINE ANNE
(1890–   )

American short story writer and novelist. Her style, which is both subtle and straightforward, has permitted her to convey penetrating and imaginative perceptions of human motivation. She has written three volumes of short stories: *Flowering Judas* (1930), *Pale Horse, Pale Rider* (1939), and *The Leaning Tower* (1944); and a novel, *Ship of Fools* (1962).

POUND, EZRA (LOOMIS)
(1885–   )

American poet and critic. He has been

a leading figure in the new movements in poetry and a considerable influence upon many of the major poets of his day. Among his critical studies are *Pavannes and Divisions* (1918), *The ABC of Reading* (1934), and *Culture* (1938). His first poems appeared in the volume *Personae* (1909). This was followed by several other collections of distinguished poetry (including translations from the Chinese and other languages), such as *Ripostes* (1912), *Lustra* (1916), *Hugh Selwyn Mauberley* (1920), *The Translations of Ezra Pound* (1953, 1963, 1964). His magnum opus is the *Cantos,* a series of complex and difficult poems that have appeared in several volumes since 1917.

RALEIGH, SIR WALTER
(1552?–1618)

English poet and essayist. His prose is somewhat meandering, but his half-ironic, sophisticated poetry is concise and aphoristic. Among his more famous poems are "Fayne Would I: But I Dare Not," "The Nimphs Reply to the Sheepheard," and "The Passionate Man's Pilgrimage." His most extensive prose work is the unfinished *The History of the World* (1621).

ROBINSON, EDWIN ARLINGTON
(1869–1935)

American poet. He was very much in the tradition of the American Transcendentalists, who dealt primarily with individual ethical conflicts, but he managed to deal with such material in a way that was original and realistic. He received a Pulitzer Prize for *Collected Poems* (1921). He also wrote a number of long narrative poems set in the time of King Arthur; for example, *Merlin* (1917), *Lancelot* (1920), *Tristram* (1927). The last was also awarded a Pulitzer Prize.

ROETHKE, THEODORE
(1908–1963)

American poet. His poetry ranges from light verse to experimental, surreal poems barbed with nightmare images; from direct, lyric evocations of childhood innocence to witty, ironic commentaries on American life. He won a Pulitzer Prize in 1954 for *The Waking, Poems 1933–1953* and both a National Book Award and Bollingen Prize for *Words for the Wind* (1959).

ROVIT, EARL H(ERBERT)
(1927–   )

American critic and novelist. He has written a number of articles on a wide range of literary subjects, though especially in the field of twentieth-century American literature. Two of his book-length studies are *Herald to Chaos: The Novels of Elizabeth Madox Roberts* (1960) and *Ernest Hemingway* (1963). He is the author of the novels *The Player King* (1965) and *A Far Cry* (1967).

SCHWARTZ, DELMORE
(1913–1966)

American poet and short story writer. From 1943 to 1956 he served as an editor of *Partisan Review,* and from 1940 to 1947 was on the faculty of Harvard University. His poetry, though concrete in imagery, usually has intriguing overtones of philosophical meaning. *Summer Knowledge: New and Selected Poems 1938–1958* appeared in 1959. "In Dreams Begin Responsibilities" (also the title of his first volume of poems—1938) is one of the stories in the collection *The World Is a Wedding* (1948). Another collection is entitled *Successful Love and Other Stories* (1961).

SEABORG, GLENN T(HEODORE)
(1912–   )

American scientist. His major contribution to science came in 1940 when he announced the discovery of a new element, plutonium; moreover, he shared with E. M. McMillan a Nobel Prize in Chemistry in 1951. He has served on the Atomic Energy Commission; since 1961 he has been its chairman. More than two hundred articles written by him or in conjunction with members of his staff have appeared in scientific and popular journals.

SEXTON, ANNE
(1928–   )

American poet. Her works have appeared in *Partisan Review, Harper's, The New Yorker,* and other magazines; her volumes include *To Bedlam and Part Way Back* (1960) and *All My Pretty Ones* (1962).

SHAKESPEARE, WILLIAM
(1564–1616)

English dramatist and poet. Few would argue with the statement that he is the greatest writer in English literature. His first plays, in the early 1590's, were principally historic and comic. Most of his sonnets were probably written between 1593 and 1596. In the first decade of the seventeenth century he wrote his great tragedies and a few bitter comedies. His final comedies present a serene acceptance of human predicaments that he had formerly treated tragically.

SHAPIRO, KARL
(1913–   )

American poet and critic. His best poems are usually considered to be those written on his experiences during World War II. *V-Letter and Other Poems* was awarded a Pulitzer Prize in 1945. The poems in *Poems 1940–1953* are often savagely satirical, especially when attack-

ing modern intellectualism and excessive complexity. His own style is vigorous and idiomatic. His critical views have appeared in verse in *Essay on Rime* (1945) and in prose in such collections of essays as *In Defense of Ignorance* (1960).

SHELLEY, PERCY BYSSHE
(1792–1822)

English poet. His lyric gift, with its seemingly spontaneous music and its straining after ethereal beauty, may be the purest in the whole range of English poetry. Among his more famous Romantic poems are "Hymn to Intellectual Beauty" (1816), *Prometheus Unbound* (1820), "Episychidion" (1822), and "Adonais" (1812).

SITWELL, EDITH
(1887–1964)

English poet, critic, and biographer. Her poetry is usually associated with the bizarre experimentations in sound and imagery and the ultrasophisticated stance of many of the poems in such collections as *Gold Coast Customs and Other Poems* (1929) and *Collected Poems* (1930). Yet beneath the façade of "terrible gaiety" are often genuine emotions, especially in terms of religious feeling. This is particularly true of her post-World War II volumes (e.g., *Gardeners and Astronomers*—1953; *Music and Ceremonies*—1963). Her best known volumes of criticism are *Poetry and Criticism* (1925) and *Aspects of Modern Poetry* (1934). Her biographies and studies include *Pope* (1930), *Bath* (1932), and *The English Eccentrics* (1933).

SNODGRASS, W(ILLIAM)
(1926–   )

American poet. Characteristic of his poetry are a traditional form and intensity of feeling (especially when dealing with personal experiences). He is also capable of ironic wit. In 1960 he received a Pulitzer Prize for his first volume of poetry, *Heart's Needle*.

SNYDER, GARY
(1930–   )

American poet. Associated with the "beat" group of San Francisco (he is said to be the prototype of the hero of Jack Kerouac's novel *Dharma Bums*). He is familiar with a number of Oriental languages and lived in Japan from 1956 to 1964; he has written on Zen Buddhism and translated Japanese poetry. In his own poems, in the "beat" style, three influences are evident: Zen Buddhism, American Indian myths, and the landscape of the American Northwest. Three of his collections of poems are *Riprap* (1959), *Myths and Texts* (1960), and *The Back Country* (1967).

SPENDER, STEPHEN
(1909–   )

English poet and critic. His earlier collections of poetry, such as *Poems* (1933) and *Vienna* (1935), suggest a committed, even belligerent, revolutionary fervor. His later poems, such as the majority of those in *Collected Poems* (1954), deal with more personal and universal themes. Although at times his images are strained and his approach didactic, at his best he has produced poems memorable for their rich suggestiveness and nobility. His best known critical studies are *The Destructive Element* (1935) and *The Creative Element* (1953). He has also written an autobiography entitled *World Within World* (1951).

STACE, W(ALTER) T(ERENCE)
(1886–1967)

English philosopher and writer. He is essentially a philosophical naturalist who nevertheless admits the validity of religious experience. Since the publication of his first book, *A Critical History of Greek Philosophy* (1920), he has written on several major areas of philosophical thought. His range of interests is suggested by the following partial list: *The Meaning of Beauty* (1929), *The Nature of the World* (1940), *The Concept of Morals* (1937), *Time and Eternity* (1952), and *Mysticism and Philosophy* (1960).

STEVENS, WALLACE
(1879–1955)

American poet. His poetry is noted for its richness of imagery, verbal luxuriance, and structural complexity. His earliest poems appeared in *Harmonium* (1923) and seemed to strive toward "absolute" poetry. His later poems, which appeared in *The Man with the Blue Guitar* (1937), *Transport to Summer* (1947), and other volumes, show a greater concern with the problem of order in a chaotic society. His *Collected Poems* (1954) won the Pulitzer Prize in 1955.

STEVENSON, ROBERT LOUIS
(1850–1894)

English novelist, poet, and short story writer, and essayist. Though such novels as *Treasure Island* (1884) and *The Strange Case of Dr. Jekyll and Mr. Hyde* (1886) are thrillers, they are memorable because of his power of invention and his psychological awareness. His essays are distinguished by their unique blend of personal charm and Calvinistic moral concern. Among his collections of essays are *Virgibus Puerisque* (1881) and *Familiar Studies of Men and Books* (1882).

TENNYSON, ALFRED LORD
(1809–1892)

English poet. One of the great Victorian poets, Tennyson believed totally in the sacredness of his poetic calling. Reception of his first works was spotty, with one devastating attack upon his 1830 volume, *Poems, Chiefly Lyrical*. However, by 1850 with the publication of *In Memoriam A. H. H.* he had earned his public, received a pension, and been appointed Poet Laureate. Later volumes include *Maud* (1855) and *Idylls of the King* (collected in 1888).

THOMAS, DYLAN (MARLAIS)
(1914–1953)

English poet and short story writer. His poems attracted attention in his early twenties for the vividness of his complex images, which often focused on nature and the unconscious. His *Collected Poems* appeared in 1953. *Portrait of the Artist as a Young Dog* (1940) is an anecdotal semiautobiography. A collection of his stories, sketches, and essays was published in 1954 under the title *Quite Early One Morning*. Another collection of stories and essays, *A Prospect of the Sea*, appeared in 1955.

THOREAU, HENRY DAVID
(1817–1862)

American essayist and philosopher. Thoreau's belief in the individual, nature, and a moral law that transcended civil statutes is expressed in a style that incorporated both a Yankee twang and an almost antique purity. His works include *Walden* (1854), *Civil Disobedience* (1849), and *The Maine Woods* (1864).

TOLSTOI, LEV
(1828–1910)

Russian novelist, short story writer, and playwright. Tolstoi's world fame rests largely on the masterpieces *War and Peace* (1869) and *Anna Karenina*

(1887), in both of which truth and directness are the bases on which he created fictional characters with distinct personalities. Among his other fictional works are *The Death of Ivan Ilyich* (1886), *The Kreutzer Sonata* (1889), and *Resurrection* (1899). Among his best known plays are *The Power of Darkness* (1887) and *The Living Corpse* (1902).

TOMLINSON, CHARLES
(1927–   )

British poet. Before joining the faculty of the University of Bristol, he taught elementary school in London, lived in Italy, and visited the United States. His rhetorical and experimental yet visually precise poetry has appeared in such volumes as *The Necklace* (1955), *Seeing Is Believing* (1958), and *A Peopled Landscape* (1963).

VAN DEN HAAG, ERNEST
(1914–   )

American psychologist and writer. A practicing psychoanalyst and teacher. As a writer, his chief interest has been to explore, with clarity and verve, American culture and mores in terms of the insights offered by psychoanalysis and the social sciences. His essays have appeared in *Partisan Review, Harper's, Commonweal, Modern Age,* and numerous anthologies and collections. Among his books are *The Fabric of Society* (with Ralph Ross —1957) and *Passion and Social Constraint* (1963).

VERGA, GIOVANNI
(1840–1922)

Italian novelist and short story writer. In his most important work, he vividly describes the often desperate struggle for existence yet spirit of endurance that permeates the world of the Sicilian peasantry. His finest novels of this type are *I*

Malavoglia (1881—translated as *The House by the Medlar Tree*) and *Maestra Don Gesualdo* (1889—translated by D. H. Lawrence in 1923). Lawrence also translated two collections of stories: *Little Novels of Sicily* (1925) and *Cavalleria Rusticana and Other Stories* (1928).

WEIL, SIMONE
(1909–1943)

French philosopher and writer. After becoming convinced that social and political action were mere "ersatz Divinity," she turned her search for meaning in the direction of religion itself. Her studies of Greek, Hindu, and Christian philosophies led her to an awareness of, as the title of her most famous work has it, *The Need for Roots* (1952). Among her other major works in translation are *Waiting for God* (1951), *Gravity and Grace* (1952), and *Selected Essays, 1934–1943* (1962).

WELTY, EUDORA
(1909–   )

American short story writer and novelist. Most of her work has as its setting the Mississippi Delta. She is known for her insights into Southern society, sympathy for the innocent and the frustrated, as well as comic effects and a superb ear for dialogue. Among her collections of short stories are *A Curtain of Green* (1941), *The Golden Apples* (1949), and *The Bride of the Innisfallen* (1955). *Delta Wedding* (1946) and *The Ponder Heart* (1954) are novels.

WHITE, E(LWYN) B(ROOKS)
(1899–   )

American essayist. His wryly humorous observations on the peculiarities, lunacy, and charms of modern life have delighted readers of *The New Yorker*

and other magazines since 1926. Many of his articles and essays have been published in book form: *Every Day Is Saturday* (1934), *One Man's Meat* (1942), *The Second Tree from the Corner* (1954), and *The Points of My Compass* (1962).

WHITMAN, WALT(ER)
(1819–1892)

American poet. His great poetic work is *Leaves of Grass,* which went through a series of revisions from 1855 to his death. In this work, employing fluid, dramatic rhythms, he attempted to show how man might attain freedom for the mind through democracy, for the heart through love, and for the soul through religion. He also wrote *Drum-Taps* (1865) and *Sequel to Drum-Taps* (1866).

WILBUR, RICHARD
(1921–   )

American poet. Awards for his poetry include two Guggenheim fellowships, a Prix de Rome (1954) and a Pulitzer Prize (1957 for *Things of This World*). *Poems 1943–1957* appeared in 1957. His cultivated, formal poetry is often witty and always urbane and intellectual. He has also translated Molière's *Le Misanthrope* and *Tartuffe* and contributed to the lyrics for the Lillian Hellman–Leonard Bernstein musical adaptation of *Candide* (1956).

WILSON, EDMUND
(1895–   )

American critic and fiction writer. Perhaps *the* preeminent American critic of our time. He is a literary humanist who follows his personal intellectual interests and moral values regardless of popular tastes. Among his works of criticism and social commentary are *Axel's Castle* (1930), *The Wound and the Bow* (1941), *The Shock of Recognition* (1943), *The Shores of Light* (1952), and *Patriotic Gore* (1962). His best known work of fiction is the novel *I Thought of Daisy* (1929).

WOOLF, VIRGINIA (STEPHEN) (1882–1941)

English novelist and essayist. In her fiction she uses the stream-of-consciousness technique and such devices as recurrent symbols and poetic images. Her goal is to explore the interrelations between the internal thoughts and feelings of individuals and external reality. Her best known novels are *Mrs. Dalloway* (1925), *To the Lighthouse* (1927), *Orlando* (1928), and *The Waves* (1931). Among her collections of essays, personal in approach and subtle in style, are *The Common Reader* (1925), *A Room of One's Own* (1929), *The Second Common Reader* (1932), and *The Captain's Death Bed* (1950).

WORDSWORTH, WILLIAM (1770–1850)

English poet. The great nature-poet of the Romantics. He found, for a while, a kindred spirit in Coleridge and together they produced the first great work of the Romantic movement, *Lyrical Ballads* (1798); he contributed most of the poems, and, in the 1800 edition, a highly influential preface. His best poetry was written during the next few years while he lived with his wife and sister in a cottage in the Lake District. These appeared in *Poems in Two Volumes* (1807). His next major work was a long autobiographical poem in blank verse entitled *The Prelude* (completed in 1805 but not published until 1850). He became Poet Laureate of England in 1843.

YEATS, WILLIAM BUTLER (1865–1939)

English poet and playwright. Considered by many the greatest of twentieth-century poets writing in English. His poetic career is usually divided into three periods: 1) 1889–1902, artificial, aesthetic works often dealing with Irish myths. Examples: *The Celtic Twilight* (1893), *The Secret Rose* (1897). 2) 1904–1929, poetry "cold and passionate as the dawn," which combines the colloquial with the formal and uses concise symbols that partake simultaneously of the personal, the traditional, and the archetypal. Examples: *The Green Helmet and Other Poems* (1910), *The Wild Swans at Coole* (1917), *The Tower* (1928). 3) 1929–1939, vigorous, inventive, personal, even bawdy poems are characteristic of this period. Examples: *Words for Music Perhaps* (1933), *Last Poems* (1939). His plays were collected in 1934. In 1923 he was awarded the Nobel Prize in Literature.

INDEX

1119